EXTRACTION OF SIGNALS FROM NOISE

EXTRACTION OF SIGNALS FROM NOISE

L. A. WAINSTEIN
V. D. ZUBAKOV

Translated from the Russian by
Richard A. Silverman

1962
PRENTICE-HALL, INC.
Englewood Cliffs, New Jersey

Library of Congress Catalog Number 62-9316

Printed in the United States of America
29813C

AUTHORS' PREFACE

This book is devoted to problems involving extraction of signals from a background of random noise. By "extraction," we mean not only restoration of unknown (random) signals, but also detection of signals of known form together with measurement of unknown parameters of such signals. Much attention is given to radar problems. Thus, in addition to ordinary radio noise, resembling noise in the receiver itself, we study noise due to chaotic reflections from a large number of objects randomly located in space. This means that from the very beginning, we are obliged to take into account both "white noise" and "correlated noise." This makes our treatment more general, and even simplifies it, since the mathematical analysis of "pure" white noise involves certain difficulties.

Historically, our subject evolved in the following way: The behavior of signals and noise was first studied in concrete situations, and much research was done on the *analysis* of different systems. In particular, detailed investigations were made of how signals and noise behave in passing through the linear (and sometimes nonlinear) circuits encountered in radio receivers, and various ways of separating signals from noise were examined. It is only in comparatively recent times that an attempt has been made to solve the problem of *synthesis* of optimum systems, which extract signals from the combination of signal plus noise by utilizing to the full the differences between the properties of the signal and those of the noise. It is largely problems of this kind which form the subject matter of the present book.

It is interesting to note that often the optimum circuits obtained by solving the synthesis problem either coincide with or are very close to the circuits already used in practice, which were developed by using simple intuitive notions. This fact, which we shall encounter repeatedly throughout the book, in no way diminishes the significance of the synthesis problem. Indeed, it is only by solving the synthesis problem that we can be assured that it is impossible to construct a better device, subject to the given constraints. In other words, knowledge of which circuits are theoretically optimum makes it unnecessary to consider a large number of modifications. (Similarly, the law of conservation of energy makes it superfluous to analyze different ways of constructing perpetual motion machines.)

In choosing the material for this book, we tried to confine ourselves to problems whose solutions can be considered to some extent definitive. Therefore, we had to omit many interesting problems of practical importance, for which a sufficiently complete and rigorous solution cannot yet be given.

The book consists of three parts. Part 1 is devoted to optimum linear filters, and we first discuss Wiener's theory of optimum filtering, the first "synthetic" theory of the type that interests us. Although this realm of ideas is closely related to automatic control, nevertheless, both the statement of the problem and a whole series of results obtained in the theory are of vital interest in radio engineering. In Part 1, we also study other optimum linear filters, where this time the signal-to-noise ratio serves as the criterion of optimality. In every case, the characteristics of the optimum linear filters are completely determined by the correlation function of the noise and by the correlation function or form of the signals. Part 1 is essentially an introduction to Part 2, and is intended to simplify the study of the latter.

In Part 2, which is the central part of the book, we systematically develop the basic ideas and results of the theory of optimum receivers. Here, we consider problems of optimum detection of a useful signal in the presence of noise, which is taken to be a normal (Gaussian) stationary random process. We solve a variety of problems of interest in radar, beginning with the simplest and ending with very complicated problems (depending on the assumptions made about the signals). Part 2 also includes problems involving measurement of parameters of the useful signal in the presence of noise, but not very many, since most of the mathematical questions arising here have yet to be treated adequately.

Part 3 contains auxiliary material, both mathematical and physical, to be used in connection with Parts 1 and 2. A more detailed idea of the subject matter of the book can be found in the table of contents.

To avoid misunderstanding, we remark that optimum filters and receivers are studied here only from the standpoint of the mathematical operations which they have to perform on the received mixture of signals and noise. Problems pertaining to the practical implementation of the corresponding operations lie outside the scope of this book.

Although we try to keep the theoretical considerations simple, wherever possible, the reader must have a solid mathematical background, particularly in the elements of probability theory. However, we hope that our approach, in which the difficulty of the problems gradually increases, will help make things easier. We also attempt, while studying different statistical problems, to explain the significance and precise meaning of the parameter which serves to generalize the ordinary signal-to-noise ratio.

Parts 1 and 3 (and also Chapter 7) were written by L. A. Wainstein, Part 2 (except for Chapter 7) was written by V. D. Zubakov, and Chapter 8 was written jointly. The overall editing was done by L. A. Wainstein. The book contains some new results obtained by the authors.

The authors gratefully acknowledge conversations with Y. B. Kobzarev, which drew their attention to a variety of new problems, and to a considerable extent stimulated their work in this field.

L.A.W.
V.D.Z.

TRANSLATOR'S PREFACE

The present volume, the third in a new series of Russian translations under my editorship, is devoted to a topic of great technological importance, which has attracted the the attention of mathematicans, physicists and engineers alike. While producing the book, I have been in constant communication with Professor Wainstein, who has suggested various improvements, which have all been duly incorporated. I have also checked all the mathematical derivations in detail; this has allowed me to correct some typographical errors which survived in the Russian edition. The Bibliography is for the most part due to the authors themselves. However, bearing in mind the needs of the English-language readership, I have suitably modified the list of books cited there.

R. A. S.

CONTENTS

EXTRACTION OF SIGNALS FROM NOISE

Part 1

STATISTICAL THEORY OF OPTIMUM LINEAR FILTERS

1

BASIC CONCEPTS OF THE THEORY OF FILTERING OF RANDOM PROCESSES

1. Statement of the Problem

The problem of extracting useful signals from different kinds of noise can be stated in various ways. In this book, we shall regard both the signal and the noise as random processes, and the problem of greatest interest to us will be the problem of *filtering*, i.e., of separating the signal as "cleanly" as possible from the "contaminated" combination of the signal plus the noise. It is physically clear that complete separation of the signal from the noise can be achieved only if the properties of the signal and the noise are radically different. In general, as we shall see later, even the optimum filter reproduces the signal with some error.

Sometimes it is appropriate to interpret the problem of filtering more broadly. For example, it is often not the signal itself which is of interest, but its derivative or perhaps its time integral. Then, the corresponding filter must be chosen in such a way that it reproduces (with the least possible error) the derivative or the integral of the useful signal. Another problem of interest is to *predict* or *extrapolate* the signal, i.e., to predict the future values of the signal from its past behavior and its statistical properties. The problem of extrapolating a signal is meaningful both in the presence of noise and in the absence of noise.

Mathematically, the problem of filtering can be stated as follows: Let the function

$$f(t) = m(t) + n(t) \tag{1.01}$$

(called the *input function*), which is equal to the sum of a useful signal $m(t)$ and the noise $n(t)$, be applied to the input of a system $\mathscr{K}$ (a *filter*). Both the useful signal $m(t)$ and the noise $n(t)$ are assumed to be *random processes* (random functions of t). The system $\mathscr{K}$ performs certain mathematical operations on the function $f(t)$, as a result of which we obtain a function $x(t)$ (called the *output function*) at the output of $\mathscr{K}$. This situation is indicated schematically in Fig. 1.

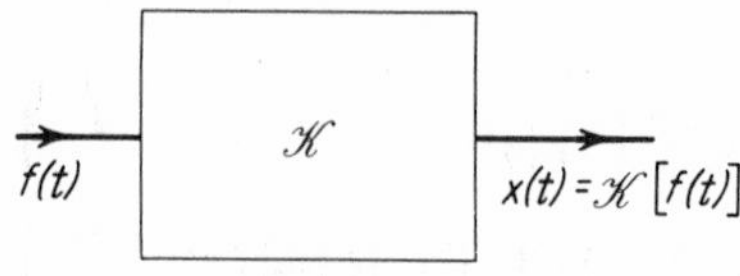

FIG. 1. Schematic representation of the filter $\mathscr{K}$.

The output function $x(t)$ can be regarded as the result of applying an operator $\mathscr{K}$ to the input function $f(t)$. The problem is now to choose the operator $\mathscr{K}$ in such a way that it reproduces some function $h(t)$ with the least possible error. Here $h(t)$ is a transformed version of the useful signal and can be written in the form

$$h(t) = \mathscr{L}[m(t)], \tag{1.02}$$

where $\mathscr{L}$ is a known mathematical operator. In the simple filtering problem it is the useful signal which must be reproduced; in this case

$$h(t) = m(t), \tag{1.03}$$

and $\mathscr{L}$ is the "unit" operator, which leaves a function unchanged.

The difference

$$\varepsilon(t) = x(t) - h(t) \tag{1.04}$$

can be regarded as the instantaneous error of reproduction. It is clear that the value of $\varepsilon(t)$ will fluctuate in time. The "intensity" of these fluctuations can be characterized by their *mean square value*, i.e., by the *mathematical expectation* of their square, denoted by $\overline{\varepsilon^2(t)}$.[1] We thereby introduce statistical (probabilistic) concepts into the theory, and in fact, we regard not only the noise but also the signal as statistical quantities.

In the absence of noise $[n(t) \equiv 0]$, we are interested only in the problem of predicting the value of a signal after a time interval s. In this case

$$h(t) = m(t + s). \tag{1.05}$$

The prediction can be made either by using the entire "past" of the function $m(t)$ or only a part of its past, but in both cases, we exploit the statistical properties of the function $m(t)$. It is usually assumed that these statistical properties are given beforehand, and are known from previous statistical measurements of the random process $m(t)$ or of one like it.

---

[1] The mathematical expectation (or *ensemble average*) is indicated by an overbar.

The most important statistical characteristics of the random process $m(t)$ are its mean value $\overline{m(t)}$ and its *correlation function* $R_m(\tau)$, defined by the formula

$$R_m(\tau) = \overline{[m(t) - \overline{m(t)}][m(t - \tau) - \overline{m(t - \tau)}]}. \tag{1.06}$$

If $\overline{m(t)} \equiv 0$, this formula simplifies and becomes

$$R_m(\tau) = \overline{m(t)m(t - \tau)}. \tag{1.07}$$

The correlation function characterizes to some extent the statistical relation between the values of the function m at the times t and $t - \tau$, where τ can be both positive and negative. In fact, if the values $m(t)$ and $m(t - \tau)$ can be regarded as being statistically independent, then the mean value of the products in (1.06) and (1.07) are equal to the product of the mean values, which leads to $R_m(\tau) = 0$. Conversely, for *normal* random processes, the equation $R_m(\tau) = 0$ implies that $m(t)$ and $m(t - \tau)$ are statistically independent (see Chap. 9). A more complete characterization of the statistical relation between $m(t)$ and $m(t - \tau)$ is given by the *correlation coefficient*, defined as the ratio $R_m(\tau)/R_m(0)$.

Henceforth, we shall assume that all the random functions under consideration have mean values which are identically zero. This constitutes no loss of generality. If, for example, $\overline{m(t)} \not\equiv 0$, then we introduce a new random function $\Delta m(t) = m(t) - \overline{m(t)}$, and consider $\Delta m(t)$ instead of $m(t)$. In fact, if a message is transmitted by using the function $m(t)$, the mean value $\overline{m(t)}$ conveys no information and hence plays no essential role. Similarly, in suppressing the noise $n(t)$, one must contend only with the fluctuation of $n(t)$ about its mean value $\overline{n(t)}$, since suppression of the known mean value $\overline{n(t)}$ can be accomplished without difficulty.

The function $R_m(\tau)$ is also called the *autocorrelation function* of the random function (process) $m(t)$, as opposed to the *cross-correlation function*, which will be introduced later.

In general, as τ is increased, the statistical relation between the values $m(t)$ and $m(t - \tau)$ becomes "weaker," and in fact, approaches zero as $|\tau| \to \infty$, so that these two values become statistically independent as $|\tau| \to \infty$. Therefore, the correlation function approaches zero as $|\tau| \to \infty$, and takes its largest value for $\tau = 0$ (see Sec. 3 below).

A random process $m(t)$ can be characterized by more complicated quantities, e.g., by the probability that at the times $t_1, t_2, \ldots, t_n$, the corresponding values $m(t_1), m(t_2), \ldots, m(t_n)$ lie in specified intervals. However, these quantities are not needed in problems of linear filtering and prediction, since it turns out that the correlation function gives everything that is needed.

Above, we have tacitly assumed that the random process $m(t)$ is *homogeneous in time* or *stationary*; it is for this reason that $R_m(\tau)$ depends only on τ, and not on t. Moreover, because of the stationarity of the process, the mean values $\overline{m(t)}$, $\overline{m^2(t)}$, $\overline{m(t)m(t-\tau)}$, etc., are all independent of time. In particular, we must have

$$\overline{m(t)m(t-\tau)} = \overline{m(0)m(-\tau)} = \overline{m(\tau)m(0)}. \tag{1.08}$$

The last equation implies an important property of a correlation function of any random process $m(t)$, namely, the fact that $R_m(\tau)$ is even:

$$R_m(\tau) = R_m(-\tau). \tag{1.09}$$

The problem with which we shall be most concerned is the problem of suppressing noise by filtering. In this regard we introduce the following classification of filters.[2] A filter of type I works as follows: The input function $f(t)$ is stored (recorded) for a certain interval of time (theoretically, for $-\infty < t < \infty$) and is then "processed," i.e., subjected to some mathematical operation as a result of which the function $x(t)$ appears at the output of the system. Such a filter resembles a computer, which records the input data, processes it and finally delivers it in the form of a curve or a table. In a filter of type II, the functions of recording, processing and delivering the data are not separated in time (at least, not significantly), but are performed continuously. Consequently, the output function $x(t)$ is influenced only by the input data available at the moment (i.e., by the values of the function $f(t)$ in the present and in the past). A filter of type II can also be a computer, but in principle such filters can be constructed without recourse to computers, and in fact can be ordinary electrical filters. In particular, a linear filter of type II can be "realized" by a circuit containing resistances, inductances and capacitances; for example, the function $f(t)$ might be the input voltage and $x(t)$ might be the output voltage of a four-terminal network, and then $\mathscr{K}$ would be the operator corresponding to the network. For linear systems, the operator $\mathscr{K}$ is simply related to the frequency characteristics of the network (see Sec. 2).

The advantages of filters of type II are the simplicity with which they can be implemented, and the rapidity with which the output data is delivered. The advantage of filters of type I is the more complete use they make of the input signal, with the consequent more effective suppression of the noise. A comparison of both types of filters and their filtering action will be given in Chap. 2. It should be noted that there is no sharp boundary between the two types of filters (see the end of Sec. 14).

Thus, to form $x(t)$, a filter of type I uses the values $f(t')$ for all possible values of t', namely, for

$$-\infty < t' < \infty, \tag{I}$$

[2] This classification of filters is not standard, and is introduced only for convenience.

whereas a filter of type II uses only the semi-infinite time interval

$$-\infty < t' \leqslant t, \tag{II}$$

namely, the present moment ($t' = t$) and the entire "past" ($t' < t$). A device that uses only a finite amount of the past, e.g., the interval

$$t - T \leqslant t' \leqslant t, \tag{III}$$

may be called a filter of type III; such a filter has a *finite memory* of length T. However, the theory of filters of type III will not be discussed below.

The problem of filtering is often stated in conjunction with the problem of predicting the useful signal [cf. (1.05)] with the least possible error. The prediction problem is particularly relevant to the filtering problem in view of the fact that filtering requires time, during which the data can "age." Thus, to a certain extent, prediction can compensate for the time lag introduced during filtering. It is clear that the prediction problem only arises in the case of filters of types II and III, since for filters of type I, there is no distinction between prediction and filtering.

In what follows we shall be concerned exclusively with *linear filters*, which perform only linear operations on the input function. In other words, we will look for the best system characterized by a linear operator $\mathscr{K}$. For such filters, the relation between the input and output can be written in the form

$$x(t) = \int_{-\infty}^{\infty} k(t')f(t - t')\, dt' \tag{1.10}$$

or

$$x(t) = \int_{-\infty}^{\infty} k(t - t')f(t')\, dt'. \tag{1.11}$$

It is clear from these formulas that the value of $x(t)$ at the output of the filter is a linear combination of the values of the input function $f(t)$ at all instants of time. More precisely, according to formula (1.11), the value $x(t)$ at time t is formed from the values $f(t')$ at past times ($t' < t$) and future times ($t' > t$), taken with the "weight" $k(t - t')\, dt'$, which depends on the difference $t - t'$.[3] A filter whose operation is described by (1.10) or (1.11) is called a *time-invariant* (or *stationary*) linear filter. Such a filter has the following property: If the input function $f(t)$ corresponds to the output function $x(t)$, then $f(t + \tau)$ corresponds to $x(t + \tau)$, i.e., if the input function is shifted in time, the output function is shifted by just the same amount. It is clear that in problems involving stationary random processes (whose

[3] For this reason, the function $k(t)$ is called the *weighting function* of the filter $\mathscr{K}$. It is also called the *impulse response* of the filter, for a reason given in the next section.

statistical properties are invariant under time shifts), one should use time-invariant filters. *Time-varying* filters correspond to more general linear transformations of the form

$$x(t) = \int_{-\infty}^{\infty} k(t, t')f(t')\, dt', \tag{1.12}$$

with which we shall not be concerned.

We note that the formulas (1.10) to (1.12) are still not the most general way of writing linear transformations. For example, in the trivial problem of filtering in the absence of noise, where $n(t) \equiv 0$, we have $\mathscr{L} = 1$, and the optimum filter carries out the trivial operation $x(t) = f(t) = m(t)$ with no error. However, we can only write this operation in the form of an integral by using an improper function, the so-called *delta function* $\delta(t)$, which has the properties

$$\begin{gathered} \delta(t) = 0 \quad \text{for} \quad t \neq 0, \qquad \delta(0) = \infty, \\ \int_{-\varepsilon}^{\varepsilon} \delta(t)\, dt = 1 \quad \text{for any} \quad \varepsilon > 0, \\ \int_{-\varepsilon}^{\varepsilon} F(t)\,\delta(t)\, dt = F(0) \quad \text{for any function } F(t). \end{gathered} \tag{1.13}$$

In fact, if we set $k(t) = \delta(t)$, formula (1.10) gives $x(t) = f(t)$. Nevertheless, the use of improper functions is often undesirable, and a form of filtering theory which avoids the use of improper functions will be given in Sec. 5.

For a filter of type II, the function $k(t)$ must satisfy the condition

$$k(t) = 0 \quad \text{for} \quad t < 0, \tag{1.14}$$

and instead of formulas (1.10) and (1.11), we have

$$x(t) = \int_{0}^{\infty} k(t')f(t - t')\, dt' = \int_{-\infty}^{t} k(t - t')f(t')\, dt'. \tag{1.15}$$

For filters of type III, we have

$$k(t) = 0 \quad \text{for} \quad t < 0 \quad \text{and} \quad t > T, \tag{1.16}$$

so that

$$x(t) = \int_{0}^{T} k(t')f(t - t')\, dt' = \int_{t-T}^{t} k(t - t')f(t')\, dt'. \tag{1.17}$$

Introducing the function

$$g(t) = k(-t), \tag{1.18}$$

we can rewrite formula (1.17) as

$$x(\tau) = \int_{-T}^{0} g(t)f(t + \tau)\, dt = \int_{\tau-T}^{\tau} g(t - \tau)f(t)\, dt. \tag{1.19}$$

The integrals (1.19) are analogs of a *cross-correlation function* (cf. Sec. 2), except that the product of the fixed function g and the random function f is not averaged, but integrated over time. We shall encounter similar expressions in Chap. 3. Thus, a filter of type III acts as a *correlator* of the given function g and the input function f, i.e., it is a device which integrates the product of the two functions over the time interval T. Filters of types I and II perform the same operation over an infinite time interval, as shown by formulas (1.10) and (1.15).

2. The Integral Equation of the Optimum Linear Filter

We now study the properties of the linear filter $\mathscr{K}$ which reproduces the useful signal with the greatest accuracy, for given signal and noise characteristics. We shall assume that the useful signal and the noise are stationary random processes. The accuracy of reproduction will be characterized by the *mean square error* $\overline{\varepsilon^2}$, where ε is defined by formula (1.04). Our problem can be formulated as follows: Find the filter $\mathscr{K}$ such that the mean square error with which the output function $x(t)$ reproduces the required signal $h(t)$ is a minimum. Such a filter is said to be *optimum*. As we shall see, the solution of this problem reduces to the solution of an integral equation determining the weighting function $k(t)$, which characterizes the optimum filter.

Thus, let $f(t)$ appear at the input of a linear filter with weighting function $k(t)$. Then, the output function is

$$x(t) = \int_{-\infty}^{\infty} k(\tau)f(t - \tau)\, d\tau, \tag{2.01}$$

and the corresponding reproduction error is

$$\varepsilon(t) = \int_{-\infty}^{\infty} k(\tau)f(t - \tau)\, d\tau - h(t). \tag{2.02}$$

The square of this error equals

$$\varepsilon^2(t) = \left[\int_{-\infty}^{\infty} k(\tau)f(t - \tau)\, d\tau\right]^2 - 2h(t)\int_{-\infty}^{\infty} k(\tau)f(t - \tau)\, d\tau + h^2(t).$$

Transforming the square of the first term in the right-hand side into a double integral, we obtain

$$\varepsilon^2(t) = \iint_{-\infty}^{\infty} k(\tau)k(\sigma)f(t - \tau)f(t - \sigma)\, d\tau\, d\sigma - 2\int_{-\infty}^{\infty} k(\tau)h(t)f(t - \tau)\, d\tau + h^2(t), \tag{2.03}$$

where the factor $h(t)$ can be written behind the integral sign, since it does not depend on the variable of integration τ. The mean square of $\varepsilon^2(t)$ is equal to

$$\overline{\varepsilon^2(t)} = \iint_{-\infty}^{\infty} k(\tau)k(\sigma)\,\overline{f(t - \tau)f(t - \sigma)}\, d\tau\, d\sigma - 2\int_{-\infty}^{\infty} k(\tau)\overline{h(t)f(t - \tau)}\, d\tau + \overline{h^2(t)}. \tag{2.04}$$

We now introduce the functions

$$R_f(\tau - \sigma) = \overline{f(t - \tau)f(t - \sigma)}, \tag{2.05}$$

$$R_{hf}(\tau) = \overline{h(t)f(t - \tau)}. \tag{2.06}$$

By the definition (1.07), $R_f(\tau)$ is the *autocorrelation function* of the random process (1.01) appearing at the input of the filter $\mathscr{K}$; according to (1.09), $R_f(\tau)$ is an even function of its argument. The function $R_{hf}(\tau)$ is called the *cross-correlation function* of the stationary random processes $h(t)$ and $f(t)$. It expresses the statistical relation between the random variables $h(t)$ and $f(t - \tau)$, whose mean values are assumed to be zero. We also define the autocorrelation function

$$R_h(\tau) = \overline{h(t)h(t - \tau)}, \tag{2.07}$$

which for $\tau = 0$ reduces to

$$R_h(0) = \overline{h^2(t)}. \tag{2.08}$$

Thus, finally, we can write the mean square error in the form

$$\overline{\varepsilon^2} = \int_{-\infty}^{\infty} k(\tau)k(\sigma)R_f(\tau - \sigma)\, d\tau\, d\sigma - 2\int_{-\infty}^{\infty} k(\tau)R_{hf}(\tau)\, d\tau + R_h(0), \tag{2.09}$$

which does not depend on the functions $h(t)$ and $f(t)$ themselves, but rather on their correlation functions.

Under what condition on the function $k(t)$ does the expression (2.09) for $\overline{\varepsilon^2}$ have a minimum? As we shall now show, the answer to this question is that $\overline{\varepsilon^2}$ takes its minimum value if and only if the weighting function $k(t)$ is the solution of the integral equation

$$\int_{-\infty}^{\infty} k(\sigma)R_f(\tau - \sigma)\, d\sigma = R_{hf}(\tau). \tag{2.10}$$

The proof goes as follows: Let the optimum filter have weighting function $k(\tau)$ and mean square error E. Then, any other filter will have weighting function $k(\tau) + \delta k(\tau)$ and mean square error E'. We are trying to find a function $k(\tau)$ such that E' is always greater than E. To do this, we first replace $k(\tau)$ in (2.09) by $k(\tau) + \delta k(\tau)$, obtaining

$$\begin{aligned} E' = \iint_{-\infty}^{\infty} &[k(\tau) + \delta k(\tau)][k(\sigma) + \delta k(\sigma)]R_f(\tau - \sigma)\, d\tau\, d\sigma \\ &- 2\int_{-\infty}^{\infty} [k(\tau) + \delta k(\tau)]R_{hf}(\tau)\, d\tau + R_h(0) \end{aligned}$$

or

$$\begin{aligned} E' = &\iint_{-\infty}^{\infty} k(\tau)k(\sigma)R_f(\tau - \sigma)\, d\tau\, d\sigma - 2\int_{-\infty}^{\infty} k(\tau)R_{hf}(\tau)\, d\tau + R_h(0) \\ &+ \iint_{-\infty}^{\infty} k(\tau)\, \delta k(\sigma)R_f(\tau - \sigma)\, d\tau\, d\sigma + \iint_{-\infty}^{\infty} \delta k(\tau)k(\sigma)R_f(\tau - \sigma)\, d\tau\, d\sigma \\ &- 2\int_{-\infty}^{\infty} \delta k(\tau)R_{hf}(\tau)\, d\tau + \iint_{-\infty}^{\infty} \delta k(\sigma)\, \delta k(\tau)R_f(\tau - \sigma)\, d\tau\, d\sigma. \end{aligned}$$

The sum of the three integrals in the first row of the right-hand side of this formula is equal to E. The first and second double integrals in the second row are equal, since the function $R_f(\tau - \sigma)$ is even. Therefore, the expression for E' can be written in the form

$$E' = E + 2\int_{-\infty}^{\infty} \delta k(\tau)\, d\tau\left[\int_{-\infty}^{\infty} k(\sigma)R_f(\tau - \sigma)\, d\sigma - R_{hf}(\tau)\right] + J, \quad (2.11)$$

where the term J equals

$$\begin{aligned} J &= \iint_{-\infty}^{\infty} \delta k(\tau)\, \delta k(\sigma) R_f(\tau - \sigma)\, d\tau\, d\sigma \\ &= \iint_{-\infty}^{\infty} \delta k(\tau)\, \delta k(\sigma)\, \overline{f(t - \tau) f(t - \sigma)}\, d\tau\, d\sigma \quad (2.12) \\ &= \overline{\left[\int_{-\infty}^{\infty} \delta k(\tau) f(t - \tau)\, d\tau\right]^2}, \end{aligned}$$

from which it is clear that

$$J \geqslant 0. \quad (2.13)$$

For the mean square error corresponding to the weighting function $k(\tau)$ to be a minimum, it is necessary and sufficient that the term in brackets in (2.11) vanish, i.e., that the integral equation (2.10) be satisfied. For if this term were nonzero, then for a suitable choice of the function $\delta k(\tau)$, the integral (with respect to τ) in which it appears would be nonzero, e.g., negative. Then, we would have $E' < E$ (since for sufficiently small $\delta k(\tau)$, the quadratic term J can be neglected), so that the weighting function $k(\tau)$ would correspond to a nonoptimum filter. If the integral were positive, we would obtain the same result by merely changing the sign of $\delta k(\tau)$. This proves that a necessary condition for $k(\tau)$ to be the weighting function of the optimum filter is that it satisfy the integral equation (2.10). The sufficiency of the condition follows from the fact that if (2.10) holds, then the formula (2.11) for the mean square error takes the form

$$E' = E + J, \quad (2.14)$$

which, because of (2.13), implies that

$$E' \geqslant E, \quad (2.15)$$

i.e., the filter $\mathscr{K}$ is really the optimum filter, since any other filter gives a mean square error which is larger (or perhaps the same).

To find the optimum filter, we have to solve the integral equation (2.10) for the unknown function $k(\tau)$. The solution of this equation for filters of types II and III is quite complicated, since then the function $k(\tau)$ must satisfy the supplementary conditions (1.14) and (1.16). However, for filters of type I, the equation can be solved quite simply, as we shall soon see.

Given a correlation function $R(\tau)$, we introduce the function

$$S(\omega) = \int_{-\infty}^{\infty} e^{-i\omega\tau} R(\tau)\, d\tau. \tag{2.16}$$

Then, inverting this Fourier transform, we can write

$$R(\tau) = \frac{1}{2\pi} \int_{-\infty}^{\infty} e^{i\omega\tau} S(\omega)\, d\omega. \tag{2.17}$$

The function $S(\omega)$, which we shall call the (*power*) *spectral density*, has deep physical significance, as will be apparent from *Khinchin's theorem* (Sec. 3).

Next, we introduce the function

$$K(\omega) = \int_{-\infty}^{\infty} e^{-i\omega\tau} k(\tau)\, d\tau, \tag{2.18}$$

and inverting the Fourier transform, we obtain

$$k(\tau) = \frac{1}{2\pi} \int_{-\infty}^{\infty} e^{i\omega\tau} K(\omega)\, d\omega. \tag{2.19}$$

The function $k(\tau)$ is the response of the filter $\mathscr{K}$ to a unit impulse, and hence is often called the *impulse response* (*function*) of $\mathscr{K}$. In fact, if we choose the input function in formula (1.11) to be a unit impulse, i.e., the delta function $\delta(t)$ defined by (1.13), we obtain

$$x(t) = \int_{-\infty}^{\infty} k(t - t')\, \delta(t')\, dt' = k(t). \tag{2.20}$$

The function $K(\omega)$ is called the *transfer function* (or *system function*) of the filter $\mathscr{K}$. This designation comes about as follows: Suppose the function

$$f(t) = f_\omega e^{i\omega t}, \tag{2.21}$$

appears at the input of the linear filter $\mathscr{K}$. Then the output of $\mathscr{K}$ is

$$x(t) = \int_{-\infty}^{\infty} k(t') f_\omega e^{i\omega(t-t')}\, dt' = f_\omega e^{i\omega t} \int_{-\infty}^{\infty} k(t') e^{-i\omega t'}\, dt'.$$

It follows that the function $x(t)$ equals

$$x(t) = x_\omega e^{i\omega t}, \tag{2.22}$$

where

$$x_\omega = K(\omega) f_\omega. \tag{2.23}$$

Thus, the transfer function $K(\omega)$ is the ratio between x_ω and f_ω, the *complex amplitudes* of the output and input functions, respectively. As is always the case in using complex notation, it is not the formulas (2.21) and (2.22) which have direct physical meaning, but rather their real parts

$$f(t) = \mathrm{Re}\{f_\omega e^{i\omega t}\}, \qquad x(t) = \mathrm{Re}\{x_\omega e^{i\omega t}\}, \tag{2.24}$$

which specify the steady-state sinusoidal oscillations (of frequency ω) at the input and output of the filter $\mathscr{K}$.

We can now easily solve the integral equation (2.10). To do so, we multiply both sides of (2.10) by $e^{\ i\omega\tau}$ and then integrate with respect to τ from $-\infty$ to ∞, obtaining

$$\int_{-\infty}^{\infty} e^{\ i\omega\tau}\,d\tau \int_{-\infty}^{\infty} k(\sigma)R_f(\tau-\sigma)\,d\sigma = \int_{-\infty}^{\infty} e^{-i\omega\tau} R_{hf}(\tau)\,d\tau. \tag{2.25}$$

Making the change of variable $t = \tau - \sigma$, we can transform the left-hand side of (2.25) into

$$\begin{aligned}
\int_{-\infty}^{\infty} e^{-i\omega\tau}\,d\tau \int_{-\infty}^{\infty} k(\sigma)R_f(\tau-\sigma)\,d\sigma \\
&= \int_{-\infty}^{\infty} k(\sigma)\,d\sigma \int_{-\infty}^{\infty} e^{\ i\omega\tau} R_f(t-\sigma)\,d\tau \\
&= \int_{-\infty}^{\infty} e^{-i\omega\sigma} k(\sigma)\,d\sigma \int_{-\infty}^{\infty} e^{\ i\omega t} R_f(t)\,dt \qquad (2.26)\\
&= K(\omega)S_f(\omega).
\end{aligned}$$

The integral in the right-hand side of (2.25), according to the notation just introduced, is $S_{hf}(\omega)$. Therefore, equation (2.25) takes the form

$$K(\omega)S_f(\omega) = S_{hf}(\omega), \tag{2.27}$$

and the transfer function of the optimum filter is given very simply as the ratio of the spectral densities $S_{hf}(\omega)$ and $S_f(\omega)$:

$$K(\omega) = \frac{S_{hf}(\omega)}{S_f(\omega)}. \tag{2.28}$$

In view of equation (2.10), the expression (2.09) for the mean square error of the optimum filter becomes

$$\overline{\varepsilon^2} = R_h(0) - \iint_{-\infty}^{\infty} k(\tau)k(\sigma)R_f(\tau-\sigma)\,d\tau\,d\sigma. \tag{2.29}$$

Using (2.17) and (2.19), we carry out the following transformations:

$$R_h(0) = \frac{1}{2\pi}\int_{-\infty}^{\infty} S_h(\omega)\,d\omega,$$

$$\begin{aligned}
\int_{-\infty}^{\infty} k(\tau)k(\sigma)R_f(\tau-\sigma)\,d\tau\,d\sigma \\
&= \frac{1}{2\pi}\iint_{-\infty}^{\infty} k(\tau)k(\sigma)\,d\tau\,d\sigma \int_{-\infty}^{\infty} e^{i\omega(\tau-\sigma)} S_f(\omega)\,d\omega \\
&= \frac{1}{2\pi}\int_{-\infty}^{\infty} S_f(\omega)\,d\omega \int_{-\infty}^{\infty} e^{i\omega\tau} k(\tau)\,d\tau \int_{-\infty}^{\infty} e^{-i\omega\sigma} k(\sigma)\,d\sigma \qquad (2.30)\\
&= \frac{1}{2\pi}\int_{-\infty}^{\infty} K(\omega)K(-\omega)S_f(\omega)\,d\omega,
\end{aligned}$$

from which it follows that

$$\overline{\varepsilon^2} = \frac{1}{2\pi}\int_{-\infty}^{\infty} [S_h(\omega) - K(\omega)K(-\omega)S_f(\omega)]\, d\omega. \tag{2.31}$$

Then, using formula (2.28), we obtain

$$\overline{\varepsilon^2} = \frac{1}{2\pi}\int_{-\infty}^{\infty} \frac{S_h(\omega)S_f(\omega) - S_{hf}(\omega)S_{hf}(-\omega)}{S_f(\omega)}\, d\omega, \tag{2.32}$$

where we have used the evenness of the function

$$S_f(\omega) = S_f(-\omega), \tag{2.33}$$

which follows from the evenness of the function $R_f(\tau)$ [see formula (1.09) and Sec. 3].

Consider now the problem of simple filtering (without further operations on the signal). In this case

$$h(t) = m(t) \quad \text{and} \quad K(\omega) = \frac{S_{mf}(\omega)}{S_f(\omega)}. \tag{2.34}$$

For simplicity, we assume that there is no cross correlation between the useful signal and the noise, i.e., that

$$R_{mn}(\tau) = \overline{m(t)n(t-\tau)} = 0. \tag{2.35}$$

Then, the correlation functions R_{mf} and R_f are equal to

$$\begin{aligned} R_{mf}(\tau) &= \overline{m(t)f(t-\tau)} = \overline{m(t)m(t-\tau)} + \overline{m(t)n(t-\tau)} = R_m(\tau), \\ R_f(\tau) &= \overline{[m(t)+n(t)][m(t-\tau)+n(t-\tau)]} = R_m(\tau) + R_n(\tau), \end{aligned} \tag{2.36}$$

and therefore

$$S_{mf}(\omega) = S_m(\omega), \qquad S_f(\omega) = S_m(\omega) + S_n(\omega). \tag{2.37}$$

Taking all this into account, we find that the transfer function (2.28) is

$$K(\omega) = \frac{S_m(\omega)}{S_m(\omega) + S_n(\omega)}, \tag{2.38}$$

where if $S_m(\omega) = 0$ and $S_n(\omega) = 0$, the function $K(\omega)$ can be chosen arbitrarily, e.g., can be set equal to zero.[4] Formula (2.38) gives the transfer function of the optimum filter under the condition that the useful signal and the noise are uncorrelated. According to (2.32), the mean square error for this filter is

$$\overline{\varepsilon^2} = \frac{1}{2\pi}\int_{-\infty}^{\infty} \frac{S_m(\omega)S_n(\omega)}{S_m(\omega) + S_n(\omega)}\, d\omega. \tag{2.39}$$

As we shall see in Sec. 3, $S_m(\omega)$, $S_n(\omega)$, etc., are nonnegative functions of ω.

[4] A similar remark applies to formulas (2.28) and (2.34).

Next, we consider some special cases of these formulas. First we assume that the spectral densities $S_m(\omega)$ and $S_n(\omega)$ of the signal and the noise, respectively, do not overlap (Fig. 2). Then, formula (2.38) gives

$$K(\omega) = 1 \quad \text{for} \quad S_m(\omega) \neq 0, \qquad K(\omega) = 0 \quad \text{for} \quad S_m(\omega) = 0, \tag{2.40}$$

and from formula (2.35), we obtain

$$\overline{\varepsilon^2} = 0. \tag{2.41}$$

Thus, in this case, the filtering takes place without error, and the useful signal $m(t)$ is reproduced exactly at the output of the filter $\mathcal{K}$. However, if the spectral densities $S_m(\omega)$ and $S_n(\omega)$ overlap, then a certain error accompanies the filtering. For example, if the spectral densities $S_m(\omega)$ and $S_n(\omega)$ are chosen as in Fig. 3, then $K(\omega) = 1$ for $\omega < \omega_1$, while for $\omega_1 < \omega < \omega_2$, the function $K(\omega)$ falls off continuously to zero. In this case, the error (2.38) is not zero. The error arises both because a part of the noise spectrum passes through the filter (in fact, the frequency range $\omega_1 < \omega < \omega_2$) and because the useful signal is distorted as a result of the attenuation of part of its spectrum (in the same frequency range). The larger the function $S_n(\omega)$ is in the range of overlap $\omega_1 < \omega < \omega_2$ and the smaller $S_m(\omega)$ is in this range, the less this range will be allowed to pass through the optimum filter.

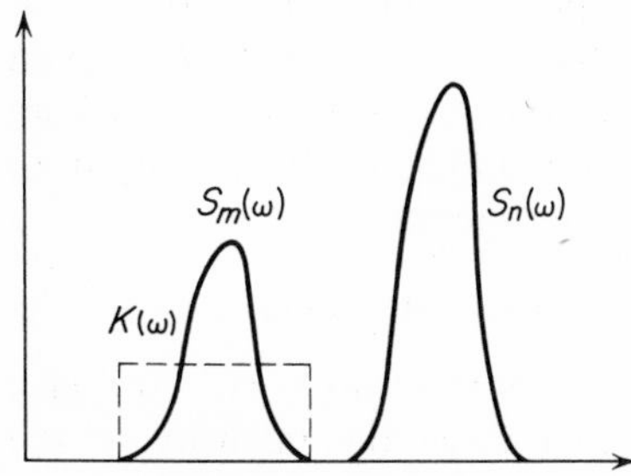

FIG. 2. Filtering of random processes with nonoverlapping spectra.

We recall that these results pertain to filters of type I. However, aside from certain special features (see Chap. 2), they also apply *qualitatively* to filters of type II.

It is interesting to examine the transfer function of the optimum filter under the condition

$$S_n(\omega) \gg S_m(\omega), \tag{2.42}$$

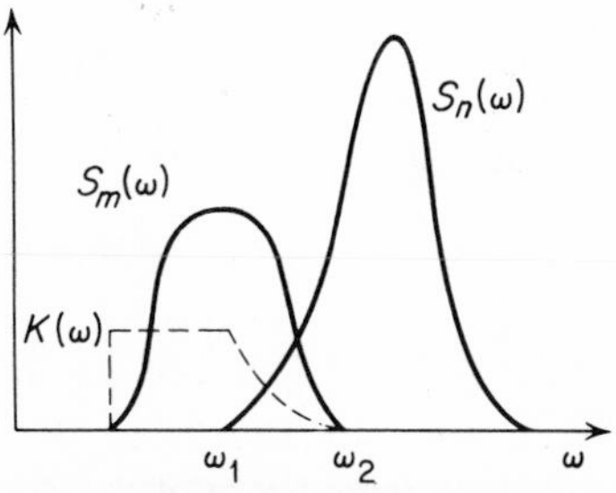

FIG. 3. Filtering in the case where the spectrum of the noise partially overlaps the spectrum of the useful signal.

i.e., when the spectral density of the noise is very large compared to that of the signal, as shown, for example, in Fig. 4. In this case, we have approximately

$$K(\omega) = \frac{S_m(\omega)}{S_n(\omega)}, \tag{2.43}$$

where we have neglected the term $S_m(\omega)$ in the denominator of formula (2.38). With the same approximation, formula (2.39) gives

$$\overline{\varepsilon^2} = \frac{1}{2\pi}\int_{-\infty}^{\infty} S_m(\omega)\, d\omega = R_m(0), \tag{2.44}$$

or, according to formula (1.07),

$$\overline{\varepsilon^2} = \overline{m^2}. \tag{2.45}$$

Thus, the mean square error at the output of the optimum filter equals the mean square of the useful signal.

The mean square error can be described quite generally as the (*mean*) *intensity of the filter output noise.* In fact, the filter is supposed to reproduce the useful signal $h(t)$, but at the output we obtain instead the function $x(t)$, which deviates from $h(t)$ by the amount $\varepsilon(t)$. It is natural to characterize the "output noise"

$$\varepsilon(t) = h(t) - m(t)$$

by its mean square or *intensity* $\overline{\varepsilon^2}$. We have just shown that when the intensity of the input noise is considerably greater than that of the useful signal and occupies the same frequency range, then the intensity of the output noise equals the signal intensity, i.e., the *output signal-to-noise ratio* equals 1. From this, one could draw the erroneous conclusion that the optimum filter can effectively separate the signal from input noise which is arbitrarily intense. However, when the input noise is very intense, the intensity of the process $x(t)$ at the filter output is extremely weak, since the function (2.43) is small, and the error (2.45) is obtained because we have approximately

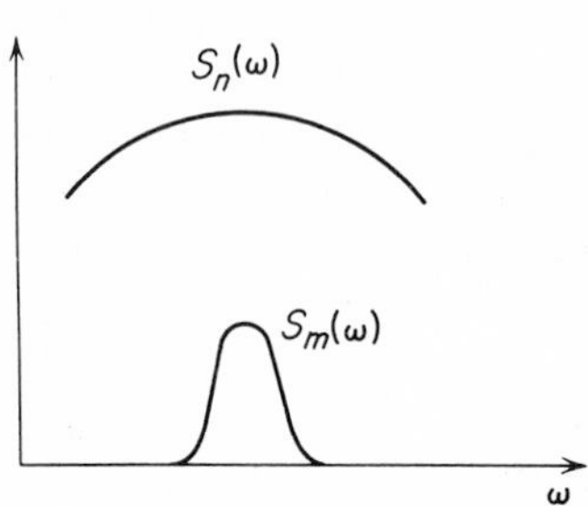

FIG. 4. A noise spectrum which completely overlaps and greatly exceeds the spectrum of the useful signal.

$$x(t) = 0 \quad \text{and} \quad \varepsilon(t) = -m(t).$$

Although it often happens in radio engineering that when the signal-to-noise ratio equals 1, it is still possible to effect a separation of the useful signal from the noise (by using the fact that the properties of the signal differ somehow from those of the noise), this difference has already been exploited in applying the optimum filter, so that even when the signal-to-noise ratio equals 1, it is in fact no longer possible to separate the useful signal from the noise background.

Finally, we note that the inequality

$$\overline{\varepsilon^2} \leqslant \overline{m^2} \tag{2.46}$$

is an easy consequence of (2.29) or (2.39). This inequality shows that the signal-to-noise ratio of the output filter is greater than 1 under more favorable conditions, i.e., for smaller noise intensities.

3. Correlation Functions and Power Spectral Densities

In the preceding section, we introduced the (power) spectral densities $S_f(\omega)$, $S_m(\omega)$, etc., in a formal way. The physical meaning of the spectral density associated with an autocorrelation function stems from *Khinchin's theorem*, which we now discuss.

It follows from the evenness of the function $R_f(\tau)$ that its Fourier transform $S_f(\omega)$ is also even. In fact, according to (1.09), formula (2.16) becomes

$$S_f(\omega) = \int_{-\infty}^{\infty} R_f(\tau) \cos \omega\tau \, d\tau = 2\int_0^{\infty} R_f(\tau) \cos \omega\tau \, d\tau, \tag{3.01}$$

which implies that

$$S_f(\omega) = S_f(-\omega). \tag{3.02}$$

Khinchin's theorem states that *the function $S_f(\omega)$ is nonnegative for any random process $f(t)$*:

$$S_f(\omega) \geqslant 0. \tag{3.03}$$

Moreover, it turns out that the product $S_f(\omega)\, d\omega$ is proportional to the intensity of the oscillations at the output of a narrow-band filter which passes only the frequency range $(\omega, \omega + d\omega)$, when the random process $f(t)$ is applied at the filter input. Formula (2.17) implies that

$$R_f(0) = \overline{f^2(t)} = \frac{1}{2\pi}\int_{-\infty}^{\infty} S_f(\omega)\, d\omega, \tag{3.04}$$

where the quantity $R_f(0) = \overline{f^2}$ is the *intensity* (or *average power*) of the process $f(t)$. (For example, if $f(t)$ is a voltage applied to the terminals of a resistance, the quantity $\overline{f^2}$ is proportional to the average power dissipated in the resistance.) Since the right-hand side of (3.04) is an integral over the (angular) frequency ω, it is natural to identify the contribution to this integral made by the frequency range $(\omega, \omega + d\omega)$ with the power "lying in" the range $(\omega, \omega + d\omega)$, i.e., associated with the sinusoidal oscillations of the process $f(t)$ in $(\omega, \omega + d\omega)$.

To prove Khinchin's theorem, we proceed as follows: Let the process $f(t)$ pass through a linear filter $\mathscr{K}$. Then, at the output of $\mathscr{K}$, we obtain the random process

$$x(t) = \int_{-\infty}^{\infty} k(t')f(t - t')\, dt', \tag{3.05}$$

whose intensity (average power) equals

$$
\begin{aligned}
\overline{x^2(t)} &= \iint_{-\infty}^{\infty} k(t')k(t'')\overline{f(t-t')f(t-t'')}\,dt'\,dt'' \\
&= \iint_{-\infty}^{\infty} k(t')k(t'')R_f(t'-t'')\,dt'\,dt'' \\
&= \frac{1}{2\pi}\int_{-\infty}^{\infty} K(\omega)K(-\omega)S_f(\omega)\,d\omega,
\end{aligned}
\tag{3.06}
$$

where we have used the second of the formulas (2.30). Since the function $k(t)$ is real, it follows from (2.18) that

$$K(-\omega) = K^*(\omega), \tag{3.07}$$

where the asterisk denotes the complex conjugate. Therefore, we have

$$K(\omega)K(-\omega) = |K(\omega)|^2 \tag{3.08}$$

and

$$\overline{x^2} = \frac{1}{2\pi}\int_{-\infty}^{\infty} |K(\omega)|^2\, S_f(\omega)\,d\omega. \tag{3.09}$$

Formula (3.09) relates the intensity of the oscillations at the filter output to the transfer function of the filter $\mathscr{K}$ and the spectral density $S_f(\omega)$.

Consider now a filter whose transfer function $K(\omega)$ is such that $K(\omega) = 1$ for frequencies in the intervals $(\omega, \omega + d\omega)$ and $(-\omega - d\omega, -\omega)$, but $K(\omega) = 0$ otherwise. Then formula (3.09) gives

$$\overline{x^2} = S_f(\omega)\frac{d\omega}{2\pi} + S_f(-\omega)\frac{d\omega}{2\pi} = 2S_f(\omega)\frac{d\omega}{2\pi}. \tag{3.10}$$

Since the left-hand side of (3.10) is nonnegative, we have proved the inequality (3.03).

The filter $\mathscr{K}$ used to derive (3.10) passes without change all sinusoidal oscillations in the frequency ranges $(\omega, \omega + d\omega)$ and $(-\omega - d\omega, -\omega)$, and "cuts off" oscillations of other frequencies [cf. formula (2.23)]. The physical meaning of the spectral density $S_f(\omega)$ is apparent from (3.10). Since ω is an angular frequency (the ordinary frequency equals $\omega/2\pi$), $S_f(\omega)$ is the average power (or intensity) of the oscillations in a unit frequency band (e.g., $d\omega/2\pi = 1$ cycle per second), provided we make a distinction between positive and negative frequencies. If we consider only positive frequencies, i.e., if we write formulas (3.04) and (3.09) as

$$
\begin{aligned}
\overline{f^2} &= \frac{1}{\pi}\int_0^{\infty} S_f(\omega)\,d\omega, \\
\overline{x^2} &= \frac{1}{\pi}\int_0^{\infty} |K(\omega)|^2 S_f(\omega)\,d\omega,
\end{aligned}
\tag{3.11}
$$

then $2S_f(\omega)$ is the average power corresponding to a frequency range of 1 cps. This explains why $S_f(\omega)$ is called the *power spectral density*.[5]

From formulas (2.17) and (3.03), we can deduce the inequality

$$|R_f(\tau)| = \frac{1}{2\pi}\left|\int_{-\infty}^{\infty} e^{i\omega\tau}S_f(\omega)\,d\omega\right| \leqslant \frac{1}{2\pi}\int_{-\infty}^{\infty} S_f(\omega)\,d\omega,$$

i.e.,

$$|R_f(\tau)| \leqslant R_f(0). \tag{3.12}$$

Thus, a correlation function takes its largest value at $\tau = 0$. This fact can be derived even more simply by starting from the inequality

$$[f(t) \pm f(t - \tau)]^2 \geqslant 0$$

or

$$f^2(t) + f^2(t - \tau) \geqslant \pm\, 2f(t)f(t - \tau).$$

Taking the mathematical expectation of both sides of the last formula, we obtain

$$R_f(0) \geqslant \pm R_f(\tau), \tag{3.13}$$

which is equivalent to the inequality (3.12).

Together with the concept of an autocorrelation function, we can introduce the concept of a *cross-correlation function*. The cross-correlation function of the two processes $m(t)$ and $n(t)$ is defined as

$$R_{mn}(\tau) = \overline{m(t)n(t - \tau)}, \tag{3.14}$$

and expresses the statistical relation between two different processes at two different instants of time. If the two processes are independent, then the cross-correlation function vanishes.

Unlike autocorrelation functions, cross-correlation functions are not even, but it can easily be shown that

$$R_{mn}(\tau) = R_{nm}(-\tau), \tag{3.15}$$

where

$$R_{nm}(\tau) = \overline{n(t)m(t - \tau)}. \tag{3.16}$$

In fact,

$$R_{nm}(-\tau) = \overline{n(t)m(t + \tau)} = \overline{n(t - \tau)m(t)},$$

which proves (3.15). The relation (3.15) carries over to the corresponding spectral densities:

$$S_{mn}(\omega) = S_{nm}(-\omega). \tag{3.17}$$

[5] Sometimes called the *intensity spectrum*, the *power spectrum*, or simply the *spectrum*. (*Translator*)

Using the Fourier transform

$$S_{mn}(\omega) = \int_{-\infty}^{\infty} e^{-i\omega\tau} R_{mn}(\tau)\, d\tau, \tag{3.18}$$

we can also easily verify the relation

$$S_{mn}(-\omega) = S_{mn}^*(\omega), \tag{3.19}$$

from the fact that $R_{mn}(\tau)$ is real.

The function $S_{mn}(\omega)$ is in general complex, and hence it has no simple physical interpretation. To clarify its meaning, we take a random process

$$f(t) = m(t) + n(t), \tag{3.20}$$

which is equal to the sum of two processes $m(t)$ and $n(t)$, and then calculate the function

$$\begin{aligned} R_f(\tau) &= \overline{[m(t) + n(t)][m(t-\tau) + n(t-\tau)]} \\ &= R_m(\tau) + R_n(\tau) + R_{mn}(\tau) + R_{nm}(\tau). \end{aligned} \tag{3.21}$$

Going over to spectral densities and using the relations (3.17) and (3.19), we find that

$$\begin{aligned} S_f(\omega) &= S_m(\omega) + S_n(\omega) + S_{mn}(\omega) + S_{nm}(\omega) \\ &= S_m(\omega) + S_n(\omega) + 2\mathrm{Re}\{S_{mn}(\omega)\}. \end{aligned} \tag{3.22}$$

The physical meaning of the terms $S_m(\omega)$ and $S_n(\omega)$ is clear from Khinchin's theorem, i.e., their sum equals the spectral density $S_f(\omega)$ in the absence of correlation between $m(t)$ and $n(t)$. The additional term $2\mathrm{Re}\{S_{mn}(\omega)\}$ is the "interference intensity" caused by the statistical relation between $m(t)$ and $n(t)$. The imaginary part of the complex function $S_{mn}(\omega)$ does not have such an explicit physical meaning.

We now study some examples of autocorrelation functions and the corresponding spectral densities. Letting α denote a real parameter with the dimension of frequency, consider the pair of functions

$$R(\tau) = R(0)e^{-\alpha|\tau|}, \qquad S(\omega) = \frac{2\alpha R(0)}{\alpha^2 + \omega^2}, \tag{3.23}$$

and the "converse" pair

$$R(\tau) = \frac{R(0)}{1 + \alpha^2\tau^2}, \qquad S(\omega) = \frac{\pi R(0)}{\alpha} e^{-|\omega|/\alpha}. \tag{3.24}$$

We can easily verify (3.23) by using (2.16) and calculating $S(\omega)$ from $R(\tau)$, while (3.24) is easily verified by using (2.17) and calculating $R(\tau)$ from $S(\omega)$. In both cases, the functions $S(\omega)$ satisfy the condition (3.03). If the correlation function $R(\tau)$ has "Gaussian form," then the spectral density also has Gaussian form:

$$R(\tau) = R(0)e^{-\alpha^2\tau^2/2}, \qquad S(\omega) = \frac{\sqrt{2\pi}R(0)}{\alpha} e^{-\omega^2/2\alpha^2}. \tag{3.25}$$

As a last example, consider the pair

$$R(\tau) = R(0)\frac{\sin \omega_0 \tau}{\omega_0 \tau}, \qquad S(\omega) = \begin{cases} \dfrac{\pi R(0)}{\omega_0} & \text{for} \quad -\omega_0 < \omega < \omega_0, \\ 0 & \text{otherwise,} \end{cases} \tag{3.26}$$

which is easily verified by using formula (2.17). An interesting feature of this example is that the roles of R and S cannot be interchanged in (3.26), as they can in (3.23) and (3.24). In fact, if we set

$$R(\tau) = \begin{cases} R(0) & \text{for} \quad -\tau_0 < \tau < \tau_0, \\ 0 & \text{otherwise,} \end{cases} \tag{3.27}$$

we obtain a function $S(\omega)$ which is proportional to $\sin \omega\tau_0/\omega\tau_0$, and which therefore takes negative values, which is not permissible in view of the condition (3.03) proved above. This makes it clear that Khinchin's theorem imposes certain restrictions on an autocorrelation function $R(\tau)$. In fact, not every even function of τ can be an autocorrelation function, but only those which have nonnegative Fourier transforms (i.e., nonnegative spectral densities).

The functions R and S in examples (3.23) to (3.25) take their maxima for $\tau = 0$ and $\omega = 0$, and then fall off monotonically on both sides. If we define the *correlation time* $\Delta\tau$ in such a way that the correlation function $R(\tau)$ takes values of the same order of magnitude as $R(0)$ inside the interval $-\Delta\tau < \tau < \Delta\tau$ and values much less than $R(0)$ outside this interval, then in all three examples we have $\Delta\tau \sim 1/\alpha$, where the sign $\sim$ denotes approximate equality. Similarly, if we define the (*spectral*) *bandwidth* $\Delta\omega$ as the interval $-\Delta\omega < \omega < \Delta\omega$ within which "most of the spectral intensity is concentrated," and outside of which the function $S(\omega)$ is small compared to $S(0)$, then in all three examples, $\Delta\omega \sim \alpha$, and we arrive at the relation

$$\Delta\omega\, \Delta\tau \sim 1. \tag{3.28}$$

In the example (3.26), obviously $\Delta\omega = \omega_0$, while $\Delta\tau \sim \pi/\omega_0$, since $R(\tau) = 0$ for $\tau = \pi/\omega_0$, whereas for larger values of τ, $R(\tau)$ takes comparatively small values. In this case

$$\Delta\omega\, \Delta\tau \sim \pi, \tag{3.29}$$

which does not differ essentially from (3.28).

For functions R and S of the type considered above, we can derive a more precise expression for the product $\Delta\omega\, \Delta\tau$, if we introduce more exact definitions of the quantities $\Delta\omega$ and $\Delta\tau$, in an appropriate manner. Thus, suppose that we define the (spectral) bandwidth $\Delta\omega$ by the formula

$$\int_{-\infty}^{\infty} S(\omega)\, d\omega = 2\int_{0}^{\infty} S(\omega)\, d\omega = 2S(0)\,\Delta\omega, \tag{3.30}$$

i.e., we define $\Delta\omega$ in such a way that if we approximate the curve $S(\omega)$ by a rectangle of height $S(0)$ and width $2\Delta\omega$, the area of the rectangle will be the same as the area under the whole curve $S(\omega)$, as shown in Fig. 5. The correlation time is defined similarly:

$$\int_{-\infty}^{\infty} R(\tau)\, d\tau = 2\int_{0}^{\infty} R(\tau)\, d\tau = 2R(0)\,\Delta\tau. \tag{3.31}$$

Then, using the formulas

$$S(0) = \int_{-\infty}^{\infty} R(\tau)\, d\tau, \qquad R(0) = \frac{1}{2\pi}\int_{-\infty}^{\infty} S(\omega)\, d\omega, \tag{3.32}$$

we arrive at the *exact* relation

$$\Delta\omega\,\Delta\tau = \frac{\pi}{2}. \tag{3.33}$$

The relations (3.28), (3.29), and (3.33) are applicable to any pairs of functions which are Fourier transforms of each other, in particular, to the functions $k(\tau)$ and $K(\omega)$ which characterize a linear filter [cf. formulas (2.18) and (2.19)]. In this case, the quantity $\Delta\omega$ defines the *pass-band* of the filter, and the quantity $\Delta\tau$ defines the "memory" of the filter, i.e., the time interval during which the input signal appreciably affects the value of the output signal at a given time. In other words, $\Delta\tau$ characterizes the time duration of the function $k(\tau)$, i.e., the time during which the filter responds appreciably to a unit impulse.

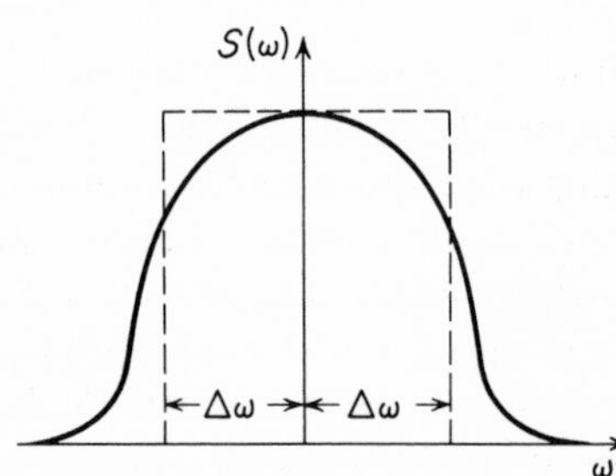

FIG. 5. Illustrating the definition of bandwidth.

We conclude this section by making the following remarks: The integral equation (2.10) shows that the properties of the optimum filter are given in terms of the correlation functions R_{hf} and R_f, or equivalently, in terms of the corresponding spectral densities. Therefore, the theory presented above leads to *filtering in the frequency domain*, an approach which is a familiar one in radio engineering. In fact, it has been known for a long time that separation of two random processes which occupy nonoverlapping frequency bands (see Fig. 2), e.g., the separation of two radio transmissions using different wavelengths, involves no difficulties and is accomplished by using a receiver with suitable frequency selectivity. On the other hand, the filtering out of noise occupying the same frequency band as the signal itself (see Figs. 3 and 4), e.g., the suppression of receiver noise itself, represents a problem lying outside the scope of "classical" radio engineering. As was shown in Sec. 2, this is just the basic problem of the theory of optimum filters; in this sense, the theory generalizes the accumulated experience of radio engineers in trying to combat the effects of random noise.

4. Transfer Functions of Linear Operators

We now consider the following important problem arising in the theory of linear filters: Let the processes $m(t)$ and $n(t)$ be related by the formula

$$h(t) = \mathscr{L}[m(t)], \tag{4.01}$$

where $\mathscr{L}$ is a linear operator. Then, what is the relation between the spectral density $S_{hf}(\omega)$ and the spectral density $S_{mf}(\omega)$, where $f(t)$ is an arbitrary random process?

We begin by studying operators $\mathscr{L}$ which can be represented as *linear integral operators*. (As already remarked in Sec. 1, not all linear operators can be represented in integral form.) In this case, we have

$$h(t) = \int_{-\infty}^{\infty} l(t')m(t - t')\, dt'. \tag{4.02}$$

We also know that

$$\begin{aligned} S_{hf}(\omega) &= \int_{-\infty}^{\infty} e^{-i\omega\tau} R_{hf}(\tau)\, d\tau \\ &= \int_{-\infty}^{\infty} e^{-i\omega\tau}\, \overline{h(t)f(t-\tau)}\, d\tau. \end{aligned} \tag{4.03}$$

Substituting $h(t)$ from (4.02) into (4.03), we obtain

$$\begin{aligned} S_{hf}(\omega) &= \int_{-\infty}^{\infty} e^{-i\omega\tau}\, d\tau \int_{-\infty}^{\infty} l(t')\overline{m(t-t')f(t-\tau)}\, dt' \\ &= \int_{-\infty}^{\infty} e^{-i\omega\tau}\, dt \int_{-\infty}^{\infty} l(t')R_{mf}(\tau - t')\, dt'. \end{aligned} \tag{4.04}$$

Introducing a new variable of integration, we obtain

$$S_{hf}(\omega) = \int_{-\infty}^{\infty} e^{-i\omega\tau} l(t)\, dt \int_{-\infty}^{\infty} e^{-i\omega\tau} R_{mf}(\tau)\, d\tau \tag{4.05}$$

or

$$S_{hf}(\omega) = L(\omega)S_{mf}(\omega), \tag{4.06}$$

where we have written

$$L(\omega) = \int_{-\infty}^{\infty} e^{-i\omega t} l(t)\, dt \tag{4.07}$$

and used the relation

$$S_{mf}(\omega) = \int_{-\infty}^{\infty} e^{-i\omega\tau} R_{mf}(\tau)\, d\tau. \tag{4.08}$$

The function $L(\omega)$ will be called the *transfer function* corresponding to the linear operator $\mathscr{L}$ [cf. formula (2.18)]. According to (3.17) and a formula like (3.19), we can also write

$$S_{fh}(\omega) = S_{hf}(-\omega) = L(-\omega)S_{mf}(-\omega) = L(-\omega)S_{fm}(\omega)$$

or

$$S_{fh}(\omega) = L(-\omega)S_{fm}(\omega) = L^*(\omega)S_{fm}(\omega). \tag{4.09}$$

For example, let $S_f(\omega)$ and $S_x(\omega)$ be the spectral densities of the random functions $f(t)$ and $x(t)$, appearing at the input and output, respectively, of a filter $\mathscr{K}$. Then, using (4.06) and (4.09), we obtain

$$S_x(\omega) \equiv S_{xx}(\omega) = K(\omega)S_{fx}(\omega) = K(\omega)K^*(\omega)S_{ff}(\omega)$$

or

$$S_x(\omega) = |K(\omega)|^2 S_f(\omega). \tag{4.10}$$

The expression (4.10) shows that the spectral density $S_x(\omega)$ at the output of a linear filter equals the absolute value squared of the transfer function $K(\omega)$ times the input spectral density $S_f(\omega)$. This is just the formula (3.09) derived previously.

As already noted, not all linear operators can be written in the form (4.02), and then the integral (4.07) defining $L(\omega)$ is meaningless. In such cases, we *define* the transfer function corresponding to the operator $\mathscr{L}$ by the formula

$$L(\omega) = \frac{S_{hf}(\omega)}{S_{mf}(\omega)}. \tag{4.11}$$

The following examples illustrate how this is done:

1. Let $h(t) = m(t)$. Strictly speaking, we cannot represent this simple formula by an integral of the form (4.02). Formally, of course, we could use a delta function [cf. formula (1.13)], but for our purposes there is no need to do so. Since $\mathscr{L}$ is the "unit" operator, in this case it is natural to set

$$L(\omega) = 1, \tag{4.12}$$

which agrees with formula (4.11).

2. Let

$$h(t) = m(t + s), \tag{4.13}$$

i.e., let $\mathscr{L}$ be the time shift operator. Then, it is easy to show that

$$L(\omega) = e^{i\omega s}, \tag{4.14}$$

since

$$S_{hf}(\omega) = \int_{-\infty}^{\infty} e^{-i\omega\tau}\overline{m(t + s)f(t - \tau)}\, d\tau = \int_{-\infty}^{\infty} e^{-i\omega\tau} R_{mf}(\tau + s)\, d\tau$$

or

$$S_{hf}(\omega) = e^{i\omega s}\int_{-\infty}^{\infty} e^{-i\omega\tau} R_{mf}(\tau)\, d\tau = e^{i\omega s}S_{mf}(\omega), \tag{4.15}$$

which gives (4.14).

3. Let $\mathscr{L}$ be the differentiation operator

$$h(t) = \frac{dm(t)}{dt}. \tag{4.16}$$

Then

$$\begin{aligned} R_{hf}(\tau) &= \overline{\frac{dm(t)}{dt} f(t-\tau)} = \overline{\frac{dm(t+\tau)}{dt} f(t)} \\ &= \frac{d}{d\tau}\overline{m(t+\tau)f(t)} = \frac{d}{d\tau} R_{mf}(\tau) \end{aligned} \tag{4.17}$$

and

$$\begin{aligned} S_{hf}(\omega) &= \int_{-\infty}^{\infty} e^{-i\omega\tau} \frac{d}{d\tau} R_{mf}(\tau)\, d\tau \\ &= i\omega \int_{-\infty}^{\infty} e^{-i\omega\tau} R_{mf}(\tau)\, d\tau = i\omega S_{mf}(\omega), \end{aligned} \tag{4.18}$$

so that

$$L(\omega) = i\omega. \tag{4.19}$$

4. Finally, let $\mathscr{L}$ be the integration operator

$$h(t) = \int^{t} m(t)\, dt, \tag{4.20}$$

so that

$$m(t) = \frac{dh(t)}{dt} \tag{4.21}$$

and

$$S_{mf}(\omega) = i\omega S_{hf}(\omega), \qquad S_{hf}(\omega) = \frac{1}{i\omega} S_{mf}(\omega). \tag{4.22}$$

Thus, the transfer function corresponding to the integration operator is

$$L(\omega) = \frac{1}{i\omega}. \tag{4.23}$$

It should be remarked that the process (4.20) is not always stationary even if the process $m(t)$ is stationary, and then the formulas (4.22) and (4.23) lose their meaning.

Generalizing formulas (4.12) and (4.19), we can say that if the transfer function $L(\omega)$ is a polynomial

$$L(\omega) = \sum_{\alpha=0}^{q} Q_\alpha (i\omega)^\alpha, \tag{4.24}$$

where the Q_α are constants, then the corresponding operator $\mathscr{L}$ equals

$$\mathscr{L} = \sum_{\alpha=0}^{q} Q_\alpha \left(\frac{d}{dt}\right)^\alpha, \tag{4.25}$$

since the term $Q_\alpha(i\omega)^\alpha$ corresponds to multiplication by the coefficient Q_α and α-fold differentiation with respect to t. The formulas (4.09) and (4.10) can also be easily generalized to the case of the operators just considered.

Earlier, we found the expression (2.28) for the transfer function of the optimum linear filter of type I. Applying formula (4.11), we can easily write (2.28) in the form

$$K(\omega) = L(\omega)\frac{S_{mf}(\omega)}{S_f(\omega)}. \tag{4.26}$$

If the signal and the noise are uncorrelated, then, according to (2.37), formula (4.26) becomes

$$K(\omega) = L(\omega)\frac{S_m(\omega)}{S_m(\omega) + S_n(\omega)}. \tag{4.27}$$

This formula for $K(\omega)$ has a simple physical meaning: In the absence of noise, i.e., when $S_n(\omega) \equiv 0$, we have

$$K(\omega) = L(\omega), \tag{4.28}$$

and the factor

$$K_0(\omega) = \frac{S_m(\omega)}{S_m(\omega) + S_n(\omega)} \tag{4.29}$$

gives the correction due to the noise. As is clear from (2.38), formula (4.29) is the transfer function of the optimum linear system performing *simple filtering* [where $h(t) = m(t)$]. Thus, for example, the output of a differentiation filter of type I is obtained by first reproducing the signal with the least possible error, and then differentiating the result. Symbolically, this can be written as

$$\mathscr{K} = \mathscr{L}\mathscr{K}_0, \tag{4.30}$$

where $\mathscr{K}_0$ is the operator corresponding to simple filtering. The mean square error corresponding to a system performing *general filtering* [where $h(t) \neq m(t)$] turns out to be

$$\overline{\varepsilon^2} = \frac{1}{2\pi}\int_{-\infty}^{\infty} |L(\omega)|^2 \frac{S_m(\omega)S_f(\omega) - S_{mf}(\omega)S_{mf}(-\omega)}{S_f(\omega)}\, d\omega, \tag{4.31}$$

which becomes

$$\overline{\varepsilon^2} = \frac{1}{2\pi}\int_{-\infty}^{\infty} |L(\omega)|^2 \frac{S_m(\omega)S_n(\omega)}{S_m(\omega) + S_n(\omega)}\, d\omega. \tag{4.32}$$

If $L(\omega) = 1$, formula (4.32) reduces to (2.39).

In the theory of filtering, the spectral densities are often written as rational functions of the form

$$S(\omega) = \frac{P_\nu(\omega)}{P_\mu(\omega)}, \tag{4.33}$$

where P_ν and P_μ are polynomials of degree ν and μ, respectively. Since the integral

$$\int_{-\infty}^{\infty} S(\omega)\, d\omega$$

has to converge, we must have $\mu > \nu$. Spectral densities corresponding to autocorrelation functions must be even functions, so that for them the polynomials P_ν and P_μ can contain only even powers of ω. When the spectral densities are of this form, the transfer function of the optimum filter $\mathscr{K}$ will also be a rational function, and can therefore be written in the form

$$K(\omega) = \frac{P_b(\omega)}{P_a(\omega)}, \tag{4.34}$$

where P_a and P_b are polynomials of degree a and b, respectively.

If $a > b$ in (4.34), then the whole theory of optimum filtering developed in Sec. 2 is applicable. However, if $a \leqslant b$, then as $\omega \to \pm\infty$, the numerator grows more rapidly than the denominator, and if we try to find an expression for $k(\tau)$, the integral

$$k(\tau) = \frac{1}{2\pi}\int_{-\infty}^{\infty} e^{i\omega\tau} K(\omega)\, d\omega \tag{4.35}$$

will not converge. Thus, the whole theory of optimum filtering is no longer meaningful, since we cannot find the impulse response $k(\tau)$ from a knowledge of the transfer function $K(\omega)$.

To deal with this case, we divide the numerator by the denominator, thereby representing $K(\omega)$ in the form of a sum

$$K(\omega) = Q(\omega) + K_1(\omega), \tag{4.36}$$

where the first term $Q(\omega)$ is a polynomial of degree $q = b - a$, and the second term $K_1(\omega)$, which is the remainder when the numerator is divided by the denominator, goes to zero as $\omega \to \pm\infty$. According to (4.24) and (4.25), the polynomial

$$Q(\omega) = \sum_{\alpha=0}^{q} Q_\alpha (i\omega)^\alpha, \tag{4.37}$$

corresponds to the operator

$$\sum_{\alpha=0}^{q} Q_\alpha \left(\frac{d}{dt}\right)^\alpha. \tag{4.38}$$

Thus, we can assume that the function $x(t)$ at the output of a filter with the transfer function (4.36) is equal to

$$x(t) = \sum_{\alpha=0}^{q} Q_\alpha \frac{d^\alpha f(t)}{dt^\alpha} + \int_{-\infty}^{\infty} k_1(\tau) f(t - \tau)\, d\tau, \tag{4.39}$$

where

$$k_1(\tau) = \frac{1}{2\pi}\int_{-\infty}^{\infty} e^{i\omega\tau}K_1(\omega)\,d\omega. \tag{4.40}$$

However, in deriving the integral equation (2.10), we did not allow for the possibility that the action of the optimum linear filter might be described by formula (4.39), which is more general than formula (2.01). Therefore, in the next section, we shall generalize the theory of optimum filtering to cover this case, thereby justifying the statement that the transfer function (4.36) corresponds to the filter (4.39).

5. Generalization of the Integral Equation of the Optimum Filter

We now assume that the linear filter acts according to formula (4.39), and formulate the problem as follows: How should the function $k_1(\tau)$ and the coefficients Q_α be chosen so as to obtain a function $x(t)$ at the system output which differs from the required function $h(t)$ by as little as possible? Again, we look for an optimum filter, i.e., a filter whose mean square error $\overline{\varepsilon^2}$ is a minimum. Since

$$\varepsilon(t) = x(t) - h(t), \tag{5.01}$$

we have

$$\overline{\varepsilon^2(t)} = \overline{x^2(t)} - 2\overline{x(t)h(t)} + \overline{h^2(t)} \tag{5.02}$$

or

$$\begin{aligned}\overline{\varepsilon^2} = {} & \overline{\Big[\sum_\alpha Q_\alpha f^{(\alpha)}(t)\Big]^2} + 2\overline{\sum_\alpha Q_\alpha f^{(\alpha)}(t)\int k_1(\tau)f(t-\tau)\,d\tau} \\ & + \overline{\Big[\int k_1(\tau)f(t-\tau)\,d\tau\Big]^2} - 2\sum_\alpha Q_\alpha \overline{f^{(\alpha)}(t)h(t)} \\ & - 2\int k_1(\tau)\,\overline{f(t-\tau)h(t)}\,d\tau + \overline{h^2}.\end{aligned} \tag{5.03}$$

Transforming the square of the sum and the square of the integral into a double sum and a double integral, we obtain

$$\begin{aligned}\overline{\varepsilon^2} = {} & \sum_\alpha\sum_\beta Q_\alpha Q_\beta \overline{f^{(\alpha)}(t)f^{(\beta)}(t)} + 2\sum_\alpha Q_\alpha \int k_1(\tau)\,\overline{f^{(\alpha)}(t)f(t-\tau)}\,d\tau \\ & + \int\int k_1(\tau)k_1(\sigma)\,\overline{f(t-\tau)f(t-\sigma)}\,d\tau\,d\sigma - 2\sum_\alpha Q_\alpha \overline{h(t)f^{(\alpha)}(t)} \\ & - 2\int k_1(\tau)\overline{h(t)f(t-\tau)}\,d\tau + \overline{h^2}.\end{aligned} \tag{5.04}$$

We now differentiate the relation (2.06) α times with respect to τ, and the relation (2.05) α times with respect to σ, obtaining

$$\begin{aligned} R_{hf}^{(\alpha)}(\tau) &= (-1)^\alpha \overline{h(t)f^{(\alpha)}(t-\tau)}, \\ R_{hf}^{(\alpha)}(0) &= (-1)^\alpha \overline{h(t)f^{(\alpha)}(t)}, \\ R_f^{(\alpha)}(\tau-\sigma) &= \overline{f(t-\tau)f^{(\alpha)}(t-\sigma)}, \\ R_f^{(\alpha)}(\tau) &= \overline{f^{(\alpha)}(t)f(t-\tau)}. \end{aligned} \tag{5.05}$$

Then, we differentiate the last formula β times with respect to τ, obtaining

$$\begin{aligned} R_f^{(\alpha+\beta)}(\tau) &= (-1)^\beta \overline{f^{(\alpha)}(t)f^{(\beta)}(t-\tau)}, \\ R_f^{(\alpha+\beta)}(0) &= (-1)^\beta \overline{f^{(\alpha)}(t)f^{(\beta)}(t)} = (-1)^\alpha \overline{f^{(\alpha)}(t)f^{(\beta)}(t)}. \end{aligned} \tag{5.06}$$

This allows us to rewrite the expression (5.04) in the form

$$\begin{aligned} \overline{\varepsilon^2} = \sum_\alpha \sum_\beta Q_\alpha Q_\beta (-1)^\beta R_f^{(\alpha+\beta)}(0) &+ 2\sum_\alpha Q_\alpha \int k_1(\tau) R_1^{(\alpha)}(\tau)d\tau \\ &+ \iint k_1(\tau)k_1(\sigma)R_f(\tau-\sigma)\,d\tau\,d\sigma - 2\sum_\alpha Q_\alpha(-1)^\alpha R_{hf}^\alpha(0) \\ &- 2\int k_1(\tau)R_{hf}(\tau)\,d\tau + R_h(0), \end{aligned} \tag{5.07}$$

which expresses the mean square error in terms of the correlation functions.

Next, as in Sec. 2, we denote the mean square error of the optimum filter by E and that of any other filter by E'. Then, in order for the function $k_1(\tau)$ and the coefficients Q_α to be such that the expression (5.07) for the mean square error is a minimum, it is necessary and sufficient that they satisfy the equation

$$\sum_{\alpha=0}^{q} Q_\alpha R_f^{(\alpha)}(\tau) + \int_{-\infty}^{\infty} k_1(\sigma)R_f(\tau-\sigma)\,d\sigma = R_{hf}(\tau). \tag{5.08}$$

This is proved in the same way as in Sec. 2: Let Q_α and $k_1(\tau)$ correspond to the optimum filter, while $Q_\alpha + \delta Q_\alpha$ and $k_1(\tau) + \delta k_1(\tau)$ correspond to a nonoptimum filter. Then the mean square error E' equals

$$\begin{aligned} E' = \sum_\alpha \sum_\beta (Q_\alpha + \delta Q_\alpha)(Q_\beta + \delta Q_\beta)(-1)^\beta R_f^{(\alpha+\beta)}(0) \\ + 2\sum_\alpha (Q_\alpha + \delta Q_\alpha) \int [k_1(\tau) + \delta k_1(\tau)] R_f^{(\alpha)}(\tau)\,d\tau \\ + \iint [k_1(\tau) + \delta k_1(\tau)][k_1(\sigma) + \delta k_1(\sigma)] R_f(\tau-\sigma)\,d\tau\,d\sigma \\ - 2\sum_\alpha (Q_\alpha + \delta Q_\alpha)(-1)^\alpha R_{hf}^{(\alpha)}(0) \\ - 2\int [k_1(\tau) + \delta k_1(\tau)] R_{hf}(\tau)\,d\tau + R_h(0). \end{aligned} \tag{5.09}$$

Subtracting the expression for the mean square error E of the optimum filter, we obtain

$$\begin{aligned} E' = E &+ \sum_{\alpha}\sum_{\beta} \delta Q_{\alpha} Q_{\beta}[(-1)^{\alpha} + (-1)^{\beta}]R_f^{(\alpha+\beta)}(0) \\ &+ 2\sum_{\alpha} \delta Q_{\alpha} \int k_1(\tau)R_f^{(\alpha)}(\tau)\,d\tau + 2\sum_{\alpha} Q_{\alpha} \int \delta k_1(\tau)R_f^{(\alpha)}(\tau)\,d\tau \\ &+ 2\iint \delta k_1(\tau)k_1(\sigma)R_f(\tau-\sigma)\,d\tau\,d\sigma - 2\sum_{\alpha} \delta Q_{\alpha}(-1)^{\alpha}R_{hf}^{(\alpha)}(0) \\ &- 2\int \delta k_1(\tau)R_{hf}(\tau)\,d\tau + J, \end{aligned} \tag{5.10}$$

where

$$\begin{aligned} J &= \sum_{\alpha}\sum_{\beta} \delta Q_{\alpha}\delta Q_{\beta}(-1)^{\beta}R_f^{(\alpha+\beta)}(0) + 2\sum_{\alpha} \delta Q_{\alpha} \int \delta k_1(\tau)R_f^{(\alpha)}(\tau)\,d\tau \\ &\quad + 2\iint \delta k_1(\tau)\delta k_1(\sigma)R_f(\tau-\sigma)\,d\tau\,d\sigma \\ &= \overline{\Big[\sum_{\alpha} \delta Q_{\alpha} f^{(\alpha)}(t) + \int \delta k_1(\tau)f(t-\tau)\,d\tau\Big]^2}. \end{aligned} \tag{5.11}$$

It is clear from (5.11) that

$$J \geqslant 0. \tag{5.12}$$

Using (5.06), we can write the expression (5.10) in the form

$$\begin{aligned} E' = E &+ 2\sum_{\alpha}(-1)^{\alpha}\delta Q_{\alpha}\Big[\sum_{\beta} Q_{\beta}R_f^{(\alpha+\beta)}(0) \\ &\quad + (-1)^{\alpha}\int k_1(\tau)R_f^{(\alpha)}(\tau)\,d\tau - R_{hf}^{(\alpha)}(0)\Big] \\ &+ 2\int \delta k_1(\tau)\,d\tau\Big[\sum_{\alpha} Q_{\alpha}R_f^{(\alpha)}(\tau) \\ &\quad + \int k_1(\sigma)R_f(\tau-\sigma)\,d\sigma - R_{hf}(\tau)\Big] + J. \end{aligned} \tag{5.13}$$

It is now easy to show that for the inequality

$$E' \geqslant E \tag{5.14}$$

to hold, it is necessary that the two expressions in brackets in (5.13) vanish, in particular, that the integral equation (5.08) be satisfied. If (5.08) holds identically in τ, then the first expression in brackets in (5.13) vanishes, as well as the second expression. To see this, we observe that the vanishing of the first expression in brackets follows from the identity (5.08), if we differentiate (5.08) α times with respect to τ and then set $\tau = 0$. Symbolically, we can write (5.08) as

$$\mathscr{K}[R_f(\tau)] = R_{hf}(\tau) \tag{5.15}$$

[cf. equation (4.39)]. We can also show that equation (5.15) is a sufficient condition for the filter to be optimum. This is proved just as in Sec. 2, by using the inequality (5.12).

We now try to solve equation (5.05) or (5.15). If we multiply both sides by $e^{-i\omega\tau}\,d\tau$ and integrate from $-\infty$ to ∞, the right-hand side becomes the expression for the spectral density $S_{hf}(\omega)$, and we obtain

$$\sum_{\alpha=0}^{q} Q_\alpha \int e^{-i\omega\tau} R_f^{(\alpha)}(\tau)\,d\tau + \iint k_1(\sigma) R_f(\tau-\sigma) e^{-i\omega\tau}\,d\tau\,d\sigma = S_{hf}(\omega). \quad (5.16)$$

Integrating by parts, we obtain

$$\int_{-\infty}^{\infty} e^{-i\omega\tau} R_f^{(\alpha)}(\tau)\,d\tau = e^{-i\omega\tau} R_f^{(\alpha-1)}(\tau)\Big|_{-\infty}^{\infty} + i\omega \int_{-\infty}^{\infty} e^{-i\omega\tau} R_f^{(\alpha-1)}(\tau)\,d\tau \quad (\alpha = 1, 2, \ldots, q). \quad (5.17)$$

Since $R_f^{(\alpha-1)}(\tau)$ goes to zero as $\tau \to \pm\infty$, we have

$$\int_{-\infty}^{\infty} e^{-i\omega\tau} R_f^{(\alpha)}(\tau)\,d\tau = i\omega \int_{-\infty}^{\infty} e^{-i\omega\tau} R_f^{(\alpha-1)}(\tau)\,d\tau. \quad (5.18)$$

Repeating this operation α times gives

$$\int_{-\infty}^{\infty} e^{-i\omega\tau} R_f^{(\alpha)}(\tau)\,d\tau = (i\omega)^\alpha \int_{-\infty}^{\infty} e^{-i\omega\tau} R_f(\tau)\,d\tau = (i\omega)^\alpha S_f(\omega). \quad (5.19)$$

According to formula (2.26), we have

$$\iint k_1(\sigma) R_f(\tau-\sigma) e^{-i\omega\tau}\,d\tau\,d\sigma = K_1(\omega) S_f(\omega). \quad (5.20)$$

Thus, equation (5.16) becomes

$$\left[\sum_{\alpha=0}^{q} Q_\alpha (i\omega)^\alpha + K_1(\omega)\right] S_f(\omega) = S_{hf}(\omega), \quad (5.21)$$

and we see that the transfer function of the optimum type I filter is

$$K(\omega) = \sum_{\alpha=0}^{q} Q_\alpha (i\omega)^\alpha + K_1(\omega) = \frac{S_{hf}(\omega)}{S_f(\omega)}. \quad (5.22)$$

This formula has the same appearance as formula (2.28), but it has now been established for a much wider class of filters. In fact, $K_1(\omega)$ corresponds to the "integral part" of the operator $\mathscr{K}$ associated with the optimum filter, and the polynomial $\sum Q_\alpha (i\omega)^\alpha$ corresponds to the linear differential operator $\sum Q_\alpha (d/dt)^\alpha$. The expression for the transfer function of the optimum filter can also be written in the form (4.26) or (4.27).

We now express the mean square error of the optimum filter in terms of spectral densities. Starting from formula (5.07) and taking into account the integral equation (5.08), we obtain the expression

$$\overline{\varepsilon^2} = R_h(0) - \Big[\sum_\alpha \sum_\beta Q_\alpha Q_\beta (-1)^\beta R_f^{(\alpha+\beta)}(0)$$

$$+ 2\sum_\alpha Q_\alpha \int k_1(\tau) R_f^{(\alpha)}(\tau)\, d\tau + \iint k_1(\tau) k_1(\sigma) R_f(\tau - \sigma)\, d\tau\, d\sigma\Big]$$

$$= R_h(0) - \frac{1}{2\pi}\int \Big|\sum_\alpha Q_\alpha (i\omega)^\alpha + K_1(\omega)\Big|^2 S_f(\omega)\, d\omega \tag{5.23}$$

or

$$\overline{\varepsilon^2} = R_h(0) - \frac{1}{2\pi}\int_{-\infty}^{\infty} |K(\omega)|^2 S_f(\omega)\, d\omega. \tag{5.24}$$

If we use formula (2.30), we can also write

$$\overline{\varepsilon^2} = \frac{1}{2\pi}\int_{-\infty}^{\infty} [S_h(\omega) - |K(\omega)|^2 S_f(\omega)]\, d\omega. \tag{5.25}$$

If we substitute the expression (5.22) into (5.25), we obtain formula (4.31) for optimum filters of type I, but under more general assumptions about the nature of the filter. It should be pointed out that many of the above calculations apply to filters of types II and III, as well as to filters of type I, but with important differences (to be discussed in Chap. 2).

The integral in the right-hand side of (5.24) must converge, and this has to be verified in each concrete case. However, the integral diverges only when a derivative $R_f^{(\alpha)}(\tau)$ becomes infinite at $\tau = 0$.[6] Then, we cannot write even the generalized equation of the optimum filter, i.e., the problem has no solution.

We can also write formula (5.24) in the form

$$\overline{\varepsilon^2} = \overline{h^2} - \overline{x^2}, \tag{5.26}$$

where the term $\overline{h^2}$ measures the dispersion of the values of $h(t)$ about its mean value $\bar{h} = 0$. Since $\overline{x^2} \geqslant 0$, we have

$$\overline{\varepsilon^2} \leqslant \overline{h^2}. \tag{5.27}$$

For an optimum system performing simple filtering, we have

$$\overline{\varepsilon^2} \leqslant \overline{m^2}. \tag{5.28}$$

In the case of simple filtering, $\overline{\varepsilon^2}$ approaches $\overline{m^2}$ when the input signal is deeply immersed in noise with the same spectral composition as the signal

[6] For example, the correlation function (3.23) has a discontinuity in its derivative $R'(\tau)$ at $\tau = 0$ and hence $R''(0) = \infty$.

itself [cf. the end of Sec. 2]. Then, according to (2.42) and (2.43), the function $K(\omega)$ is small, and the filter output function $x(t)$ is also small. If $x(t) \equiv 0$, then obviously we have $\overline{\varepsilon^2} = \overline{h^2}$ or $\overline{\varepsilon^2} = \overline{m^2}$.

6. Filtering of Quasi-Monochromatic Signals by Using Filters of Type I

Suppose that we have a signal

$$m(t) = a \cos \omega_0 t + b \sin \omega_0 t = e \cos (\omega_0 t - \vartheta), \tag{6.01}$$

where

$$a = e \cos \vartheta, \qquad b = e \sin \vartheta. \tag{6.02}$$

For fixed parameters a and b, or e and ϑ, the signal (6.01) is not a random process. However, let a and b be random variables which are independent of the time and which satisfy the relations

$$\bar{a} = \bar{b} = 0, \qquad \overline{a^2} = \overline{b^2}, \qquad \overline{ab} = 0. \tag{6.03}$$

Then, the signal (6.01) can be regarded as a random process. The spectrum of this process consists of just the two frequencies $\omega = \pm\, \omega_0$ and hence such a signal can be called *monochromatic*. A monochromatic signal can be regarded as the limiting case of a *quasi-monochromatic* signal, in which a, b, e and ϑ vary slowly in time, in accordance with some statistical law. Strictly monochromatic signals cannot be produced in practice; instead, one can only produce quasi-monochromatic signals which closely approximate monochromatic signals.

Random modulation of a harmonic oscillation of frequency ω_0 produces a new random process. In order for this process to qualify as a quasi-monochromatic signal, the bandwidth $\Delta\omega$ of the modulation must be very small compared to the carrier frequency ω_0, i.e.,

$$\Delta\omega << \omega_0. \tag{6.04}$$

We shall assume that the stationary random functions $a(t)$ and $b(t)$ have the following statistical properties:

$$\overline{a(t)} = \overline{b(t)} = 0, \tag{6.05}$$

$$\overline{a(t)a(t - \tau)} = \overline{b(t)b(t - \tau)} = c^2 r(\tau), \tag{6.06}$$

$$\overline{a(t)b(t - \tau)} = 0 \quad \text{for arbitrary } \tau. \tag{6.07}$$

The process $c^2 r(\tau)$ appearing in (6.06) is the autocorrelation function of the random processes $a(t)$ and $b(t)$, between which there is no cross correlation.

The constant c^2 is given by

$$c^2 = \overline{a^2} = \overline{b^2}, \tag{6.08}$$

so that

$$r(0) = 1. \tag{6.09}$$

A correlation function $r(\tau)$ satisfying the relation (6.09) is said to be *normalized* (or to be a *correlation coefficient*).

The assumptions just made concerning the statistical properties of the functions $a(t)$ and $b(t)$ imply various properties of the functions $e(t)$ and $\vartheta(t)$ [which are related to the functions $a(t)$ and $b(t)$ by the formulas (6.02)]. The function $e(t)$ is called the *envelope* of the random process $m(t)$, and $\vartheta(t)$ is called the *phase* of $m(t)$. A rigorous definition of the envelope and phase for *any* random process was first given by V. I. Bunimovich in 1944, and is discussed in detail in his book.[7] There, the reader will find the proof that if the condition (6.04) holds, then the functions $a(t)$ and $b(t)$ always satisfy the relations (6.06) and (6.07).

We now calculate the correlation function of the useful signal $m(t)$, obtaining

$$\begin{aligned} R_m(\tau) &= \overline{[a(t)\cos\omega_0 t + b(t)\sin\omega_0 t]\,[a(t-\tau)\cos\omega_0(t-\tau) +} \\ &\qquad \overline{+\, b(t-\tau)\sin\omega_0(t-\tau)]} \\ &= c^2 r(\tau)[\cos\omega_0 t\cos\omega_0(t-\tau) + \sin\omega_0 t\sin\omega_0(t-\tau)] \end{aligned}$$

or

$$R_m(\tau) = c^2 r(\tau)\cos\omega_0\tau. \tag{6.10}$$

For $\tau = 0$, we have

$$c^2 = R_m(0) = \overline{m^2(t)}, \tag{6.11}$$

which shows the physical meaning of the constant c^2. Next, we introduce the spectral density

$$s(\omega) = \int_{-\infty}^{\infty} e^{-i\omega\tau} r(\tau)\,d\tau, \tag{6.12}$$

corresponding to the normalized correlation function $r(\tau)$. The inverse Fourier transform of (6.12) is

$$r(\tau) = \frac{1}{2\pi}\int_{-\infty}^{\infty} e^{i\omega\tau} s(\omega)\,d\omega. \tag{6.13}$$

Using the spectral density $s(\omega)$ of the random processes $a(t)$ and $b(t)$, we can find the spectral density of the quasi-monochromatic signal $m(t)$ itself:

$$S_m(\omega) = \int_{-\infty}^{\infty} e^{-i\omega\tau} R_m(\tau)\,d\tau = c^2\int_{-\infty}^{\infty} e^{-i\omega\tau}\, r(\tau)\cos\omega_0\tau\,d\tau. \tag{6.14}$$

---

[7] V. I. Bunimovich, Флюктуационные Процессы в Радиоприёмных Устройствах (*Fluctuation Processes in Radio Receivers*), Sovietskoye Radio, Moscow (1951).

Since

$$\cos \omega_0 \tau = \frac{e^{i\omega_0\tau} + e^{-i\omega_0\tau}}{2},$$

we can write (6.14) in the form

$$S_m(\omega) = \frac{c^2}{2}\left[\int_{-\infty}^{\infty} e^{-i(\omega-\omega_0)\tau} r(\tau)\, d\tau + \int_{-\infty}^{\infty} e^{-i(\omega+\omega_0)\tau} r(\tau)\, d\tau\right].$$

Then, using (6.12), we have

$$S_m(\omega) = \frac{c^2}{2}\,[s(\omega - \omega_0) + s(\omega + \omega_0)]. \tag{6.15}$$

The quantity $\Delta\omega$ appearing in formula (6.04) characterizes the bandwidth of the function $s(\omega)$, as defined in Sec. 3. We shall assume that $s(\omega)$ is a "bell-shaped curve" (not necessarily Gaussian), with its maximum at $\omega = 0$. According to (3.33), the inequality (6.04) implies that

$$\omega_0\, \Delta\tau \gg 1. \tag{6.16}$$

The correlation time $\Delta\tau$ characterizes the rapidity with which the random functions $a(t)$ and $b(t)$ vary in time. The condition (6.16) shows that the functions $\cos \omega_0 t$ and $\sin \omega_0 t$ undergo many oscillations in the time during which $a(t)$ and $b(t)$ change appreciably. In other words, if the condition (6.04) is met, the functions $a(t)$, $b(t)$ and $\vartheta(t)$ are slowly varying as compared to $\cos \omega_0 t$ and $\sin \omega_0 t$. According to (6.15), the spectral density $S_m(\omega)$ has the form shown in Fig. 6, and according to (6.04) it consists of two nonoverlapping peaks centered at $\omega \sim \omega_0$ and $\omega \sim -\omega_0$.

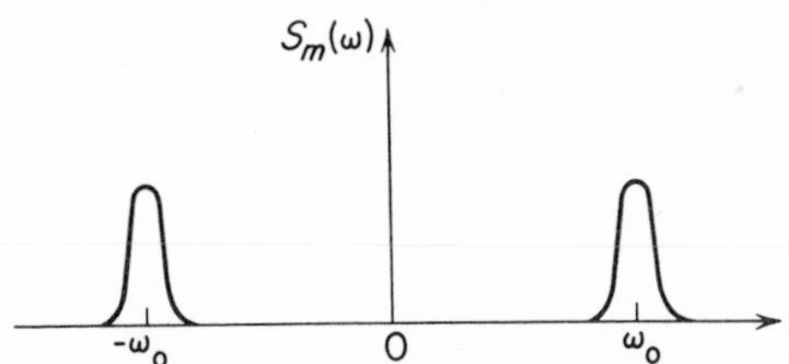

FIG. 6. Spectrum of a quasi-monochromatic signal.

In the explicit calculations which follow, we choose

$$r(\tau) = e^{-\alpha|\tau|}, \tag{6.17}$$

so that, using formula (3.23), we have

$$s(\omega) = \frac{2\alpha}{\alpha^2 + \omega^2}. \tag{6.18}$$

The parameter α determines the spectral bandwidth. In fact, according to (6.09) and (6.13),

$$\frac{1}{2\pi}\int_{-\infty}^{\infty} s(\omega)\,d\omega = 1, \tag{6.19}$$

and the relation (3.30) gives

$$\omega = \frac{\pi}{2}\alpha. \tag{6.20}$$

We now study the optimum filters which separate quasi-monochromatic signals from a background of so-called "white noise," i.e., noise with constant spectral density

$$S_n(\omega) = S_n = \text{const.} \tag{6.21}$$

The designation "white noise" stems from the analogy with "white light," which is made up of all colors of the spectrum, corresponding to different optical frequencies. Similarly, "white noise" is made up of oscillations of all frequencies, but with the same intensity. Obviously, white noise is not realizable in its pure form, since it would correspond to an infinitely large noise intensity [cf. formula (3.04)]. Therefore, we have to assume that $S_n(\omega)$ is constant over a sufficiently large interval and then drops off to zero for higher frequencies. Actually, for the validity of all the results that follow, we only have to require that $S_n(\omega)$ be constant in the frequency band occupied by the signal (see Fig. 6).

In the case of simple filtering, when there is no correlation between the signal and the noise, the transfer function of the optimum type I filter is given by formula (2.38):

$$K(\omega) = \frac{S_m(\omega)}{S_m(\omega) + S_n}. \tag{6.22}$$

In calculating the function $k(\tau)$ by the formula

$$k(\tau) = \frac{1}{2\pi}\int_{-\infty}^{\infty} \frac{e^{i\omega\tau}\,d\omega}{1 + [S_n/S_m(\omega)]}, \tag{6.23}$$

we can confine ourselves to positive values of τ, since $k(\tau)$ is an even function. We let $N(\omega)$ denote the denominator of the integrand in (6.23), and then look for the roots of the equation $N(\omega) = 0$. In the case of the function (6.18), $N(\omega)$ has four complex zeros (two zeros for $\omega \sim \omega_0$ and two for $\omega \sim -\omega_0$). To calculate these zeros, we use the fact that for $\omega \sim \omega_0$, we have the approximation

$$S_m(\omega) \sim \frac{c^2}{2} s(\omega - \omega_0) = \frac{c^2\alpha}{(\omega - \omega_0)^2 + \alpha^2},$$

since the term $s(\omega + \omega_0) \sim s(2\omega_0)$ can be neglected here. Then, the denominator equals

$$N(\omega) = 1 + S_n \frac{(\omega - \omega_0)^2 + \alpha^2}{c^2\alpha}, \tag{6.24}$$

which vanishes for

$$\omega = \omega_0 \pm i\beta, \tag{6.25}$$

where

$$\beta = \sqrt{\alpha^2 + (c^2\alpha/S_n)}.$$

Similarly, the other two zeros of $N(\omega)$ are at $\omega = -\omega_0 \pm i\beta$.

Thus, we see that two of the zeros of $N(\omega)$ lie in the upper half-plane, and two lie in the lower half-plane. To calculate $k(\tau)$ for $\tau > 0$, only the zeros in the upper half-plane are important, since in this case we close the contour of integration in the upper half-plane and reduce the integral to a sum of residues, using Jordan's lemma (see Sec. 8). At the poles $\omega = \pm\,\omega_0 + i\beta$ of the integrand in (6.23), the derivative $dN/d\omega$ is equal to

$$\frac{dN}{d\omega} = \frac{2S_n}{c^2\alpha}\, i\beta, \tag{6.26}$$

and the final expression for $k(\tau)$ can be written in the form

$$k(\tau) = \frac{\rho\alpha^2}{\beta}\, e^{-\beta|\tau|} \cos \omega_0\tau, \tag{6.27}$$

where we have introduced the dimensionless parameter

$$\rho = \frac{c^2}{S_n\alpha}, \tag{6.28}$$

which in this problem plays the role of a *signal-to-noise (power) ratio*. In terms of ρ, the parameter β is

$$\beta = \alpha\sqrt{1 + \rho}. \tag{6.29}$$

The dimensionless parameter ρ shows the extent to which the signal is stronger than the noise. In fact, according to (6.11), c^2 is the average power of the quasi-monochromatic signal, while according to (6.20), the product $S_n\alpha$ gives the noise power in the frequency band occupied by the signal.

When the signal-to-noise ratio is small ($\rho \ll 1$), formula (6.29) implies that $\alpha \sim \beta$, so that

$$k(\tau) = \frac{R_m(\tau)}{S_n} \tag{6.30}$$

and

$$K(\omega) = \frac{S_m(\omega)}{S_n}, \tag{6.31}$$

which agrees with formula (2.43). When the signal-to-noise ratio is large ($\rho \gg 1$), formula (6.29) implies that $\beta \gg \alpha$.

The pass-band of the optimum filter corresponds to the frequency intervals $(\omega_0 - \Delta\omega', \omega_0 + \Delta\omega')$ and $(-\omega_0 - \Delta\omega', -\omega_0 + \Delta\omega')$, where

$$\Delta\omega' = \frac{\pi}{2}\beta = \frac{\pi}{2}\alpha\sqrt{1 + \rho}. \tag{6.32}$$

We see from (6.32) that the pass-band of the filter should be widened if the noise power is decreased. Widening the pass-band of the filter when the noise level is low leads to a shortening of the "memory" of the filter, i.e., of the time (of order $1/\beta$) during which the signal is "extracted" from the noise. This is quite understandable, since in the absence of noise, no time at all is needed to obtain the useful signal. It should also be noted that the process of extracting a quasi-monochromatic signal from noise by using a filter has to be done in times less than the correlation time of the signal, and hence we always have $\beta > \alpha$.

Finally, we calculate the mean square filtering error

$$\overline{\varepsilon^2} = \overline{m^2} - \frac{1}{2\pi}\int_{-\infty}^{\infty} |K(\omega)|^2 S_f(\omega)\, d\omega \tag{6.33}$$

or

$$\overline{\varepsilon^2} = c^2 - \frac{1}{2\pi}\int_{-\infty}^{\infty} \frac{S_m^2(\omega)\, d\omega}{S_m(\omega) + S_n}. \tag{6.34}$$

Writing the integrand in the form

$$\frac{S_m(\omega)}{1 + [S_n/S_m(\omega)]}, \tag{6.35}$$

we can use residues to calculate the integral (6.34). Here we have two kinds of residues, those connected with the zeros of the denominator ($\omega = \pm\,\omega_0 + i\beta$) and those connected with the poles of the numerator ($\omega = \pm\omega_0 + i\alpha$). The result of the calculation is

$$\overline{\varepsilon^2} = \frac{c^2}{\sqrt{1 + \rho}}. \tag{6.36}$$

To see this, we proceed as in the derivation of formula (6.27), writing

$$\begin{aligned}\overline{\varepsilon^2} &= c^2 - \frac{1}{2\pi}\int_{-\infty}^{\infty} \frac{S_m(\omega)\, d\omega}{1 + [S_n/S_m(\omega)]}\\ &= -\frac{S_m(\omega_0 + i\beta) + S_m(-\omega_0 + i\beta)}{2S_n\,\beta/c^2\alpha}\\ &= \frac{c^2\alpha}{\beta} = \frac{c^2}{\sqrt{1 + \rho}}.\end{aligned} \tag{6.37}$$

Suppose that α approaches zero, so that the signal becomes more monochromatic. Then ρ increases and $\overline{\varepsilon^2}$ decreases. This happens because the pass-band of the filter (6.32) becomes narrower and hence its memory increases, i.e., the time (of order $\Delta t' \sim 1/\beta$) during which it makes effective use of the input signal increases. However, β does not decrease in proportion to α, and in fact,

$$\beta \sim \alpha\sqrt{\rho} = \sqrt{c^2\alpha/S_n}, \tag{6.38}$$

since, as shown above, the filter pass-band should not be made as narrow as the frequency band occupied by the signal, but should be kept somewhat wider. We observe that for the bandpass filter under consideration, with the transfer function (6.22), the quantities $\Delta\omega'$ and $\Delta t'$ are connected by the relation (3.33), as usual.

In the case of a strictly monochromatic signal (which is not physically realizable), we have $\alpha = 0$, $\beta = 0$, $\omega = 0$, $\overline{\varepsilon^2} = 0$ and

$$k(\tau) \sim \gamma \cos \omega_0\tau, \tag{6.39}$$

where the coefficient γ is "infinitely small." It should be noted that the infinitely small error achieved here is due to the infinite working time of the filter. If the input signal is used for only a finite amount of time, then it is clear that the error must be greater than zero.

7. Some General Remarks on the Statistical Theory of Filtering

This section is devoted to some remarks concerning the foundations of the statistical theory of filtering. First of all, we observe that both the useful signal and the noise are assumed to be stationary random processes with known correlation properties. The stationarity of the processes means that each has statistical properties which do not change in time, i.e., the properties of each process do not depend on the time interval in which the process is examined. It is also assumed that the correlation functions are known, which means that some preliminary investigations of the processes have been made.

In the statistical theory of filtering, by the *optimum filter* is meant the filter which operates with the minimum mean square error. This criterion, which leads to the simplest results, is applicable in practice only when the undesirability of an error increases as its size increases. However, there are cases where all errors exceeding a certain threshold are equally undesirable. In such cases, it is natural to use another error criterion.

The theory presented above is restricted to *linear* filters, and we have not considered the possibility of using *nonlinear* filters. In Chap. 8 we shall discuss the theory of filtering of normal (Gaussian) processes and sequences from a more general point of view. We shall show that in this case the optimum linear filter is actually optimum as compared to *any* other filter, linear or nonlinear, and that the mean square error criterion is equivalent to various other criteria. Roughly speaking, this means that all statistical characteristics of normal processes with zero mean values are given by their correlation functions. It is just these correlation functions that are exploited by linear filters, and the need for nonlinear filters arises only when dealing with random processes whose statistical properties are not completely described by their correlation functions. Thus, nonlinear filters are significant only for random processes which do not obey the normal law. The advantage of nonlinear filters as compared to linear filters ought to become more pronounced as the given random process deviates more from a normal process. The theory of nonlinear filters is very complicated, and so far it has not yielded any tangible practical results.

In radar, the problem of filtering has to be posed somewhat differently. Although the noise can still be regarded as a random process, the useful signal now has a definite form (e.g., a rectangular pulse), but with certain unknown parameters. Therefore, in this case, the filtering problem does not consist in reproducing the useful signal with the least distortion, but rather it consists in transforming the useful signal in such a way that it can be detected and its parameters measured with the least error in the presence of noise. Filters of this type will be considered in Chap. 3.

The problem of linear extrapolation of stationary random sequences and processes was first investigated in the works of A. N. Kolmogorov and other Soviet mathematicians. However, it was only because of Norbert Wiener's work on optimum linear filtering and extrapolation of stationary random processes that the whole subject emerged from the confines of pure mathematics and acquired practical significance.

The filtering problem has become the prototype for "optimum" solutions of a host of other statistical problems of engineering interest. Therefore, in the next chapter, we shall continue our study of the filtering problem. The reader can find a detailed exposition of this and related matters in the review article by A. M. Yaglom,[8] as well as in numerous books.

---

[8] A. M. Yaglom, Введение в Теорию Стационарных Случайных Функций (*An Introduction to the Theory of Stationary Random Functions*), Uspekhi Mat. Nauk, **7**, 3 (1952). Revised English translation by R. A. Silverman in this series,published by Prentice-Hall, Inc., Englewood Cliffs, N.J. (1962).

2

FILTERING AND PREDICTION OF STATIONARY RANDOM PROCESSES[1]

8. The Integral Equation of the Optimum Linear Filter of Type II

For filters of type II, the function $k_1(\tau)$ satisfies the additional condition

$$k_1(\tau) = 0 \quad \text{for} \quad \tau < 0, \tag{8.01}$$

similar to condition (1.14), and formula (4.39) becomes

$$x(t) = \sum_{\alpha=0}^{q} Q_\alpha f^{(\alpha)}(t) + \int_{-\infty}^{\infty} k(\tau) f(t-\tau)\, d\tau. \tag{8.02}$$

Thus, a filter of type II uses the input process for a semi-infinite time interval, while a filter of type I uses the input "information" for an interval which goes to infinity in both directions. Hence, a filter of type I is more effective than one of type II, and, in particular, its mean square error is less. For $\tau \geqslant 0$, the coefficients Q_α and the function $k_1(\tau)$ of the optimum filter of type II must satisfy the same equation (5.08) as in the case of filters of type I:

$$\sum_{\alpha=0}^{q} Q_\alpha R_f^{(\alpha)}(\tau) + \int_0^{\infty} k_1(\sigma) R_f(\tau-\sigma)\, d\sigma = R_{hf}(\tau). \tag{8.03}$$

[1] This chapter may be omitted on first reading, but the reader should become familiar with the representation of a random process as a superposition of pulses of standard form (given in Sec. 12).

However, for $\tau < 0$, this equation does not have to be satisfied, since

$$\delta k_1(\tau) = 0 \quad \text{for} \quad \tau < 0. \tag{8.04}$$

Instead, the condition (8.01) must be met, and as a result, the problem becomes much more complicated.

We now take the Fourier transform of equation (8.03), using the formulas

$$\begin{aligned} R_f(\tau) &= \frac{1}{2\pi}\int_{-\infty}^{\infty} e^{i\omega\tau} S_f(\omega)\, d\omega, \\ R_f^{(\alpha)}(\tau) &= \frac{1}{2\pi}\int_{-\infty}^{\infty} e^{i\omega\tau}(i\omega)^{\alpha} S_f(\omega)\, d\omega, \\ \sum_{\alpha=0}^{q} Q_\alpha R_f^{(\alpha)}(\tau) &= \frac{1}{2\pi}\int_{-\infty}^{\infty} e^{i\omega\tau}\left[\sum_{\alpha=0}^{q} Q_\alpha (i\omega)^{\alpha}\right] S_f(\omega)\, d\omega, \end{aligned} \tag{8.05}$$

and

$$\begin{aligned} \int_0^{\infty} k_1(\sigma) R_f(\tau-\sigma)\, d\sigma &= \frac{1}{2\pi}\int_0^{\infty} k_1(\sigma)\, d\sigma \int_{-\infty}^{\infty} e^{i\omega(\tau-\sigma)} S_f(\omega)\, d\omega \\ &= \frac{1}{2\pi}\int_{-\infty}^{\infty} e^{i\omega\tau} S_f(\omega)\, d\omega \int_0^{\infty} e^{-i\omega\sigma} k_1(\sigma)\, d\sigma \\ &= \frac{1}{2\pi}\int_{-\infty}^{\infty} e^{i\omega\tau} K_1(\omega) S_f(\omega)\, d\omega. \end{aligned} \tag{8.06}$$

Then, also using the relation

$$R_{hf}(\tau) = \frac{1}{2\pi}\int_{-\infty}^{\infty} e^{i\omega\tau} S_{hf}(\omega)\, d\omega, \tag{8.07}$$

we transform (8.03) into the form

$$\int_{-\infty}^{\infty} e^{i\omega\tau}[K(\omega)S_f(\omega) - S_{hf}(\omega)]\, d\omega = 0 \quad \text{for} \quad \tau \geqslant 0, \tag{8.08}$$

where

$$K(\omega) = \sum_{\alpha=0}^{q} Q_\alpha (i\omega)^{\alpha} + K_1(\omega) \tag{8.09}$$

is the unknown transfer function (system function) of the required filter. The term $K_1(\omega)$ has a Fourier transform, and vanishes as $\omega \to \pm\infty$, and the spectral densities $S_f(\omega)$, $S_{hf}(\omega)$ are known functions.

If we knew the transfer function $K(\omega)$, then we could write it in the form (8.09) and then use $K_1(\omega)$ to calculate the weighting function

$$k_1(\tau) = \frac{1}{2\pi}\int_{-\infty}^{\infty} e^{i\omega\tau} K_1(\omega)\, d\omega \tag{8.10}$$

[cf. formula (4.40)], which must satisfy the condition (8.01). Therefore, in addition to equation (8.08), the following relation must hold:

$$\int_{-\infty}^{\infty} e^{i\omega\tau} K_1(\omega)\, d\omega = 0 \quad \text{for} \quad \tau < 0. \tag{8.11}$$

The whole difficulty of the problem lies in the fact that the function $K(\omega)$ has to satisfy the two relations (8.08) and (8.11).

We now solve for the unknown function $K(\omega)$, assuming first that the functions $S_f(\omega)$ and $S_{hf}(\omega)$ are given not in the form of empirical curves, but as formulas which can be continued analytically into the complex frequency domain, i.e., we shall assume that $S_f(\omega)$ and $S_{hf}(\omega)$ are functions of a complex variable ω which are analytic in some neighborhood of the real axis in the complex ω-plane. Introducing the function

$$J(\omega) = K(\omega)S_f(\omega) - S_{hf}(\omega), \tag{8.12}$$

we can write (8.08) as

$$\int_{-\infty}^{\infty} e^{i\omega\tau}J(\omega)\,d\omega = 0 \quad \text{for} \quad \tau \geqslant 0. \tag{8.13}$$

For our subsequent purposes, we transform (8.13) as follows: We multiply both sides of (8.13) by $e^{-iw\tau}$ and integrate from 0 to ∞, obtaining

$$\int_0^{\infty} e^{-iw\tau}\,d\tau \int_{-\infty}^{\infty} e^{i\omega\tau}J(\omega)\,d\omega = 0. \tag{8.14}$$

If w is a complex number lying in the lower half-plane (below the real axis), so that $\operatorname{Im} w < 0$, then we can change the order of integration in (8.14). The result is

$$\int_0^{\infty} e^{-iw\tau}\,d\tau \int_{-\infty}^{\infty} e^{i\omega\tau}J(\omega)\,d\omega = \int_{-\infty}^{\infty} J(\omega)\,d\omega \int_0^{\infty} e^{i(\omega-w)\tau}\,d\tau, \tag{8.15}$$

since the inner integral

$$\int_0^{\infty} e^{i(\omega-w)\tau}\,d\tau = -\frac{1}{i(\omega - w)} \tag{8.16}$$

converges. Thus, finally, equation (8.08) becomes

$$\int_{-\infty}^{\infty} \frac{J(\omega)\,d\omega}{\omega - w} = 0 \quad \text{for} \quad \operatorname{Im} w < 0. \tag{8.17}$$

Treating equation (8.11) in the same way, i.e., multiplying both sides by $e^{-iw\tau}$ and integrating from $-\infty$ to 0, we transform (8.11) into the form

$$\int_{-\infty}^{\infty} \frac{K_1(\omega)\,d\omega}{\omega - w} = 0 \quad \text{for} \quad \operatorname{Im} w > 0. \tag{8.18}$$

In the theory of functions of a complex variable, integrals like (8.17) and (8.18) are called integrals of *Cauchy's type*. In the next section, we shall see how complex variable theory permits us to solve for the unknown functions $K(\omega)$ and $K_1(\omega)$ by using equations (8.17) and (8.18). But first, we discuss certain results of complex variable theory, which will be needed below.

Cauchy's theorem. According to Cauchy's theorem, *if a function $F(\omega)$ is analytic in a simply-connected region R, then the formula*

$$F(w) = \frac{1}{2\pi i}\int_C \frac{F(\omega)\,d\omega}{\omega - w} \tag{8.19}$$

gives the value of $F(\omega)$ at any point w of R, in terms of its values on a closed contour C, which surrounds w and lies entirely within R (see Fig. 7). Here, ω is the variable of integration, and the integral along C is evaluated in the positive (i.e., counterclockwise) direction.

FIG. 7. A contour C in the complex plane, illustrating Cauchy's theorem.

Jordan's lemma. This lemma can be stated as follows:

If the function $F(w)$ satisfies the condition

$$F(w) \to 0 \quad \textit{uniformly as} \quad |w| \to \infty \tag{8.20}$$

in the upper half-plane and on the real axis, i.e., for $\operatorname{Im} w \geqslant 0$, *and if τ is a positive number, then as $R \to \infty$ we have*

$$\lim_{R\to\infty} \int_{C_R} e^{iw\tau} F(w)\,dw = 0 \quad (\tau > 0), \tag{8.21}$$

where C_R is a semicircle drawn in the upper half-plane, with radius R and center at the origin of coordinates (see Fig. 8). If $\tau < 0$, then (8.21) *holds if $F(w)$ satisfies the same conditions in the lower half-plane and on the real axis, i.e., for* $\operatorname{Im} w \leqslant 0$, *but then the semicircle C_R must lie in the lower half-plane.*

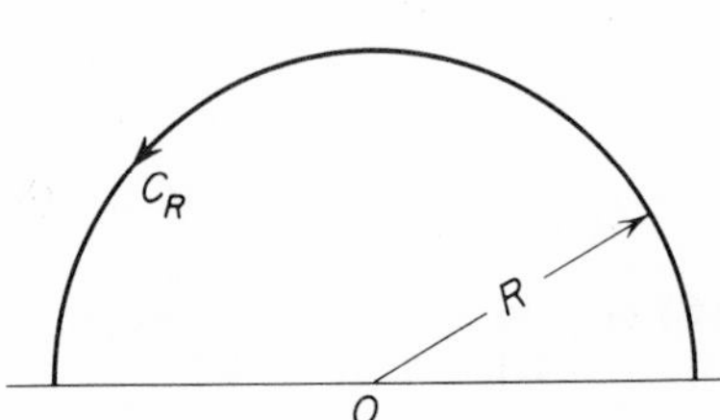

FIG. 8. A contour C_R in the complex plane, illustrating Jordan's lemma.

We shall also need the following lemma:

LEMMA 1. *Let the function $G(w)$ be analytic in the strip*

$$\gamma_1 \leqslant \operatorname{Im} w \leqslant \gamma_2, \tag{8.22}$$

and let $G(w)$ fall off sufficiently rapidly at the ends of the strip (as $\operatorname{Re} w \to \pm\infty$), *i.e., at least as rapidly as $w^{-\sigma}$ where $\sigma > 0$.* [*In practice, we shall take $\gamma_1 \leqslant 0$, $\gamma_2 \geqslant 0$, so that the strip* (8.22) *will include the real axis.*] *Then, no matter what the function $G(w)$ is outside the strip, it can be written as the sum*

$$G(w) = G^+(w) + G^-(w), \tag{8.23}$$

where $G^+(w)$ is a function which is analytic in the entire upper half-plane and in the strip (8.22), *i.e., for* $\operatorname{Im} w \geqslant \gamma_1$, *and $G^-(w)$ is a function which* *is analytic in the entire lower half-plane and in the strip* (8.22), *i.e., for* $\operatorname{Im} w \leqslant \gamma_2$.

The proof of this lemma is a consequence of Cauchy's theorem (8.19), as applied to the function $G(w)$. In fact, let the contour of integration be a rectangle (Fig. 9), described in the counterclockwise direction, and let the ends of the rectangular contour extend to infinity in both directions. Then, since $G(w)$ falls off more rapidly than $w^{-\sigma}$ as $\operatorname{Re} w \to \pm\infty$, it follows that the contributions to $G(w)$ coming from the integrals over each horizontal line converge more rapidly than the integral

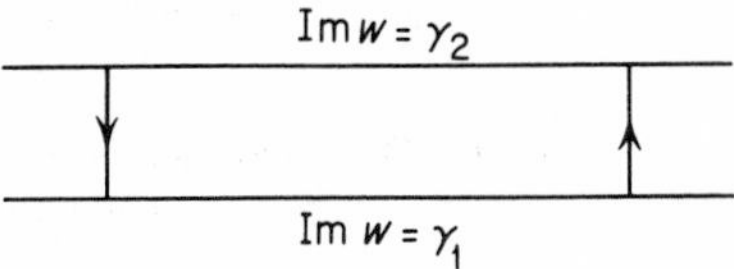

FIG. 9. A rectangular contour, illustrating Lemma 1.

$$\int \frac{d\omega}{\omega^{1+\sigma}}, \tag{8.24}$$

and hence converge to definite limits, whereas the contributions to the integral coming from the vertical ends of the rectangle converge to zero (for the same reason). Therefore, in the strip (8.22), we can represent $G(w)$ as

$$G(w) = \frac{1}{2\pi i}\int_{i\gamma_1-\infty}^{i\gamma_1+\infty}\frac{G(\omega)\,d\omega}{\omega - w} - \frac{1}{2\pi i}\int_{i\gamma_2-\infty}^{i\gamma_2+\infty}\frac{G(\omega)\,d\omega}{\omega - w}, \tag{8.25}$$

where the first integral is taken over the lower edge of the strip, and the second integral is taken over the upper edge.

We now write

$$G^+(w) = \frac{1}{2\pi i}\int_{i\gamma_1-\infty}^{i\gamma_1+\infty}\frac{G(\omega)\,d\omega}{\omega - w}, \qquad G^-(w) = -\frac{1}{2\pi i}\int_{i\gamma_2-\infty}^{i\gamma_2+\infty}\frac{G(\omega)\,d\omega}{\omega - w}. \tag{8.26}$$

Then, the first integral is an analytic function above its path of integration. In fact, $G^+(w)$ is also an analytic function below the path of integration, but a different one, since $G^+(w)$ suffers a jump in crossing the path of integration. The second integral in (8.26) represents a function which is analytic below its path of integration, i.e., $G^-(\omega)$ can be continued analytically into the entire lower half-plane.

Next, we study the behavior at infinity of the functions $G^+(w)$ and $G^-(w)$; this behavior is different, depending on whether $\sigma > 1$ or $\sigma \leqslant 1$. If $\sigma > 1$, then, as $|w| \to \infty$,

$$G^+(w) \sim \frac{M}{w}, \tag{8.27}$$

where the integral

$$M = -\frac{1}{2\pi i}\int_{i\gamma_1-\infty}^{i\gamma_1+\infty} G(\omega)\,d\omega \tag{8.28}$$

converges, since $\sigma > 1$. If σ lies between 0 and 1 (or if $\sigma = 1$), then (8.28) diverges ($M = \infty$). In this case, it can be shown that the function $G^+(w)$ falls off more slowly than w^{-1}.

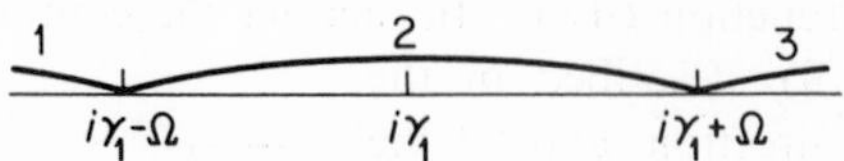

FIG. 10. Decomposition of the interval of integration into three parts (in connection with Lemma 1).

To see this, we divide the integral defining $G^+(w)$ into three integrals, along the three different line segments shown in Fig. 10. Then, the integral along segment 2 is an integral between finite limits, and the estimate (8.27) holds for this integral. As for the integrals along segments 1 and 3, for sufficiently large Ω, they can be estimated by writing

$$G(\omega) = \frac{C}{\omega^\sigma},$$

where C is a constant. Thus, for example, the integral along segment 3 equals approximately

$$\frac{C}{2\pi i}\int_{i\gamma_1+\Omega}^{\infty}\frac{d\omega}{\omega^\sigma(\omega - w)} = \frac{C}{2\pi i w^\sigma}\int_{(i\gamma_1+\Omega)/w}^{\infty}\frac{dx}{x^\sigma(x-1)}, \tag{8.29}$$

where $x = \omega/w$. As $w \to \infty$, the integral in the right-hand side of (8.29) is either finite (if $\sigma < 1$) or else grows like $\ln w$ (if $\sigma = 1$),[2] since

$$\int_{(i\gamma_1+\Omega)/w}^{\infty}\frac{dx}{x(x-1)} \sim -\ln\frac{i\gamma_1+\Omega}{w}. \tag{8.30}$$

A similar estimate holds for the integral along the segment 1. Consequently, $G^+(w)$ falls off like $w^{-\sigma}$ or like $\ln w/w$, i.e., more slowly than w^{-1}. The function $G^-(w)$ has similar properties.

The theory of the kind of integral equations to which one is led in studying optimum filters of type II was first given by N. Wiener and E. Hopf,[3] and then, from a more general point of view, by V. A. Fock.[4] In our discussion of the technique of solving equation (8.03), we shall essentially follow Fock's approach.

[2] The logarithm to the base e is denoted by ln, and the logarithm to the base 10 by log.

[3] N. Wiener and E. Hopf, Über eine Klasse singulärer Integralgleichungen (*On a class of singular integral equations*), S. B. Preuss. Akad. Wiss. (1931), p. 696.

[4] V. A. Fock, О некоторых интегральных уравнениях математической физики (*On some integral equations of mathematical physics*), Mat. Sbornik, **14**, 3 (1944).

9. Determination of the Transfer Function of the Optimum Filter of Type II

In Sec. 8, we reduced equation (8.03) for the optimum filter of type II to the two relations (8.17) and (8.18). We now assume that the functions $S_f(\omega)$ and $S_{hf}(\omega)$ are analytic inside the strip

$$-\gamma \leqslant \operatorname{Im} \omega \leqslant \gamma \tag{9.01}$$

containing the real axis, and that the function $S_f(\omega)$ does not vanish anywhere inside the strip. In particular, we assume that

$$S_f(\omega) > 0 \tag{9.02}$$

for all real ω. Later on, in Sec. 11, we shall try to free ourselves of these restrictions, but the treatment given in this section makes essential use of them.

We now apply Lemma 1 to the relations (8.17) and (8.18). We shall assume that $J(\omega)$ and $K_1(\omega)$ also satisfy the conditions of the lemma (including the restriction on their behavior at infinity, since otherwise the integrals which we have written have no meaning). Then, according to Lemma 1, we can write

$$\begin{aligned} J(w) &= J^+(w) + J^-(w), \\ K_1(w) &= K_1^+(w) + K_1^-(w). \end{aligned} \tag{9.03}$$

If in the lemma, we take a strip lying below the real axis ($\gamma_1 < 0, \gamma_2 = 0$), then, according to (8.17) and (8.26), in this strip we have

$$J^-(w) = -\frac{1}{2\pi i}\int_{-\infty}^{\infty} \frac{J(\omega)\, d\omega}{\omega - w} = 0, \tag{9.04}$$

and hence

$$J(w) = J^+(w). \tag{9.05}$$

Similarly, in a strip lying above the real axis ($\gamma_1 = 0$ and $\gamma_2 > 0$), equations (8.18) and (8.26) give

$$K_1^+(w) = 0 \tag{9.06}$$

and

$$K_1(w) = K_1^-(w). \tag{9.07}$$

Thus, it follows from (8.17) and (8.18) that a necessary condition for obtaining the optimum filter is that the function $J(w)$ be an analytic function in the entire upper half-plane, and that $K_1(w)$ be an analytic function in the entire lower half-plane. The sufficiency of these conditions is easily proved by using Cauchy's theorem, in the case of (8.17) and (8.18), or by using Jordan's lemma, in the case of (8.11) and (8.13), provided that the functions

$J(w)$ and $K_1(w)$ fall off uniformly at infinity in the half-planes in which they are analytic. In fact, since $J(w)$ is analytic in the upper half-plane, we can transform the integral in the left-hand side of formula (8.13) into a contour integral along the infinite semicircle C_R shown in Fig. 8:

$$\int_{-\infty}^{\infty} e^{i\omega\tau}J(\omega)\,d\omega = \lim_{R\to\infty}\int_{-R}^{R} e^{i\omega\tau}J(\omega)\,d\omega = \lim_{R\to\infty}\int_{C_R} e^{i\omega\tau}J(\omega)\,d\omega. \quad (9.08)$$

If $J(\omega)$ falls off uniformly at infinity, this integral vanishes for $\tau > 0$. The integral also vanishes for $\tau = 0$, if $J(\omega)$ falls off faster than $\omega^{-(1+\sigma)}$, where $\sigma > 0$, for then the integral along the semicircle C_R vanishes for $\tau = 0$ also. Similarly, if the function $K_1(\omega)$ falls off uniformly at infinity, then, applying Jordan's lemma again, we obtain

$$\int_{-\infty}^{\infty} e^{i\omega\tau}K_1(\omega)\,d\omega = \lim_{R\to\infty}\int_{C_R} e^{i\omega\tau}K_1(\omega)\,d\omega = 0 \quad (9.09)$$

for $\tau < 0$, where C_R is now a semicircular contour in the lower half-plane.

Thus, we have finally arrived at the following requirements:

A. *The function $K_1(\omega)$ must be analytic in the lower half-plane* (Im $\omega \leqslant 0$), *where it must go to zero uniformly as $|\omega| \to \infty$. Hence, according to formula* (8.09), *the transfer function $K(\omega)$ must be an analytic function in the lower half-plane, where it can grow no faster than some polynomial*

$$Q(\omega) = \sum_{\alpha=0}^{q} Q_\alpha (i\omega)^\alpha.$$

B. *The function $J(\omega) = K(\omega)S_f(\omega) - S_{hf}(\omega)$ must be analytic in the upper half-plane* (Im $\omega \geqslant 0$), *where it must go to zero faster than $\omega^{-(1+\sigma)}$* ($\sigma > 0$) *as $|\omega| \to \infty$.*

From the requirements A and B, we can obtain a solution of our problem in terms of two auxiliary functions $S_f^+(\omega)$ and $S_f^-(\omega)$ whose product is the given function $S_f(\omega)$:

$$S_f(\omega) = S_f^+(\omega)S_f^-(\omega). \quad (9.10)$$

Here, the functions $S_f^+(\omega)$ and $S_f^-(\omega)$, like the function $S_f(\omega)$, are analytic and nonvanishing in the strip (9.01). Moreover, $S_f^+(\omega)$ is analytic and nonvanishing in the entire upper-half-plane (Im $\omega \geqslant -\gamma$), while $S_f^-(\omega)$ is analytic and nonvanishing in the entire lower half-plane (Im $\omega \leqslant \gamma$). Of course, the factors in the decomposition (9.10) are not unique, and some extra requirements must be imposed in order to determine S_f^+ and S_f^-. As we know [cf. formula (3.02)], $S_f(\omega)$ is an even function, and hence

$$S_f^+(\omega)S_f^-(\omega) = S_f^+(-\omega)S_f^-(-\omega). \quad (9.11)$$

This suggests requiring that

$$S_f^+(\omega) = S_f^-(-\omega), \qquad S_f^-(\omega) = S_f^+(-\omega). \quad (9.12)$$

We shall also assume that inside our strip, the function $S_f(\omega)$ falls off at infinity like $c^2\omega^{-2r}$, where r is some positive integer and c is a constant. This means that

$$\lim_{\omega \to \pm\infty} \frac{\omega^{2r} S_f(\omega)}{c^2} = 1. \tag{9.13}$$

To actually find S_f^+ and S_f^-, we introduce the function

$$G(\omega) = \ln \frac{(\omega^2 + \tilde{\gamma}^2)^r S_f(\omega)}{c^2}, \tag{9.14}$$

where $\tilde{\gamma}$ is any number larger than γ [cf. formula (9.01)]. We shall assume that $G(\omega)$ is real for real values of ω, which we achieve by taking the principal value of the logarithm. Clearly, $G(\omega)$ is an analytic function within the strip. Hence, Lemma 1 is applicable to $G(\omega)$, since $G(\omega) \to 0$ as $\operatorname{Re} \omega \to \pm\infty$. Thus, using formula (9.10) and the identity

$$\omega^2 + \tilde{\gamma}^2 = (\tilde{\gamma} + i\omega)(\tilde{\gamma} - i\omega), \tag{9.15}$$

we obtain

$$G(\omega) = \ln \frac{(\tilde{\gamma} - i\omega)^r S_f^+(\omega)}{c} + \ln \frac{(\tilde{\gamma} + i\omega)^r S_f^-(\omega)}{c}. \tag{9.16}$$

The first logarithm in (9.16) is a function which is analytic in the upper half-plane, while the second logarithm is a function which is analytic in the lower half-plane. In other words, according to formula (8.23), we can write

$$G^+(\omega) = \ln \frac{(\tilde{\gamma} - i\omega)^r S_f^+(i\omega)}{c}, \qquad G^-(\omega) = \ln \frac{(\tilde{\gamma} + i\omega)^r S_f^-(\omega)}{c}, \tag{9.17}$$

from which we obtain the functions S_f^+ and S_f^- in the form

$$S_f^+(\omega) = \frac{c}{(\tilde{\gamma} - i\omega)^r} e^{G^+(\omega)}, \qquad S_f^-(\omega) = \frac{c}{(\tilde{\gamma} + i\omega)^r} e^{G^-(\omega)}, \tag{9.18}$$

where the functions G^+ and G^- are themselves given by (8.26). The defect of these formulas is that they contain the arbitrary parameter $\tilde{\gamma}$ and that they are derived subject to the condition (9.13). Later, we shall try to get rid of these restrictions. It is clear that the functions S_f^+ and S_f^- defined by (9.18) have the properties formulated above. Thus, finally, using Lemma 1, we have been able to carry out the factorization (9.10). Henceforth, we shall always understand S_f^+ and S_f^- to be the expressions (9.18): In the half-planes in which they are analytic, these expressions satisfy the following limiting relations at infinity:

$$\lim_{|\omega| \to \infty} \frac{(-i\omega)^r S_f^+(\omega)}{c} = 1, \qquad \lim_{|\omega| \to \infty} \frac{(i\omega)^r S_f^-(\omega)}{c} = 1. \tag{9.19}$$

At first glance, the formulas just written may appear rather complicated. However, in the applications, it is very often possible to take $S_f(\omega)$ to be a rational function, i.e., a ratio of two polynomials [cf. formula (4.33)]:

$$S_f(\omega) = \frac{P_b(\omega^2)}{P_a(\omega^2)} \quad (a > b). \tag{9.20}$$

The polynomials $P_a(\omega^2)$ and $P_b(\omega^2)$ are of degree a and b, respectively, in the variable ω^2 (since they must be even functions). We shall assume that

$$P_a(\omega^2) = 0 \quad \text{for} \quad \omega = \pm x_a \quad (\alpha = 1, 2, \ldots, a) \tag{9.21}$$

and

$$P_b(\omega^2) = 0 \quad \text{for} \quad \omega = \pm y_\beta \quad (\beta = 1, 2, \ldots, b). \tag{9.22}$$

Here, we have used x_α and y_β to denote the zeros of the numerator and denominator, respectively, which are located in the upper half-plane ($\text{Im } x_\alpha > 0$ and $\text{Im } y_\beta > 0$), and we have used $-x_\alpha$ and $-y_\beta$ to denote the zeros in the lower half-plane. Then, the function $S_f(\omega)$ can be written as a product of the form

$$S_f(\omega) = c^2 \frac{\prod(\omega^2 - y_\beta^2)}{\prod(\omega^2 - x_\alpha^2)} = (-1)^r c^2 \frac{\prod(y_\beta^2 - \omega)}{\prod(x_\alpha^2 - \omega)} \quad (r = a - b), \tag{9.23}$$

and the functions S_f^+ and S_f^- are equal to

$$S_f^+(\omega) = i^r c \frac{\prod(y_\beta + \omega)}{\prod(x_\alpha + \omega)}, \qquad S_f^-(\omega) = i^r c \frac{\prod(y_\beta - \omega)}{\prod(x_\alpha - \omega)}. \tag{9.24}$$

It is clear that the expressions (9.24) satisfy (9.10), (9.12) and (9.19), and therefore they must coincide with the expressions (9.18).

Using formula (9.10), we find that

$$J(\omega) = K(\omega) S_f^+(\omega) S_f^-(\omega) - S_{hf}(\omega), \tag{9.25}$$

which implies the formula

$$\frac{S_{hf}(\omega)}{S_f^+(\omega)} = K(\omega) S_f^-(\omega) - \frac{J(\omega)}{S_f^+(\omega)}, \tag{9.26}$$

where S_f^+, S_f^- and S_{hf} are known functions, while J and K are unknown functions. Thus, the left-hand side of (9.26) is a known function, which we denote by $H(\omega)$, whereas the right-hand side of (9.26) is an unknown function whose first term, according to condition A above, is analytic in the lower half-plane, and whose second term, according to condition B, is analytic in the upper half-plane. It follows from the properties of the functions S_{hf} and S_f^+ that $H(\omega)$ satisfies the conditions of Lemma 1, except perhaps the condition pertaining to the behavior at infinity. If the latter condition is also satisfied, then, according to Lemma 1, the function $H(\omega)$ can be represented in the form

$$H(\omega) = \frac{S_{hf}(\omega)}{S_f^+(\omega)} = H^+(\omega) + H^-(\omega), \tag{9.27}$$

where H^+ is a function which is analytic in the upper half-plane, and H^- is a function which is analytic in the lower half-plane. If we identify the terms in the right-hand sides of equations (9.26) and (9.27) which are analytic functions in the same half-plane, then we obtain

$$-\frac{J(\omega)}{S_f^+(\omega)} = H^+(\omega), \qquad K(\omega)S_f^-(\omega) = H^-(\omega), \tag{9.28}$$

so that

$$J(\omega) = -S_f^+(\omega)H^+(\omega) \quad \text{and} \quad K(\omega) = \frac{H^-(\omega)}{S_f^-(\omega)}, \tag{9.29}$$

where

$$H^+(w) = \frac{1}{2\pi i}\int_{-i\gamma-\infty}^{-i\gamma+\infty} \frac{H(\omega)\,d\omega}{\omega - w}, \qquad H^-(w) = -\frac{1}{2\pi i}\int_{i\gamma-\infty}^{i\gamma+\infty} \frac{H(\omega)\,d\omega}{\omega - w}. \tag{9.30}$$

If we define the functions $J(\omega)$ and $K(\omega)$ by using the formulas (9.29), then they will obviously be analytic in the half-planes required in conditions A and B. As for the behavior at infinity, condition B holds since the functions S_f^+ and H^+ both fall off at infinity in the upper half-plane, and condition A holds if S_{hf} and S_f are rational functions.

We now consider the case where $S_f(\omega)$ and $S_{hf}(\omega)$ are rational functions, but the function $H(\omega)$ does not fall off at infinity. Then $H(\omega)$ can be represented as the sum of two functions, a polynomial $P(\omega)$ and a function $H_1(\omega)$, which now satisfies all the conditions of Lemma 1:

$$H(\omega) = P(\omega) + H_1(\omega). \tag{9.31}$$

We form H_1^+ and H_1^-, using Lemma 1, and set

$$H^+(\omega) = P(\omega) + H_1^+(\omega), \qquad H^-(\omega) = H_1^-(\omega). \tag{9.32}$$

Then, we again use the formulas (9.29) to define the functions $J(\omega)$ and $K(\omega)$. To verify that the part of condition B pertaining to the behavior at infinity holds, we let the functions S_f, S_f^+ and S_f^- satisfy the conditions (9.13) and (9.19) at infinity. Assuming that $S_{hf}(\omega)$ falls off as ω^{-s}, where $s > 1$, we have

$$H(\omega) \sim \omega^{r-s} \qquad (\text{as } \omega \to \infty) \tag{9.33}$$

and

$$H^+(\omega) \sim \omega^{r-s}, \qquad J(\omega) \sim \omega^{-s}, \tag{9.34}$$

so that $J(\omega)$ really satisfies condition B. The part of condition A pertaining to the behavior at infinity is automatically satisfied, since the spectral densities are rational functions.

In the above analysis, we did not point out a very important fact, in the absence of which, the problem would not have a unique solution, and the solution (9.29) would be only one of several possible solutions. Thus, suppose that together with the decomposition of the function $H(\omega)$ already chosen, there is another possible decomposition

$$H(\omega) = H^{++}(\omega) + H^{--}(\omega), \tag{9.35}$$

where the functions H^{++} and H^{--} are analytic in the same half-planes as H^{+} and H^{-}, but behave differently at infinity. Then, comparing (9.35) with (9.27), we see that

$$H^{--}(\omega) - H^{-}(\omega) = H^{+}(\omega) - H^{++}(\omega), \tag{9.36}$$

where the left-hand side is an analytic function in the upper half-plane, and the right-hand side is an analytic function in the lower half-plane. Therefore, either side of (9.36) defines a function which is analytic in the entire complex ω-plane. We now use *Liouville's theorem*, which states that if a function is analytic in the entire complex ω-plane, then as $|\omega| \to \infty$, it either increases without limit, or else it reduces to a constant. It follows that H^{--} cannot decrease at infinity, but can only increase or approach a constant.

We now calculate the intensity of the process at the output of the optimum filter:

$$\overline{x^2} = \frac{1}{2\pi}\int_{-\infty}^{\infty} |K(\omega)|^2 S_f(\omega)\, d\omega. \tag{9.37}$$

This quantity appears in the expression (5.26) for the mean square error. For real values of ω, we have the identity

$$|S_f^+(\omega)|^2 = |S_f^-(\omega)|^2 = S_f(\omega), \tag{9.38}$$

which will be proved later (see Sec. 11). Therefore, formulas (9.29) and (9.37) give

$$\overline{x^2} = \frac{1}{2\pi}\int_{-\infty}^{\infty} |H^{-}(\omega)|^2\, d\omega, \tag{9.39}$$

so that to obtain a finite value of $\overline{x^2}$, as we must if our solution is to make any sense, the function $|H^{-}(\omega)|$ must fall off faster than $\omega^{-1/2}$ as $\omega \to \pm\infty$. The functions H^{-} defined by formulas (9.30) and (9.32) satisfy this condition, whereas any other function H^{--}, like the one discussed above, will give $\overline{x^2} = \infty$. Thus, it is just the condition

$$\overline{x^2} < \infty \tag{9.40}$$

which guarantees that our problem has a unique solution, at least within the framework of the present method of solution.

10. Investigation of the Functions $S_f^+(\omega)$ and $S_f^-(\omega)$

We now examine in more detail the properties of the functions appearing in the expression

$$K(\omega) = \frac{H^-(\omega)}{S_f^-(\omega)} \tag{10.01}$$

for the transfer function of the optimum filter [cf. formula (9.29)]. We begin by considering the function

$$G^-(w) = -\frac{1}{2\pi i}\int_{i\gamma-\infty}^{i\gamma+\infty} \frac{G(\omega)\,d\omega}{\omega - w}, \tag{10.02}$$

defined by Lemma 1. Differentiating both sides of (10.02) with respect to w, we obtain

$$\frac{dG^-(w)}{dw} = -\frac{1}{2\pi i}\int_{i\gamma-\infty}^{i\gamma+\infty} \frac{G(\omega)\,d\omega}{(\omega - w)^2}. \tag{10.03}$$

Noting that

$$-\frac{1}{(\omega - w)^2} = \frac{d}{d\omega}\frac{1}{\omega - w},$$

we integrate by parts, obtaining

$$\frac{dG^-(w)}{dw} = \frac{1}{2\pi i}\frac{G(\omega)}{\omega - w}\bigg|_{i\gamma-\infty}^{i\gamma+\infty} - \frac{1}{2\pi i}\int_{i\gamma-\infty}^{i\gamma+\infty} \frac{G'(\omega)\,d\omega}{\omega - w}, \tag{10.04}$$

where $G'(\omega)$ is the derivative of $G(\omega)$ with respect to ω. Since

$$\frac{G(\omega)}{\omega - w}$$

vanishes at infinity, the first term in the right-hand side of (10.04) is zero, and we have

$$\frac{dG^-(w)}{dw} = -\frac{1}{2\pi i}\int_{i\gamma-\infty}^{i\gamma+\infty} \frac{G'(\omega)\,d\omega}{\omega - w}. \tag{10.05}$$

We now take $G(\omega)$ to be the function (9.14). To eventually get rid of the auxiliary parameter $\tilde{\gamma}$, we write $G(\omega)$ in the form

$$G(\omega) = \psi(\omega) + \chi(\omega), \tag{10.06}$$

where

$$\psi(\omega) = \ln\frac{(\omega^2 + \tilde{\gamma}^2)^r}{c^2}, \qquad \chi(\omega) = \ln S_f(\omega). \tag{10.07}$$

Then, the functions G^+ and G^- likewise can be written in the form

$$\begin{aligned} G^+(\omega) &= \psi^+(\omega) + \chi^+(\omega), \\ G^-(\omega) &= \psi^-(\omega) + \chi^-(\omega). \end{aligned} \tag{10.08}$$

If we now try to use formulas like (8.26) to find ψ^+, ψ^-, χ^+ or χ^-, the integrals will diverge individually, even though the corresponding integrals for the function G itself (which goes to zero at infinity) are guaranteed to converge. Instead, we calculate the derivatives of the functions ψ^+, ψ^-, χ^+ and χ^-. It follows from the second of the formulas (10.08) that

$$\frac{dG^-(w)}{dw} = \frac{d\psi^-(w)}{dw} + \frac{d\chi^-(w)}{dw}. \tag{10.09}$$

Since

$$\psi(\omega) = r \ln (\omega + i\tilde{\gamma}) + r \ln (\omega - i\tilde{\gamma}) - \ln c^2 \tag{10.10}$$

and

$$\psi'(\omega) = r\left(\frac{1}{\omega + i\tilde{\gamma}} + \frac{1}{\omega - i\tilde{\gamma}}\right), \tag{10.11}$$

the integral

$$\frac{d\psi^-(w)}{dw} = -\frac{1}{2\pi i}\int_{i\gamma-\infty}^{i\gamma+\infty} \frac{\psi'(\omega)\, d\omega}{\omega - w} \tag{10.12}$$

will converge, since the function $\psi'(\omega)$ falls off at infinity like $1/\omega$, and the whole integrand falls off like $1/\omega^2$.

The derivative $d\psi^-(w)/dw$ can easily be found. The integrand in (10.12) has one pole above the path of integration ($\omega = i\tilde{\gamma}$), and two poles below the path of integration ($\omega = -i\tilde{\gamma}$ and $\omega = w$). Deforming the path of integration upward, calculating the residue at the point $\omega = i\tilde{\gamma}$, and using the fact that the integral over the semicircle C_R in Fig. 8 goes to zero as $R \to \infty$, we obtain

$$\frac{d\psi^-(w)}{dw} = \frac{r}{\omega - i\tilde{\gamma}}, \tag{10.13}$$

which implies that

$$\psi^-(\omega) = r \ln (\omega - i\tilde{\gamma}) + \text{const.} \tag{10.14}$$

We choose the constant in such a way that

$$\psi^-(\omega) = \ln \frac{(\tilde{\gamma} + i\omega)^r}{c}. \tag{10.15}$$

Then, introducing the function ψ^+ in the form

$$\psi^+(\omega) = \psi^-(-\omega) = \ln \frac{(\tilde{\gamma} - i\omega)^r}{c}, \tag{10.16}$$

we can rewrite the formula (9.18) as

$$S_f^+(\omega) = e^{\chi^+(\omega)}, \qquad S_f^-(\omega) = e^{\chi^-(\omega)}, \tag{10.17}$$

since

$$e^{\psi^+(\omega)} = \frac{(\tilde{\gamma} - i\omega)^r}{c}, \qquad e^{\psi^-(\omega)} = \frac{(\tilde{\gamma} + i\omega)^r}{c}. \tag{10.18}$$

Next, consider the functions χ^+ and χ^-. Differentiating the second of the formulas (10.07), we obtain

$$\chi'(\omega) = \frac{S_f'(\omega)}{S_f(\omega)}, \tag{10.19}$$

from which it follows that

$$\begin{aligned}\frac{d\chi^-(w)}{dw} &= -\frac{1}{2\pi i}\int_{i\gamma-\infty}^{i\gamma+\infty} \frac{\chi'(\omega)\,d\omega}{\omega - w} \\ &= -\frac{1}{2\pi i}\int_{i\gamma-\infty}^{i\gamma+\infty} \frac{S_f'(\omega)\,d\omega}{S_f(\omega)(\omega - w)}.\end{aligned} \tag{10.20}$$

This formula allows us to determine the function $\chi^-(w)$ to within a constant.

As an example, we examine the case where $S_f(\omega)$ is the rational function (9.23). Then, we have

$$\begin{aligned}\chi(\omega) = \ln S_f(\omega) = \ln c^2 &+ \sum_{\beta=1}^{b} [\ln(\omega + y_\beta) + \ln(\omega - y_\beta)] \\ &- \sum_{\alpha=1}^{a} [\ln(\omega + x_\alpha) + \ln(\omega - x_\alpha)],\end{aligned}$$

and

$$\chi'(\omega) = \sum_{\beta=1}^{b}\left(\frac{1}{\omega + y_\beta} + \frac{1}{\omega - y_\beta}\right) - \sum_{\alpha=1}^{a}\left(\frac{1}{\omega + x_\alpha} + \frac{1}{\omega - x_\alpha}\right). \tag{10.21}$$

Substituting (10.21) into (10.19) and (10.20) and evaluating the integral by residues [just as was done in deriving formula (10.13)], we obtain

$$\frac{d\chi^-(w)}{dw} = \sum_\beta \frac{1}{w - y_\beta} - \sum_\alpha \frac{1}{w - x_\alpha}, \tag{10.22}$$

and similarly

$$\frac{d\chi^+(w)}{dw} = \sum_\beta \frac{1}{w + y_\beta} - \sum_\alpha \frac{1}{w + x_\alpha}. \tag{10.23}$$

Then, integrating (10.22) and (10.23), we find that

$$\begin{aligned}\chi^-(w) &= \sum_\beta \ln(w - y_\beta) - \sum_\alpha \ln(w - x_\alpha) + \text{const}, \\ \chi^+(w) &= \sum_\beta \ln(w + y_\beta) - \sum_\alpha \ln(w + x_\alpha) + \text{const},\end{aligned} \tag{10.24}$$

and the formulas (10.17) become

$$S_f^+(\omega) = C^+\frac{\prod(y_\beta + \omega)}{\prod(x_\alpha + \omega)}, \qquad S_f^-(\omega) = C^-\frac{\prod(y_\beta - \omega)}{\prod(x_\alpha - \omega)}, \tag{10.25}$$

where C^+ and C^- are as yet undetermined multiplicative constants. It follows from (9.12) that

$$C^+ = C^-, \tag{10.26}$$

and from formula (9.10) that

$$\begin{aligned} S_f(\omega) = S_f^+(\omega)S_f^-(\omega) &= (-1)^r c^2 \frac{\prod(y_\beta^2 - \omega^2)}{\prod(x_a^2 - \omega^2)} \\ &= C^+C^- \frac{\prod(y_\beta^2 - \omega^2)}{\prod(x_\alpha^2 - \omega^2)}. \end{aligned} \tag{10.27}$$

Therefore, we have

$$C^+ = C^- = \pm\, i^r c. \tag{10.28}$$

Choosing the plus sign, we finally obtain

$$S_f^+(\omega) = i^r c \frac{\prod(y_\beta + \omega)}{\prod(x_\alpha + \omega)}, \qquad S_f^-(\omega) = i^r c \frac{\prod(y_\beta - \omega)}{\prod(x_\alpha - \omega)}. \tag{10.29}$$

Moreover, the minus sign gives exactly the same solution for the optimum filter of type II. In fact, if we change the signs of S_f^+ and S_f^-, then the function H (and hence H^+ and H^-) also changes its sign, and consequently the system function (10.01) remains the same.

Thus, we have again obtained the formulas (9.24), which were not derived in Sec. 9, but only verified indirectly. The method of calculating the functions S_f^+ and S_f^- given in this section is obviously more general, and can be applied in cases where $S_f(\omega)$ is not a rational function.

11. Construction of the Optimum Filter of Type II

The solution of the integral equation of the optimum type II filter which was obtained in Sec. 9 made essential use of the theory of functions of a complex variable. In this section, we modify the solution in such a way that it involves only the values of $S_f(\omega)$ and $S_{hf}(\omega)$ for *real* ω, since it is only for real ω that we can actually find $S_f(\omega)$ and $S_{hf}(\omega)$ by "analyzing the spectra" of the appropriate random processes.

First, we calculate the functions S_f^+ and S_f^-. It turns out that these functions can be calculated by a different method, which is particularly suitable for real frequencies ω. In fact, as we shall see, this method establishes a relation between the functions S_f^+, S_f^- and certain concepts of circuit theory. We start from the function

$$G^-(w) = -\frac{1}{2\pi i}\int_{i\gamma-\infty}^{i\gamma+\infty} \frac{G(\omega)\, d\omega}{\omega - w}, \tag{11.01}$$

defined in connection with Lemma 1, and taking w to be real, we reduce the integral in (11.01) to an integral along the real axis. To do so, we use the analyticity of the function $G(\omega)$ to lower the contour of integration to the real axis, except at the pole $\omega = w$ which we by-pass, using a small semicircle in the upper half-plane (see Fig. 11). We cannot let the path of integration go through this pole, since then the integral would diverge. In fact, the limit

$$\lim_{\substack{\varepsilon_1 \to 0 \\ \varepsilon_2 \to 0}} \int_{-\infty}^{w-\varepsilon_1} \frac{G(\omega)\,d\omega}{\omega - w} + \int_{w+\varepsilon_2}^{\infty} \frac{G(\omega)\,d\omega}{\omega - w} \tag{11.02}$$

does not exist if the positive numbers ε_1 and ε_2 approach zero independently. However, if $\varepsilon_1 = \varepsilon_2 \to 0$, the integral does exist, and is called the *Cauchy principal value* of the integral, which we denote in the same way as an ordinary integral:

$$\int_{-\infty}^{\infty} \frac{G(\omega)\,d\omega}{\omega - w} = \lim_{\varepsilon \to 0} \left[\int_{-\infty}^{w-\varepsilon} \frac{G(\omega)\,d\omega}{\omega - w} + \int_{w+\varepsilon}^{\infty} \frac{G(\omega)\,d\omega}{\omega - w} \right]. \tag{11.03}$$

Thus, the integral along the real axis can be given a definite meaning, but it differs from the original integral (11.01).

In the theory of functions of a complex variable, it is shown that the integral (11.01) equals

$$G^-(w) = \frac{1}{2} G(w) - \frac{1}{2\pi i} \int_{-\infty}^{\infty} \frac{G(\omega)\,d\omega}{\omega - w}. \tag{11.04}$$

In fact, the integral along the contour shown in Fig. 11 equals one half the residue at the point $\omega = w$ (i.e., the integral around the infinitesimal semi-circle) plus the integral along the real axis (i.e., the principal value). If $G(\omega)$ is an even function, then

FIG. 11. A contour of integration going along the real axis and passing above the point $\omega = w$.

$$\begin{aligned} \int_{-\infty}^{\infty} \frac{G(\omega)\,d\omega}{\omega - w} &= \int_0^{\infty} G(\omega) \left(\frac{1}{\omega - w} - \frac{1}{\omega + w} \right) d\omega \\ &= 2w \int_0^{\infty} \frac{G(\omega)\,d\omega}{\omega^2 - w^2}, \end{aligned} \tag{11.05}$$

and formula (11.04) becomes

$$G^-(w) = \frac{1}{2} G(w) + \frac{iw}{\pi} \int_0^{\infty} \frac{G(\omega)\,d\omega}{\omega^2 - w^2}. \tag{11.06}$$

As $\omega \to \infty$, this integral converges better than the integral (11.04).

We now apply (11.06) to the functions

$$\begin{gathered} \chi(\omega) = \ln S_f(\omega), \\ \chi^+(\omega) = \ln S_f^+(\omega), \qquad \chi^-(\omega) = \ln S_f^-(\omega) \end{gathered} \tag{11.07}$$

(cf. Sec. 10), obtaining

$$\chi^-(w) = \frac{1}{2}\chi(w) + \frac{iw}{\pi} \int_0^{\infty} \frac{\chi(\omega)\,d\omega}{\omega^2 - w^2}, \tag{11.08}$$

where we assume that the integral in the right-hand side converges (as it certainly does if S_f is a rational function). Bearing in mind that

$$\chi^+(\omega) = \chi^-(-\omega), \tag{11.09}$$

and writing

$$\varphi(w) = \frac{w}{\pi}\int_0^\infty \frac{\ln S_f(\omega)\,d\omega}{\omega^2 - w^2}, \tag{11.10}$$

we finally obtain the formulas

$$S_f^+(\omega) = \sqrt{S_f(\omega)}e^{-i\varphi(\omega)}, \qquad S_f^-(\omega) = \sqrt{S_f(\omega)}e^{i\varphi(\omega)} \tag{11.11}$$

for real ω. Thus, the first term in the right-hand side of (11.08) gives the absolute value of the functions S_f^+ and S_f^-, while the second term gives the phase. Moreover, for real ω, we have the formula

$$|S_f^+(\omega)|^2 = |S_f^-(\omega)|^2 = S_f(\omega), \tag{11.12}$$

which has already been used in Sec. 9.

In the theory of electrical circuits, the following problem often arises: Suppose that one is given the absolute value $|K(\omega)|$ of the transfer function of a filter of type II, for all frequencies from 0 to ∞. Then, what is the phase function $\varphi(\omega)$ of the filter? This phase function must be such that the transfer function

$$K(\omega) = |K(\omega)|e^{i\varphi(\omega)} \tag{11.13}$$

defines a filter which uses the input function only in the past and in the present, but not in the future. One way of defining $\varphi(\omega)$ is to use the formula

$$\varphi(w) = \frac{2w}{\pi}\int_0^\infty \frac{\ln|K(\omega)|\,d\omega}{\omega^2 - w^2}, \tag{11.14}$$

which is similar to (11.10). In fact, for a filter of type II, the function $K(\omega)$ must be analytic in the lower half-plane (cf. Sec. 9, condition A), and moreover, $K(\omega)$ must satisfy the formula (3.08), i.e.,

$$K(\omega)K(-\omega) = |K(\omega)|^2, \tag{11.15}$$

where the function $K(-\omega)$ must obviously be analytic in the upper half-plane. It is easy to see that the relation (11.15) is also applicable to transfer functions of the form (8.09). Therefore, the problem of finding $K(\omega)$ from $|K(\omega)|$ reduces to the problem of decomposing a given function $|K(\omega)|^2$ into the factors (11.15), and this gives rise to formula (11.14).

For calculational purposes, it is convenient to write formula (11.10) in the form

$$\varphi(w) = \frac{w}{\pi}\int_0^\infty \frac{\ln S_f(\omega) - \ln S_f(w)}{\omega^2 - w^2}\,d\omega, \tag{11.16}$$

where the extra term $-\ln S_f(w)$ guarantees the convergence of the integral at the point $\omega = w$. In view of the identity

$$w \int_0^\infty \frac{d\omega}{\omega^2 - w^2} = \frac{1}{2} \int_0^\infty \left(\frac{1}{\omega - w} - \frac{1}{\omega + w} \right) d\omega$$

$$= \frac{1}{2} \lim_{\varepsilon \to 0} \left(\ln \frac{\varepsilon}{2w - \varepsilon} - \ln \frac{\varepsilon}{2w + \varepsilon} \right) \tag{11.17}$$

$$= \frac{1}{2} \lim_{\varepsilon \to \infty} \ln \frac{2w + \varepsilon}{2w - \varepsilon} = 0,$$

this extra term does not change the result.

For our subsequent work, we need the following result:

LEMMA 2. *Let the function $G(\omega)$ satisfy the conditions of Lemma 1 in some strip*

$$-\gamma \leqslant \operatorname{Im} \omega \leqslant \gamma, \tag{11.18}$$

and let the function $g(\tau)$ be equal to

$$g(\tau) = \frac{1}{2\pi} \int_{-\infty}^{\infty} e^{i\omega\tau} G(\omega)\, d\omega. \tag{11.19}$$

Then, the functions G^+ and G^- can be calculated by using the formulas

$$G^+(\omega) = \int_{-\infty}^{0} e^{-i\omega\tau} g(\tau)\, d\tau, \qquad G^-(\omega) = \int_0^\infty e^{-i\omega\tau} g(\tau)\, d\tau. \tag{11.20}$$

The proof of Lemma 2 is almost obvious: Substituting the expression

$$G(\omega) = G^+(\omega) G^-(\omega) \tag{11.21}$$

into formula (11.19), we obtain

$$g(\tau) = g^+(\tau) + g^-(\tau), \tag{11.22}$$

where

$$g^+(\tau) = \frac{1}{2\pi} \int_{-\infty}^{\infty} e^{i\omega\tau} G^+(\omega)\, d\omega, \quad g^-(\tau) = \frac{1}{2\pi} \int_{-\infty}^{\infty} e^{i\omega\tau} G^-(\omega)\, d\omega. \tag{11.23}$$

According to Lemma 1, the functions $G^+(\omega)$ and $G^-(\omega)$ decrease at infinity, and the integrals (11.23) are meaningful. The function $G^+(\omega)$ is analytic in the upper half-plane, and therefore, for $\tau > 0$, we can deform the path of integration upward, and change it into an infinite semicircle which has the real axis as its diameter. Then, the integral along this semicircle vanishes, by Jordan's lemma (the conditions for which are met in this case). Therefore, we have

$$g^+(\tau) = 0 \quad \text{for} \quad \tau > 0, \tag{11.24}$$

and similarly

$$g^-(\tau) = 0 \quad \text{for} \quad \tau < 0. \tag{11.25}$$

Inverting the integrals (11.23), we obtain

$$G^{+}(\omega) = \frac{1}{2\pi}\int_{-\infty}^{\infty} e^{-i\omega\tau}\, g^{+}(\tau)\, d\tau,$$
$$G^{-}(\omega) = \frac{1}{2\pi}\int_{-\infty}^{\infty} e^{-i\omega\tau}\, g^{-}(\tau)\, d\tau. \tag{11.26}$$

Finally, according to formulas (11.22), (11.24) and (11.25), the integrals (11.26) and (11.20) are the same, which completes the proof of Lemma 2.

This lemma allows us to give a new approach to the problem of finding the optimum linear filter of type II. In fact, in view of the foregoing, we can construct the optimum linear filter in the following steps:

Step 1. Calculate S_f^+ and S_f^- by one of the methods given above. If the function $S_f(\omega)$ is given analytically (e.g., as a rational function), then it is better to use the functions χ^+ and χ^-. If $S_f(\omega)$ is given empirically (in the form of a curve), this cannot be done, and we have to use formulas (11.11) and (11.16).

Step 2. Form the function $H(\omega)$, using the expression

$$H(\omega) = \frac{S_{hf}(\omega)}{S_f^+(\omega)}, \tag{11.27}$$

and then take the Fourier transform

$$\eta(\tau) = \frac{1}{2\pi}\int_{-\infty}^{\infty} e^{i\omega\tau}\, H(\omega)\, d\omega \tag{11.28}$$

of $H(\omega)$, provided $H(\omega)$ satisfies the conditions of Lemma 1. However, if

$$H(\omega) = P(\omega) + H_1(\omega), \tag{11.29}$$

where $P(\omega)$ is a polynomial and $H_1(\omega)$ satisfies the conditions of Lemma 1 (cf. the end of Sec. 9), then calculate $\eta(\tau)$ by using the formula

$$\eta(\tau) = \frac{1}{2\pi}\int_{-\infty}^{\infty} e^{i\omega\tau}\, H_1(\omega)\, d\omega. \tag{11.30}$$

We shall only need $\eta(\tau)$ for $\tau > 0$.

Step 3. Use Lemma 2 to calculate the function $H^{-}(\omega)$ by means of the formula

$$H^{-}(\omega) = \int_{0}^{\infty} e^{-i\omega\tau}\, \eta(\tau)\, d\tau. \tag{11.31}$$

If all the spectral densities are given analytically, then instead of the function $\eta(\tau)$, we can use the formulas of Sec. 9.

Step 4. This step is completely elementary, and consists in calculating the desired transfer function by using the formula

$$K(\omega) = \frac{H^{-}(\omega)}{S_f^{-}(\omega)}. \tag{11.32}$$

Here, the functions are taken with a minus sign, since a filter of type II does not use the input process in the "future."

It is convenient to consider these four steps separately in the case where the functions S_f and S_{hf} are given empirically. Sometimes, however, it makes sense to write one overall formula

$$K(\omega) = \frac{1}{2\pi S_f^{-}(\omega)} \int_0^{\infty} e^{-i\omega\tau}\, d\tau \int_{-\infty}^{\infty} e^{iw\tau} \frac{S_{hf}(w)}{S_f^{+}(w)}\, dw, \tag{11.33}$$

instead of the four separate formulas. This is the final formula for filters of type II. If the function $H(\omega) = S_{hf}(\omega)/S_f^{+}(\omega)$ does not satisfy the conditions of Lemma 1, then we divide out $H_1(\omega)$, the fractional part of $H(\omega)$, for which the integral with respect to w in (11.33) exists. In formula (11.33), we have already freed ourselves of the need to work in the domain of complex frequencies, where $S_f(\omega)$ and $S_{hf}(\omega)$ cannot be measured.

The considerations above pertain to all filters of type II, both to predicting filters and to filters which only suppress the noise, as well as to filters which combine noise suppression with prediction or transformation of the useful signal. Later, we shall consider some special cases of filters of type II. It should be noted that if $K(\omega)$ is a rational function of the frequency, then it is always possible to synthesize a circuit containing inductances, capacitances and resistances, which realizes the given optimum filter. Thus, the theory of optimum linear filters leads to frequency filters, like those widely used in electrical engineering. An elementary example of such a filter will be given in Sec. 15.

12. Physical Interpretation of the Theory of Filtering and Prediction

Until now, we have studied filters of types I and II from a purely mathematical point of view. We shall now see what physical meaning can be ascribed to the mathematical formulas derived above. To do this, it is convenient to consider a particularly simple model of a random process, in which the process is conceived of as being a superposition of irregularly occurring pulses (disturbances) of standard form. We shall assume that the time of occurrence of each pulse is random, but that the form of each pulse is perfectly definite. If t_α is the time of occurrence of the αth pulse, then its behavior in time is characterized by the function $v(t - t_\alpha)$, as shown in Fig. 12.

It turns out that many random processes can actually be represented in this way. Consider the example of *shot noise*, where electrons are emitted from the cathode of a vacuum tube at random times. Let the time axis in Fig. 12 be divided into many small intervals Δt_α, and let N_α denote the number of electrons emitted in the time interval Δt_α. The subsequent motion of the electrons will depend on the field between the cathode and anode of the tube. If we let $v(t)$ be the current produced in an external circuit by an electron which leaves the cathode at the time $t = 0$, then the resulting current $u(t)$ equals

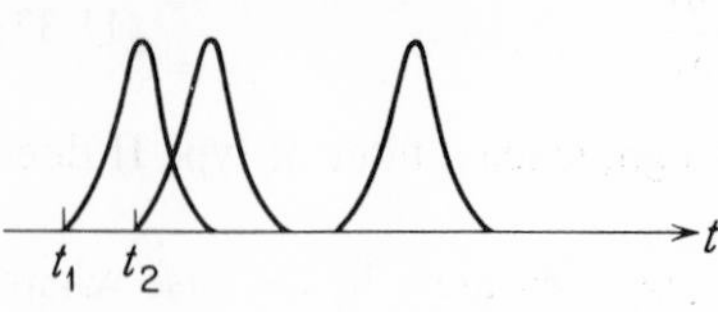

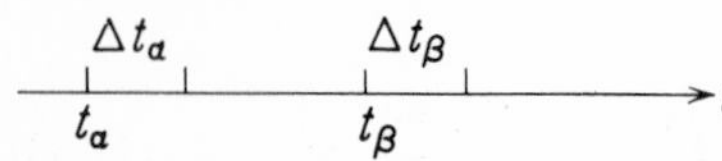

FIG. 12. Representation of a random process as a superposition of pulses of standard form.

$$u(t) = \sum_\alpha N_\alpha v(t - t_\alpha). \tag{12.01}$$

The mean value of the quantity N_α is obviously proportional to Δt_α, so that

$$\overline{N}_\alpha = \nu\, \Delta t_\alpha, \tag{12.02}$$

where ν is the average number of electrons emitted per unit time. The mean value of the random function $u(t)$ is

$$\overline{u(t)} = \sum_\alpha \overline{N}_\alpha v(t - t_\alpha) = \nu \sum_\alpha v(t - t_\alpha)\, \Delta t_\alpha, \tag{12.03}$$

or, passing to the limit as $\Delta t_\alpha \to 0$,

$$\bar{u} = \nu \int_{-\infty}^{\infty} v(t - \tau)\, d\tau = \nu \int_{-\infty}^{\infty} v(t)\, dt. \tag{12.04}$$

Because of the obvious condition

$$v(t) = 0 \quad \text{for} \quad t < 0, \tag{12.05}$$

we can write (12.04) as

$$\bar{u} = \nu \int_0^\infty v(t)\, dt. \tag{12.06}$$

The expression (12.01) can be used to construct a "model" of a random process with any correlation function (for certain exceptions, see Sec. 13). So far, we have only considered random processes with mean value zero. Therefore, in constructing a model of a random process $u(t)$ by using the present method, we must also assume that (12.06) vanishes. A sufficient condition for this is that

$$\nu = 0, \tag{12.07}$$

i.e., that the mean value (12.02) vanishes. This makes sense if N_α takes both positive and negative values in such a way that the pulse $v(t - t_\alpha)$ or the pulse $-v(t - t_\alpha)$ occurs with equal probability. Moreover, we assume that if the intervals Δt_α and Δt_β are nonoverlapping, then

$$\overline{N_\alpha N_\beta} = 0 \quad \text{for} \quad \alpha \neq \beta. \tag{12.08}$$

Thus, the pulses occurring in different time intervals are statistically independent of one another. As for the pulses occurring in the same time interval, we assume that

$$\overline{N_\alpha^2} = \sigma \, \Delta t_\alpha, \tag{12.09}$$

i.e., the mean square of the number of pulses is proportional to the length of the interval Δt_α.

Suppose we assume that $N_\alpha = M_\alpha - \overline{M}_\alpha$, where the random variables M_α obey a Poisson distribution law, and suppose we define the random process

$$U(t) = \sum_\alpha M_\alpha v(t - t_\alpha),$$

which is connected with the process (12.01) by the relation

$$u(t) = U(t) - \overline{U}.$$

Then, the number σ has a perfectly definite meaning: In fact, it is just the mean number of pulses making up the process $U(t)$, per unit time. To justify this interpretation of (12.09), we observe that with the Poisson law we have

$$\overline{N_\alpha^2} = \overline{M_\alpha^2} - (\overline{M}_\alpha)^2 = \overline{M}_\alpha.$$

Returning to the process $u(t)$, we calculate the autocorrelation function

$$R_u(\tau) = \overline{u(t)u(t - \tau)} = \sum_{\alpha, \beta} \overline{N_\alpha N_\beta} v(t - t_\alpha)v(t - \tau - t_\beta). \tag{12.10}$$

Using formulas (12.08) and (12.09), we obtain

$$\begin{aligned} R_u(\tau) &= \sum_\alpha \overline{N_\alpha^2} v(t - t_\alpha)v(t - \tau - t_\alpha) \\ &= \sigma \sum_\alpha v(t - t_\alpha)v(t - \tau - t_\alpha)\, \Delta t_\alpha. \end{aligned} \tag{12.11}$$

Letting $\Delta t_\alpha \to 0$, we finally have

$$\begin{aligned} R_u(\tau) &= \sigma \int_{-\infty}^{\infty} v(t - s)v(t - s - \tau)\, ds \\ &= \sigma \int_{-\infty}^{\infty} v(t)v(t - \tau)\, dt. \end{aligned} \tag{12.12}$$

Thus, the autocorrelation function of the given random process can be represented by integrals similar to those considered at the end of Sec. 1.

If we assume that the "standard" pulse $v(t)$ satisfies the condition (12.05) and dies out quite rapidly as $t \to \infty$, then we can take the Fourier transform of $v(t)$. Thus, let $V(\omega)$ be the "amplitude spectrum" of the pulse $v(t)$, equal to

$$V(\omega) = \int_{-\infty}^{\infty} e^{-i\omega\tau} v(t)\, dt. \tag{12.13}$$

Then, the inversion of (12.13) is

$$v(t) = \frac{1}{2\pi} \int_{-\infty}^{\infty} e^{i\omega t} V(\omega)\, d\omega.$$

It should be noted that although the standard pulse $v(t)$ can be represented as a Fourier integral, the stationary random process $u(t)$ itself cannot. Therefore, it only makes sense to talk about the "power spectrum" of $u(t)$, but not about its "amplitude spectrum."

We now observe that the autocorrelation function of the process $u(t)$ equals

$$R(\tau) = \frac{\sigma}{2\pi} \int_{-\infty}^{\infty} v(t-\tau)\, dt \int_{-\infty}^{\infty} e^{i\omega t} V(\omega)\, d\omega$$

$$= \frac{\sigma}{2\pi} \int_{-\infty}^{\infty} e^{i\omega\tau} V(\omega)\, d\omega \int_{-\infty}^{\infty} e^{i\omega t} v(t)\, dt$$

or

$$R_u(\tau) = \frac{\sigma}{2\pi} \int_{-\infty}^{\infty} e^{i\omega\tau} |V(\omega)|^2\, d\omega.$$

Comparing this formula with (2.16), which relates the autocorrelation function of the random process $u(t)$ to its power spectral density $S_u(\omega)$, we easily obtain the formula

$$S_u(\omega) = \sigma |V(\omega)|^2. \tag{12.14}$$

Thus, $S_u(\omega)$ is proportional to the square of the absolute value of the Fourier transform of the pulse $v(t)$. This formula shows how to construct an appropriate pulse model of any given random process. It is clear that the problem does not have a unique solution, and in fact we can construct various different pulse models for a random process which is specified only by its correlation function, e.g., by giving $V(\omega)$ various phases.

In Sec. 3, we derived the formula (3.33), relating the correlation time $\Delta\tau$ and the (spectral) bandwidth $\Delta\omega$. In the present model, $\Delta\tau$ is determined by the duration of the pulse $v(t)$. In particular, pulses of infinitely short duration correspond to an infinitely wide spectrum, like the spectrum of so-called "white noise," about which we spoke in Sec. 6 [cf. formula (6.21)]. We shall hereafter denote white noise by $w(t)$; it has the spectral density

$$S_w(\omega) = \text{const.} \tag{12.15}$$

Of course, (12.15) is just a limiting case. In practice, every random process has a power spectral density which falls off when the frequency is sufficiently high. This is also clear from our pulse model: Pulses of zero duration cannot be produced, and pulses of finite (although short) duration always lead to a spectral density which vanishes as $\omega \to \pm\infty$. However, as remarked in Sec. 6, we can always assume that (12.15) holds in such a large frequency band (how large this band is depends on the particular problem) that we are in effect led to the same results as those we would get if "real" white noise, rigorously obeying (12.15) for *all* frequencies, could actually be produced.

If we try to calculate the correlation function of white noise, then the integral (2.17) will diverge, so that one cannot talk about the correlation function of such a process. If we start from the idea of white noise as an aggregate of instantaneous pulses and bear in mind that in formula (12.12) the correlation function is different from zero for $\tau \neq 0$ only because of the finite duration of the pulses, then we can conclude that the correlation function of white noise vanishes for $\tau \neq 0$. Thus, white noise is an "absolutely random" process, in which there is no correlation between the present and the future, or between the past and the present. In particular, white noise cannot be predicted.

Suppose now that white noise passes through a filter which admits only some specific range of frequencies. Then, at the output of the filter, there appears a process which is correlated in time. If we regard white noise as an aggregate of irregularly occurring instantaneous pulses, then this correlation is explained by the fact that in going through the filter each pulse has been "smeared out" in a definite way, i.e., each pulse has been converted into the *impulse response* of the filter (see Sec. 2). Therefore, the process at the filter output exhibits time correlation. Thus, if we consider a random process only from the standpoint of its correlation properties and the corresponding spectral densities, any process can be identified with white noise which has passed through an appropriate filter.

Specifically, suppose that the white noise $w(t)$, with spectral density $S_w(\omega) = 1$, appears at the output of a filter of type II, with transfer function $S_f^-(\omega)$. Then, according to formulas (4.10) and (11.12), we can write

$$S_x(\omega) = |K(\omega)|^2 S_w(\omega) = |S_f^-(\omega)|^2 = S_f(\omega), \tag{12.16}$$

i.e., at the output of the filter we obtain a random process with spectral density $S_f(\omega)$. In this way, we can regard the process $f(t)$ as being the result of passing white noise through a type II filter with a suitably chosen transfer function $S_f^-(\omega)$, as illustrated by Fig. 13. Conversely, if we pass the random process $f(t)$ through a filter with the transfer function $1/S_f^-(\omega)$, then we obtain white noise with spectral density 1 (see Fig. 14).

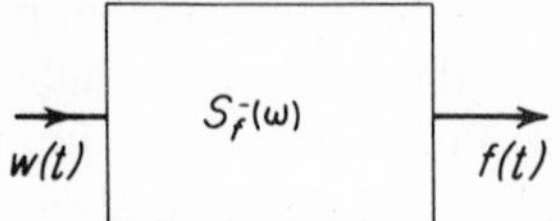

FIG. 13. A filter with transfer function $S_f^-(\omega)$, which converts white noise $w(t)$ into the random process $f(t)$, or into its pulse model.

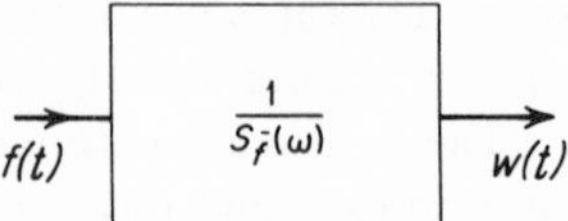

FIG. 14. A filter with transfer function $1/S_f^-(\omega)$, which converts the random process $f(t)$ into white noise.

We are now in a position to explain the meaning of the formula

$$K(\omega) = \frac{H^-(\omega)}{S_f^-(\omega)} \tag{12.17}$$

for the transfer function of the optimum filter of type II: Let $K(\omega)$ consist of two filters in series; first, a filter with the transfer function $1/S_f^-(\omega)$, which converts our input random process $f(t)$ into the white noise $w(t)$, followed by a filter with the transfer function $H^-(\omega)$. To clarify the physical meaning of the second filter, we find the filter with which it should be replaced in order to obtain the optimum filter *of type* I. According to formulas (2.28) and (9.10), we have to set

$$H(\omega) = \frac{S_{hf}(\omega)}{S_f^+(\omega)}. \tag{12.18}$$

since then, the transfer function of the overall filter shown in Fig. 15 will be

$$K(\omega) = \frac{H(\omega)}{S_f^-(\omega)} = \frac{S_{hf}(\omega)}{S_f(\omega)}. \tag{12.19}$$

However, if we restrict ourselves to filters of type II, then, instead of $H(\omega)$, we have to use $H^-(\omega)$, i.e., the filter which uses only "past" pulses of the white noise. In fact, according to Lemma 2 of Sec. 11, the response of the filter $H^-(\omega)$ to a unit pulse is the same as that of $H(\omega)$ for $\tau \geqslant 0$, but vanishes for $\tau < 0$.

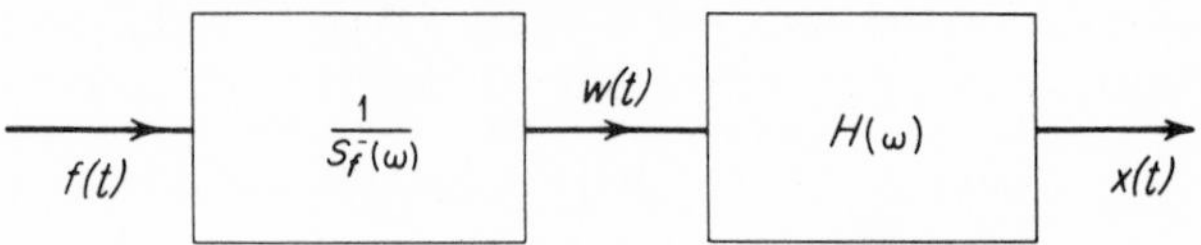

FIG. 15. Illustrating the action of a filter with the transfer function (12.19).

By representing $f(t)$ as "filtered white noise," we can also form an intuitive picture of statistical prediction (sometimes called *extrapolation* or *anticipation*). Thus, let

$$f(t) = m(t), \qquad n(t) = 0, \qquad h(t) = m(t + s). \tag{12.20}$$

Then, according to formula (4.15), we have

$$S_{hf}(\omega) = e^{i\omega s} S_f(\omega), \tag{12.21}$$

and the function $H(\omega)$ is equal to

$$H(\omega) = e^{i\omega s} S_f^-(\omega). \tag{12.22}$$

This function $H(\omega)$ satisfies the conditions of Lemma 1, and formula (11.28) becomes

$$\eta(\tau) = \frac{1}{2\pi} \int_{-\infty}^{\infty} e^{i\omega(\tau+s)} S_f^-(\omega)\, d\omega = \xi(t + s), \tag{12.23}$$

where, according to Lemma 2, the function

$$\xi(\tau) = \frac{1}{2\pi} \int_{-\infty}^{\infty} e^{i\omega\tau} S_f^-(\omega)\, d\omega \tag{12.24}$$

satisfies the condition

$$\xi(\tau) = 0 \quad \text{for} \quad \tau < 0. \tag{12.25}$$

It is easy to see that $\xi(\tau)$ is the impulse response of the filter with the transfer function $S_f^-(\omega)$. Moreover, $\xi(\tau)$ gives the form of the white noise pulses after they have gone through the filter $S_f^-(\omega)$, i.e., $\xi(\tau)$ gives the form of the pulses representing the process $f(t)$ (see Fig. 13).

According to Lemma 2, the filter with transfer function $H^-(\omega)$ has an impulse response $\eta^-(\tau)$ equal to

$$\begin{aligned} \eta^-(\tau) &= \eta(\tau) = \xi(\tau + s) \quad && \text{for} \quad \tau > 0, \\ \eta^-(\tau) &= 0 && \text{for} \quad \tau < 0, \end{aligned} \tag{12.26}$$

i.e., it acts as described by the formula

$$x(t) = \int_0^{\infty} \eta^-(\tau) w(t - \tau)\, d\tau = \int_0^{\infty} \xi(\tau + s) w(t - \tau)\, d\tau \tag{12.27}$$

or

$$x(t) = \int_{-\infty}^{t-s} \xi(t - t') w(t' + s)\, dt'. \tag{12.28}$$

The operation of the predicting filter is illustrated by Fig. 16. The first row of Fig. 16 shows white noise. After this white noise passes through the filter $S_f^-(\omega)$, each of its pulses at time t_α is smeared out and converted into the pulse $\xi(t - t_\alpha)$. The second row gives the pulse representation of the random process $f(t)$, and shows graphically what is meant by predicting $f(t)$. The value $f(t + s)$ can be regarded as being the superposition of the pulses $\xi(t - t_\alpha)$ which have already occurred prior to the time t and which are then "extended" (into the future) in the "standard" way. Of course, during the time s, new pulses occur, representing the unpredictable part of the value $f(t + s)$. It is due to these pulses that the prediction becomes less accurate, when we try to predict further ahead. In other words, the more "long-range" our prediction, the less reliable it is. In fact, it can be shown

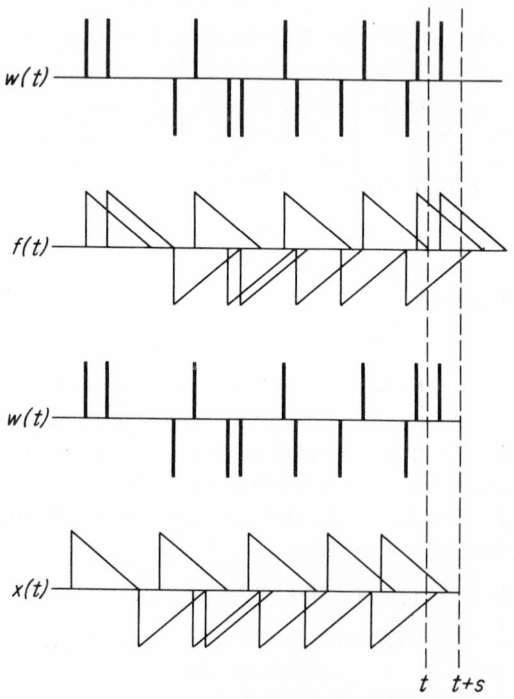

FIG. 16. Illustrating the action of the filter which predicts $f(t + s)$.

that in the limit as $s \to \infty$, the mean square error approaches $\overline{f^2}$, i.e., the mean square of the process f itself, whereas the predicted value $f(t + s)$ converges to zero.

The third and fourth rows of Fig. 16 are constructed in accordance with formula (12.17) for $K(\omega)$, and they show that in statistical prediction theory, everything happens as previously described. In passing through the filter $1/S_f^-(\omega)$, the process $f(t)$ is converted into precisely the same white noise as initially (the first and third rows are identical). The final filter $H^-(\omega)$, whose operation is described by (12.28), shifts each pulse of the white noise s seconds backward in time, and then "extends" it in accordance with the law $\xi(t - t')$. Thus, finally, the function $x(t)$ shown in the fourth row predicts the value of $f(t + s)$ corresponding to this "extension."

13. Prediction of Singular Random Processes

The results given above, in particular the theory of the "predicting" filter, were based on the assumption that the functions $S_f^+(\omega)$ and $S_f^-(\omega)$ exist. In the case where $S_f(\omega)$ is a rational function of the frequency, these functions can always be constructed (see Sec. 9 and 10); hence, the process $f(t)$ can always be converted into white noise by using a suitable filter of type II (see Fig. 14), and conversely we can obtain an equivalent "pulse version" of the process $f(t)$ by passing white noise through an "inverse" filter of type II (see Fig. 13). Moreover, in this case, the transfer functions of both filters are also rational functions [cf. formula (9.24)], so that they can be easily realized as electrical circuits with lumped constants L, C and R (see Sec. 15, below).

The problem of decomposing a given function $S_f(\omega)$ into factors $S_f^+(\omega)$ and $S_f^-(\omega)$ can be interpreted by using the pulse model of random processes, considered in Sec. 12. Thus, suppose that $f(t)$ is a superposition of randomly occurring pulses $v(t - t_\alpha)$ of a definite form. Then, according to formula (12.14), the amplitude spectrum $V(\omega)$ of these pulses is connected with the given power spectral density $S_f(\omega)$ by the relation

$$S_f(\omega) = \sigma |V(\omega)|^2 = \sigma V(\omega) V(-\omega). \tag{13.01}$$

Since the function $v(t)$ has to satisfy the condition (12.05), the function $V(\omega)$ must be analytic in the lower half-plane $\operatorname{Im} \omega \leqslant 0$, and the function $V(-\omega)$ must be analytic in the upper half-plane. In particular, $V(\omega)$ can be defined by the relation

$$S_f^-(\omega) = \sqrt{\sigma}\, V(\omega), \tag{13.02}$$

in which case, the function $v(t)$ differs only by the constant factor $\sqrt{\sigma}$ from the impulse response of the filter $S_f^-(\omega)$, about which we spoke in Sec. 12.

If now we choose $S_f(\omega)$ from a class of functions which is wider than the class of rational functions, then we can encounter the so-called *singular* random processes, for which the functions $S_f^-(\omega)$ and $V(\omega)$ do not exist. Examples of singular random processes are furnished by the processes with the autocorrelation functions and spectral densities given by formulas (3.24) and (3.25). Such random processes do not obey the theory developed above, and for them, the integrals (11.08), (11.10) and (11.16) diverge, since $\log S_f(\omega)$ falls off too slowly as $\omega \to \pm\infty$. The random process defined by the formula (3.26) is also singular, since for this process, $\log S_f(\omega) = \infty$ for $|\omega| > \omega_0$.

A random process is said to be *singular* if the integral

$$\int_0^\infty \frac{\ln S_f(\omega)\, d\omega}{\omega^2 - w^2} \tag{13.03}$$

diverges. In order to emphasize that it is the divergence as $\omega \to \infty$ (and not at $\omega = \pm w$) which is at issue here, we can write ω_1^2 instead of $-w^2$ in the integral (13.03). Then, the condition for the process to be singular becomes

$$\int_0^\infty \frac{\ln S_f(\omega)\, d\omega}{\omega^2 + \omega_1^2} = -\infty \qquad (\omega_1^2 > 0). \tag{13.04}$$

The fact that a process is singular means that it cannot be converted into the equivalent of white noise by using a filter of type II, and that it cannot be represented as a superposition of irregularly occurring pulses. Below, we shall convince ourselves by an example that singular processes have greater "stability" in time than the so-called "regular" processes considered above, and hence that singular processes can be predicted as far ahead as we please, with arbitrarily small error. On the other hand, we have already seen that a regular process can be reliably predicted ahead only for a time comparable to the correlation time of the process, i.e., the duration of one of the pulses making up the pulse model of the process.

Consider now a singular process $f(t)$ which satisfies the condition

$$S_f(\omega) = 0 \quad \text{for} \quad \omega < -\omega_0 \quad \text{and} \quad \omega > \omega_0. \tag{13.05}$$

A special case of this process is the process whose spectral density $S_f(\omega)$ is constant in the interval $(-\omega_0, \omega_0)$ and vanishes outside this interval [cf. formula (3.26)]. However, more generally, the even function $S_f(\omega)$ can vary in any way within the interval $(-\omega_0, \omega_0)$, and we shall assume only that it is bounded, i.e., that

$$S_f(\omega) \leqslant S_0 \quad \text{for} \quad -\omega_0 < \omega < \omega_0. \tag{13.06}$$

Then, the process $f(t)$ can be extrapolated ahead as far as we please. To prove this, we express the value $f(t)$ in terms of the values of the function f at the earlier times $t - \tau, t - 2\tau, \ldots$, where $\tau > 0$ is a suitably chosen time interval [cf. formula (13.17) below].

Thus, consider the random variable

$$\Delta_p(t) = f(t) - \binom{p}{1} f(t - \tau) + \binom{p}{2} f(t - 2\tau) - \cdots + (-1)^p \binom{p}{p} f(t - p\tau), \tag{13.07}$$

where $\binom{p}{q}$ is the binomial coefficient

$$\binom{p}{q} = \frac{p!}{q!(p-q)!} = \frac{p(p-1)\dots(p-q+1)}{q!}. \tag{13.08}$$

The quantity $\Delta_p(t)$ is called the pth *difference* of the function $f(t)$. In particular, for $p = 1$ and $p = 2$, we obtain the first and second differences

$$\begin{aligned}\Delta_1(t) &= f(t) - f(t-\tau),\\ \Delta_2(t) &= f(t) - 2f(t-\tau) + f(t-2\tau).\end{aligned} \tag{13.09}$$

The random processes $f(t)$ and $\Delta_p(t)$ are connected by a linear transformation. To calculate the transfer function of the filter which produces this transformation, we use formula (2.21). The result is

$$\begin{aligned}\Delta_p(t) &= \left[1 - \binom{p}{1}e^{-i\omega\tau} + \binom{p}{2}e^{-2i\omega\tau} - \cdots \right.\\ &\qquad \left. + (-1)^p\binom{p}{p}e^{-pi\omega\tau}\right] f_\omega e^{i\omega\tau}\\ &= (1 - e^{-i\omega\tau})^p f_\omega e^{i\omega t},\end{aligned} \tag{13.10}$$

and hence, the transfer function is

$$\begin{aligned}K(\omega) &= (1 - e^{-i\omega\tau})^p,\\ |K(\omega)|^2 &= \left(2 \sin \frac{\omega\tau}{2}\right)^{2p}\end{aligned} \tag{13.11}$$

Calculating the mean square of the random variable $\Delta_p(t)$ by the general formula (3.09), we obtain

$$\begin{aligned}\overline{\Delta_p^2} &= \frac{1}{2\pi}\int_{-\infty}^{\infty} |K(\omega)|^2 S_f(\omega)\, d\omega\\ &= \frac{1}{\pi}\int_0^{\omega_0} \left(2 \sin \frac{\omega\tau}{2}\right)^{2p} S_f(\omega)\, d\omega.\end{aligned} \tag{13.12}$$

It follows from the inequality (13.06) that

$$\overline{\Delta_p^2} \leqslant \frac{S_0}{\pi}\int_0^{\omega_0} \left(2 \sin \frac{\omega\tau}{2}\right)^{2p} d\omega. \tag{13.13}$$

If we choose a value of τ such that

$$2 \sin \frac{\omega_0\tau}{2} < 1, \tag{13.14}$$

i.e., such that

$$\tau < \frac{\pi}{3\omega_0}, \tag{13.15}$$

then we have the limiting formula

$$\lim_{p\to\infty} \overline{\Delta_p^2} = 0. \tag{13.16}$$

Consequently, writing (13.07) in the form

$$f(t) = \binom{p}{1}f(t-\tau) - \binom{p}{2}f(t-2\tau) + \cdots - (-1)^p\binom{p}{p}f(t-p\tau) + \Delta_p(t), \tag{13.17}$$

we can predict $f(t)$ from a knowledge of its past values $f(t-\tau)$, $f(t-2\tau)$, $\ldots, f(t-p\tau)$, and if we neglect the unknown term $\Delta_p(t)$, we make an error whose mean square error vanishes as $p\to\infty$. Then, having found $f(t)$ with arbitrary accuracy, we can use this value to predict $f(t+\tau)$, $f(t+2\tau)$, etc., again tolerating only an arbitrarily small error. In connection with this proof, we add that the applicability of formula (3.07) to the linear operator $\mathscr{K}$, as a result of which the quantity (13.09) is obtained, was proved in Sec. 4 [consider formulas (4.13) and (4.14), and set $s = -\tau$, $s = -2\tau$, etc.]. This justifies the use of formula (13.12) to calculate $\overline{\Delta_p^2}$.

The result just proved is intimately related to *Kotelnikov's theorem*, which we shall discuss later, in Sec. 19. In fact, it follows from formula (19.10) that a random function $f(t)$ with spectral density (13.05) is an *analytic* function of time and, hence, can be extrapolated by using a Taylor series. If we take only a finite number of terms in this Taylor series (e.g., $p-1$ terms), then we essentially commit the same error as made in neglecting the term $\Delta_p(t)$ in formula (13.17). We also note that the time interval Δt which plays a role in Kotelnikov's theorem is at least three times larger than the interval (13.15) necessary for prediction using (13.17):

$$\Delta t > 3\tau. \tag{13.18}$$

The fact that "band-limited" random processes, i.e., processes with spectral densities satisfying the condition (13.05), are singular requires us to exercise caution in formulating problems. After all, a radio station transmits in a given frequency band, a telephone conversation occupies a given frequency band, etc. If the boundaries of these bands were completely sharp, and if the transmitted messages, regarded as random processes, had vanishing spectral densities outside of these bands, then such a process would really be singular, and then its "past" would uniquely determine its "future." Of course, an actual radio broadcast or telephone conversation does not have this determinacy, which shows that the boundaries of the frequency bands are diffuse. Moreover, the spectrum of actual noise cannot satisfy the condition (13.05), since, in this case, the noise would be singular, and we could suppress it by predicting it and then subtracting it off. In this regard, we shall consider noise with arbitrary spectral density, when we develop the theory of the optimum receiver (Part II).

It should be emphasized that from a physical point of view, singular random processes are the result of a drastic idealization of actual random processes. This can easily be seen merely from the fact that in forming the higher-order differences $\Delta_p(t)$, the significant figures "disappear," and we need more and more accurate knowledge of the values $f(t - \tau)$, $f(t - 2\tau)$, $\cdots, f(t - p\tau)$, which unavoidable measurement errors and noise prevent us from obtaining. Even if arbitrarily weak noise $n(t)$, e.g., white noise, is superimposed on a singular process $m(t)$, the total process

$$f(t) = m(t) + n(t) \tag{13.19}$$

ceases to be singular. In fact, if $m(t)$ and $n(t)$ are uncorrelated, we have

$$S_f(\omega) = S_m(\omega) + S_n(\omega) \tag{13.20}$$

[cf. formula (2.37)], and the function S_f can now be decomposed into the factors S_f^+ and S_f^-. In this case, prediction of the process $m(t)$ must be combined with filtering out the noise $n(t)$, and it turns out that the prediction has "standard" character, i.e., the further ahead we try to predict, the larger the mean square error (cf. Sec. 12). Of course, as the intensity of the noise approaches zero, we obtain the formal possibility of predicting $m(t)$ arbitrarily far ahead. However, to substantially increase the time interval for which reliable prediction is possible, we must enormously increase the signal-to-noise ratio.

14. Some General Observations on Filtering

Consider filtering in the presence of very strong noise which is uniformly distributed over the spectrum of the useful signal:

$$S_n(\omega) = S_n = \text{const} \quad \text{for} \quad S_m \neq 0. \tag{14.01}$$

As in Sec. 2, we assume that,

$$S_f(\omega) = S_m(\omega) + S_n, \tag{14.02}$$

i.e., that the useful signal and the noise are statistically independent. Writing $S_f(\omega)$ in the form

$$S_f(\omega) = S_n\left[1 + \frac{S_m(\omega)}{S_n}\right], \tag{14.03}$$

we can express S_f^+ and S_f^- in terms of an unknown function $E(\omega)$ by writing

$$\begin{aligned} S_f^-(\omega) &= \sqrt{S_n}\left[1 + \frac{E(\omega)}{S_n}\right], \\ S_f^+(\omega) &= \sqrt{S_n}\left[1 + \frac{E(-\omega)}{S_n}\right]. \end{aligned} \tag{14.04}$$

Thus, we have

$$S_f^+(\omega)S_f^-(\omega) = S_n\left[1 + \frac{E(\omega) + E(-\omega)}{S_n} + \frac{E(\omega)E(-\omega)}{S_n^2}\right]. \tag{14.05}$$

If we neglect the last term in the brackets, (14.05) becomes

$$S_f^+(\omega)S_f^-(\omega) = S_n\left[1 + \frac{E(\omega) + E(-\omega)}{S_n}\right] = S_n + E(\omega) + E(-\omega). \tag{14.06}$$

Comparing (14.06) and (14.02), we see that

$$S_m(\omega) = E(\omega) + E(-\omega), \tag{14.07}$$

up to terms of the second order of smallness.

Since the function $S_f^-(\omega)$ is analytic in the lower half-plane, it is clear from formula (14.04) that the function $E(\omega)$ must also be analytic in the lower half-plane. Similarly, the function $E(-\omega)$ must be analytic in the upper half-plane. This means that to find $E(\omega)$, we must decompose $S_m(\omega)$ into a sum of two terms, by using Lemma 1 or Lemma 2. According to Lemma 2, we have

$$E(\omega) = \frac{1}{2\pi}\int_0^\infty e^{-i\omega t}\,dt \int_{-\infty}^\infty e^{i\omega t}S_m(\omega)\,d\omega. \tag{14.08}$$

Since $S_m(\omega)$ is even,

$$E(-\omega) = E^*(\omega) \tag{14.09}$$

for real ω. Moreover, since the signal and noise are assumed to be statistically independent,

$$S_{hf}(\omega) = S_m(\omega), \tag{14.10}$$

and to a first approximation, the function $H(\omega)$ equals

$$H(\omega) = \frac{S_m(\omega)}{\sqrt{S_n}}. \tag{14.11}$$

Next, we use Lemma 1 to decompose $H(\omega)$. The result is

$$H^-(\omega) = \frac{E(\omega)}{\sqrt{S_n}}, \tag{14.12}$$

since the denominator in (14.11) is constant. Therefore, to the same approximation, the transfer function of the optimum filter of type II is

$$K(\omega) = \frac{E(\omega)}{S_n}. \tag{14.13}$$

The impulse response of this filter is

$$k(\tau) = \frac{1}{2\pi}\int_{-\infty}^\infty e^{i\omega\tau}\frac{E(\omega)}{S_n}\,d\omega, \tag{14.14}$$

or

$$k(\tau) = \frac{R_m(\tau)}{S_n} \quad \text{for} \quad \tau > 0,$$
$$k(\tau) = 0 \qquad \text{for} \quad \tau < 0. \tag{14.15}$$

The corresponding mean square error is

$$\overline{\varepsilon^2} = \overline{m^2} - \frac{1}{2\pi S_n}\int_{-\infty}^{\infty} |E(\omega)|^2\, d\omega, \tag{14.16}$$

i.e.,

$$\overline{\varepsilon^2} \sim \overline{m^2}. \tag{14.17}$$

This is the same result as we obtained earlier for type I filters (cf. Sec. 2). Formula (14.15) shows that under the given conditions, the function $k(\tau)$ is proportional to the correlation function of the useful signal. For type II filters, this is true only for $\tau > 0$, since $k(\tau)$ must vanish for $\tau < 0$. For type I filters, formula (2.43) gives

$$K(\omega) = \frac{S_m(\omega)}{S_n}, \tag{14.18}$$

so that

$$k(\tau) = \frac{R_m(\tau)}{S_n} \tag{14.19}$$

for all τ.

Type I filters must have less mean square error than type II filters, since type I filters use the input process $f(t)$ for all times from $-\infty$ to $+\infty$, whereas type II filters use the input process only for a semi-infinite time interval. Because of the restriction imposed on type II filters, they will always give a larger error, since clearly every minimum subject to a constraint is less than the absolute minimum. In general, we can say that any shortening of the time interval during which the input function is used imposes additional constraints and hence increases the mean square error. Therefore, in general, a type III filter has a mean square error which increases as the "memory" of the filter is decreased.

It should also be noted that there is no sharp boundary between type I filters and type II filters. In fact, there is an intermediate case, the so-called *lagging filters*. These are filters of type II for which, by definition,

$$h(t) = m(t + s), \quad \text{where} \quad s < 0, \tag{14.20}$$

i.e., the filter tries to reproduce the signal at an earlier time, and hence, in a manner of speaking, uses the part of the "future" of the signal from $t + s$ to t. Therefore, for $s = 0$, this filter is a "pure" filter of type II, while for $s = \infty$, it goes into a filter of type I.

In Sec. 1, we also introduced the concept of filters of type III, which use the given process only for a finite time interval [cf. formulas (1.16) to (1.19)]. The theory of such filters is quite complicated, and will not be given in this book. We merely note that there is also no sharp boundary between filters of this type and the filters of types I and II, considered above.

15. Filtering of Quasi-Monochromatic Signals by Using Filters of Type II

In electrical engineering, the practical aspects of filtering signals in the frequency domain have been well explored. Therefore, it is interesting to compare the results of statistical filtering theory with what is already known. The statement of the problem is the same as in Sec. 6. As before, we take the power spectral densities of the useful signal $m(t)$ and the total process $f(t) = m(t) + n(t)$ to be

$$S_m(\omega) = c^2\alpha\left[\frac{1}{(\omega - \omega_0)^2 + \alpha^2} + \frac{1}{(\omega + \omega_0)^2 + \alpha^2}\right] \tag{15.01}$$

and

$$S_f(\omega) = S_m(\omega) + S_n \sim S_n\frac{[\omega^2 - (\omega_0 + i\beta)^2][\omega^2 - (\omega_0 - i\beta)^2]}{[\omega^2 - (\omega_0 + i\alpha)^2][\omega^2 - (\omega_0 - i\alpha)^2]}, \tag{15.02}$$

as in formulas (6.15), (6.18) and (6.25). We note that this is a special case of formulas (9.23) and (9.24), corresponding to $r = 0$. The functions S_f^+ and S_f^- are equal to

$$\begin{aligned} S_f^+(\omega) &= \sqrt{S_n}\frac{(\omega + \omega_0 + i\beta)(\omega - \omega_0 + i\beta)}{(\omega + \omega_0 + i\alpha)(\omega - \omega_0 + i\alpha)}, \\ S_f^-(\omega) &= \sqrt{S_n}\frac{(\omega + \omega_0 - i\beta)(\omega - \omega_0 - i\beta)}{(\omega + \omega_0 - i\alpha)(\omega - \omega_0 - i\alpha)}. \end{aligned} \tag{15.03}$$

The second step in constructing the optimum linear filter of type II is to determine the function (11.27), which in this case is

$$\begin{aligned} H(\omega) = \frac{S_m(\omega)}{S_f^+(\omega)} &= \frac{c^2}{2i\sqrt{S_n}}\frac{(\omega + \omega_0 + i\alpha)(\omega - \omega_0 + i\alpha)}{(\omega + \omega_0 + i\beta)(\omega - \omega_0 + i\beta)} \\ &\times \left[\frac{1}{\omega - \omega_0 - i\alpha} - \frac{1}{\omega - \omega_0 + i\alpha} + \frac{1}{\omega + \omega_0 - i\alpha} - \frac{1}{\omega + \omega_0 + i\alpha}\right]. \end{aligned} \tag{15.04}$$

The third step is to calculate the function $H^-(\omega)$. Here, we can use either Lemma 1 or Lemma 2. Using Lemma 1, we obtain

$$H^-(w) = -\frac{1}{2\pi i}\int_{i\gamma-\infty}^{i\gamma+\infty}\frac{H(\omega)\,d\omega}{\omega - w}. \tag{15.05}$$

Substituting (15.04) into (15.05), and evaluating the integral by using the residues at the poles lying above the path of integration, we obtain

$$H^{-}(\omega) = \frac{ic^2}{\sqrt{S_n}} \frac{2\alpha}{\alpha + \beta} \left[\frac{\omega_0 + i\alpha}{2\omega_0 + i\alpha + i\beta} \frac{1}{\omega - \omega_0 - i\alpha} + \frac{\omega_0 - i\alpha}{2\omega_0 - i\alpha - i\beta} \frac{1}{\omega + \omega_0 - i\alpha} \right]. \tag{15.06}$$

Then, finally, we find that the transfer function of the optimum filter is

$$K(\omega) = \frac{ic^2\alpha}{S_n(\alpha + \beta)} \frac{1}{(\omega - \omega_0 - i\beta)(\omega + \omega_0 - i\beta)} \times \left[\frac{(\omega_0 + i\alpha)(\omega + \omega_0 - i\alpha)}{\omega_0 + i(\alpha + \beta)/2} + \frac{(\omega_0 - i\alpha)(\omega - \omega_0 - i\alpha)}{\omega_0 - i(\alpha + \beta)/2} \right]. \tag{15.07}$$

We find the impulse response $k(\tau)$ for $\tau > 0$ by evaluating the Fourier transform of $K(\omega)$ by residues at the points $\omega = \pm\omega + i\beta$. Thus, we have

$$k(\tau) = \frac{1}{2\pi} \int_{-\infty}^{\infty} e^{i\omega\tau} K(\omega)\, d\omega = \frac{c^2\alpha}{S_n(\alpha + \beta)} [Ae^{i(\omega_0 + i\beta)\tau} + A^* e^{i(-\omega_0 + i\beta)\tau}], \tag{15.08}$$

where we have introduced the symbol

$$A = |A| e^{-i(\psi - \pi)} = -\frac{(\omega_0 + i\alpha)(2\omega_0 - i\alpha + i\beta)}{\omega_0(2\omega_0 + i\alpha + i\beta)} - \frac{i(\omega_0 - i\alpha)(\beta - \alpha)}{\omega_0(2\omega_0 - i\alpha - i\beta)}. \tag{15.09}$$

In its final form, we can write the function $k(\tau)$ as

$$\begin{aligned} k(\tau) &= \frac{2c^2\alpha}{S_n(\alpha + \beta)} |A| e^{-\beta\tau} \cos(\omega_0\tau - \psi) \quad \text{for} \quad \tau > 0, \\ k(\tau) &= 0 \quad \text{for} \quad \tau < 0. \end{aligned} \tag{15.10}$$

In these formulas

$$\beta = \alpha\sqrt{1 + \rho}, \tag{15.11}$$

where ρ is the signal-to-noise ratio introduced in formula (6.28). For $\rho \ll 1$, we have approximately

$$\alpha = \beta, \quad -A = |A| = 1, \qquad \psi = 0, \tag{15.12}$$

and formula (15.10) becomes

$$k(\tau) = \frac{c^2 e^{-\alpha\tau} \cos \omega_0\tau}{S_n} \quad \text{for} \quad \tau > 0, \tag{15.13}$$

which agrees with (14.15).

The formulas given above are valid when the condition (6.04), expressing the fact that the signal is quasi-monochromatic, is satisfied. If the stronger condition

$$\omega_0 \gg \beta = \alpha\sqrt{1 + \rho} \tag{15.14}$$

holds, then, according to (15.09), $A \sim -1$, $\psi \sim 0$, and the above formulas simplify to

$$k(\tau) = \frac{2\alpha\rho}{1 + \sqrt{1 + \rho}} e^{-\beta\tau} \cos \omega_0\tau \quad \text{for} \quad \tau > 0, \tag{15.15}$$

$$K(\omega) = \frac{\rho}{(1 + \sqrt{1 + \rho})\sqrt{1 + \rho}} \frac{2i\beta\omega}{\omega_0^2 - \omega^2 + 2i\beta\omega}, \tag{15.16}$$

and

$$H^-(\omega) = \frac{ic^2\alpha}{(\alpha + \beta)\sqrt{S_n}} \left(\frac{1}{\omega - \omega_0 - i\alpha} + \frac{1}{\omega + \omega_0 - i\alpha}\right). \tag{15.17}$$

We note that α specifies the bandwidth of the signal [cf. formula (6.20)], while β specifies the bandwidth of the filter, which is in fact equal to

$$\Delta\omega' = \frac{\pi}{2}\beta. \tag{15.18}$$

We now find the mean square error of the optimum type II filter. Evaluating integrals by using residue theory, and neglecting terms of order $1/\omega_0$ as compared to terms of order $1/\alpha$, we obtain

$$\begin{aligned} \overline{\varepsilon^2} &= c^2 - \frac{1}{2\pi}\int_{-\infty}^{\infty} |H^-(\omega)|^2\, d\omega = c^2 - \frac{c^4\alpha}{(\alpha + \beta)^2 S_n} \\ &= c^2\left[1 - \frac{\rho}{(1 + \sqrt{1 + \rho})^2}\right], \end{aligned} \tag{15.19}$$

or

$$\overline{\varepsilon^2} = c^2 \frac{2}{1 + \sqrt{1 + \rho}}. \tag{15.20}$$

In Sec. 6, we found that

$$\overline{\varepsilon^2} = c^2 \frac{1}{\sqrt{1 + \rho}} \tag{15.21}$$

for type I filters. For $\rho \ll 1$, the mean square errors for both type I and type II filters have the same value c^2. This means that both filters work equally poorly when the noise level is high. If $\rho \gg 1$, then the mean square error of the type II filter is approximately twice as large as that of the type I filter, which uses more complete information about the input process.

The system function (15.16) of the optimum type II filter can be written as

$$K(\omega) = \Theta \frac{2i\beta\omega}{\omega_0^2 - \omega^2 + 2i\beta\omega}, \qquad \Theta = \frac{\rho}{\sqrt{1+\rho}(1 + \sqrt{1+\rho})}. \tag{15.22}$$

This is the transfer function of the simple resonant circuit shown in Fig. 17, with time constant β, combined with an attenuator. (The constant of proportionality Θ is always less than 1, and becomes 1 only in the limiting case $\rho = \infty$.)

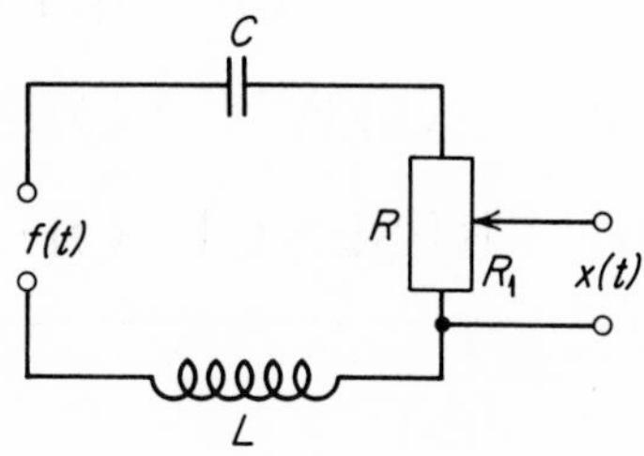

FIG. 17. A filter with the transfer function (15.22):
$R_1 = \Theta R, \qquad \omega_0 = 1/\sqrt{LC}, \qquad 2\beta = R/L.$

Strictly monochromatic processes are characterized by the parameters $\rho = \infty$ and $\alpha = \beta = 0$. In this case, the mean square error vanishes for both type I and type II filters. This happens because the circuit is perfectly selective when it operates for an infinitely long time on the input process (a mixture of noise and a monochromatic signal).

3

DETECTION OF SIGNALS OF KNOWN FORM IN THE PRESENCE OF NOISE

16. Filters for Detecting Signals of Known Form

In Chapters 1 and 2, we assumed that the signal and the noise are random processes with known correlation properties. However, as we have already remarked (see Sec. 7), in radar and in various other branches of radio engineering, the useful signal arriving at the receiver has a fixed shape. In this case, the useful signal must be regarded not as a random process, but as a given function with one or several unknown parameters (e.g., amplitude, arrival time, r-f phase, etc.). The purpose of filtering is now no longer to reproduce the signal (which is of known form) with the minimum mean square error, but rather to make the most reliable observations of the useful signal in the presence of random noise, and to make the most precise measurements of the parameters of the signal (in particular, of its arrival time, from which we can determine the distance to the reflecting object). Therefore, an index of the performance of a filter extracting a signal of known form is the signal-to-noise ratio at the filter output. The relation between this ratio and more precise probabilistic properties of the receiver will be investigated in Part 2.

Thus, suppose that the useful signal has a perfectly well-defined form, and consider what happens when the signal passes through a linear filter $\mathscr{K}$

with the transfer function $K(\omega)$. At the filter input, there may appear a mixture of the useful signal $m(t)$, which has a known form, and the noise $n(t)$, which is a stationary random process, i.e., the input signal may be

$$f(t) = m(t) + n(t). \tag{16.01}$$

On the other hand, the useful signal may be absent, in which case only the noise appears at the filter input, so that

$$f(t) = n(t). \tag{16.02}$$

We shall assume first that the function $m(t)$ is completely known, so that the desired filter should simplify as much as possible the task of observing the useful signal, i.e., the filter should help as much as possible to decide which of the two possibilities (16.01) and (16.02) actually occurs in a given experiment. The more complicated situation, where the signal $m(t)$ depends on unknown parameters, will be examined at the end of this section.

In the presence of a signal, we obtain the function

$$\varphi(t) = \mu(t) + \nu(t) \tag{16.03}$$

at the filter output, where $\mu(t)$ is the result of passing the useful signal $m(t)$ through the filter $\mathscr{K}$, and $\nu(t)$ is the result of passing the noise $n(t)$ through $\mathscr{K}$. For example, the signal $m(t)$ might be a rectangular pulse, such as is often used in radar applications. Assuming that the useful signal is of finite duration (or else falls off sufficiently rapidly as $t \to \pm\infty$), we can write it as the Fourier transform

$$m(t) = \frac{1}{2\pi}\int_{-\infty}^{\infty} e^{i\omega t} M(\omega)\, d\omega, \tag{16.04}$$

where

$$M(\omega) = \int_{-\infty}^{\infty} e^{-i\omega t} m(t)\, dt. \tag{16.05}$$

Then, the function $\mu(t)$, i.e., the useful signal at the filter output, is equal to

$$\mu(t) = \frac{1}{2\pi}\int_{-\infty}^{\infty} e^{i\omega t} K(\omega) M(\omega)\, d\omega, \tag{16.06}$$

where $K(\omega)$ is the (complex) transfer function of the filter $\mathscr{K}$ [cf. formula (2.23)].

Since the noise $n(t)$ is a random process, instead of a Fourier transform like (16.06), we use Khinchin's theorem (see Sec. 3), one consequence of which is the relation

$$\overline{n^2(t)} = \frac{1}{2\pi}\int_{-\infty}^{\infty} S_n(\omega)\, d\omega. \tag{16.07}$$

Here $\overline{n^2}$ is the average noise power (as usual, the overbar denotes the operation of ensemble averaging), and $S_n(\omega)$ is the power spectral density of the noise at the input of the filter $\mathscr{K}$. At the output of the filter $\mathscr{K}$, the noise has intensity

$$\overline{\nu^2(t)} = \frac{1}{2\pi}\int_{-\infty}^{\infty} |K(\omega)|^2 S_n(\omega)\, d\omega, \tag{16.08}$$

according to formula (3.09). We define the *signal-to-noise* (*power*) *ratio* ρ at the filter output by the expression

$$\rho = \frac{\mu^2(t_0)}{\overline{\nu^2}}, \tag{16.09}$$

where $\mu(t_0)$ is the value of the signal at the output at some time t_0. Using formulas (16.06) and (16.08), we find that

$$\rho = \frac{1}{2\pi}\frac{\left|\int_{-\infty}^{\infty} e^{i\omega t_0} K(\omega)M(\omega)\, d\omega\right|^2}{\int_{-\infty}^{\infty} |K(\omega)|^2 S_n(\omega)\, d\omega}. \tag{16.10}$$

We now look for the filter which gives a value of ρ at the filter output which is larger than all other values of ρ. In other words, we intend to use the value

$$\varphi(t_0) = \mu(t_0) + \nu(t_0) \tag{16.11}$$

to decide whether or not the signal is present, and therefore it is important that the absolute value of $\mu(t_0)$ exceed the quantity $\sqrt{\overline{\nu^2(t_0)}} = \sqrt{\overline{\nu^2}}$ by as much as possible. The transfer function of the filter we are looking for can be found by using the inequality

$$\left|\int_{-\infty}^{\infty} e^{i\omega t_0} K(\omega)M(\omega)\, d\omega\right|^2 \leqslant \int_{-\infty}^{\infty} |K(\omega)|^2 S_n(\omega)\, d\omega \int_{-\infty}^{\infty} \frac{|M(\omega)|^2}{S_n(\omega)}\, d\omega, \tag{16.12}$$

to be proved presently. This inequality shows that

$$\rho \leqslant \frac{1}{2\pi}\int_{-\infty}^{\infty} \frac{|M(\omega)|^2}{S_n(\omega)}\, d\omega, \tag{16.13}$$

i.e., it gives an upper bound for ρ. Then, if we take

$$K(\omega) = c e^{-i\omega t_0}\frac{M^*(\omega)}{S_n(\omega)}, \tag{16.14}$$

where c is an arbitrary constant, the filter actually achieves the maximum value of ρ, equal to

$$\rho = \frac{1}{2\pi}\int_{-\infty}^{\infty} \frac{|M(\omega)|^2}{S_n(\omega)}\, d\omega. \tag{16.15}$$

Turning to the proof of the inequality (16.12), we observe that it is just a form of the familiar *Schwarz inequality*. To prove the Schwarz inequality itself, consider the double integral

$$\begin{aligned}\iint_{-\infty}^{\infty} &|A(\omega)B^*(\omega') - A(\omega')B^*(\omega)|^2\, d\omega\, d\omega' \\ &= \iint_{-\infty}^{\infty} [A(\omega)B^*(\omega') - A(\omega')B^*(\omega)][A^*(\omega)B(\omega') \\ &\qquad\qquad - A^*(\omega')B(\omega)]\, d\omega\, d\omega' \qquad (16.16) \\ &= \iint_{-\infty}^{\infty} [|A(\omega)|^2|B(\omega')|^2 + |A(\omega')|^2|B(\omega)|^2 - A(\omega)B(\omega)A^*(\omega')B^*(\omega') \\ &\qquad\qquad - A(\omega')B(\omega')A^*(\omega)B^*(\omega)]\, d\omega\, d\omega' \geqslant 0.\end{aligned}$$

Since the original integral is obviously nonnegative, so is the last integral in (16.16). Then, bearing in mind that

$$\begin{aligned}\iint_{-\infty}^{\infty} |A(\omega)|^2|B(\omega')|^2\, d\omega\, d\omega' &= \iint_{-\infty}^{\infty} |A(\omega')|^2|B(\omega)|^2\, d\omega\, d\omega' \\ &= \int_{-\infty}^{\infty} |A(\omega)|^2\, d\omega \int_{-\infty}^{\infty} |B(\omega)|^2\, d\omega,\end{aligned}$$

$$\begin{aligned}\iint_{-\infty}^{\infty} &A(\omega)B(\omega)A^*(\omega')B^*(\omega')\, d\omega\, d\omega' \qquad (16.17) \\ &= \iint_{-\infty}^{\infty} A(\omega')B(\omega')A^*(\omega)B^*(\omega)\, d\omega\, d\omega' \\ &= \int_{-\infty}^{\infty} A(\omega)B(\omega)\, d\omega \int_{-\infty}^{\infty} A^*(\omega)B^*(\omega)\, d\omega = \left|\int_{-\infty}^{\infty} A(\omega)B(\omega)\, d\omega\right|^2,\end{aligned}$$

we obtain the inequality

$$\left|\int_{-\infty}^{\infty} A(\omega)B(\omega)\, d\omega\right|^2 \leqslant \int_{-\infty}^{\infty} |A(\omega)|^2\, d\omega \int_{-\infty}^{\infty} |B(\omega)|^2\, d\omega \qquad (16.18)$$

for any two functions $A(\omega)$ and $B(\omega)$, provided that the integrals written have meaning (converge). Finally, setting

$$A(\omega) = e^{i\omega t_0}K(\omega)\sqrt{S_n(\omega)}, \qquad B(\omega) = \frac{M(\omega)}{\sqrt{S_n(\omega)}}, \qquad (16.19)$$

we arrive at the inequality (16.12).

As we have seen above, among all linear filters, the best filter is the one with the transfer function (16.14). If the noise $n(t)$ is a normal (Gaussian) random process, then the filter (16.14) is an absolute optimum, as we shall show in Part 2. Thus, the need for nonlinear filters arises only when the noise is not normal, but then the mathematical analysis of optimum filters and optimum receivers becomes so complicated that no tangible results have been obtained.

The physical meaning of formula (16.14) is very simple: The larger the "amplitude spectrum" of the useful signal and the smaller the "power spectrum" of the noise in the frequency interval $(\omega, \omega + d\omega)$, the more the optimum linear filter $\mathscr{K}$ passes the frequencies in $(\omega, \omega + d\omega)$. Moreover, as shown by formula (16.15), the greater the difference between the signal spectrum and the noise spectrum, the greater the signal-to-noise ratio at the output of $\mathscr{K}$ (cf. the end of Sec. 2). For example, if the spectral density $S_n(\omega)$ is very small in some interval of the frequency band occupied by the signal, and large elsewhere, then the optimum filter $\mathscr{K}$ essentially passes only frequencies in this interval, and the quantity (16.15) will be very large. In this case, it is true that $\mu(t)$, the form of the signal at the filter output, will differ greatly from $m(t)$, the form of the signal at the filter input (cf. Secs. 17 and 20 below), but since $\mu(t)$ is known, this change in the shape of the signal presents no difficulties.

We note that formulas (16.06) and (16.14) imply the relation

$$\mu(t) = \frac{c}{2\pi} \int_{-\infty}^{\infty} e^{i\omega(t-t_0)} \frac{|M(\omega)|^2}{S_n(\omega)} \, d\omega, \tag{16.20}$$

from which it follows (cf. Sec. 3) that

$$|\mu(t)| \leqslant |\mu(t_0)| = |c|\rho. \tag{16.21}$$

In using the filter (16.14) to detect a completely known signal, we need only the quantity (16.11), i.e., the value of the output function of the filter at the time t_0, since, according to (16.21), the absolute value of the useful signal at the filter output is smaller at other times. However, the results are somewhat different if the useful signal has the form

$$m(t) = Gm_0(t - \tau), \tag{16.22}$$

where the parameters G and τ are *unknown*; here, G is the signal amplitude, τ is its time of arrival, and $m_0(t)$ is a known function of time. First of all, according to formula (16.05), we now have

$$M(\omega) = GM_0(\omega)e^{-i\omega\tau}, \tag{16.23}$$

where

$$M_0(\omega) = \int_{-\infty}^{\infty} e^{-i\omega t} m_0(t) \, dt, \qquad m_0(t) = \frac{1}{2\pi} \int_{-\infty}^{\infty} e^{i\omega t} M_0(\omega) \, d\omega, \tag{16.24}$$

so that the function $M(\omega)$ depends on the unknown parameters. To avoid introducing the unknown parameter τ in (16.14), we change this formula to

$$K(\omega) = ce^{-i\omega t_0} \frac{M_0^*(\omega)}{S_n(\omega)}, \tag{16.25}$$

since otherwise, we would need as many different filters as there are different values of τ. Then, formula (16.20) becomes

$$\mu(t) = \frac{cG}{2\pi} \int_{-\infty}^{\infty} e^{i\omega(t-t_0-\tau)} \frac{|M_0(\omega)|^2}{S_n(\omega)} \, d\omega, \tag{16.26}$$

so that

$$|\mu(t)| \leqslant |\mu(t_0 + \tau)| = |c|G\rho_0, \tag{16.27}$$

where

$$\rho_0 = \frac{1}{2\pi}\int_{-\infty}^{\infty} \frac{|M_0(\omega)|^2}{S_n(\omega)}\, d\omega \tag{16.28}$$

is the signal-to-noise ratio at the output of the filter with transfer function (16.25). In the present case, ρ_0 is defined as

$$\rho_0 = \frac{\mu^2(t_0 + \tau)}{\overline{\nu^2}} \quad \text{for} \quad G = 1. \tag{16.29}$$

For arbitrary G, we can define the signal-to-noise ratio by the formula

$$\rho = \frac{\mu^2(t_0 + \tau)}{\overline{\nu^2}} = G^2\rho_0, \tag{16.30}$$

or we can use the formula

$$\bar{\rho} = \overline{G^2}\rho_0, \tag{16.31}$$

obtained by averaging (16.31), using the distribution law of the random variable G.

It is clear that the transfer function (16.25) leads to the maximum value of the parameters (6.30) and (6.31), where in this case the random process $\varphi(t)$ at the filter output is used more completely than it was before. In fact, if the parameter τ can take the values $\tau_1, \ldots, \tau_n$, then we need the values $\varphi(t_0 + \tau_1), \ldots, \varphi(t_0 + \tau_n)$. In particular, if τ can take all values in the interval $0 \leqslant \tau \leqslant T$, then we have to use the function $\varphi(t)$ from $t_0 \leqslant t \leqslant t_0 + T$. In the absence of noise ($\rho = \infty$), the function $\varphi(t) = \mu(t)$ allows us to completely determine the parameters τ and G, i.e., we find τ from the position of the maximum of $\varphi(t)$, and G from the size of this maximum [see formula (16.27)]. However, in the presence of weak noise (for large values of ρ), errors will be made in determining τ and G, since the noise randomly displaces the maximum of $\varphi(t)$ [with respect to the maximum of $\mu(t)$] in such a way that its position along the time axis and its absolute value vary. As the noise is increased, i.e., as ρ is decreased, these errors become larger, and in sufficiently strong noise (for sufficiently small ρ), the presence or absence of the useful signal is almost completely masked by the noise, and even the optimum filter, which guarantees the maximum value of ρ, does not help to distinguish the signal in the noise background. This describes qualitatively the operation of the optimum linear filter, in the case of variable signal parameters.

Finally, we note that if we set $c = 1$ in formula (16.14), then, according to (16.09) and (16.20), we have

$$\mu(t_0) = \rho, \qquad \overline{\nu^2(t)} = \rho, \tag{16.32}$$

so that the signal-to-noise ratio gives us simultaneously the useful signal $\mu(t_0)$ and the noise power $\overline{\nu^2}$ at the output of the optimum linear filter. In this case, we have the interesting formula

$$\mu(t) = R_\nu(t_0 - t), \tag{16.33}$$

relating the useful signal and the correlation function of the noise, at the output of the optimum filter. Similar formulas for $c = 1$ can be derived in the more general case, corresponding to the transfer function (16.25).

17. The Matched Filter or Correlator

In this section, we consider the optimum filters obtained when the condition

$$S_n(\omega) = S_n = \text{const} \tag{17.01}$$

is met, i.e., when the noise spectrum is uniformly distributed over the frequency band occupied by the useful signal. Noise of this kind is usually called *white noise* (cf. Secs. 7 and 12), and the corresponding optimum filter $\mathscr{K}$ is called the *matched filter*. The transfer function of this filter is equal to

$$K(\omega) = e^{-i\omega t_0} M^*(\omega), \tag{17.02}$$

so that $K(\omega)$ is completely determined by the form of the signal $m(t)$ to which it is "matched." Formula (17.02) is obtained by setting

$$c = S_n \tag{17.03}$$

(for simplicity) in formula (16.14).

We now study in more detail the action of the matched filter. Since $m(t)$ is real, it follows from (16.05) that

$$M^*(\omega) = M(-\omega). \tag{17.04}$$

According to (16.06) and (17.02), the signal at the output of the matched filter is

$$\begin{aligned} \mu(t) &= \frac{1}{2\pi} \int_{-\infty}^{\infty} e^{i\omega(t-t_0)} M(-\omega) M(\omega)\, d\omega \\ &= \frac{1}{2\pi} \int_{-\infty}^{\infty} e^{i\omega(t-t_0)} M(-\omega)\, d\omega \int_{-\infty}^{\infty} e^{-i\omega t'} m(t')\, dt'. \end{aligned} \tag{17.05}$$

Changing the order of integration, we obtain

$$\begin{aligned} \mu(t) &= \frac{1}{2\pi} \int_{-\infty}^{\infty} m(t')\, dt' \int_{-\infty}^{\infty} e^{i\omega(t-t_0-t')} M(-\omega)\, d\omega \\ &= \frac{1}{2\pi} \int_{-\infty}^{\infty} m(t')\, dt' \int_{-\infty}^{\infty} e^{i\omega(t'-t+t_0)} M(\omega)\, d\omega, \end{aligned} \tag{17.06}$$

where we have replaced $-\omega$ by ω. Then, using formula (16.04), we obtain

$$\mu(t) = \int_{-\infty}^{\infty} m(t')m(t' - t + t_0)\, dt'. \tag{17.07}$$

The integral

$$R_m(\tau) = \int_{-\infty}^{\infty} m(t)m(t - \tau)\, dt \tag{17.08}$$

is called the *autocorrelation function* of the signal $m(t)$ of known form. The quantity $R_m(\tau)$ differs from the autocorrelation functions which we considered earlier in that instead of taking the ensemble average of the quantity $m(t)m(t - \tau)$, we now simply integrate with respect to t (see, however, the end of Sec. 1). It is clear from (17.08) that

$$R_m(0) = \int_{-\infty}^{\infty} m^2(t)\, dt = E, \tag{17.09}$$

i.e., in this case $R_m(0)$ is just the energy E of the useful signal (or a number proportional to the energy), whereas for a stationary random process, the quantity $R_m(0)$ gives the average power of the process (or a number proportional to the average power).

Returning to formula (17.05), giving the useful signal at the output of the filter, and using the definition of the correlation function, we see that

$$\mu(t) = R_m(t - t_0). \tag{17.10}$$

Thus, we obtain the following remarkable result: The matched filter is just a correlator, whose response to the useful signal $m(t)$ is not $m(t)$ itself, but rather the autocorrelation function of $m(t)$. For $t = t_0$, the useful signal at the output of the matched filter takes the value

$$\mu(t_0) = E. \tag{17.11}$$

It is not hard to show that formulas (3.12) and (3.13) also apply to the correlation function (17.08). Therefore we have

$$R_m(0) \geqslant |R_m(\tau)| \quad \text{and} \quad \mu(t_0) \geqslant |\mu(t)|, \tag{17.12}$$

so that $\mu(t_0)$ is the maximum value of the useful signal at the filter output, as already shown in Sec. 16. Thus, we see that regardless of the form of the useful signal, the maximum value of the signal at the output of the matched filter is just the total energy of the signal at the filter input.

With the condition (17.01), formula (16.15) becomes

$$\rho = \frac{1}{2\pi S_n} \int_{-\infty}^{\infty} |M(\omega)|^2\, d\omega. \tag{17.13}$$

It follows from formulas (17.04) to (17.09) that

$$\frac{1}{2\pi} \int_{-\infty}^{\infty} |M(\omega)|^2\, d\omega = \int_{-\infty}^{\infty} m^2(t)\, dt = E, \tag{17.14}$$

an identity which is well known in the theory of the Fourier integral. If we use (17.14), formula (17.13) takes the particularly simple form

$$\rho = \frac{E}{S_n}. \tag{17.15}$$

Thus, the signal-to-noise ratio at the output of the matched filter is determined by two physical quantities, the total energy E of the signal, and the spectral density S_n of the noise, i.e., the noise power passing through a frequency band whose width is 1 cycle per second (cf. the beginning of Sec. 3). This shows that the only way to improve the detection of a known signal in a background of white noise, which is an "absolutely random process" (cf. Sec. 12), is to increase the energy of the useful signal, whereas for other kinds of noise the same result can be obtained by changing the spectrum of the signal, i.e., the shape of the signal (see Sec. 16).

According to formula (2.19), the impulse response of the matched filter is equal to

$$k(t) = \frac{1}{2\pi}\int_{-\infty}^{\infty} e^{i\omega t}\, K(\omega)\, d\omega = \frac{1}{2\pi}\int_{-\infty}^{\infty} e^{i\omega(t-t_0)} M(-\omega)\, d\omega$$

or

$$k(t) = m(t_0 - t). \tag{17.16}$$

Therefore, the action of the matched filter is described by the formula

$$\varphi(t) = \int_{-\infty}^{\infty} f(t')m(t' - t + t_0)\, dt' \tag{17.17}$$

[cf. (1.11)], so that as applied to the total process (16.01), the matched filter forms the *cross correlation* between the useful signal $m(t)$ and the input function $f(t)$. Thus, the matched filter can also be called a *correlator*.

If the useful signal has the form (16.22), i.e., if it contains unknown parameters G and τ, then, according to (16.25) and (17.03), the transfer function of the matched filter is

$$K(\omega) = e^{-i\omega t_0} M_0^*(\omega), \tag{17.18}$$

and its impulse response is

$$k(t) = m_0(t_0 - t). \tag{17.19}$$

Thus, at the output of the matched filter, we obtain the function

$$\varphi(t) = \int_{-\infty}^{\infty} f(t')m_0(t_0 - t + t')\, dt', \tag{17.20}$$

i.e., we again have a cross-correlation function of the form (17.17), so that the matched filter is still a correlator. The difference between formulas (17.17) and (17.20) is the following: In the case of a completely known signal, we have to form only one value $\varphi(t_0)$ by using (17.17), while in the case of a signal with unknown τ, we need the values $\varphi(t_0 + \tau)$, calculated for all possible values of τ by using (17.20). In the case of a signal containing unknown parameters G and τ, the useful signal at the output of the matched filter can be written in the form

$$\begin{aligned} \mu(t) &= G \int_{-\infty}^{\infty} m_0(t' - \tau) m_0(t_0 - t + t')\, dt' \\ &= G R_{m_0}(t - t_0 - \tau) \end{aligned} \tag{17.21}$$

[cf. (16.22) and (17.08)], where R_{m_0} is the autocorrelation function of the signal $m_0(t)$. Using the function (17.21), we can determine the parameters G and τ of the original signal and also detect its presence, with an error which decreases as the parameter ρ increases (see Sec. 16).

In this and the preceding section, we have imposed no restrictions on the functions $K(\omega)$ and $k(\tau)$, so that in the general case, we obtain a filter of type I (with the classification of Sec. 1). However, if in the case of the matched filter, we choose the parameter t_0 so that

$$m(t) = 0 \quad \text{or} \quad m_0(t - \tau) = 0 \quad \text{for} \quad t > t_0, \tag{17.22}$$

then the matched filter will be a filter of type II. This result is obvious, since the matched filter begins its operation when the least delayed version of the signal arrives, but it cannot finish its operation until the most delayed version of the signal has "died out."

In order to properly appraise the operation of the matched filter, we must bear in mind that in radio engineering, the band occupied by the useful signal always coincides with the pass-band of the receiver, i.e., the pass-band of the receiver's r-f filter. Thus, consider a filter with the "rectangular" transfer function

$$\begin{aligned} K(\omega) &= 1 \quad \text{for} \quad -\omega_0 - \Delta\omega < \omega < -\omega_0 + \Delta\omega, \\ &\qquad \text{and} \quad \omega_0 - \Delta\omega < \omega < \omega_0 + \Delta\omega, \\ K(\omega) &= 0 \quad \text{for all other values of } \omega, \end{aligned} \tag{17.23}$$

which acts on the rectangular r-f pulse given by formula (20.01) of Sec. 20, with corresponding amplitude spectrum (20.03) satisfying the condition

$$M(-\omega) = M(\omega). \tag{17.24}$$

In this case, according to formula (16.06), the useful signal at the output of the filter $\mathscr{K}$ equals

$$\begin{aligned} \mu(t) &= \frac{1}{2\pi} \left[\int_{-\omega_0 - \Delta\omega}^{-\omega_0 + \Delta\omega} e^{i\omega t} M(\omega)\, d\omega + \int_{\omega_0 - \Delta\omega}^{\omega_0 + \Delta\omega} e^{i\omega t} M(\omega)\, d\omega \right] \\ &= \frac{1}{\pi} \int_{\omega_0 - \Delta\omega}^{\omega_0 + \Delta\omega} \cos \omega t \cdot M(\omega)\, d\omega. \end{aligned} \tag{17.25}$$

Keeping only the first term in brackets in the expression (20.03) (which is permissible if the condition $\omega_0 T_0 \gg 1$ holds, where T_0 is the duration of the pulse), we obtain

$$\mu(t) = \frac{A}{\pi} \int_{\omega_0 - \Delta\omega}^{\omega_0 + \Delta\omega} \cos \omega t \, \frac{\sin [(\omega - \omega_0)T_0/2]}{\omega - \omega_0} \, d\omega. \tag{17.26}$$

It is not hard to see that for sufficiently small $\Delta\omega$, the function (17.26) achieves its maximum value for $t = 0$. In fact, if the condition

$$\frac{\Delta\omega T_0}{2} \leqslant \pi \tag{17.27}$$

is satisfied, then the factor

$$\frac{\sin [(\omega - \omega_0)T_0/2]}{\omega - \omega_0}$$

is nonnegative over the interval of integration, and we have

$$|\mu(t)| \leqslant \frac{A}{\pi} \int_{\omega_0 - \Delta\omega}^{\omega_0 + \Delta\omega} |\cos \omega t| \, \frac{\sin [(\omega - \omega_0)T_0/2]}{\omega - \omega_0} \, d\omega \leqslant \mu(0), \tag{17.28}$$

where

$$\mu(0) = \frac{A}{\pi} \int_{\omega_0 - \Delta\omega}^{\omega_0 + \Delta\omega} \frac{\sin [(\omega - \omega_0)T_0/2]}{\omega - \omega_0} \, d\omega = \frac{2A}{\pi} \int_0^X \frac{\sin x}{x} \, dx \tag{17.29}$$

and

$$X = \frac{\Delta\omega T_0}{2}. \tag{17.30}$$

According to formulas (16.08) and (17.01), noise of intensity

$$\overline{\nu^2} = \frac{2}{\pi} S_n \Delta\omega \tag{17.31}$$

appears at the output of the filter with transfer function (17.23). Therefore, by formula (16.09), the signal-to-noise ratio equals

$$\rho = \frac{\mu^2(0)}{\overline{\nu^2}} = \frac{2A^2}{\pi S_n \Delta\omega} (\text{si } X)^2, \tag{17.32}$$

where

$$\text{si } X = \int_0^X \frac{\sin x}{x} \, dx \tag{17.33}$$

is the integral sine.

To compare formula (17.32) with the expression (17.15) obtained earlier, we calculate the energy of the rectangular pulse (20.01); the result is

$$E = \int_{-T_0/2}^{T_0/2} m^2(t) \, dt = A^2 \frac{T_0}{2}, \tag{17.34}$$

since the mean value of $\cos^2 \omega t$ is 1/2. Using (17.30) and (17.34), we finally obtain

$$\rho = \frac{2E}{\pi S_n} \frac{(\text{si } X)^2}{X} \tag{17.35}$$

or

$$\frac{\rho}{\rho_0} = \frac{2(\text{si } X)^2}{\pi X}, \tag{17.36}$$

where ρ_0 denotes the signal-to-noise ratio at the output of the matched filter, as given by formula (17.15).

In Fig. 18, we show how the ratio ρ/ρ_0 depends on the parameter X. We see that the maximum is obtained when

$$X \sim 2.15, \tag{17.37}$$

i.e., when

$$\omega \sim \frac{4.3}{T_0}. \tag{17.38}$$

For this "optimum" receiver bandwidth, we have

$$\frac{\rho}{\rho_0} \sim 0.825, \tag{17.39}$$

i.e., ρ is about 1 decibel less than ρ_0. The matched filter gives a larger value of the signal-to-noise ratio because its transfer function is chosen to correspond to the spectrum of the signal, as regards both its bandwidth and its shape. However, the advantage of using the matched filter is small.

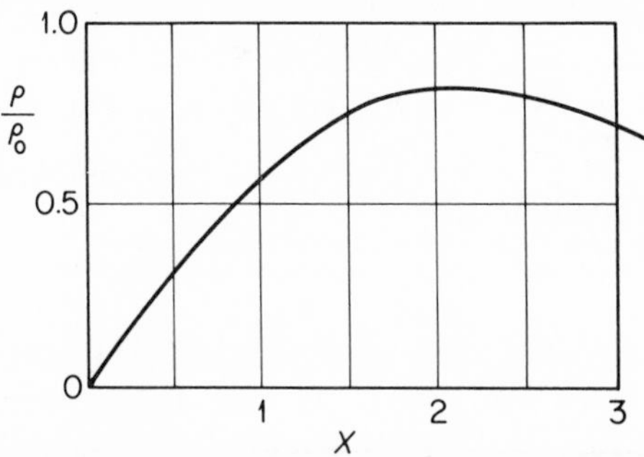

FIG. 18. Comparison of the matched filter and the filter with a rectangular transfer function.

18. Use of a Correlator in the Video Stage of a Radar Receiver

At one time, certain writers had high hopes that correlation methods would be very successful in separating signals from a background of random noise. In fact, in Sec. 17, we showed that the optimum filter for detecting a signal of given form in the presence of white noise is the matched filter or correlator, which forms the cross-correlation function of the expected signal with the mixture of signal and noise arriving at the filter input. However, it has turned out that the correlation method of handling the input processes leads to a result which was only slightly better than that given by ordinary frequency methods of separating signals from noise.

Later, in Sec. 20, we shall study the effectiveness of correlation methods when a sequence of coherent pulses arrives at the receiver, but in this section we confine ourselves to a study of the operation of a correlator in the video stage of the receiver of a pulse radar system. Thus, let the useful signal $m(t)$ be a regular sequence of L rectangular pulses of duration T_0, with unknown amplitude G and unknown time shift τ, i.e.,

$$m(t) = Gm_0(t - \tau) \tag{18.01}$$

[cf. formula (16.22) and Fig. 19(a)], and let the presence and the position of the useful signal (18.01) be masked by white noise. According to formula (17.20), the optimum method for detecting the signal in the noise background is to form the cross-correlation of the input process

$$f(t) = m(t) + n(t) \tag{18.02}$$

with the "standard" signal $m_0(t)$, shown in Fig. 19(b). The expression (17.20), describing the correlator output, can be written in the form

$$\varphi(t) = R_{fm_0}(s), \qquad s = t - t_0, \tag{18.03}$$

where R_{fm_0} is the cross-correlation function of the input process (18.02) with the given function $m_0(t)$ [cf. the end of Sec. 1]. In the absence of noise, $R_{fm_0}(s)$ reduces to the function $R_{mm_0}(s)$ shown in Fig. 19(c), consisting of "correlated" video pulses of triangular form, with various amplitudes. The maximum value of the function

$$R_{mm_0}(s) = GR_{m_0}(t - t_0 - \tau)$$

is achieved for $s = \tau$, when every pulse $m(t)$ of Fig. 19(a) coincides with the corresponding pulse of Fig. 19(b). If τ is slightly increased or slightly decreased, then the function $R_{mm_0}(s)$ falls off linearly, and vanishes when the time shift is $\pm T_0$. The "subsidiary" maxima of the function (18.04) are arranged with period T, equal to the repetition period of the pulses. These subsidiary maxima decrease as we go away from the central maximum, since when two finite pulse trains are superimposed [cf. Figs. 19(a) and 19(b)], the number of pulses falling on top of one another decreases as the two pulse trains are shifted further apart. In addition to the central maximum, there are $2(L - 1)$ subsidiary maxima.

We have just described the specific form which the correlator introduced in Sec. 17 takes for a sequence of L rectangular video pulses. Since the useful signal [Fig. 19(a)] is masked by noise, the "correlated" pulses [Fig. 19(c)] are contaminated by noise. However, the energy of the useful signal is still concentrated in the central maximum, which is the easiest of the maxima to detect in the noise background, since it has the largest signal-to-noise ratio. It should be noted that because of the particularly simple form of the signal $m_0(t)$ shown in Fig. 19(b), the mathematical operations involved in calculating the integral

$$\varphi(t) = R_{fm_0}(s) = \int_{-\infty}^{\infty} f(t')m_0(t' - s)\,dt' \tag{18.04}$$

have simple physical counterparts. In fact, calculating (18.04) reduces to "stroboscoping," i.e., isolating an interval of length T_0 (equal to the pulse duration) from each repetition period T, followed by signal "accumulation," i.e., adding up all the products obtained from the given L repetition periods. These operations are easily implemented by simple electrical engineering methods, so that the use of computers is not ordinarily required.

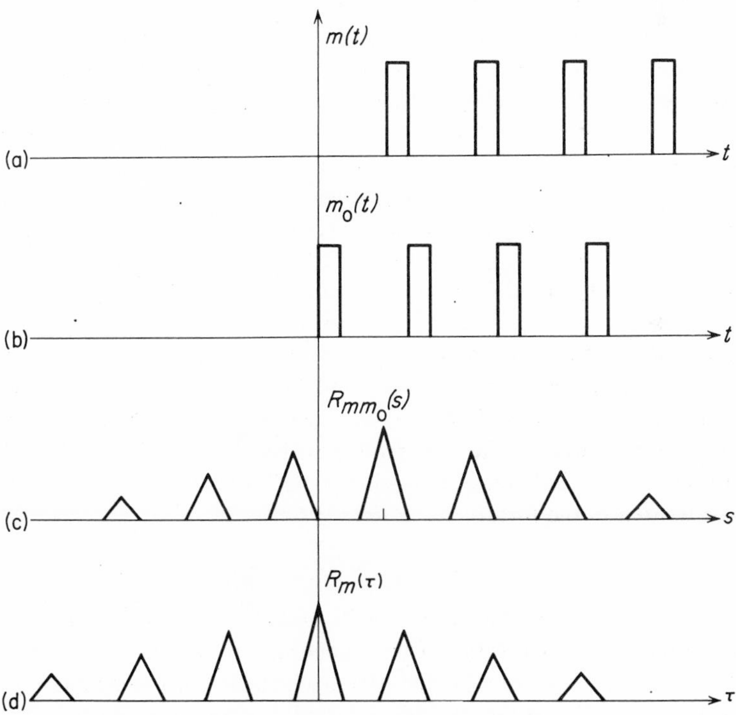

FIG. 19. Detection of a video pulse train by the correlation method.

We now ask how the signal-to-noise ratio after correlation depends on L, the number of pulses. The answer is given by the formula

$$\rho_L = L\rho_1, \tag{18.05}$$

where ρ_L is the value of ρ for L pulses, and ρ_1 is its value for one pulse. This formula is an immediate consequence of (17.15), since, all other things being equal, the energy E of a sequence of L pulses is L times greater than the energy of one pulse. Formula (18.05) can also be easily derived by a more elementary argument, by interpreting the action of the correlator as *integration*. In fact, if one sweep of the stroboscope [invoked above in explaining the physical meaning of (18.04)] reveals the useful signal, then the signal will be present in all the other sweeps of the pulse train; hence, as a result of the integration, the signal amplitude is increased L times, and its power is increased L^2 times. As for the noise, its values in the L different sweeps of the pulse train are statistically independent of one another; hence, the integration leads to an "incoherent" superposition of the noise, i.e., the noise "adds like power" instead of "like amplitude." As a result, the noise power is only L times greater than if only one pulse were present, and we again obtain formula (18.05).

The entire discussion given so far in this section is based on the tacit assumption that we can talk about the "signal" and the "noise" in the video stage of the receiver as if they were distinct and statistically independent entities, whose sum is the given input process (18.02). Strictly speaking, this assumption is valid only in the r-f stage of the receiver, where the useful signal and the noise are simply added together; moreover, since the transition from the r-f stage to the i-f stage can be regarded as linear, the assumption is still justified in the i-f stage. However, the conversion of the signal and the noise to video frequencies is usually accomplished by using a nonlinear device, namely, the *detector*, and as a result, the total process is more complicated than just the sum of signal and noise.

Thus, we now consider in more detail the operation of detection, since in what follows we shall often be concerned with this operation. Since the r-f stage of the receiver has a narrow pass-band, the noise in the r-f stage has the character of a "quasi-monochromatic" process (cf. Sec. 6), and hence can be written in the form

$$n(t) = e_n \cos(\omega_0 t - \vartheta_n), \tag{18.06}$$

where $e_n = e_n(t)$ is the envelope and $\vartheta_n = \vartheta_n(t)$ is the ("supplementary") phase of the random process. These functions are slowly varying compared to the r-f phase $\omega_0 t$ (here ω_0 is the carrier frequency of the signal). Even if the noise acting on the receiver has a broad spectrum (i.e., even if the noise is white), nevertheless, only the part of the noise which can be written in the form (18.06) passes through the receiver. Similarly, we can write the useful signal in the form

$$m(t) = e_m \cos(\omega_0 t - \vartheta_m), \tag{18.07}$$

where e_m is its envelope and ϑ_m is its (supplementary) phase; e_m and ϑ_m are again "slowly varying" functions of time, but for a signal of a given form, they are fixed (i.e., nonrandom) functions, unlike e_n and ϑ_n. Finally, we can also represent the total process (18.02) in the r-f stage in the form

$$f(t) = e_f \cos(\omega_0 t - \vartheta_f), \tag{18.08}$$

where

$$e_f = \sqrt{e_m^2 + 2e_m e_n \cos(\vartheta_m - \vartheta_n) + e_n^2} \tag{18.09}$$

is the envelope of the total process (signal plus noise). The same formulas are also valid in the i-f stage, provided that now ω_0 denotes the intermediate frequency.

The operation of detection consists in making a nonlinear transformation of the signal, e.g., with a (half-wave) linear detector or with a quadratic detector, and then passing the signal through a linear filter which suppresses the high-frequency components. In what follows, by the *detector* we shall mean this combination of a nonlinear device and a filter. At the output of the linear detector, we obtain the envelope (18.09) of the input process $f(t)$, while at the output of the quadratic detector, we obtain the square of the envelope of $f(t)$:

$$e_f^2 = e_m^2 + 2e_m e_n \cos(\vartheta_m - \vartheta_n) + e_n^2. \tag{18.10}$$

In the absence of noise, these two detectors give the function e_m and e_m^2, while in the absence of signal, they give the functions e_n and e_n^2 instead. However, when both signal and noise are present, the resulting function at the detector output does not reduce to just a sum of contributions from the signal and from the noise separately. Instead, in addition to the term $e_m^2 + e_n^2$, the expression (18.10) contains the "interference" term $2e_m e_n \cos(\vartheta_m - \vartheta_n)$, which has a "mixed" character, depending as it does on the phase difference between the signal and the noise; this term is a consequence of the nonlinearity of the transformation. Similar terms also appear in the expression (18.09). In fact, if the noise is much stronger than the signal, so that

$$e_m \ll e_n, \tag{18.11}$$

then, using the formula

$$\sqrt{1 + x} = 1 + \tfrac{1}{2}x - \tfrac{1}{8}x^2 + \cdots, \tag{18.12}$$

we can write (18.09) in the form

$$e_f = e_n + e_m \cos(\vartheta_m - \vartheta_n) + \frac{e_m^2}{4e_n}[1 - \cos 2(\vartheta_m - \vartheta_n)]. \tag{18.13}$$

Both the second term in the right-hand side of (18.12) and part of the third term have an "interference" character, i.e., depend on $\vartheta_m - \vartheta_n$.

In making a theoretical analysis of detection, the interference terms can be regarded as noise. Then, formulas (18.10) and (18.13) immediately reveal an important and interesting effect, i.e., *a weak signal is suppressed by strong noise when the combination of signal plus noise is detected.* In fact, let the signal-to-noise amplitude ratio before detection be

$$r' = \frac{e_m}{e_n}. \tag{18.14}$$

Then, if r' is small, according to formula (18.10), after quadratic detection we have

$$r'' = \frac{e_m^2}{e_n^2} = (r')^2 \ll r', \tag{18.15}$$

while, according to formula (18.13), after linear detection, we have

$$r'' = \frac{e_m^2}{4e_n^2} = \left(\frac{r'}{2}\right)^2 \ll r'. \tag{18.16}$$

Conversely, *weak noise is suppressed by a strong signal during detection.* In fact, if the quantity (18.14) is large, then at the output of the quadratic detector, we have

$$r'' = \frac{e_m^2}{e_n^2} = (r')^2 \gg r', \tag{18.17}$$

while if

$$e_m \gg e_n, \tag{18.18}$$

formula (18.13) becomes

$$e_f = e_m + e_n \cos(\vartheta_m - \vartheta_n) + \frac{e_n^2}{4e_m}[1 - \cos 2(\vartheta_m - \vartheta_n)], \tag{18.19}$$

so that

$$r'' = \frac{4e_m^2}{e_n^2} = (2r')^2 \gg r' \tag{18.20}$$

at the output of the linear detector. In deriving formulas (18.17) and (18.20), we did not take into account the interference terms, and it is assumed that they can be eliminated by some kind of averaging of the quantity e_f^2 or e_f at the detector output.

The expressions (18.15) and (18.16) show that for small signal-to-noise ratios, the quadratic detector is better than the linear detector, since the quadratic detector gives a value of r'' which is four times larger. On the other hand, for large signal-to-noise ratios, the linear detector is better than the quadratic detector, since this time, the linear detector gives a value of r'' which is four times larger.

We assumed above that the larger the signal-to-noise ratio at the detector output, the better the detector. However, it should be noted that in the case of nonlinear transformations of the signal plus noise, the definition of this important parameter (i.e., the signal-to-noise ratio) is not entirely unique, since the interference terms contain some information about the signal, and hence can be regarded both as signal and as noise. This lack of determinacy does not occur in the case of linear transformations, which are more completely characterized by their signal-to-noise ratios.

The *weak-signal suppression effect* just found shows that the correlation method of detecting signals[1] must be less effective in the video stage than in the r-f or i-f stage. The problem of detecting a coherent sequence of pulses in the r-f or i-f stage will be studied in Sec. 20, after we have developed the necessary mathematical tools in the next section.

It should be noted that in the literature, a *correlator* is often understood to be a device forming the autocorrelation function of the input process $f(t)$, i.e., the function

$$R_f(\tau) = \int_{-\infty}^{\infty} f(t)f(t - \tau)\, dt, \tag{18.21}$$

where, for example, $f(t)$ means the sum (18.02) of the signal and noise after L repetition periods. However, the correlator (18.21) is useless in the video stage of a radar system, since even in the absence of the noise $n(t)$, it gives the function $R_m(\tau)$, shown in Fig. 19(d), which has a maximum at $\tau = 0$, regardless of the time delay with which the useful signal arrives (this leads to a loss of the target range information) and regardless of whether one or two useful signals with different delay times arrive (this leads to a loss of resolving power). It can also be shown that in the presence of strong noise, the correlator described by the formula (18.21) leads to an additional suppression of weak signals. This suppression is of the same nature as that occurring in a quadratic detector. Moreover, if the integral in (18.21) is performed over a finite time, and if $f(t)$ is understood to be the sum of an r-f signal and noise, then we get the so-called "sliding" autocorrelation function. It can be shown that a device which forms such an autocorrelation function differs only slightly from a quadratic detector (to which it reduces for $\tau = 0$).

We said above that it is hard to appraise nonlinear data processing[2] by using the signal-to-noise ratio. Therefore, in looking for optimum nonlinear operations, it is better to rely on the more exact statistical theory to be developed in Part 2.

---

[1] I.e., "stroboscoping and accumulation," as described above.

[2] As described, for example, by formulas (18.09), (18.10) and (18.21).

19. Kotelnikov's Theorem and Its Conjugate

Kotelnikov's theorem gives a representation of band-limited signals, i.e., signals with a limited spectrum. To derive the theorem, we first write the signal $f(t)$ as a Fourier integral

$$f(t) = \frac{1}{2\pi}\int_{-\infty}^{\infty} e^{i\omega t}F(\omega)\, d\omega, \tag{19.01}$$

where

$$F(\omega) = \int_{-\infty}^{\infty} e^{-i\omega t}f(t)\, dt. \tag{19.02}$$

We assume that

$$F(\omega) = 0 \quad \text{for} \quad \omega < -\Omega \quad \text{and} \quad \omega > \Omega. \tag{19.03}$$

This means that the (amplitude) spectrum $F(\omega)$ of the signal is different from zero only in the band $-\Omega < \omega < \Omega$, and hence in this interval, $F(\omega)$ can be expanded in a Fourier series, which we write in complex form:

$$F(\omega) = \sum_{\alpha=-\infty}^{\infty} D_\alpha e^{i\pi\alpha\omega/\Omega}. \tag{19.04}$$

The corresponding Fourier coefficients are equal to

$$D_\alpha = \frac{1}{2\Omega}\int_{-\Omega}^{\Omega} e^{-i\pi\alpha\omega/\Omega}F(\omega)\, d\omega. \tag{19.05}$$

Comparing (19.05) and (19.01), we find that

$$D_\alpha = \frac{\pi}{\Omega} f\left(-\frac{\pi\alpha}{\Omega}\right). \tag{19.06}$$

Next, introducing the notation

$$\Delta t = \frac{\pi}{\Omega}, \tag{19.07}$$

we can write formulas (19.06) and (19.04) as

$$D_\alpha = \Delta t f(-\alpha\Delta t),$$

$$F(\omega) = \Delta t \sum_{\alpha=-\infty}^{\infty} f(-\alpha\,\Delta t)e^{i\alpha\omega\,\Delta t} = \Delta t \sum_{\alpha=-\infty}^{\infty} f(\alpha\,\Delta t)e^{-i\alpha\omega\,\Delta t}. \tag{19.08}$$

Substituting (19.08) into (19.01), and bearing in mind the condition (19.03), we obtain

$$\begin{aligned} f(t) &= \frac{\Delta t}{2\pi}\sum_{\alpha=-\infty}^{\infty} f(\alpha\,\Delta t)\int_{-\Omega}^{\Omega} e^{i\omega(t-\alpha\,\Delta t)}\, d\omega \\ &= \sum_{\alpha=-\infty}^{\infty} f(\alpha\,\Delta t)\frac{\Delta t}{\pi}\,\frac{\sin\Omega(t-\alpha\,\Delta t)}{t-\alpha\,\Delta t} \end{aligned} \tag{19.09}$$

or

$$f(t) = \sum_{\alpha=-\infty}^{\infty} f(\alpha\,\Delta t)\,\frac{\sin \Omega(t - \alpha\,\Delta t)}{\Omega(t - \alpha\,\Delta t)}. \tag{19.10}$$

Formula (19.10), known as *Kotelnikov's theorem*,[3] shows that if the signal $f(t)$ is band-limited, then its value at *any* time t is determined by the values it takes at the times $t_\alpha = \alpha\,\Delta t$, which are Δt seconds apart [where Δt is given by (19.07)]. It should be noted that the value of the sum (19.10) at the time $t_\alpha = \alpha\,\Delta t$ is determined by only one term, i.e., the αth term, since all the other terms vanish. This follows from the fact that the expression

$$\frac{\sin \Omega(\alpha - \beta)\,\Delta t}{\Omega(\alpha - \beta)\,\Delta t}$$

is zero if $\alpha \neq \beta$.

There is another theorem of this type, which we shall call the *conjugate* of Kotelnikov's theorem, dealing with signals of finite duration ("time-limited" signals). Suppose that

$$f(t) = 0 \quad \text{for} \quad t < -T \quad \text{or} \quad t > T. \tag{19.11}$$

Then, in the interval $-T < t < T$, the function $f(t)$ can be expanded in a Fourier series

$$f(t) = \sum_{\alpha=-\infty}^{\infty} C_\alpha e^{i\pi\alpha t/T}, \tag{19.12}$$

where

$$C_\alpha = \frac{1}{2T}\int_{-T}^{T} e^{-i\pi\alpha t/T} f(t)\,dt = \frac{1}{2T}F\left(\frac{\pi\alpha}{T}\right) = \frac{\Delta\omega}{2\pi}F(\alpha\,\Delta\omega) \tag{19.13}$$

and

$$\Delta\omega = \frac{\pi}{T}. \tag{19.14}$$

Using (19.13), we find that

$$f(t) = \frac{\Delta\omega}{2\pi}\sum_{\alpha=-\infty}^{\infty} F(\alpha\,\Delta\omega)e^{i\alpha\,\Delta\omega t}. \tag{19.15}$$

Substituting (19.15) into (19.02) and bearing in mind the condition (19.11), we obtain the following expression for the complex amplitude spectrum $F(\omega)$ of a signal of finite duration:

$$F(\omega) = \sum_{\alpha=-\infty}^{\infty} F(\alpha\,\Delta\omega)\,\frac{\sin(\omega - \alpha\,\Delta\omega)T}{(\omega - \alpha\,\Delta\omega)T}. \tag{19.16}$$

---

[3] Often called *Shannon's theorem* or simply the *sampling theorem*. (*Translator*)

This result, called the *conjugate of Kotelnikov's theorem*, shows that if $F(\omega)$ is the spectrum of a signal of finite duration, then its value at *any* frequency ω is determined by the values it takes at the frequencies $\omega_\alpha = \alpha\,\Delta\omega$.

It should be noted that formula (19.10) can be applied to the function

$$f(t) = f_1(t_0 + t), \tag{19.17}$$

where t_0 is an arbitrary time. The result is

$$f_1(t_0 + t) = \sum_{\alpha=-\infty}^{\infty} f_1(t_0 + \alpha\,\Delta t)\,\frac{\sin \Omega(t - \alpha\,\Delta t)}{\Omega(t - \alpha\,\Delta t)}. \tag{19.18}$$

Here, f_1 like f is a band-limited function. Replacing $t_0 + t$ by t', and then dropping the prime on t' and the subscript on f_1, we obtain the formula

$$f(t) = \sum_{\alpha=-\infty}^{\infty} f(t_0 + \alpha\,\Delta t)\,\frac{\sin \Omega(t - t_0 - \alpha\,\Delta t)}{\Omega(t - t_0 - \alpha\,\Delta t)}, \tag{19.19}$$

which is a slight generalization of (19.10).

In deriving Kotelnikov's theorem (19.10) or (19.19), we assumed that $f(t)$ could be written as a Fourier integral (19.01). For random functions $f(t)$, the amplitude spectrum $F(\omega)$ is replaced by the power spectrum $S_f(\omega)$ (cf. Sec. 3). Therefore, for random functions (e.g., for noise), Kotelnikov's theorem, although obvious from a physical point of view, strictly speaking needs a special proof, which we now give.

Let the power spectral density $S_f(\omega)$ satisfy the condition

$$S_f(\omega) = 0 \quad \text{for} \quad \omega < -\Omega \quad \text{or} \quad \omega > \Omega, \tag{19.20}$$

analogous to the condition (19.03). Then the correlation function

$$R_f(\tau) = \frac{1}{2\pi}\int_{-\infty}^{\infty} e^{i\omega\tau} S_f(\omega)\,d\omega, \tag{19.21}$$

related to $S_f(\omega)$ by (19.21) and by the inverse Fourier transform

$$S_f(\omega) = \int_{-\infty}^{\infty} e^{-i\omega\tau} R_f(\tau)\,d\tau, \tag{19.22}$$

can obviously be written in a form similar to (19.10). Therefore, we have

$$R_f(\tau) = \sum_{\alpha=-\infty}^{\infty} R_f(\alpha\,\Delta t)\,\frac{\sin \Omega(\tau - \alpha\,\Delta t)}{\Omega(\tau - \alpha\,\Delta t)} \tag{19.23}$$

or, as in formula (19.19),

$$R_f(\tau) = \sum_{\beta=-\infty}^{\infty} R_f(t_0 + \beta\,\Delta t)\,\frac{\sin \Omega(\tau - t_0 - \beta\,\Delta t)}{\Omega(\tau - t_0 - \beta\,\Delta t)}, \tag{19.24}$$

where t_0 is an arbitrary time. In fact, in deriving (19.10) and (19.19), we only used the properties of Fourier transforms and the condition (19.03).

To prove formula (19.10) for the random function $f(t)$ itself, we write

$$x(t) = \sum_{\alpha=-\infty}^{\infty} f(\alpha\,\Delta t)\,\frac{\sin\Omega(t-\alpha\,\Delta t)}{\Omega(t-\alpha\,\Delta t)} \tag{19.25}$$

and show that the mean square of the difference

$$\varepsilon(t) = x(t) - f(t) \tag{19.26}$$

equals zero. In fact, we have

$$\overline{\varepsilon^2(t)} = \overline{x^2(t)} - 2\overline{x(t)f(t)} + \overline{f^2(t)}, \tag{19.27}$$

and bearing in mind that

$$R_f(\tau) = \overline{f(t)f(t-\tau)}, \tag{19.28}$$

we find that

$$\overline{x^2(t)} = \sum_\alpha \sum_\beta R_f(\beta\,\Delta t - \alpha\,\Delta t) \times \frac{\sin\Omega(t-\alpha\,\Delta t)}{\Omega(t-\alpha\,\Delta t)}\,\frac{\sin\Omega(t-\beta\,\Delta t)}{\Omega(t-\beta\,\Delta t)}, \tag{19.29}$$

$$\overline{x(t)f(t)} = \sum_\alpha R_f(t-\alpha\,\Delta t)\,\frac{\sin\Omega(t-\alpha\,\Delta t)}{\Omega(t-\alpha\,\Delta t)}, \tag{19.30}$$

and

$$\overline{f^2(t)} = R_f(0). \tag{19.31}$$

Setting $t_0 = -\alpha\,\Delta t$ and $\tau - t_0 = t$ in formula (19.24), we obtain

$$\sum_\beta R_f(-\alpha\,\Delta t + \beta\,\Delta t)\,\frac{\sin\Omega(t-\beta\,\Delta t)}{\Omega(t-\beta\,\Delta t)} = R_f(t-\alpha\,\Delta t). \tag{19.32}$$

It follows that

$$\overline{x^2(t)} = \sum_\alpha R_f(t-\alpha\,\Delta t)\,\frac{\sin\Omega(t-\alpha\,\Delta t)}{\Omega(t-\alpha\,\Delta t)} = \overline{x(t)f(t)}. \tag{19.33}$$

Then, setting $t_0 = -\tau$ and $\tau = 0$ in formula (19.24), and using the evenness of the function $R_f(\tau)$, we find that

$$\overline{f^2(t)} = R_f(0) = \sum_\beta R_f(-t+\beta\,\Delta t)\,\frac{\sin\Omega(t-\beta\,\Delta t)}{\Omega(t-\beta\,\Delta t)} = \overline{x(t)f(t)}. \tag{19.34}$$

Using (19.33), (19.34) and the expression (19.27) for $\overline{\varepsilon^2(t)}$, we obtain the desired result

$$\overline{\varepsilon^2(t)} = 0, \tag{19.35}$$

which proves formula (19.10) for a band-limited random process.

20. The Comb Filter and the Matched Filter (Correlator) for a Sequence of R-F Pulses

In this section, we shall study sequences of rectangular pulses. Consider first a single pulse, which has the form

$$\begin{aligned} m(t) &= A \cos \omega_0 t \quad \text{for} \quad -\frac{T_0}{2} < t < \frac{T_0}{2}, \\ m(t) &= 0 \qquad\qquad \text{for} \quad t < -\frac{T_0}{2} \quad \text{and} \quad t > \frac{T_0}{2}. \end{aligned} \tag{20.01}$$

Here, ω_0 is the carrier frequency, A is the amplitude of the pulse and T_0 is the duration of the pulse. The amplitude spectrum $M(\omega)$ of a single pulse is

$$M(\omega) = \int_{-\infty}^{\infty} e^{-i\omega t} m(t)\, dt = A \int_{-T_0/2}^{T_0/2} e^{-i\omega t} \cos \omega_0 t\, dt \tag{20.02}$$

or

$$M(\omega) = A\left\{\frac{\sin [(\omega - \omega_0)T_0/2]}{\omega - \omega_0} + \frac{\sin [(\omega + \omega_0)T_0/2]}{\omega + \omega_0}\right\}. \tag{20.03}$$

The function $M(\omega)$ is shown in Fig. 20 for positive frequencies ω. For $\omega < 0$, we obtain the same curve, since

$$M(-\omega) = M(\omega). \tag{20.04}$$

These formulas have already been used in Sec. 17.

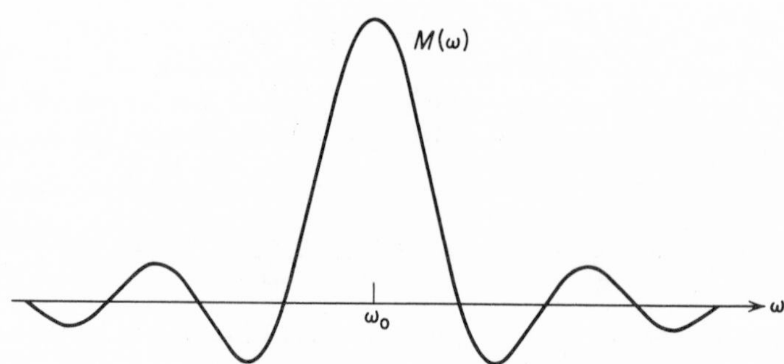

FIG. 20. Amplitude spectrum $M(\omega)$ of a rectangular r-f pulse.

The pulse (20.01) is symmetric with respect to the time $t = 0$. If we take a rectangular pulse of the more general form

$$\begin{aligned} m(t) &= A \cos (\omega_0 t - \vartheta) \quad \text{for} \quad \tau - \frac{T_0}{2} < t < \tau + \frac{T_0}{2}, \\ m(t) &= 0 \qquad\qquad\qquad\quad \text{for all other } t, \end{aligned} \tag{20.05}$$

then, instead of (20.03), we obtain

$$M(\omega) = Ae^{-i\omega\tau}\left\{e^{i(\omega_0\tau-\vartheta)}\frac{[\sin(\omega-\omega_0)T_0/2]}{\omega-\omega_0} + e^{-i(\omega_0\tau-\vartheta)}\frac{[\sin(\omega+\omega_0)T_0/2]}{\omega+\omega_0}\right\}. \qquad (20.06)$$

Suppose now that the rectangular pulses occur irregularly. Then, as shown in Sec. 12, we obtain a random process with the power spectral density

$$S(\omega) = \sigma|M(\omega)|^2, \qquad (20.07)$$

where the parameter σ equals the average number of pulses which occur per unit time. The relation (20.07) is also applicable to the case of interest in radar, where the pulses occur periodically (with repetition period T), but where each pulse has a random phase ϑ which is independent of the phases of all the other pulses, a case which is referred to as a *sequence of incoherent pulses*. If every position of the sequence along the time axis is equally likely, then the resulting random process (consisting of a randomly located incoherent pulse train) has the spectral density (20.07), where the coefficient σ equals

$$\sigma = \frac{1}{T}, \qquad (20.08)$$

and the correlation function

$$R(\tau) = \frac{\sigma}{2\pi}\int_{-\infty}^{\infty} e^{i\omega\tau}|M(\omega)|^2\,d\omega = \sigma\int_{-\infty}^{\infty} m(t)m(t-\tau)\,dt, \qquad (20.09)$$

as follows from formulas (17.05) to (17.08). The relations (20.07) to (20.09) hold for any infinite sequence of incoherent signals, but for the special case of the rectangular pulse (20.01) and for $0 < \tau < T_0$, (20.09) becomes

$$\begin{aligned} R(\tau) &= \sigma A^2 \int_{-(T_0/2)+\tau}^{T_0/2} \cos\omega_0 t\cos\omega_0(t-\tau)\,dt \\ &= \frac{\sigma A^2}{2}\int_{-(T_0/2)+\tau}^{T_0/2} [\cos\omega_0\tau + \cos\omega_0(2t-\tau)]\,dt \qquad (20.10) \\ &= \frac{\sigma A^2}{2}(T_0-\tau)\cos\omega_0\tau, \end{aligned}$$

where we have neglected the integral of $\cos\omega_0(2t-\tau)$, since it is of order $\omega_0 T_0$ times less than the integral which has been retained, and since the product $\omega_0 T_0$ is assumed to be large, i.e., it is assumed that the pulse contains many periods of the r-f carrier. Therefore, we finally have

$$\begin{aligned} R(\tau) &= \sigma E\left(1-\frac{|\tau|}{T_0}\right)\cos\omega_0\tau \quad \text{for} \quad -T_0 < \tau < T_0, \\ R(\tau) &= 0 \quad \text{for} \quad \tau < -T_0 \quad \text{and} \quad \tau > T_0, \end{aligned} \qquad (20.11)$$

where E is the energy of the pulse, given by (17.34). Thus, for this random process, because of the incoherence of the different pulses, the correlation extends only for a time interval of order T_0, as shown in Fig. 21.

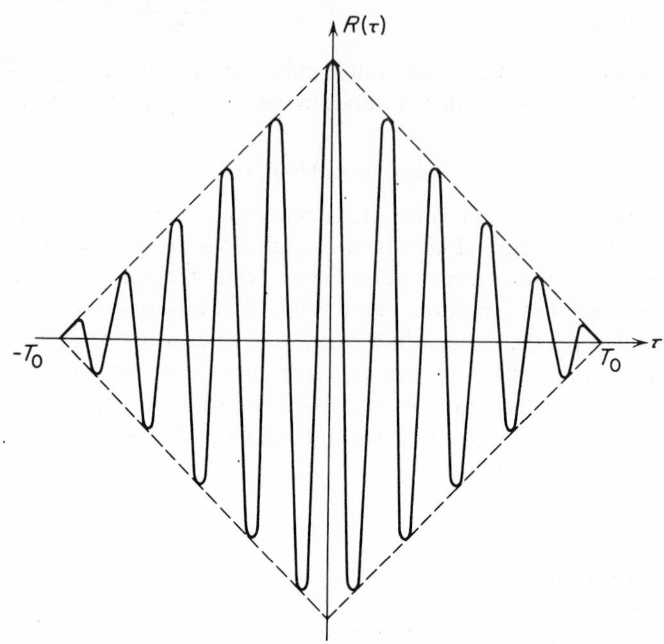

FIG. 21. Correlation function of a rectangular r-f pulse.

Next, we find the spectrum of an infinite periodic sequence of *coherent* pulses, i.e., we assume that formula (20.01) holds in the interval $-T/2 < t < T/2$ (where T is the repetition period), and that the function $m(t)$ is continued periodically outside this interval. Then, $m(t)$ can be expanded in a Fourier series

$$m(t) = \sum_{\alpha=-\infty}^{\infty} M_\alpha e^{i2\pi\alpha t/T}, \tag{20.12}$$

whose coefficients M_α are

$$M_\alpha = \frac{1}{T}\int_{-T_0/2}^{T_0/2} e^{-i2\pi\alpha t/T} m(t)\,dt. \tag{20.13}$$

Comparing formulas (20.13) and (20.02), we see that

$$M_\alpha = \frac{1}{T} M\left(\frac{2\pi\alpha}{T}\right) = \frac{1}{T} M(\alpha\omega_1), \tag{20.14}$$

where

$$\omega_1 = \frac{2\pi}{T} \tag{20.15}$$

is the repetition frequency.

The coefficient M_α gives the *weight* of the αth harmonic, i.e., it shows what amplitude is assigned to the frequency $\omega_\alpha = \alpha\omega_1$. If we omit the factor $1/T$, then we can represent M_α as shown in Fig. 22. Comparing Figs. 22

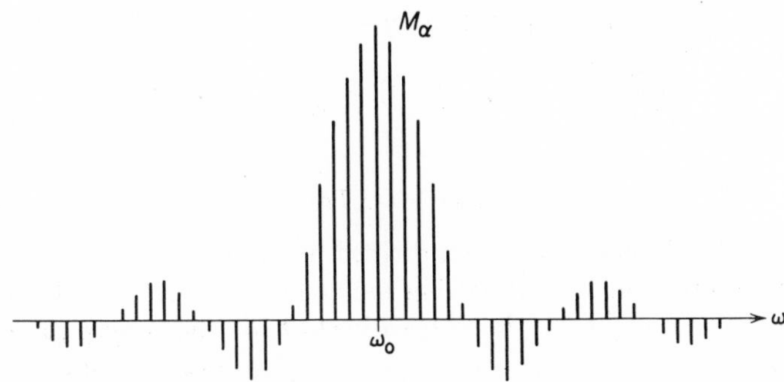

FIG. 22. Spectral coefficients M_α for an infinite periodic sequence of rectangular r-f pulses.

and 20, we see that the amplitude spectrum of a single pulse of a periodic pulse train is a kind of "spectral envelope" for the *line spectrum* of the whole train. Since $T \gg T_0$, the spectral lines M_α are very close together.

It is also of interest to consider the spectrum of a periodic pulse train of *finite* length. In this case, the signal is written as a Fourier *integral* and has a continuous spectrum, but as L, the number of pulses, is increased, the energy of the pulses becomes concentrated in the vicinity of the frequencies $\omega_\alpha = \alpha\omega_1$. Thus, suppose we have a periodic sequence of L pulses of the form (20.01). Then, the spectrum $M(\omega)$ of this pulse train is given by

$$\begin{aligned} M(\omega) &= \int_{-\infty}^{\infty} e^{-i\omega t} m(t)\, dt \\ &= \int_{-T_0/2}^{T_0/2} e^{-i\omega t} m(t)\, dt + \int_{T-(T_0/2)}^{T+(T_0/2} e^{-i\omega t} m(t)\, dt \\ &\qquad + \cdots + \int_{(L-1)T-(T_0/2)}^{(L-1)T+(T_0/2)} e^{-i\omega t} m(t)\, dt \qquad (20.16) \\ &= [1 + e^{-i\omega t} + \cdots + e^{-i\omega(L-1)T}] \int_{-T_0/2}^{T_0/2} e^{-i\omega t} m(t)\, dt. \end{aligned}$$

The expression in brackets in (20.16) is a geometric series, with the sum

$$\frac{e^{-i\omega LT} - 1}{e^{-i\omega T} - 1} = \frac{\sin(\omega LT/2)}{\sin(\omega T/2)}\, e^{-i\omega(L-1)T/2}, \tag{20.17}$$

from which it follows that

$$M(\omega) = \frac{\sin(\omega LT/2)}{\sin(\omega T/2)} e^{-i\omega(L-1)T/2} \int_{-T_0/2}^{T_0/2} e^{-i\omega t} m(t)\, dt. \tag{20.18}$$

Formula (20.18) shows that

$$M\left(\frac{\alpha\omega_1}{L}\right) = M\left(\frac{2\pi\alpha}{LT}\right) = 0 \quad \text{for} \quad \alpha \neq \varkappa L, \tag{20.19}$$

where α and $\varkappa$ are integers, since for $\omega = \alpha\omega_1/L$, the factor $\sin(\omega LT/2)$ vanishes. For $\alpha = \varkappa L$, using (20.16), we see that

$$M\left(\frac{\alpha\omega_1}{L}\right) = M(\varkappa\omega_1) = L \int_{-T_0/2}^{T_0/2} e^{-i\varkappa\omega_1 t} m(t)\, dt \tag{20.20}$$

or

$$M(\varkappa\omega_1) = LTM_\varkappa, \tag{20.21}$$

where $M_\varkappa$ is the Fourier coefficient defined by (20.14).

A more transparent way of writing the amplitude spectrum of a periodic sequence of L pulses can be given by using (19.16), the conjugate of Kotelnikov's theorem. In fact, by appropriately choosing the time origin, we can include the whole pulse train in the interval

$$-\tilde{t} < t < \tilde{t}, \quad \text{where} \quad \tilde{t} = \frac{LT + T_0}{2} \sim \frac{LT}{2}, \tag{20.22}$$

so that the quantity (19.14) equals

$$\Delta\omega = \frac{2\pi}{LT + T_0} \sim \frac{\omega_1}{L}. \tag{20.23}$$

Then, (20.19) and (20.21) show that

$$\begin{aligned} M(\alpha\,\Delta\omega) &= 0 && \text{for} \quad \alpha \neq \varkappa L, \\ M(\alpha\,\Delta\omega) &= LTM_\varkappa && \text{for} \quad \alpha = \varkappa L, \end{aligned} \tag{20.24}$$

so that (19.16) becomes

$$M(\omega) = LT \sum_{\varkappa=-\infty}^{\infty} M_\varkappa \frac{\sin[(\omega - \varkappa\omega_1)(LT/2)]}{(\omega - \varkappa\omega_1)(LT/2)}. \tag{20.25}$$

This formula shows that in the case of a finite r-f pulse train, each spectral line is "spread out" (as compared to the infinite pulse train) in accordance with the law $\sin x/x$, where $x = (\omega - \varkappa\omega_1)(LT/2)$. The larger L, the "sharper" the function $\sin x/x$ becomes. In the limit as $L \to \infty$, we obtain the discrete spectrum shown in Fig. 22, while for $L = 1$, we obtain the spectrum of a single pulse, as shown in Fig. 20. In Fig. 23(a), we show an intermediate case, corresponding to $L = 3$.

Since for large L, the spectrum of a finite pulse train is almost a line spectrum, then, to pass the useful signal $m(t)$ without appreciable loss of energy and without appreciable distortion, while at the same time keeping the noise level as low as possible, we have to choose a filter whose transfer function is comb-shaped [see Fig. 23(b)]. The "teeth" of the comb have the same height and the same width (the latter depends on L), while the midpoint of each tooth lies at one of the frequencies $\omega_\varkappa = \varkappa\omega_1$. This constitutes the so-called *comb filter*.

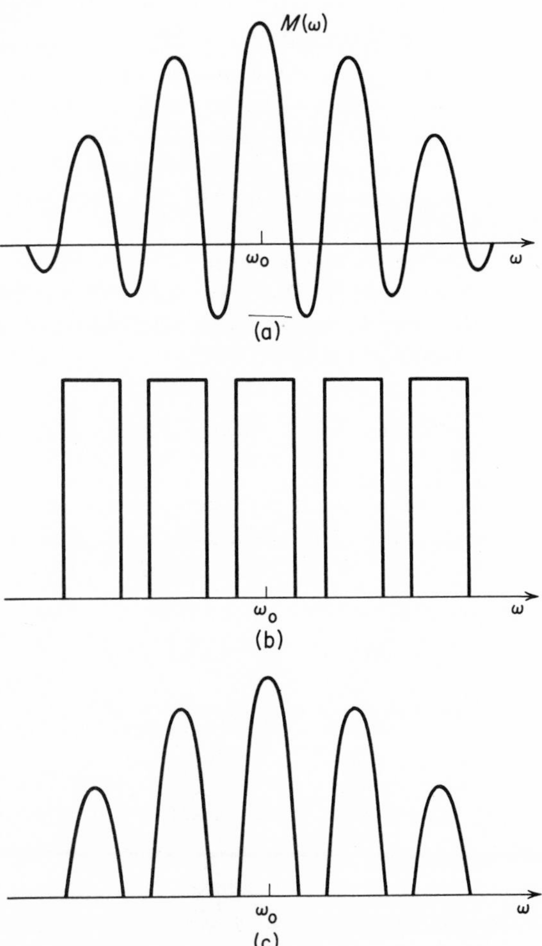

FIG. 23. The comb filter and the matched filter for a sequence of three rectangular r-f pulses.

(a) The amplitude spectrum $M(\omega)$ of three coherent pulses;
(b) The transfer function of the comb filter;
(c) The transfer function corresponding (approximately) to the matched filter.

The matched filter can be regarded as a modification of the comb filter. In the case of the matched filter, the teeth are not as high as in the comb filter, and they are not rectangular, but instead reproduce the form of the amplitude spectrum $M^*(\omega)$ of the useful signal. Unlike the comb filter, the matched filter considerably distorts the useful signal, but this makes it possible to obtain a larger output signal-to-noise ratio than in the case of the comb filter. In fact, the gain in using the matched filter amounts to 4.3 db. This is the figure obtained by George and Zamanakos,[4] making the assumption that the width of the teeth of the comb filter is $4\pi/T_0$ and that the transfer function of the matched filter is different from zero only inside the teeth, as shown in Fig. 23(c). Of course, as we have seen, an exact calculation of the matched filter shows that its transfer function must reproduce the form of the spectrum of the useful signal [Fig. 23(a)], and in particular, it must vanish only at certain points and not in entire intervals. However, the "nonoptimum" filter shown in Fig. 23(c) is only slightly less effective than the true matched filter.

We have just examined the operation of the matched filter from a frequency domain point of view (Fig. 23). To study the same problem from a time domain point of view, we must bear in mind that the matched filter is a correlator which forms the function

$$R_{fm_0}(s) = \int_{-\infty}^{\infty} f(t)m_0(t - s)\,dt \tag{20.26}$$

(cf. Secs. 17 and 18), where $m_0(t)$ is the "standard" search signal, which in this case consists of L coherent r-f pulses, while $f(t)$ is the signal received during L repetition periods. We can also write (20.26) as

$$\begin{aligned} R_{fm_0}(s) &= \sum_{\alpha=1}^{L} \int_{-\infty}^{\infty} f(t)m_\alpha(t - s)\,dt \\ &= \sum_{\alpha=1}^{L} \int_{s+(\alpha-1)T-(T_0/2)}^{s+(\alpha-1)T+(T_0/2)} f(t) \cos \omega_0(t - s)\,dt, \end{aligned} \tag{20.27}$$

where $m_\alpha(t)$ denotes the αth pulse, which, according to formulas (20.01) and (20.06), is equal to

$$\begin{aligned} m_\alpha(t) &= \cos \omega_0 t \quad \text{for} \quad (\alpha - 1)T - \frac{T_0}{2} < t < (\alpha - 1)T + \frac{T_0}{2}, \\ m_\alpha(t) &= 0 \qquad\qquad \text{for all other } t. \end{aligned} \tag{20.28}$$

[4] S. F. George and A. Zamanakos, *Comb filters for pulsed radar use*, Proc. IRE, **42**, 1159 (1954).

Thus, the action of the matched filter or correlator reduces to the following operations:

1. Multiplication by $\cos \omega_0 t$ with various time shifts. This operation can be easily implemented by using a coherent (phase) detector, which forms the product of the input voltage $f(t)$ and a cosinusoidal voltage (with carrier frequency ω_0).

2. Integration of the product over the time interval T_0. This integration (or time-averaging) is accomplished by using a linear filter which passes only sufficiently low frequencies; as is customary, this filter follows the coherent detector in the circuit. We note that the action of the averaging filter is not entirely equivalent to integrating over a well-defined time interval T_0, but, by the same token, the presence of strictly rectangular pulses of duration T_0 is also a theoretical idealization.

3. Summation or "accumulation" of the different values obtained during the L repetition periods. This operation leads once again to formula (18.05), which shows how summation increases the signal-to-noise (power) ratio. Formula (17.15) gives the signal-to-noise ratio after the whole sequence of operations.

All these operations taken together can be called "coherent integration," as opposed to the operations (described in Sec. 18) in the video stage of the receiver, which we call "incoherent integration." As we have just seen, coherent integration is easily implemented by ordinary electrical engineering methods.

In radar applications, even in the case of a single reflecting object, the received pulses do not usually form a strictly periodic sequence, since the r-f phase of the scattered pulses ranges varies randomly from pulse to pulse. Therefore, in the r-f and i-f stages of the radar receiver, a matched filter can be implemented only by means of coherent (synchronous) detection, using an oscillation with carrier (or intermediate) frequency ω_0 and with a phase corresponding to each scattered pulse. By using a coherent detector, the situation is just as if the reflecting object radiates a strictly periodic pulse train, in which each pulse has the same phase. Then, the rest of the operations are the same as those described above.

If the reflecting object (e.g., an airplane) is in rapid motion, then the practical implementation of coherent integration becomes much more complicated. From a frequency domain point of view, it is now necessary to take into account frequency shifts in the received signal due to the Doppler effect, when constructing comb filters or matched filters. Then, different filters have to be used for different frequencies, and the longer the integration time, the more filters there have to be in a given frequency range. From a time domain point of view, for every target moving with constant radial velocity, we have to deal with the received signal $f(t)$ by using the following formula [instead of formula (20.27)]:

$$\begin{aligned} R_{fm_\alpha}(s) &= \sum_{\alpha=1}^{L} \int_{-\infty}^{\infty} f(t) m_\alpha(t-s)\, dt \\ &= \sum_{\alpha=1}^{L} \int_{s+(\alpha-1)T-(T_0/2)}^{s+(\alpha-1)T+(T_0/2)} f(t) \cos\,[\omega_0(t-s) - (\alpha-1)\,\Delta\vartheta]\, dt. \end{aligned} \tag{20.29}$$

Here

$$\begin{aligned} m_\alpha(t) &= \cos\,[\omega_0 t - (\alpha-1)\,\Delta\vartheta] \\ &\qquad \text{for } (\alpha-1)T - \frac{T_0}{2} < t < (\alpha-1)T + \frac{T_0}{2}, \\ m_\alpha(t) &= 0 \qquad \text{for all other } t \end{aligned} \tag{20.30}$$

is the αth pulse of the pulse train reflected by the moving object, and $\Delta\vartheta$ is the extra phase difference between the pulses due to the motion. It is easy to show that

$$\Delta\vartheta = \zeta T, \tag{20.31}$$

where ζ is the frequency shift due to the Doppler effect (cf. Chap. 11).

The need for using different operations for different (and, in general, unknown) values of $\Delta\vartheta$, i.e., the need for implementing a "parallel combination" of coherent detectors, leads to great complications in designing the receiver.

21. The Urkowitz Filter

In Secs. 17, 18 and 20, we made a detailed study of optimum linear filters for detecting signals of known form and measuring their parameters in the presence of white noise. However, in some cases, one is interested in a different type of noise, with a spectral density which is not constant over the frequency band occupied by the signal. The most important example of this kind of noise is *clutter*, i.e., the noise produced when radar search signals are reflected by a large number of randomly located objects. A detailed examination of this kind of noise will be made in Chap. 11, and here we only mention those of its properties which are needed for the present discussion.

Noise of this type is produced by a multitude of scattering particles, e.g., raindrops, which are irregularly located in space and which, due to their large numbers, mask the useful signal reflected by the object we are trying to observe. As a first approximation to the actual situation, we assume that both the scattering particles and the object being observed are *fixed*, and that the radar signal consists of a sequence of incoherent pulses (or perhaps incoherent signals of some other kind). If the problem is stated in this way, then the useful signal differs from the noise only by being "concentrated" in time, since the reflecting object is located in a definite place, whereas the scattering particles are distributed (approximately uniformly) over a large volume surrounding the reflecting object. This physical difference can be exploited to increase the signal-to-noise ratio when the received combination of signal plus noise is "processed" for one repetition period.

Since each particle is the source of a reflected signal, and since all these signals are added incoherently because of the random (chaotic) positions of the particles, we can use formula (20.07) to calculate the power spectral density of the noise. The result is

$$S_n(\omega) = \sigma|M(\omega)|^2, \tag{21.01}$$

where $M(\omega)$ is the complex amplitude spectrum of a single pulse (i.e., during one repetition period). In this case, the transfer function of the optimum filter (16.14) equals

$$K(\omega) = \frac{c}{\sigma}\, e^{-i\omega t_0} \frac{M^*(\omega)}{|M(\omega)|^2}. \tag{21.02}$$

Choosing $c = \sigma$ and $t_0 = 0$ for simplicity, we obtain

$$K(\omega) = \frac{1}{M(\omega)}. \tag{21.03}$$

If we succeed in constructing a filter with the transfer function (21.03), then, according to (16.06), the useful signal at the output of the filter will be

$$\mu(t) = \frac{1}{2\pi}\int_{-\infty}^{\infty} e^{i\omega t}\, d\omega = \delta(t), \tag{21.04}$$

and, according to (16.15), the signal-to-noise ratio at the filter output will be

$$\rho = \frac{1}{2\pi\sigma}\int_{-\infty}^{\infty} d\omega = \infty. \tag{21.05}$$

The reason why we obtain an infinite value for ρ is that the transfer function (21.03) corresponds to an infinitely wide pass-band. In the first place, such a filter cannot be implemented in practice, and, in the second place, such a filter is very vulnerable to white noise, e.g., to the receiver noise itself.

Therefore, we now assume that the transfer function equals

$$\begin{aligned} K(\omega) &= \frac{1}{M(\omega)} \quad \text{for} \quad -\omega_0 - \Delta\omega < \omega < -\omega_0 + \Delta\omega \\ &\qquad\qquad \text{and} \quad \omega_0 - \Delta\omega < \omega < \omega_0 + \Delta\omega, \\ K(\omega) &= 0 \qquad\ \ \text{for all other } \omega, \end{aligned} \tag{21.06}$$

which defines a filter known as the *Urkowitz filter*. Then, the useful signal (16.06) at the filter output is given by the convergent integral

$$\mu(t) = \frac{1}{2\pi}\left(\int_{-\omega_0-\Delta\omega}^{-\omega_0+\Delta\omega} e^{i\omega t}\,d\omega + \int_{\omega_0-\Delta\omega}^{\omega_0+\Delta\omega} e^{i\omega t}\,d\omega\right) \tag{21.07}$$

or

$$\mu(t) = \frac{2}{\pi}\cos\omega_0 t\,\frac{\sin(t\,\Delta\omega)}{t}. \tag{21.08}$$

The maximum value of (21.08) is achieved for $t = 0$, and equals

$$\mu(0) = \frac{2\,\Delta\omega}{\pi}. \tag{21.09}$$

Formulas (21.04) and (21.08) show that the filters (21.03) and (21.06) "concentrate" the useful signal, by giving it a sharp peak at $t = 0$, whose height is proportional to $\Delta\omega$. The spectral density of the noise at the filter output is

$$S_\nu(\omega) = |K(\omega)|^2 S_n(\omega) = \sigma|K(\omega)M(\omega)|^2, \tag{21.10}$$

i.e.,

$$\begin{aligned} S_\nu(\omega) &= \sigma \quad \text{for} \quad -\omega_0 - \Delta\omega < \omega < -\omega_0 + \Delta\omega \\ &\qquad\quad \text{and} \quad \omega_0 - \Delta\omega < \omega < \omega_0 + \Delta\omega, \\ S_\nu(\omega) &= 0 \quad \text{for all other } \omega. \end{aligned} \tag{21.11}$$

Thus, the filter (21.06) "whitens" the noise, by converting it into a stationary random process with constant spectral density (within the filter pass-band). This white noise is obtained because each elementary signal returned by an individual scatterer, as well as the useful signal reflected from the object being observed, is converted into a pulse (21.08) of very short duration [in the limit into the delta function (21.04)], and the result of an aggregate of such randomly occurring pulses is just white noise (cf. Sec. 12).

We note that the matched filter considered earlier, with the transfer function (17.02), transforms noise in the opposite direction, i.e., it transforms white noise with the spectral density (17.01) into noise with the spectral density

$$S_\nu(\omega) = S_n|M(\omega)|^2. \tag{21.12}$$

This noise can be regarded as an aggregate of randomly occurring pulses with the same form as the useful signal itself at the filter input.

The noise power (16.08) at the output of the filter with the transfer function (21.06) equals

$$\overline{\nu^2} = \frac{2\sigma\,\Delta\omega}{\pi}, \tag{21.13}$$

so that formula (16.09) gives

$$\rho = \frac{2\,\Delta\omega}{\pi\sigma}. \tag{21.14}$$

It is instructive to compare this expression with the signal-to-noise ratio at the filter input. If the signal is the rectangular pulse (20.01), then, according to (20.01) and (20.10), we have

$$m(0) = A, \qquad \overline{n^2} = R_n(0) = \frac{\sigma A^2}{2} T_0, \tag{21.15}$$

so that

$$\rho_1 = \frac{m^2(0)}{\overline{n^2}} = \frac{2}{\sigma T_0} \tag{21.16}$$

and

$$\frac{\rho}{\rho_1} = \frac{T_0 \Delta\omega}{\pi}. \tag{21.17}$$

It would appear from (21.17) that the larger the product of the filter pass-band $\Delta\omega$ and the pulse duration T_0, the more effective the action of the filter defined by formula (21.06). However, it is clear from (21.14) and (21.15) that increasing the quantity T_0 by itself does not improve the detection of the signal in the presence of noise, since the noise power $\overline{n^2}$ itself is proportional to the pulse length T_0. Thus, it can only be said that detection of the signals becomes easier when the bandwidth $\Delta\omega$ is increased. Urkowitz' paper[5] discusses the practical implementation of filters with transfer functions close to (21.06).

We now compare the action of the Urkowitz filter (21.06) with that of the "rectangular" filter with the transfer function (17.23). If the condition (17.27) is met, then, according to formula (17.29), the maximum value of $\mu(t)$ is equal to

$$\mu(0) = \frac{2A}{\pi} \operatorname{si} X, \qquad X = \frac{T_0 \Delta\omega}{2}. \tag{21.18}$$

For larger values of $\Delta\omega$, the maximum value of $\mu(t)$ will somewhat exceed $\mu(0)$ and will be attained for a nonzero value of t, since then the envelope of the signal $\mu(t)$ becomes a function of t which is not monotone. If the rectangular transfer function of the filter is smoothed out somewhat, then this effect does not take place. Thus, in what follows, we shall neglect this effect, and, as before, we shall define the signal-to-noise ratio at the output of the rectangular filter by the formula

$$\rho = \frac{\mu^2(0)}{\overline{\nu^2}}, \tag{21.19}$$

[5] H. Urkowitz, *Filters for detection of small radar signals in clutter*, J. Appl. Phys., **24**, 1024 (1953).

where, according to (16.08) and (20.03),

$$\overline{\nu^2} = \frac{\sigma}{\pi}\int_{\omega_0-\Delta\omega}^{\omega_0+\Delta\omega} |M(\omega)|^2\, d\omega = \frac{\sigma A^2}{\pi}\int_{-\Delta\omega}^{\Delta\omega} \frac{\sin^2(\omega T_0/2)}{\omega^2}\, d\omega$$

or

$$\overline{\nu^2} = \frac{\sigma A^2 T_0}{\pi}\int_0^X \frac{\sin^2 x}{x^2}\, dx. \tag{21.20}$$

This last integral can be easily expressed in terms of the integral sine (17.33). In fact, integrating by parts, we obtain

$$\begin{aligned}\int_0^X \frac{\sin^2 x}{x^2}\, dx &= -\frac{\sin^2 x}{x}\Big|_0^X + \int_0^X \frac{2\sin x\cos x}{x}\, dx\\ &= -\frac{\sin^2 X}{X} + \int_0^X \frac{\sin 2x}{x}\, dx,\end{aligned} \tag{21.21}$$

so that

$$\overline{\nu^2} = \frac{\sigma A^2 T_0}{\pi}\left(\operatorname{si} 2X - \frac{\sin^2 X}{X}\right) \tag{21.22}$$

and

$$\rho = \frac{4}{\pi\sigma T_0}\,\frac{(\operatorname{si} X)^2}{\operatorname{si} 2X - (\sin^2 X/X)}. \tag{21.23}$$

Thus, finally, the action of the rectangular filter can be characterized by the ratio

$$\frac{\rho}{\rho_1} = \frac{2}{\pi}\,\frac{(\operatorname{si} X)^2}{\operatorname{si} 2X - (\sin^2 X/X)}, \tag{21.24}$$

where ρ_1 is the quantity (21.16). The ratio (21.24) is plotted in Fig. 24, from which it can be seen that up to $X \sim 3$, increasing the bandwidth leads to an increase in ρ/ρ_1, while for smaller X, the ratio ρ/ρ_1 increases almost linearly, as in formula (21.17).

If we let ρ_0 denote the quantity (21.14) corresponding to the Urkowitz filter (21.06) with the same bandwidth $\Delta\omega$, then we have

$$\frac{\rho}{\rho_0} = \frac{(\operatorname{si} X)^2}{X \operatorname{si} 2X - \sin^2 X}. \tag{21.25}$$

This ratio is plotted in Fig. 25, from which it can be seen that both filters are equally good for $X \lesssim 2$, and it is only for larger values of X (i.e., broad-band filters) that the advantage of the filter (21.06) appears.

The bandwidth $\Delta\omega$ which is attainable in practice is determined by the intensity of the white noise always present in radio receivers. If we let

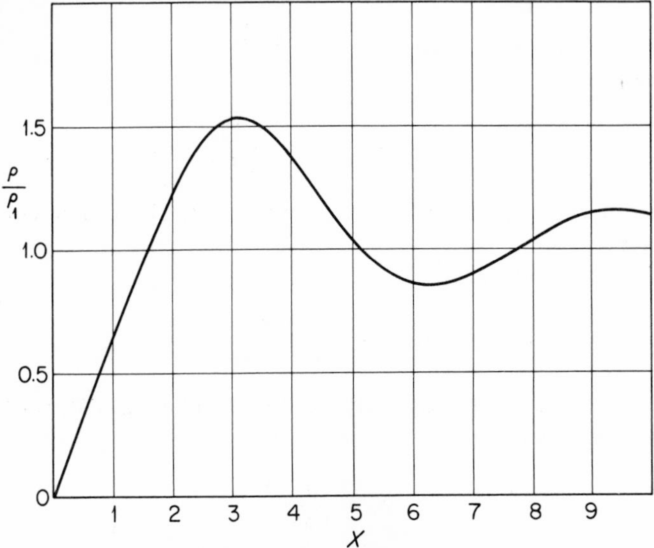

FIG. 24. Detection of a signal in a background of clutter by using a rectangular filter.

S_0 denote the constant (i.e., independent of frequency) spectral density of the white noise, then the total spectral density of the noise equals

$$S_n(\omega) = S_0 + \sigma|M(\omega)|^2, \tag{21.26}$$

so that, instead of formula (21.02), we have (setting $t_0 = 0$)

$$K(\omega) = c\,\frac{M^*(\omega)}{S_0 + \sigma|M(\omega)|^2}. \tag{21.27}$$

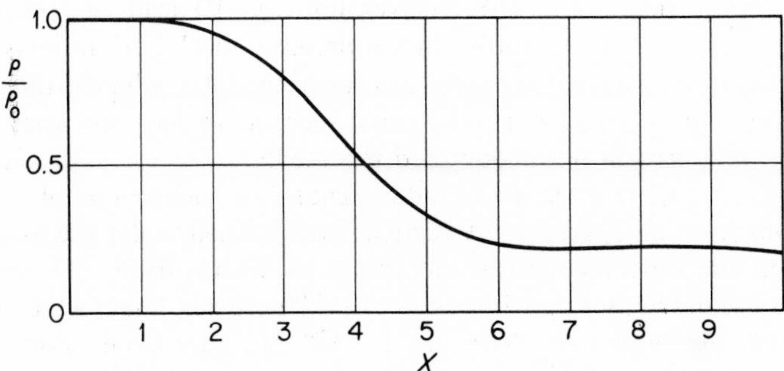

FIG. 25. Comparison of the rectangular filter with the Urkowitz filter.

If we use a rectangular pulse, then, according to formula (20.03),

$$M(\omega_0) \sim AT_0/2, \tag{21.28}$$

and if the ratio

$$\varepsilon = \frac{S_0}{\sigma|M(\omega_0)|^2} = \frac{4S_0}{\sigma A^2 T_0^2} \tag{21.29}$$

is sufficiently small, then for $\omega \sim \omega_0$, the filter (21.27) is quite close to the filter (21.06).

Because of the inequality

$$|M(\omega)|^2 \leqslant \frac{A^2}{(\omega - \omega_0)^2}, \tag{21.30}$$

the maximum value of the quantity $\Delta\omega$ for the filter (21.06) can be found from the requirement

$$S_0 = \frac{\sigma A^2}{(\Delta\omega)^2}, \tag{21.31}$$

since then, for $|\omega - \omega_0| > \Delta\omega$, the term $\sigma|M(\omega)|^2$ in the denominator will be less than the first term S_0 and the whole filter (21.27) will be closer to the matched filter (17.02) than to the Urkowitz filter (21.06). Formulas (21.29) and (21.31) give

$$\Delta\omega = \frac{2}{\sqrt{\varepsilon}T_0} \tag{21.32}$$

or

$$X_{\max} = \frac{1}{\sqrt{\varepsilon}}. \tag{21.33}$$

It should be noted that to a considerable extent, the noise due to clutter and the white noise (e.g., the receiver noise itself) lead to contradictory requirements. As shown above, in the presence of clutter, an increase in ρ is achieved by increasing the bandwidth $\Delta\omega$ of the filter, whereas the presence of the white noise prevents a substantial increase in $\Delta\omega$. In what follows, similar situations will be encountered repeatedly.

In this section, the detection of radar signals in a background of "chaotic" reflections from an aggregate of particles was studied under the assumption that both the observed object and the particles are fixed. However, the object is usually in motion with respect to the particles, a fact which presents additional possibilities for detecting it. On the other hand, motion of the scattering particles makes it more difficult to compensate for the noise (cf. Chaps. 6, 7 and 11).

22. Some General Remarks on Filters for Detecting Signals of Known Form

The theory of filters for detecting signals of known form, which was presented in this chapter, is based on two fundamental assumptions, (1) that the filter is linear, and (2) that the signal-to-noise ratio characterizes the quality of the filter's performance. This last criterion is quite customary from a practical point of view, but its relation to the visibility of the signal on indicators of various kinds is quite complicated. Thus, it is not entirely clear either from a theoretical or from a practical point of view what a given value of the signal-to-noise ratio ($\rho = 2$, say) means and in what respect it is quantitatively better than some other value ($\rho = 1$, say). In Part 2 of this book, which is devoted to the statistical theory of optimum receivers, we shall study the problem of detecting signals in a background of normal (Gaussian) noise from a more fundamental point of view, and we shall show how the quantity ρ is related quantitatively to the basic characteristics of the receiver performing the optimum detection, i.e., the probability of "false alarm" (of detecting a signal when none is present) and the probability of "false dismissal" (of failing to detect a signal when one is present).

It should be noted that the signal-to-noise ratio has direct probabilistic meaning only for linear transformations, and loses this meaning in the case of detection, for example. In particular, in the case of a single signal, both quadratic and linear detection of the sum of the signal plus the noise give the same probabilistic characteristics (see Chap. 5), whereas, according to Sec. 18, the output signal-to-noise ratios differ for these two kinds of detection.

The first assumption, concerning the linearity of the detecting filter, is quite a serious restriction, even in the case of normal processes. Filters which detect signals differ in this regard from filters which reproduce all the values of the useful signal (with minimum mean square error). Filters of the latter kind (cf. Sec. 7 and Chap. 8) are always linear, at least for normal processes, whereas detecting filters can be nonlinear as well. For the details, we refer the reader to Part 2. Here, we note only the following fact: The problem of detecting (i.e., deciding on the presence or the absence) of a useful signal, without reconstructing its values at different instants of time, can be posed not only for a signal which is a given known function of time, but also for a signal which is a random process or a random sequence. This problem requires a different approach, and it cannot be solved by using only linear filters (see Part 2).

In the next chapter, before beginning our presentation of optimum receivers, we shall study the theory of random sequences. In doing so, we shall discuss briefly those aspects of the theory of filtering of random sequences which were investigated in more detail for the case of random processes in the first three chapters.

4

RANDOM SEQUENCES

23. Filtering of Stationary Random Sequences

Together with the random processes considered in the first three chapters, we shall also be interested in *random sequences* (sequences of random variables). We shall denote the elements of a typical random sequence by $f(t)$, where t is a variable integer, i.e., $t = 0, 1, 2, \ldots$ or $t = \ldots, -2, -1, 0, 1, 2, \ldots$, which will be called the *time*, in order to give an intuitive idea of what is involved. Thus, in a random sequence $f(t)$, the time takes only discrete (integral) values. The variable t is essentially an index, and we could write f_t instead of $f(t)$. However, the notation $f(t)$ is more convenient, since we thereby achieve a certain uniformity, which makes it easier to carry over many concepts from the theory of random processes to the theory of random sequences.

Let $f(t)$ and $g(t)$ be two *stationary* random sequences, with zero mean values, so that

$$\overline{f(t)} = 0, \qquad \overline{g(t)} = 0. \tag{23.01}$$

We define their *cross-correlation function* by the formula

$$R_{fg}(\tau) = \overline{f(t)g(t - \tau)}, \tag{23.02}$$

and the *autocorrelation function* of $f(t)$, say, by the formula

$$R_f(\tau) = \overline{f(t)f(t - \tau)}. \tag{23.03}$$

These definitions differ from the corresponding definitions for random processes only in that the variables t and τ are now integers. The *stationarity* of the sequences consists of the fact that the correlation functions (23.02) and (23.03) do not depend on t.

The problem of filtering stationary random sequences can be stated as follows: Suppose we have an input sequence

$$f(t) = m(t) + n(t), \tag{23.04}$$

consisting of the useful signal $m(t)$ and the noise $n(t)$. Then, given the values of $f(t)$ at the H previous instants of time $t - H, t - H + 1, \ldots, t - 1$, it is required to determine $m(t + s)$ with the greatest possible accuracy. For $s \geqslant 0$, the filtering is accompanied by prediction (anticipation), while for $s = -1, -2, \ldots$, we have "pure" filtering.

In the general case, only the problem of *linear* filtering has been solved. In this problem, we look for the best expression of the form

$$\begin{aligned} x &= k_1 f(t-1) + k_2 f(t-2) + \cdots + k_H f(t-H) \\ &= \sum_{\tau=1}^{H} k_\tau f(t-\tau) \end{aligned} \tag{23.05}$$

for determining the quantity $x = x(t)$ which reproduces the quantity $m(t + s)$ with the smallest error. As before, we use the mean square error criterion. Thus, we introduce the error

$$\varepsilon = x - m(t+s) = \sum_{\tau} k_\tau f(t-\tau) - m(t+s), \tag{23.06}$$

and form its mean square

$$\begin{aligned} \overline{\varepsilon^2} &= \overline{m^2(t+s)} + \overline{x^2} - 2\overline{m(t+s)x} \\ &= \overline{m^2} + \sum_{\tau}\sum_{\sigma} k_\tau k_\sigma \overline{f(t-\tau)f(t-\sigma)} \\ &\quad - 2\sum_{\tau} k_\tau \overline{m(t+s)f(t-\tau)}. \end{aligned} \tag{23.07}$$

Using formulas (23.02) and (23.03), we can write

$$\begin{aligned} \overline{m^2} &= R_m(0), \\ \overline{f(t-\tau)f(t-\sigma)} &= R_f(t-\sigma), \\ \overline{m(t+s)f(t-\tau)} &= R_{mf}(\tau+s), \end{aligned} \tag{23.08}$$

so that the expression (23.07) becomes

$$E = R_m(0) + \sum_{\tau}\sum_{\sigma} k_\tau k_\sigma R_f(\tau - \sigma) - 2\sum_{\tau} k_\tau R_{mf}(\tau + s). \tag{23.09}$$

As in the case of random processes, optimum linear filtering corresponds to the minimum value of E. This minimum can be found by forming the partial derivatives $\partial E/\partial k_\tau$ and then equating them to zero. Thus, writing

$$\frac{\partial E}{\partial k_\tau} = 0 \qquad (\tau = 1, 2, \ldots, H), \tag{23.10}$$

we obtain the following system of linear algebraic equations for the coefficients k_τ:

$$\sum_{\sigma=1}^{H} k_\sigma R_f(\tau - \sigma) = R_{mf}(\tau + s) \qquad (\tau = 1, 2, \ldots, H). \tag{23.11}$$

In general, these equations uniquely determine the unknown coefficients k_τ, since the number of equations equals the number of unknowns. The system of algebraic equations (23.11) is analogous to the integral equation of the optimum linear filter (see Sec. 2) and its generalization (see Sec. 5), since the signal $h(t)$ being extracted is now

$$h(t) = m(t + s), \quad \text{i.e.,} \quad R_{hf}(\tau) = R_{mf}(\tau + s). \tag{23.12}$$

As in the theory of filters for random processes, the solution of the equations (23.11) actually gives a minimum for the mean square error (and not just an extremum); this can easily be proved in the same way as before.

If the coefficients k_τ have the values given by the equations (23.11), then the mean square filtering error becomes

$$\overline{\varepsilon^2} = R_m(0) - \sum_\tau \sum_\sigma k_\tau k_\sigma R_f(\tau - \sigma) \tag{23.13}$$

or

$$\overline{\varepsilon^2} = \overline{m^2} - \overline{x^2}. \tag{23.14}$$

The relations just obtained for linear filtering of stationary sequences are of a more elementary character than the corresponding relations for filtering of stationary processes. They involve sums and algebraic equations instead of the integrals and integral equations obtained before. However, as far as calculations are concerned, the situation is not so simple, since for large H ($H > 4$, say), the numerical solution of the equations (23.11) is a rather tedious problem, which rapidly becomes more complicated as H increases.

To form a general idea of the possibilities of linear filtering, we now assume that the random sequence $f(t)$ is completely known, i.e., that $f(t)$ is known for the values

$$t = \ldots, -2, -1, 0, 1, 2, \ldots, \tag{23.15}$$

and we look for the filtering formula

$$x(t) = \sum_{\tau=-\infty}^{\infty} k_\tau f(t - \tau), \tag{23.16}$$

which reproduces the value $m(t)$ with the least error. In the case of random processes, this statement of the problem leads to a determination of the filter of type I which gives the least mean square error (among all such filters). Here, we are again led to the same kind of optimum filtering, where we now make use of a sequence $f(t)$ which is infinite in both directions.

In the present case, the equations (23.11) become

$$\sum_{\sigma=-\infty}^{\infty} k_\sigma R_f(\tau - \sigma) = R_{mf}(\tau) \qquad (\tau = -2, -1, 0, 1, 2, \ldots), \quad (23.17)$$

and their solution can be obtained in closed form. Thus, we multiply each of the equations (23.17) by $e^{-i\omega t}$ and sum the result over all τ, obtaining

$$\sum_{\tau=-\infty}^{\infty} e^{-i\omega\tau} \sum_{\sigma=-\infty}^{\infty} k_\sigma R_f(\tau - \sigma) = \sum_{\tau=-\infty}^{\infty} e^{-i\omega\tau} R_{mf}(\tau). \qquad (23.18)$$

The left-hand side of (23.18) can be transformed as follows:

$$\begin{aligned} \sum_\tau e^{-i\omega\tau} \sum_\sigma k_\sigma R_f(\tau - \sigma) &= \sum_\sigma k_\sigma \sum_\tau e^{-i\omega\tau} R_f(\tau - \sigma) \\ &= \sum_\sigma e^{-i\omega\sigma} k_\sigma \sum_\tau e^{-i\omega\tau} R_f(\tau). \qquad (23.19) \end{aligned}$$

Then, as in Sec. 2, we introduce the quantities

$$\begin{aligned} S_f(\omega) &= \sum_{\tau=-\infty}^{\infty} e^{-i\omega\tau} R_f(\tau), \\ S_{mf}(\omega) &= \sum_{\tau=-\infty}^{\infty} e^{-i\omega\tau} R_{mf}(\tau), \end{aligned} \qquad (23.20)$$

and also the quantity

$$K(\omega) = \sum_{\tau=-\infty}^{\infty} e^{-i\omega\tau} k_\tau. \qquad (23.21)$$

Using this notation, we can write equation (23.18) in the form

$$K(\omega) S_f(\omega) = S_{mf}(\omega), \qquad (23.22)$$

from which it follows that

$$K(\omega) = \frac{S_{mf}(\omega)}{S_f(\omega)}. \qquad (23.23)$$

From a knowledge of $K(\omega)$, we can easily find the coefficients k_τ appearing in (23.16). In fact, (23.21) is essentially a Fourier series in complex form.

If we multiply both sides of (23.21) by $e^{i\omega\tau}$ and then integrate from $-\pi$ to π (or over any other interval of length 2π), we obtain

$$k_\tau = \frac{1}{2\pi}\int_{-\pi}^{\pi} e^{i\omega\tau}K(\omega)\,d\omega. \tag{23.24}$$

In the same way, we can "invert" the formulas (23.20), obtaining

$$\begin{aligned} R_f(\tau) &= \frac{1}{2\pi}\int_{-\pi}^{\pi} e^{i\omega\tau}S_f(\omega)\,d\omega, \\ R_{mf}(\tau) &= \frac{1}{2\pi}\int_{-\pi}^{\pi} e^{i\omega\tau}S_{mf}(\omega)\,d\omega. \end{aligned} \tag{23.25}$$

To calculate the mean square filtering error, we first observe that

$$\begin{aligned} \sum_\tau\sum_\sigma k_\tau k_\sigma R_f(\tau-\sigma) &= \frac{1}{2\pi}\sum_\tau\sum_\sigma k_\tau k_\sigma \int_{-\pi}^{\pi} e^{i\omega(\tau-\sigma)}S_f(\omega)\,d\omega \\ &= \frac{1}{2\pi}\int_{-\pi}^{\pi} S_f(\omega)\,d\omega \sum_\tau\sum_\sigma k_\tau k_\sigma\, e^{i\omega(\tau-\sigma)} \\ &= \frac{1}{2\pi}\int_{-\pi}^{\pi} S_f(\omega)\,d\omega \sum_\tau e^{i\omega\tau}k_\tau \sum_\sigma e^{-i\omega\sigma}k_\sigma \\ &= \frac{1}{2\pi}\int_{-\pi}^{\pi} K(\omega)K(-\omega)S_f(\omega)\,d\omega \\ &= \frac{1}{2\pi}\int_{-\pi}^{\pi} |K(\omega)|^2 S_f(\omega)\,d\omega, \end{aligned} \tag{23.26}$$

since

$$K(-\omega) = K^*(\omega), \tag{23.27}$$

because of the reality of the coefficients k_τ in formula (23.21). Then, we write the expression (23.13) in the form

$$\overline{\varepsilon^2} = \frac{1}{2\pi}\int_{-\pi}^{\pi} [S_m(\omega) - |K(\omega)|^2 S_f(\omega)]\,d\omega, \tag{23.28}$$

which resembles the expression (2.31). Here, of course,

$$S_m(\omega) = \sum_{\tau=-\infty}^{\infty} e^{-i\omega\tau}R_m(\tau).$$

Substituting (23.23) into (23.28), we obtain

$$\overline{\varepsilon^2} = \frac{1}{2\pi}\int_{-\pi}^{\pi} \frac{S_m(\omega)S_f(\omega) - |S_{mf}(\omega)|^2}{S_f(\omega)}\,d\omega. \tag{23.29}$$

If the useful signal and the noise are statistically independent (or even just uncorrelated), then

$$S_{mf}(\omega) = S_m(\omega), \qquad S_f(\omega) = S_m(\omega) + S_n(\omega), \tag{23.30}$$

and we arrive at the formulas

$$K(\omega) = \frac{S_m(\omega)}{S_m(\omega) + S_n(\omega)} \tag{23.31}$$

and

$$\overline{\varepsilon^2} = \frac{1}{2\pi}\int_{-\pi}^{\pi} \frac{S_m(\omega)S_n(\omega)}{S_m(\omega) + S_n(\omega)}\, d\omega. \tag{23.32}$$

In the next section, we shall examine in some detail the physical meaning of these formulas, which is the same as that of the corresponding formulas of Sec. 2.

24. Khinchin's Theorem for Sequences. Some Remarks on Filtering of Sequences

Guided by the analogy between random sequences and random processes, it is natural to regard the function $S_f(\omega)$ defined by the first of the formulas (23.20) as the (*power*) *spectral density* of the random sequence $f(t)$. Moreover, comparing formulas (2.18) and (2.19) with formulas (23.21) and (23.24), it is natural to call the function $K(\omega)$ the (*complex*) *transfer function*, or *system function*, of the filter whose action is described by (23.05) or (23.16). This last designation can be justified as follows: In formula (23.16), choose the input sequence $f(t)$ to be

$$f(t) = f_\omega e^{i\omega t}. \tag{24.01}$$

Then the sequence $x(t)$ at the output of the linear filter is given by the formulas

$$x(t) = x_\omega e^{i\omega t}, \qquad x_\omega = K(\omega) f_\omega, \tag{24.02}$$

where $K(\omega)$ is given by formula (23.21). This makes it clear that the function $K(\omega)$ is a transfer function, of the kind customarily used in radio engineering (cf. Sec. 2); moreover, the variable ω is obviously a (dimensionless) angular frequency.

As an example, consider the filter whose action is described by the formula

$$x(t) = f(t) - f(t-1). \tag{24.03}$$

Comparing (24.03) with (23.16), we see that

$$k_0 = 1, \qquad k_1 = -1, \tag{24.04}$$

while all other $k_\tau = 0$. Therefore, according to formula (23.21), we have

$$K(\omega) = 1 - e^{-i\omega} = 2ie^{-i\omega/2} \sin\frac{\omega}{2}. \tag{24.05}$$

Returning to the function $S_f(\omega)$, we note that in view of the relation

$$R_f(0) = \overline{f^2(t)} = \frac{1}{2\pi}\int_{-\pi}^{\pi} S_f(\omega)\, d\omega, \tag{24.06}$$

which follows from the first of the formulas (23.25), it is natural to regard the quantity

$$\frac{1}{2\pi} S_f(\omega)\, d\omega$$

as the average power (or intensity) of the random sequence lying in the angular frequency range $(\omega, \omega + d\omega)$. Thus, $S_f(\omega)$ itself can be regarded as the average power in a unit frequency band, i.e., the power spectral density (cf. the beginning of Sec. 3). This statement is easily proved by passing the given sequence through a narrow-band filter; since the proof is completely analogous to that given for random processes in Sec. 3, it will not be repeated here.

In this way, we generalize Khinchin's theorem to the case of random sequences. The spectral density of a random sequence differs from the spectral density of a random process by being periodic (with period 2π), as implied by (23.20). This property is shared by the transfer function of any linear filter acting on sequences, since

$$K(\omega + 2\pi r) = K(\omega), \qquad (r = \pm 1, \pm 2, \ldots), \tag{24.07}$$

according to formula (23.21). The periodicity of the functions $K(\omega)$ and $S_f(\omega)$ is explained by the fact that when ω is replaced by $\omega + 2\pi$, the elements of the input and output sequences (24.01) and (24.02) do not change. It follows from the interpretation of $S_f(\omega)\, d\omega$ as power that

$$S_f(\omega) \geqslant 0, \tag{24.08}$$

which imposes certain restrictions on the numbers $R_f(\tau)$. Unlike the case of the autocorrelation function, the spectral density corresponding to a cross-correlation function does not have a clear-cut interpretation as a "power density" (cf. Sec. 3).

We now consider some simple examples of random sequences. If the elements of the sequence are uncorrelated, then

$$R_f(\tau) = 0 \qquad (\tau = \pm 1, \pm 2, \ldots), \tag{24.09}$$

and such a sequence has the spectral density

$$S_f(\omega) = R_f(0) = \text{const.} \tag{24.10}$$

This is the analog of the "absolutely random process" or "white noise" of Sec. 12, which also has constant spectral density. Any correlation between elements of the sequence leads to a nonuniform spectral density. For example, if

$$R_f(\tau) = Ca^{|\tau|} \qquad (|a| < 1), \tag{24.11}$$

we obtain

$$S_f(\omega) = C\frac{1 - a^2}{|e^{i\omega} - a|^2}, \tag{24.12}$$

and as $a \to 0$, we return to formulas (24.09) and (24.10).

The use of formula (23.31) to filter stationary sequences is tantamount to separating the signal from the noise in the frequency domain (cf. Sec. 2). As formula (23.32) shows, separation without error is possible if the spectra of the useful signal and of the noise do not overlap, i.e., if

$$S_m(\omega)S_n(\omega) = 0, \tag{24.13}$$

where it is assumed that there is no cross correlation between the signal and the noise. However, if the spectra overlap, then filtering is always accompanied by an error, even if we use all the elements of the sequence $f(t)$ from $t = -\infty$ to $t = \infty$. If we use only some of these elements in carrying out the filtering, then the error will be even greater (or, in any event, not less).

As far as the application of the theory of filtering of sequences is concerned, it is above all clear that stationary processes and stationary sequences are very closely related. This is apparent not only from the analogy between the corresponding formulas, but also from Kotelnikov's theorem (Sec. 19), according to which a band-limited random process is completely determined by its sample values taken at times lying Δt apart.

Above, we studied the problem of the optimum filter whose operation is described by formula (23.05), i.e., the filter which combines H elements of a sequence in such a way as to suppress the noise and strengthen the useful signal in comparison to the noise. The calculations involved in formula (23.05) can be made either by hand or by using a computing machine. In either case, it is meaningful to speak of the transfer function of the device which performs the operations described by (23.05).

So far, we have discussed the problem of reproducing an element of the random sequence $m(t)$ with the minimum error. Generally speaking, this statement of the problem is natural in the context of communication theory, where the useful signal $m(t)$ carries an unknown message. However, it is sometimes sufficient just to *detect* the sequence $m(t)$ (i.e., to decide whether it is present or absent "as a whole") or to *measure* some of its parameters. In the theory of random processes, this statement of the problem leads to filters for signals of known form (see Chap. 3). In the next section, we shall consider the analogous problem for sequences.

25. Filters for Detecting Sequences of Known Form

We now discuss the problem of detecting a known sequence $m(t)$ in the presence of background noise $n(t)$. We shall also consider the case where the "form" of the sequence $m(t)$ is known, but where its time of occurrence τ and its amplitude G are unknown. In this case, we have

$$m(t) = Gm_0(t - \tau), \tag{25.01}$$

where the sequence $m_0(t)$ is completely known. (For example, we might have $m_0(t) = 1$ for $t = 1, 2, \ldots, 7$, and $m_0(t) = 0$ for all other t.) Linear filtering of the input sequence

$$f(t) = m(t) + n(t) \tag{25.02}$$

gives the output sequence

$$\varphi(t) = \sum_\sigma k_\sigma f(t - \sigma) = \mu(t) + \nu(t), \tag{25.03}$$

consisting of the useful signal

$$\mu(t) = \sum_\sigma k_\sigma m(t - \sigma) \tag{25.04}$$

and the noise

$$\nu(t) = \sum_\sigma k_\sigma n(t - \sigma). \tag{25.05}$$

By arguing as in Sec. 16, it is not hard to derive the formulas

$$\mu(t) = \frac{1}{2\pi}\int_{-\pi}^{\pi} e^{i\omega t}K(\omega)M(\omega)\,d\omega, \qquad M(\omega) = \sum_t e^{-i\omega t}m(t), \tag{25.06}$$

where $M(\omega)$ is the amplitude spectrum of the useful signal, and

$$\overline{\nu^2} = \frac{1}{2\pi}\int_{-\pi}^{\pi} |K(\omega)|^2 S_n(\omega)\,d\omega \tag{25.07}$$

is the noise power at the filter output. If we maximize the quantity

$$\rho = \frac{\mu^2(t_0)}{\overline{\nu^2}}, \tag{25.08}$$

equal to the signal-to-noise ratio at the filter output at time t_0, we arrive at the transfer function

$$K(\omega) = ce^{-i\omega t_0}\frac{M^*(\omega)}{S_n(\omega)}, \tag{25.09}$$

analogous to formula (16.14). If the sequence has the special form (25.01), then instead, we obtain the expression

$$K(\omega) = ce^{-i\omega t_0}\frac{M_0^*(\omega)}{S_n(\omega)}, \tag{25.10}$$

analogous to formula (16.25), where $M_0(\omega)$ is formed from $m_0(t)$ in the same way that $M(\omega)$ is formed from $m(t)$, namely, by using the second of the formulas (25.06).

If the noise is white, i.e., if its spectral density can be considered uniform, so that

$$S_n(\omega) = S_n = \text{const}, \tag{25.11}$$

then, for $c = S_n$, formula (25.09) gives the following expression for the transfer function of the "matched filter for sequences":

$$K(\omega) = e^{-i\omega t_0} M^*(\omega). \tag{25.12}$$

Substituting this expression into formula (23.24), we obtain

$$k_\sigma = m(t_0 - \sigma), \tag{25.13}$$

so that the formula for the matched filter becomes

$$\begin{aligned} \varphi(t) &= \sum_\sigma m(t_0 - \sigma) f(t - \sigma), \\ \mu(t) &= \sum_\sigma m(t_0 - \sigma) m(t - \sigma). \end{aligned} \tag{25.14}$$

If we now define the correlation function $R_m(\tau)$ for a sequence $m(t)$ of finite length by the formula

$$R_m(\tau) = \sum_{t=-\infty}^{\infty} m(t) m(t - \tau), \tag{25.15}$$

then the second of the formulas (25.14) becomes

$$\mu(t) = R_m(t_0 - t). \tag{25.16}$$

In particular, we have

$$\mu(t_0) = R_m(0) = \sum_{t=-\infty}^{\infty} m^2(t). \tag{25.17}$$

Thus, the signal-to-noise ratio at the output of the matched filter is equal to

$$\rho = \frac{E}{S_n}, \qquad E = \sum_{t=-\infty}^{\infty} m^2(t), \tag{25.18}$$

in complete analogy with the corresponding results of Chap. 3.

26. Filtering of Sequences and Processes, I

In the study just made of the problem of filtering random sequences, the notation was chosen in such a way as to emphasize the far-reaching analogy between sequences and continuous processes. However, in the theory of optimum receivers (see Part 2), it is more convenient to use a somewhat different notation, which will be presented in this and the next section. In order to simplify matters in Part 2, we shall confine ourselves for the most part to the case of sequences, since the transition to the case of continuous processes is as a rule quite simple. Since the optimum receivers studied in Part 2 often include (as essential circuit components) optimum linear filters like those studied in Part 1, it is appropriate to cast the theory of these filters in a form which is suitable for comparison with the theory of optimum receivers.

Thus, suppose we know the values

$$f_1, f_2, \ldots, f_H \tag{26.01}$$

of a random sequence, whose elements f_h are equal to the sum of elements m_h (the useful signal) and elements n_h (the noise):

$$f_h = m_h + n_h \qquad (h = 1, 2, \ldots, H). \tag{26.02}$$

Let the quantities n_h form a random sequence, with the first and second moments

$$\overline{n_h} = 0, \qquad \overline{n_g n_h} = R^n_{gh} \qquad (g, h = 1, 2, \ldots, H). \tag{26.03}$$

Then, the properties of the noise are specified by a symmetric matrix $\|R^n_{gh}\|$, of order H.

Different properties now arise, depending on the properties of the sequence m_h. If the quantities m_h are also random, with known moments

$$\overline{m_h} = 0, \qquad \overline{m_g m_h} = R^n_{gh} \qquad (g, h = 1, 2, \ldots, H), \tag{26.04}$$

then we can pose the problem of optimum restoration (or extraction) of the quantities m_h from their mixture with noise, given by (26.02). Confining ourselves to linear operations on the given numbers f_h, we look for the coefficients k_{gh} in the formula

$$x_g = \sum_h k_{gh} f_h \tag{26.05}$$

which lead to a minimum of the mean square error

$$\overline{\varepsilon_g^2} = \overline{(x_g - m_g)^2} = \sum_h \sum_j k_{gh} k_{gj} \overline{f_h f_j} - 2 \sum_h k_{gh} \overline{m_g f_h} + \overline{m_g^2}. \tag{26.06}$$

If, in addition to (26.03) and (26.04), we introduce the notation

$$R^f_{gh} = \overline{f_g f_h}, \qquad R^{mf}_{gh} = \overline{m_g f_h}, \tag{26.07}$$

then the mean square error (26.06) equals

$$\overline{\varepsilon_g^2} = \sum_h \sum_j k_{gh} k_{gj} R^f_{hj} - 2 \sum_h k_{gh} R^{mf}_{gh} + R^m_{gg}. \tag{26.08}$$

The conditions for a minimum are

$$\frac{\partial}{\partial k_{gh}} \overline{\varepsilon_g^2} = 0, \tag{26.09}$$

and lead to the equations

$$\sum_j k_{gj} R^f_{hj} = R^{mf}_{gh}, \tag{26.10}$$

which permit us, at least in principle, to determine the required coefficients k_{gh}. In fact, if we let Q^f_{gh} denote the elements of the matrix which is the inverse of $\|R^f_{gh}\|$, i.e., if the quantities Q^f_{gh} satisfy the equations

$$\sum R^f_{gj} Q^f_{jh} = \delta_{gh}, \tag{26.11}$$

where δ_{gh} is the Kronecker delta ($\delta_{gg} = 1$, $\delta_{gh} = 0$ if $g \neq h$), then the required quantities k_{gh} are equal to

$$k_{gh} = \sum_j R^{mf}_{gj} Q^f_{jh}. \tag{26.12}$$

In what follows, we shall assume for simplicity that there is no cross correlation between the sequences $m_1, m_2, \ldots, m_H$ and $n_1, n_2, \ldots, n_H$, i.e., that

$$\overline{m_g n_h} = 0 \qquad (g, h = 1, 2, \ldots, H). \tag{26.13}$$

Then, the expressions (26.07) become

$$R^f_{gh} = R^m_{gh} + R^n_{gh}, \qquad R^{mf}_{gh} = R^m_{gh}, \tag{26.14}$$

and formula (26.12) can be written in the form

$$k_{gh} = \sum_j R^m_{gj} Q^f_{jh} = \delta_{gh} - \sum_j R^n_{gj} Q^f_{jh}. \tag{26.15}$$

Moreover, the equations (26.10) themselves can be rewritten as

$$k_{gh} + \sum_{j,l} k_{gj} R^n_{lj} Q^m_{lh} = \delta_{gh} \tag{26.16}$$

or

$$k_{gh} + \sum_{j,l} k_{gj} R^m_{lj} Q^n_{lh} = \sum_j R^m_{gj} Q^n_{jh}, \tag{26.17}$$

where we have used the first of the formulas (26.14), and where $\|Q^m_{gh}\|$, $\|Q^n_{gh}\|$ denote the inverses of the matrices $\|R^m_{gh}\|$, $\|R^n_{gh}\|$, respectively. Finally, because of (26.10), the mean square error with the optimum coefficients k_{gh} equals

$$\overline{\varepsilon_g^2} = R^m_{gg} - \sum_{h,j} k_{gh} k_{gj} R^f_{hj}. \tag{26.18}$$

We now consider another case, where the sequence $m_1, m_2, \ldots, m_H$ is completely known, but where it may either be present or absent in the sequence $f_1, f_2, \ldots, f_H$. If $m_1, m_2, \ldots, m_H$ is absent, then the quantities $f_1, f_2, \ldots, f_H$ reduce to pure noise, i.e., instead of (26.02), we have

$$f_h = n_h \qquad (h = 1, 2, \ldots, H). \tag{26.19}$$

In this case, we look for coefficients k_h which are such that when the quantity

$$\varphi = \sum_h k_h f_h \tag{26.20}$$

is formed, we obtain the largest signal-to-noise ratio ρ, defined by the formula

$$\rho = \frac{\mu^2}{\overline{\nu^2}}. \tag{26.21}$$

The quantity ρ characterizes our degree of certainty in having detected the useful sequence $m_1, m_2, \ldots, m_H$ in the background noise. Here, we have

$$\varphi = \mu + \nu, \qquad \mu = \sum_h k_h m_h, \qquad \nu = \sum_h k_h n_h \tag{26.22}$$

and

$$\overline{\nu^2} = \sum_{g,h} k_g k_h R^n_{gh}. \tag{26.23}$$

The conditions for a maximum

$$\frac{\partial \rho}{\partial k_g} = 0 \qquad (g = 1, 2, \ldots, H) \tag{26.24}$$

lead to the system of equations

$$\sum_h k_h R^n_{gh} = c m_g \tag{26.25}$$

for the unknown coefficients k_h, where c is an arbitrary constant. Again using the inverse matrix $\| Q^n_{gh} \|$, we obtain

$$k_g = c \sum_h m_h Q^n_{gh}. \tag{26.26}$$

Next, suppose that instead of one sequence $m_1, m_2, \ldots, m_H$ in the input sequence (26.02), there can occur one of P sequences $m_{1p}, m_{2p}, \ldots, m_{Hp}$ $(p = 1, 2, \ldots, P)$, and suppose that we have to decide which of the P sequences actually occurs. Then, it is natural to form the P quantities

$$\varphi_p = \sum_h k_{ph} f_h \qquad (p = 1, 2, \ldots, P), \tag{26.27}$$

and look for coefficients k_{ph} such that the P parameters

$$\rho_p = \frac{\mu_p^2}{\overline{\nu_p^2}} \qquad \left(\mu_p = \sum_h k_{ph} m_{hp}, \quad \nu_p = \sum_h k_{ph} n_h\right) \tag{26.28}$$

all take their maximum values. This leads to the equations

$$\sum_h k_{ph} R^n_{gh} = c m_{gp} \qquad (p = 1, 2, \ldots, P), \tag{26.29}$$

which are not essentially different from the equations (26.25). (The same sort of relations are obtained if the useful signal appears with an unknown amplitude G, i.e., in the form of a sequence $Gm_{1p}, Gm_{2p}, \ldots, Gm_{Hp}$.) The solution of the equations (26.25) can be written in the form

$$k_{pg} = c \sum_h m_{hp} Q^n_{gh}. \tag{26.30}$$

If the sequence (26.01) is given at the times

$$t_h = t_1 + (h - 1)\,\Delta t, \qquad (h = 1, 2, \ldots, H), \tag{26.31}$$

so that

$$f_h = f(t_h), \qquad m_h = m(t_h), \qquad n_h = n(t_h), \tag{26.32}$$

then the correlation functions can be written as follows:

$$R^f_{gh} = R_f(t_g, t_h), \qquad R^m_{gh} = R_m(t_g, t_h), \qquad R^n_{gh} = R_n(t_g, t_h). \tag{26.33}$$

However, in this case, it is convenient to write the coefficients k_{gh} appearing in (26.05) in the form

$$k_{gh} = k(t_g, t_h)\,\Delta t, \tag{26.34}$$

so that (26.05) and (26.10) become

$$\begin{gathered} x(t_g) = \Delta t \sum_h k(t_g, t_h) f(t_h), \\ \Delta t \sum_j k(t_g, t_j) R_f(t_j, t_h) = R_m(t_g, t_h). \end{gathered} \tag{26.35}$$

Using these formulas, we can easily make the transition from sequences to processes, which are functions of a continuous parameter t (the time). In fact, we need only replace sums by integrals, obtaining

$$\begin{gathered} x(t) = \int_{t_1}^{t_1+T} k(t, t') f(t')\, dt', \\ \int_{t_1}^{t_1+T} k(t, s) R_f(s, t')\, ds = R_m(t, t'), \end{gathered} \tag{26.36}$$

where

$$T = (H - 1)\,\Delta t \tag{26.37}$$

is the time interval during which the function $f(t)$ is specified. If all the processes are stationary, then

$$R_m(t, t') = R_m(t - t'), \qquad R_f(t, t') = R_f(t - t'). \tag{26.38}$$

Hence, we can assume that

$$k(t, t') = k(t - t'), \tag{26.39}$$

and then the formulas (26.36) resemble certain formulas of Chap. 1.

In the case where the useful signal is completely known, we set

$$k_h = k(t_0 - t_h)\,\Delta t, \tag{26.40}$$

where t_0 is an arbitrary element of the sequence (26.31). Then, formulas (26.20) and (26.25) take the form

$$\begin{gathered}\varphi = \Delta t \sum_h k(t_0 - t_h) f(t_h),\\ \Delta t \sum_h k(t_0 - t_h) R_n(t_g, t_h) = cm(t_g),\end{gathered} \tag{26.41}$$

and for continuous processes we have

$$\begin{gathered}\varphi(t) = \int_{t_1}^{t_1+T} k(t_0 - t) f(t)\, dt,\\ \int_{t_1}^{t_1+T} k(t_0 - t') R_n(t, t')\, dt' = cm(t).\end{gathered} \tag{26.42}$$

The last equation is an integral equation for the unknown function $k(t)$. In the case where the noise $n(t)$ is a stationary random process, we have

$$R_n(t, t') = R_n(t - t'), \tag{26.43}$$

and the kernel of the integral equation is an even function of the difference $t - t'$.

Finally, confining ourselves to the case of stationary noise, we consider the detection of a useful signal of the form

$$m(t_h) = Gm_0(t_h - p\,\Delta t), \tag{26.44}$$

with unknown amplitude G and unknown time of occurrence. In this case, instead of (26.41), we have

$$\begin{gathered}\varphi(t_g) = \Delta t \sum_h k(t_g - t_h) f(t_h),\\ \Delta t \sum_h k(t_0 - t_h) R_n(t_g - t_h) = cm_0(t_g),\end{gathered} \tag{26.45}$$

or, for continuous processes,

$$\begin{gathered}\varphi(t) = \int_{t_1}^{t_1+T} k(t - t') f(t')\, dt',\\ \int_{t_1}^{t_1+T} k(t_0 - t') R_n(t - t')\, dt' = cm_0(t).\end{gathered} \tag{26.46}$$

The representation of all these operations in the frequency domain will be systematized in the next section.

27. Filtering of Sequences and Processes, II

In problems of filtering, relations in the frequency domain are of great importance, i.e., relations between power spectral densities (or amplitude spectra) and the transfer functions of appropriate filters (cf. Secs. 2, 16, 23 and 25). Such relations can be found if the corresponding random processes or random sequences are stationary.

We begin with the case of random sequences. If the correlation function $R_f(t_g, t_h)$ [cf. formula (26.33)] is an even function of the difference $t_g - t_h$, so that

$$R_f(t_g, t_h) = R_f(t_g - t_h) = R_f(|g - h|\,\Delta t), \tag{27.01}$$

then we can define the spectral density $S_f(\omega)$ by the formula

$$S_f(\omega) = \Delta t \sum_{h=-\infty}^{\infty} e^{-i\omega h\,\Delta t} R_f(h\,\Delta t), \tag{27.02}$$

with the inversion

$$R_f(h\,\Delta t) = \frac{1}{2\pi}\int_{-\pi/\Delta t}^{\pi/\Delta t} e^{i\omega h\,\Delta t} S_f(\omega)\,d\omega. \tag{27.03}$$

This last formula is easily derived by generalizing the considerations of Sec. 24.

In a similar way, we can introduce the transfer function of a filter for which the function $k(t_g, t_h)$ [cf. formula (26.39)] satisfies the relation

$$k(t_g, t_h) = k(t_g - t_h) = k[(g - h)\,\Delta t], \tag{27.04}$$

i.e., we define the (complex) transfer function of this filter as

$$K(\omega) = \Delta t \sum_{h=-\infty}^{\infty} e^{-i\omega h\,\Delta t} k(h\,\Delta t), \tag{27.05}$$

where

$$k(h\,\Delta t) = \frac{1}{2\pi}\int_{-\pi/\Delta t}^{\pi/\Delta t} e^{i\omega h\,\Delta t} K(\omega)\,d\omega. \tag{27.06}$$

According to Sec. 23, the transfer function of the optimum linear filter of type I which reproduces the elements of the stationary random sequence m_h by using the elements of the infinite sequence f_h is equal to

$$K(\omega) = \frac{S_m(\omega)}{S_m(\omega) + S_n(\omega)}, \tag{27.07}$$

where $S_m(\omega)$ is the spectral density of the useful sequence and $S_n(\omega)$ is the spectral density of the noise. In deriving this formula, it is assumed that there is no correlation between the noise and the useful signal. Then, the mean square filtering error equals

$$\overline{\varepsilon^2} = \frac{1}{2\pi}\int_{-\pi/\Delta t}^{\pi/\Delta t} \frac{S_m(\omega)S_n(\omega)}{S_m(\omega) + S_n(\omega)}\,d\omega. \tag{27.08}$$

For filters of types II and III, we obtain more complicated formulas, with mean square errors which are larger (or, in exceptional cases, remain constant).

The transition to continuous processes is obtained by letting $\Delta t \to 0$ and writing $\tau = h\,\Delta t$. Then, the series (27.02) and (27.05) become integrals, and in formulas (27.03), (27.06) and (27.08), the range of integration goes from $-\infty$ to ∞. The corresponding expressions are given in Chap. 1.

In considering the problem of detecting the sequence (26.44) in a background of random noise, we arrived at the equation

$$\Delta t \sum_h k(t_0 - t_h) R_n(|g - h|\,\Delta t) = c m_0(t_g), \tag{27.09}$$

where $R_n(\tau) = R_n(-\tau)$ is the correlation function of the noise. If we assume that we have at our disposal a sequence $f_h = f(t_h)$ which goes to infinity in both directions, then the sum in (27.09) goes from $-\infty$ to ∞. Then, according to Sec. 25, we obtain the transfer function

$$K(\omega) = c e^{-i\omega t_0} \frac{M_0^*(\omega)}{S_n(\omega)}, \tag{27.10}$$

where

$$\begin{aligned} M_0(\omega) &= \Delta t \sum_h e^{-i\omega t_h} m_0(t_h), \\ S_n(\omega) &= \Delta t \sum_h e^{-i\omega h\,\Delta t} R_n(h\,\Delta t), \end{aligned} \tag{27.11}$$

and t_0 is an arbitrary element of the sequence (26.31). In the frequency domain, the signal-to-noise ratio is given by

$$\rho = \frac{G^2}{2\pi} \int_{-\pi/\Delta t}^{\pi/\Delta t} \frac{|M_0(\omega)|^2}{S_n(\omega)}\, d\omega \tag{27.12}$$

for a fixed value of G. If the amplitude G is a random variable, then it is natural to define the average signal-to-noise ratio (at the output of the optimum detecting filter) by the formula

$$\bar{\rho} = \frac{\overline{G^2}}{2\pi} \int_{-\pi/\Delta t}^{\pi/\Delta t} \frac{|M_0(\omega)|^2}{S_n(\omega)}\, d\omega. \tag{27.13}$$

When $\Delta t \to 0$, we obtain the corresponding formulas of Sec. 16.

In the above treatment, we have tacitly assumed that the time shift of the useful signal can be arbitrary, i.e., we have assumed that the quantity p in the formula (26.44) is any integer, positive or negative. If the possible values of p are restricted, then, as before, we can introduce a transfer function for the filter, but we must now bear in mind that to extract and detect the useful signal, we need only the corresponding part of the values of $\varphi(t_g)$, namely, the values $\varphi(t_0 + p\,\Delta t)$. In particular, if p can take only one value $p = 0$, we come back to the case of a signal of known form, with a known time of occurrence. In this case, as a result of "filtering" the sequence f_h or the function $f(t)$, we obtain a *number*, and not a sequence or a function. Since we can approach this case by gradually decreasing the number of possible values of p, we can consider the filtering described by formulas (26.20), (26.22) and (26.23) to have a transfer function

$$K(\omega) = ce^{-i\omega t_0} \frac{M^*(\omega)}{S_n(\omega)}, \tag{27.14}$$

with a signal-to-noise ratio at the filter output which equals

$$\rho = \frac{1}{2\pi} \int_{-\pi/\Delta t}^{\pi/\Delta t} \frac{|M(\omega)|^2}{S_n(\omega)} \, d\omega. \tag{27.15}$$

We shall frequently encounter the filter (27.14) in the theory of optimum receivers for detecting signals of known form. To pass to the case of continuous processes, we let $\Delta t \to 0$ and $\pi/\Delta t \to \infty$.

In principle, the filter with the transfer function (27.10) or (27.14) will be a filter of type I, which uses all the values of the function $f(t)$ or the sequence $f(t_h)$ along the infinite time axis, i.e., for $-\infty < t < \infty$. However, in practice, if the noise is uncorrelated (white), the filter uses the function $f(t)$ or the sequence $f(t_h)$ for only a *finite time interval*, which begins when the earliest signal arrives and ends when the last signal dies out (cf. Sec. 17). If the noise is correlated, then both the beginning and the end of this interval have to be extended by adding extra intervals, of duration equal to the correlation time of the noise. If the function $f(t)$ or the sequence $f(t_h)$ at the input of the receiver are specified during this modified interval, then the linear filter which handles the data in the optimum way will again have the transfer function (27.10) or (27.14).

Part 2

STATISTICAL THEORY OF OPTIMUM RECEIVERS

5

RECEPTION AS A STATISTICAL PROBLEM

28. The Probabilistic Nature of Reception

The reception of useful signals in the presence of random noise always gives information of a probabilistic character, and it is only when the random noise becomes very weak that this probabilistic information becomes practically certain. In fact, the more intense the background noise, the more difficult it is to determine and distinguish useful signals. Additive background noise masks the useful signals by "contaminating" them in a random way. Thus, "guessing" is required to determine the signals, and, as a result, one signal may be confused with another or may go entirely undetected. Moreover, even when the useful signal has been properly detected, the noise leads to errors in measuring the parameters of the signal. The random character of receiver noise and other kinds of noise, and also the dependence of the useful signal on random parameters, compels us to use statistical methods in analyzing the problem of reception.

The statistical theory of reception was first studied by V. A. Kotelnikov, P. M. Woodward, I. L. Davies, D. Middleton, and other authors. The chief problem of this theory is to determine the best (optimum) means of handling the received signal, and in particular, the best way of carrying out the "guessing" mentioned above. But what is the meaning of the word "best" in this context? In Part 1, we used either the criterion of maximum signal-to-noise ratio or the criterion of minimum mean square error at the output of the system. However, there is still an essential need to put these criteria on a more solid foundation.

In this regard, the following quotation from Woodward's book[1] is instructive:

"The problem of reception is to gain information from a mixture of wanted signal and unwanted noise, and a considerable literature exists on the subject. Much of it has been concerned with methods of obtaining as large a signal-to-noise ratio as possible on the grounds that noise is what ultimately limits sensitivity and the less there is of it the better. This is a valid attitude as far as it goes, but it does not face up to the problem of extracting information. Sometimes it can be misleading, for there is no general theorem that maximum output signal-to-noise ratio ensures maximum gain of information."

As we shall see below, the statistical theory of reception involves a parameter which plays the role of a signal-to-noise ratio and which determines the characteristics of the optimum receiver. However, this parameter plays a more modest role than before, since it is not used to *choose* the optimum receiver.

The statistical theory of reception begins with the following formulation of the problem: Let the input process

$$f(t) = m(t) + n(t) \tag{28.01}$$

consist of the useful signal $m(t)$ and the noise $n(t)$, given as functions of the time t. The function $n(t)$, in its turn, may consist of different kinds of noise (e.g., the receiver noise itself, reflections from randomly arranged particles, etc.). In what follows, we shall also consider cases where there is a nonzero probability that the useful signal may be absent. In such a case, instead of formula (28.01), we have

$$f(t) = n(t), \tag{28.02}$$

i.e., the input process reduces to just the noise.

By the *optimum receiver*, we mean the device which, when the function $f(t)$ is applied to its input, forms at its output the *conditional probabilities* of the events in which we are interested, i.e., the probability $P_f(m)$ that the useful signal is present and the probability $P_f(0) = 1 - P_f(m)$ that it is absent, given that we know the input to the receiver, namely, the process $f(t)$. In problems which involve *distinguishing* one of a few or many signals in the presence of noise, the optimum receiver must form a larger set of conditional probabilities (see Chap. 8).

The conditional probabilities $P_f(m)$, $P_f(0)$, etc., are called *a posteriori* probabilities; this designation serves to emphasize the fact that they are

---

[1] P. M. Woodward, *Probability and Information Theory, with Applications to Radar*, Pergamon Press, London (1953), p. 62.

probabilities based on the "results of an experiment," which in the present case, consists in ascertaining the function $f(t)$. It is also customary to introduce the *a priori* probabilities $P(m)$ and $P(0) = 1 - P(m)$; these are the probabilities that the useful signal is present or absent in the received signal "before the experiment," i.e., in the absence of any knowledge of $f(t)$. A priori probabilities will be discussed in more detail in Sec. 30.

The definition just given of the optimum receiver reflects the fact that in the presence of random noise, one can only use the input function $f(t)$ to say that the useful signal $m(t)$ is present or absent (or has some parameters or other) *with certain probabilities*. A posteriori probabilities give the most complete and detailed description of the results of reception. Ordinarily, certain activities will be undertaken as a result of the reception, and hence, certain decisions will be made which use the a posteriori probabilities only partially and incompletely; for example, the most probable event may be regarded as actually having occurred, or some other decision rule may be used (see Sec. 30). The question of the optimum decision ("guessing") rule or the question of the optimum method for deciding, for example, whether or not the useful signal is present, is more complicated. Therefore, we begin our study by investigating the optimum receiver, i.e., the receiver which provides the a posteriori probabilities.

Two problems arise in reception:

1. Optimum detection of the useful signal in the presence of noise.
2. Optimum measurement of certain parameters of the useful signal in the presence of noise.

The useful signal $m(t)$ depends on the time t and perhaps on other parameters as well. We classify these parameters in the following three categories:

1. *Known parameters*, which we shall designate by the letter m itself. In particular, these parameters determine the form of the signal or perhaps its statistical properties, if $m(t)$ is a random sequence or a random process.
2. *Unknown parameters which are measured upon reception.* In the case of radar signals, such parameters include (for example) the target's range, its azimuth, etc. We shall denote such parameters by the letter τ. (In the case of several such parameters, when being explicit, we replace τ by a set of symbols $\tau_1, \tau_2, \ldots$).
3. *Unknown parameters which are not measured upon reception.* In the case of radar, such parameters include (for example) the r-f phase of the signal and its amplitude fluctuations. Such parameters (or groups of them) will be denoted by the letter θ.

Thus, the general form of the useful signal is

$$m = m(t, \tau, \theta). \tag{28.03}$$

As for the noise $n(t)$ at the receiver input, we shall assume that it is a random process with known statistical properties.

Using the representation (28.03), we can make the following classification of the functions which might be performed by the receiver:

1. *Simple detection*, consisting of detecting the presence of a completely known signal $m = m(t)$ in the presence of background noise.
2. *Composite detection*, consisting of detecting the signal $m = m(t, \theta)$ with unknown parameters, without measuring the latter.
3. *Simple measurement*, consisting of detecting the signal $m = m(t, \tau)$ and measuring its unknown parameters τ.
4. *Composite measurement*, consisting of detecting the signal $m = m(t, \tau, \theta)$ and measuring its unknown parameters τ.

It should be noted that in radar, one always makes composite measurements. However, by beginning our theoretical treatment with the very simplest cases, we can achieve a better understanding of the more complicated problems arising in practice.

29. A Posteriori Probabilities and Likelihood Ratios

We now use some formulas of probability theory to calculate the a posteriori probabilities obtained as a result of reception. As is well known, the probability that the events A and B occur simultaneously, which we denote by $P(A,B)$, satisfies the formula

$$P(A,B) = P(A)P_A(B) = P(B)P_B(A), \tag{29.01}$$

where $P(A)$ is the probability of the event A, $P_A(B)$ is the conditional probability of the event B, given that the event A has occurred, and the symbols $P(B)$ and $P_B(A)$ are defined similarly. The relation (29.01) can be written in the form

$$P_B(A) = \frac{P(A,B)}{P(B)} = \frac{P(A)P_A(B)}{P(B)}. \tag{29.02}$$

Suppose we have a *complete set of mutually exclusive events*

$$A_1, A_2, \cdots, A_K, \tag{29.03}$$

i.e., events such that one of them must occur, but two or more of them cannot occur simultaneously. If B is an event which can only occur if an event of the system (29.03) occurs, then the probability that B occurs is given by the expression

$$P(B) = P(A_1)P_{A_1}(B) + P(A_2)P_{A_2}(B) + \cdots + P(A_K)P_{A_K}(B)$$
$$= \sum_{k=1}^{K} P(A_k)P_{A_k}(B), \tag{29.04}$$

called the *total probability formula.* If it is known that the event B has occurred, then it is natural to ask which event A_k occurred jointly with B. In this case, the events (29.03) are called *hypotheses*, whose probabilities have to be determined. From formulas (29.02) and (29.04), we obtain the expression

$$P_B(A_k) = \frac{P(A_k)P_{A_k}(B)}{P(B)} = \frac{P(A_k)P_{A_k}(B)}{\sum_{k=1}^{K} P(A_k)P_{A_k}(B)}, \tag{29.05}$$

which is called *Bayes' formula*, or the *inverse probability formula.* Since the hypotheses form a complete system of mutually exclusive events, the probabilities $P_B(A_k)$ must satisfy the formula

$$\sum_{k=1}^{K} P_B(A_k) = 1, \tag{29.06}$$

which serves to check the calculations. In this context, the probabilities appearing in formula (29.05) have the following special designations: $P(A_k)$ is called the *a priori probability of the hypothesis* A_k (the probability "before the experiment"), $P_B(A_k)$ is called the *a posteriori probability of the hypothesis* A_k (the probability "after the experiment," i.e., after the event B has occurred), and $P_{A_k}(B)$ is called the *likelihood function.*

Next, we apply these formulas to calculate the a posteriori probability that the useful signal $m(t)$ is present in the received function $f(t)$. In our case, the event B is the appearance of the function $f(t)$ at the receiver input, and the event A is the presence of the useful signal $m(t)$ in $f(t)$. The a posteriori probability $P_f(m)$ is equal to

$$P_f(m) = \frac{P(m)P_m(f)}{P(f)}. \tag{29.07}$$

Here, $P(m)$ is the a priori probability that the useful signal occurs (the probability before reception), $P_m(f)$ is the likelihood function (the conditional probability of receiving the function $f(t)$ if the useful signal $m(t)$ is present), $P(f)$ is the a priori probability of receiving $f(t)$, and $P_f(m)$ is the a posteriori probability that the useful signal $m(t)$ is present in the received function $f(t)$ (the probability after reception).

We now consider the form of the expression (29.07) for the various cases specified in the classification at the end of Sec. 28.

1. *Simple detection.* In this case, the useful signal is completely known, and there are two possibilities for the received function: (a) $f(t)$ can consist of noise alone, i.e., $f(t) = n(t)$; (b) $f(t)$ can be a mixture of the useful signal and the noise, i.e., $f(t) = m(t) + n(t)$. Then, the probability of the compound event f can be written as

$$P(f) = P(m)P_m(f) + P(0)P_0(f),$$
$$P(m) + P(0) = 1, \tag{29.08}$$

where $P(m)$ is the a priori probability that the useful signal m is present, $P_m(f)$ is the conditional probability of f, given that m is present, $P(0)$ is the a priori probability that the useful signal is absent, and $P_0(f)$ is the conditional probability of f, given that m is absent. Using (29.08), we can write the general formula (29.07) in the form

$$P_f(m) = \frac{P(m)P_m(f)}{P(m)P_m(f) + P(0)P_0(f)} = \frac{\Lambda}{\Lambda + [P(0)/P(m)]}, \tag{29.09}$$

where the quantity

$$\Lambda = \frac{P_m(f)}{P_0(f)} \tag{29.10}$$

is called the *likelihood ratio.*

The likelihood ratio also determines the a posteriori probability that the useful signal is absent, since

$$P_f(0) = \frac{P(0)P_0(f)}{P(0)P_0(f) + P(m)P_m(f)} = \frac{P(0)/P(m)}{\Lambda + [P(0)/P(m)]}. \tag{29.11}$$

The ratio of the a posteriori probabilities (29.09) and (29.11) equals

$$\frac{P_f(m)}{P_f(0)} = \frac{P(m)}{P(0)}\Lambda. \tag{29.12}$$

2. *Composite detection.* In this case, the useful signal has an unknown parameter θ which is not measured, and there are two possibilities for the received function: (a) $f(t)$ can consist of noise alone, i.e., $f(t) = n(t)$; (b) $f(t)$ can be the sum of noise and the useful signal with some definite value θ_k of the unknown discrete parameter θ, i.e., $f(t) = m(t, \theta_k) + n(t)$. Then, the probability of the compound event f can be written as

$$P(f) = \sum_{k=1}^{K} P[m(\theta_k)]P_{m(\theta_k)}(f) + P(0)P_0(f),$$
$$\sum_{k=1}^{K} P[m(\theta_k)] + P(0) = 1, \tag{29.13}$$

where $P[m(\theta_k)]$ is the probability that the useful signal is present and has the parameter $\theta = \theta_k$, and $P_{m(\theta_k)}(f)$ is the conditional probability that the function $f(t)$ is received, given that it contains the useful signal m with parameter θ_k. The sums in (29.13) are taken over all values θ_k of the discrete parameter θ.

If the parameter θ can take a continuous set of values, then instead of the probability $P[m(\theta_k)]$, we have to introduce the probability density $p[m(\theta)]$ and replace the sums in (29.13) by integrals. Then we have

$$P(f) = \int p[m(\theta)]P_{m(\theta)}(f)\, d\theta + P(0)P_0(f), \tag{29.14}$$

where $p[m(\theta)]\, d\theta$ is the probability that the useful signal is present and has a parameter θ lying in the interval $(\theta, \theta + d\theta)$. The integral in (29.14) is taken over all possible values of θ. In this case, the normalization condition takes the form

$$P(m) + P(0) = 1, \tag{29.15}$$

where

$$P(m) = \int p[m(\theta)]\, d\theta. \tag{29.16}$$

The quantity $P(m)$ is the probability that the useful signal is present. The probability density $p[m(\theta)]$ can also be written as

$$p[m(\theta)] = P(m)p_m(\theta), \tag{29.17}$$

where $p_m(\theta)\, d\theta$ is the conditional probability that the useful signal m has a parameter θ in the interval $(\theta, \theta + d\theta)$, given that m is present in the first place. The conditional probability density $p_m(\theta)$ satisfies the relation

$$\int p_m(\theta)\, d\theta = 1. \tag{29.18}$$

The a posteriori probability that the useful signal is present and has the parameter θ_k is equal to

$$P_f[m(\theta_k)] = \frac{P[m(\theta_k)]P_{m(\theta_k)}(f)}{P(f)}. \tag{29.19}$$

Since the unknown parameter θ_k does not interest us, we form just the a posteriori probability that the useful signal is present:

$$P_f(m) = \sum_{k=1}^{K} P_f[m(\theta_k)] = \frac{\sum_{k=1}^{K} P[m(\theta_k)]P_{m(\theta_k)}(f)}{\sum_{k=1}^{K} P[m(\theta_k)]P_{m(\theta_k)}(f) + P(0)P_0(f)}. \tag{29.20}$$

If the parameter θ takes a continuous set of values, then the last formula becomes

$$P_f(m) = \frac{P(m) \int p_m(\theta) P_{m(\theta)}(f)\, d\theta}{P(m) \int p_m(\theta) P_{m(\theta)}(f)\, d\theta + P(0)P_0(f)} \tag{29.21}$$

or

$$P_f(m) = \frac{\Lambda}{\Lambda + [P(0)/P(m)]}. \tag{29.22}$$

Here, Λ is the likelihood ratio, which equals

$$\Lambda = \int \Lambda(\theta)\, d\theta, \tag{29.23}$$

where

$$\Lambda(\theta) = p_m(\theta) \frac{P_{m(\theta)}(f)}{P_0(f)}. \tag{29.24}$$

In formulas (29.22) to (29.24), we make a distinction between the quantity $\Lambda(\theta)$ and the likelihood ratio obtained by integrating (or summing) $\Lambda(\theta)$ over all possible values of θ. If we have several unknown parameters $\theta_1, \theta_2, \ldots$, then the integrals with respect to θ in the above formulas have to be replaced by multiple integrals.

Using the likelihood ratio Λ, we have just written the a posteriori probability for composite detection in the same form as for simple detection [cf. formulas (29.09) and (29.22)]. However, the likelihood ratio Λ itself is now calculated by using the more complicated formula (29.23).

It should also be kept in mind that the probabilities $P_m(f)$ and $P_0(f)$ are usually zero, so that in calculating the likelihood ratios Λ and $\Lambda(\theta)$, we have to get rid of the indeterminacy by writing

$$\Lambda = \frac{P_m(f)}{P_0(f)} = \frac{p_m(f)\, df}{p_0(f)\, df} = \frac{p_m(f)}{p_0(f)}, \qquad \Lambda(\theta) = p_m(\theta) \frac{p_{m(\theta)}(f)}{p_0(f)}. \tag{29.25}$$

In other words, instead of using the zero probabilities $P_m(f)$, $P_{m(\theta)}(f)$ and $P_0(f)$, we use the corresponding probability densities $p_m(f)$, $p_{m(\theta)}(f)$ and $p_0(f)$.

3. *Simple measurement.* In this case, the signal has an unknown parameter, which is measured. Assuming that the parameter τ varies continuously, we can write the probability of occurrence of the function $f(t)$, as in the case of composite detection, in the form

$$\begin{aligned} P(f) &= \int p[m(\tau)] P_{m(\tau)}(f)\, d\tau + P(0)P_0(f) \\ &= P(m) \int p_m(\tau) P_{m(\tau)}(f)\, d\tau + P(0)P_0(f), \\ \int p[m(\tau)]\, d\tau &+ P(0) = P(m) + P(0) = 1, \\ p[m(\tau)] &= P(m)p_m(\tau), \end{aligned} \tag{29.26}$$

where $P(m)$, $P(0)$, $p[m(\tau)]$ and $p_m(\tau)$ have the same meaning as the similar expressions for the case of composite detection.

In making the measurement, we are interested first in whether or not the signal m is present in the input signal f, and then, if it is present, we are interested in what can be said about its unknown parameter τ. After receiving f, we calculate the a posteriori probability density of all possible values of the parameter τ being measured, by using the formula

$$p_f[m(\tau)] = \frac{p[m(\tau)]P_{m(\tau)}(f)}{P(f)}. \tag{29.27}$$

Using the formulas (29.26), we find that the a posteriori probability density of the parameter τ is given by the following function of τ:

$$p_f[m(\tau)] = \frac{\Lambda(\tau)}{\Lambda + [P(0)/P(m)]}. \tag{29.28}$$

Here, we have

$$\Lambda(\tau) = p_m(\tau)\frac{P_{m(\tau)}(f)}{P_0(f)}, \tag{29.29}$$

and

$$\Lambda = \int \Lambda(\tau)\, d\tau. \tag{29.30}$$

4. *Composite measurement.* In this case, the signal has the unknown parameters τ and θ, where the parameter τ is measured, but the parameter θ is not measured. Suppose that the parameters τ and θ take continuous sets of values. Then, the probability of occurrence of the function $f(t)$ is equal to

$$\begin{aligned} P(f) &= \iint p[m(\tau, \theta)]P_{m(\tau,\theta)}(f)\, d\tau\, d\theta + P(0)P_0(f) \\ &= P(m)\iint p_m(\tau, \theta)P_{m(\tau,\theta)}(f)\, d\tau\, d\theta + P(0)P_0(f), \end{aligned} \tag{29.31}$$

$$P(m) + P(0) = 1$$

$$p[m(\tau, \theta)] = P(m)p_m(\tau, \theta), \qquad \iint p_m(\tau, \theta)\, d\tau\, d\theta = 1,$$

where the notation has the same meaning as before.

Since we are interested in the parameter τ but not in the parameter θ, we have to form the a posteriori probability density of the parameter τ by integrating over all possible values of θ. The result is

$$p_f[m(\tau)] = \int p_f[m(\tau, \theta)]\, d\theta = \frac{\int p[m(\tau, \theta)]P_{m(\tau,\theta)}(f)\, d\theta}{P_0(f)}. \tag{29.32}$$

This formula can also be written as

$$p_f[m(\tau)] = \frac{\Lambda(\tau)}{\Lambda + [P(0)/P(m)]}, \tag{29.33}$$

where we have introduced the quantities

$$\Lambda(\tau) = \int \Lambda(\tau, \theta)\, d\theta, \tag{29.34}$$

$$\Lambda = \int\int \Lambda(\tau, \theta)\, d\tau\, d\theta, \tag{29.35}$$

$$\Lambda(\tau, \theta) = p_m(\tau, \theta) \frac{P_{m(\tau,\theta)}(f)}{P_0(f)}. \tag{29.36}$$

Thus, in this problem, we have to distinguish the three quantities Λ, $\Lambda(\tau)$ and $\Lambda(\tau, \theta)$, where $\Lambda(\tau, \theta)$ is the likelihood ratio for measuring the parameters τ and θ, $\Lambda(\tau)$ is the likelihood ratio for measuring only the parameter τ, and Λ is the likelihood ratio for composite measurement of the signal $m(t, \tau, \theta)$.

If the parameters τ and θ are statistically independent, then

$$p_m(\tau, \theta) = p_m(\tau)p_m(\theta), \tag{29.37}$$

and formula (29.34) becomes somewhat simpler:

$$\Lambda(\tau) = p_m(\tau) \int p_m(\theta) \frac{P_{m(\tau,\theta)}(f)}{P_0(f)}\, d\theta. \tag{29.38}$$

The formulas given above allow us to find the form of the optimum receiver if we know the statistical properties of the noise $n(t)$ and of the unknown parameters of the useful signal $m(t)$. Before undertaking the corresponding calculations, we shall investigate the problem of a priori probabilities (in the next section).

In conclusion, we note that in the literature, the likelihood ratios $\Lambda(\tau)$, $\Lambda(\tau, \theta)$, etc., are sometimes defined by the formulas

$$\Lambda(\tau) = \frac{P_{m(\tau)}(f)}{P_0(f)}, \qquad \Lambda(\tau, \theta) = \frac{P_{m(\tau,\theta)}(f)}{P_0(f)}, \tag{29.39}$$

which do not contain the a priori probabilities $p_m(\tau)$ and $p_m(\tau, \theta)$. In this case, the expressions written above take a somewhat different form.

30. A Priori Probabilities. Decision Rules

In the preceding two sections, we have examined the basic concepts of the statistical theory of optimum receivers. In this theory, there are certain special difficulties in connection with the a priori probabilities of the useful signal. As we have seen, the a priori probabilities are needed to calculate the a posteriori probabilities, i.e., they are required for practical implementation of the optimum receiver. However, the a priori probabilities are often unknown. Thus, Woodward writes (*op. cit.*, p. 74):

"Consider, for example, the prior probability of observing an aircraft on a given radar set at a range of ten miles at nine o'clock tomorrow morning. If the set is situated at an airfield where regular services operate, statistical analysis of the past might provide us with the required probability, on the assumption that the organization of air traffic is a stationary statistical process. But in a large number of problems, no statistics are available, either because they have not been taken, or more fundamentally, because there has not been an ensemble of similar past situations from which to form any judgment."

As shown in Sec. 29, the a priori probability densities $p[m(\tau)]$, $p[m(\theta)]$ and $p[m(\tau, \theta)]$ can be written as products of two factors:

$$p[m(\tau)] = P(m)p_m(\tau), \qquad p[m(\theta)] = P(m)p_m(\theta),$$
$$p[m(\tau, \theta)] = P(m)p_m(\tau, \theta). \tag{30.01}$$

Here, $P(m)$ is the a priori probability that the useful signal is present at the receiver input, and $P(0) = 1 - P(m)$ is the a priori probability that it is absent. It is very difficult to evaluate these probabilities. On the other hand, the a priori probabilities $p_m(\tau)$, $p_m(\theta)$ and $p_m(\tau, \theta)$ describe the distribution of the unknown parameters of the useful signal, given that the useful signal is present at the receiver input, and in many cases, these distributions can be more or less accurately determined from theoretical considerations. Thus, for example, in the case of incoherent detection it is natural to assume that the random r-f phase is uniformly distributed from 0 to 2π, and that the amplitude fluctuations of the signal have a Rayleigh distribution. Also, the range and azimuth of the target can be assumed to be uniformly distributed in a certain small region of space, but as the dimensions of this region are increased, this assumption may no longer be justified.

Bearing these considerations in mind and assuming that we know the a priori distributions of the unknown parameters τ and θ of the useful signal, we can calculate the likelihood ratios Λ, $\Lambda(\tau)$ and $\Lambda(\tau, \theta)$ which were introduced in the various cases considered above. Then, forming the ratio of the a posteriori probability that the useful signal is present to the a posteriori probability that it is absent, we obtain

$$\frac{P_f(m)}{P_f(0)} = \frac{P(m)}{P(0)}\Lambda \tag{30.02}$$

in the case of detection, and

$$\frac{P_f[m(\tau)]}{P_0(0)} = \frac{P(m)}{P(0)}\Lambda(\tau) \tag{30.03}$$

in the case of measurement. These relations are easily derived from (29.09), (29.22), (29.28), (29.33), and the formulas

$$P_f(0) = 1 - P_f(m) = \frac{P(0)/P(m)}{\Lambda + [P(0)/P(m)]}, \tag{30.04}$$

$$P_f(m) = \int P_f[m(\tau)]\, d\tau. \tag{30.05}$$

Formulas (30.02) and (30.03) show that in the ratio of the a posteriori probabilities, it is only the constant factor $P(m)/P(0)$ which involves the a priori probabilities, and moreover, that it is the received signal $f(t)$ which determines the likelihood ratios Λ and $\Lambda(\tau)$.

The difficulties caused by not knowing $P(m)/P(0)$ can be avoided by changing the definition of the optimum receiver. Thus, suppose we define the optimum receiver as the receiver forming the likelihood ratios (rather than the a posteriori probabilities). Thus, *by definition*, the optimum receiver must provide the following mathematical quantities, in the various cases described above:

1. Λ, for simple detection;
2. $\Lambda = \int \Lambda(\theta)\, d\theta$, for composite detection;
3. $\Lambda(\tau)$, for simple measurement;
4. $\Lambda(\tau) = \int \Lambda(\tau, \theta)\, d\theta$, for composite measurement.

(30.06)

Next, on the basis of the input data and the quantities (30.06) formed by using them, a *decision* is usually made. If a person makes the decision (e.g., by saying "there is a signal" or "there is no signal"), then the optimum receiver can only help the person, while leaving the decision up to him. It should be noted that a person who makes the decision always uses some a priori knowledge of the probability of occurrence of the signal (although he may not be explicitly aware of it). In particular, the smaller the a priori probability of occurrence of the signal, the more the signal must exceed the noise (i.e., the larger the value of Λ must be) in order to answer "there is a signal."

It is not hard to make the decision scheme automatic. Confining ourselves to the problem of detection (simple or composite), we first note that the a posteriori probability that the useful signal is present, i.e., the quantity

$$P_f(m) = \frac{\Lambda}{\Lambda + [P(0)/P(m)]} \tag{30.07}$$

is a monotonically increasing function of the likelihood ratio Λ. It is quite natural to assume that the useful signal m is present if the probability $P_f(m)$ is large enough (i.e., close enough to unity), and that the useful signal is absent if the probability $P_f(m)$ is small enough. Therefore, the simplest decision rule has the form

$$\begin{aligned} &\text{If} \quad P_f(m) \geqslant P_*, \quad \text{the signal is present;} \\ &\text{If} \quad P_f(m) < P_*, \quad \text{the signal is absent,} \end{aligned} \tag{30.08}$$

where P_* is some "threshold" probability, e.g., $P_* = 0.5$, $P_* = 0.9$ or $P_* = 0.99$.

A more complicated decision rule is

$$\begin{aligned} &\text{If} \quad P_f(m) \geqslant P^*, \quad \text{the signal is present;} \\ &\text{If} \quad P^* > P_f(m) > P_*, \quad \text{no decision is made;} \\ &\text{If} \quad P_f(m) \leqslant P_*, \quad \text{the signal is absent,} \end{aligned} \tag{30.09}$$

with two thresholds P^* and P_*. This decision rule uses the a posteriori probabilities at the receiver more completely, but it sometimes gives an indeterminate answer. If once the signal $f(t)$ is received, there is no further information available at the receiver, and if a decision must be made on the basis of the information at hand, then there is no alternative but to use the decision rule (30.08), with one threshold. However, if information arrives at the receiver gradually, then on the basis of the input data accumulated after a certain amount of time, one might make the "indeterminate" decision, thereby indicating the need to continue the observation. In this case, we can use the "two-threshold" rule (30.09). In principle, at least, even more complicated rules could be used.

We now consider the decision rule (30.08) in more detail. As soon as one of the two possible decisions has been made, then we have always made either a correct decision or an error. Two kinds of error are possible. The first kind of error consists in making the decision "yes" when only noise is present at the receiver input. This kind of error is called a "false alarm," and we denote its probability by F. The second kind of error consists in making the decision "no" when both the signal and the noise are present at the receiver input. This kind of error is called a "false dismissal," and we denote its probability by D_0. Thus, the false alarm probability F is the probability of interpreting the noise to be the sum of signal plus noise, while the false dismissal probability D_0 is the probability of interpreting the sum of signal plus noise to be just noise.

Correct decisions can also be of two kinds, i.e., correct detection or correct "nondetection." The probability of correct detection, which we denote by D, is the probability of interpreting the sum of signal plus noise to be the sum of signal plus noise, while the probability of correct non-detection is the probability of interpreting noise to be noise. It is clear that F, D_0, D and F_0 are conditional probabilities: F_0 and F are the probabilities of making a correct or an incorrect decision, given that the useful signal is absent, whereas D and D_0 are the probabilities of making a correct or an incorrect decision, given that the useful signal is present. Therefore, the relations

$$D_0 = 1 - D, \qquad F_0 = 1 - F \tag{30.10}$$

hold. The total probability of making a correct decision obviously equals

$$W = P(m)D + P(0)F_0 = P(m)D + P(0)(1 - F), \tag{30.11}$$

where $P(0)$ and $P(m)$ are the a priori probabilities of absence and presence of the signal m, respectively.

In using the rule (30.08), the a priori probabilities $P(0)$ and $P(m)$, as well as the threshold probability P_*, must be specified. If $P(0)$ and $P(m)$ are unknown, then, as remarked above, we can use the likelihood ratio Λ to rewrite the decision rule (30.08) in the form

$$\begin{aligned} &\text{If} \quad \Lambda \geqslant \Lambda_*, \quad \text{the signal is present;} \\ &\text{If} \quad \Lambda < \Lambda_*, \quad \text{the signal is absent,} \end{aligned} \tag{30.12}$$

where

$$\Lambda_* = \frac{P(0)}{P(m)} \frac{P_*}{1 - P_*} \tag{30.13}$$

is the threshold value of the likelihood ratio. Similarly, the "two-threshold" decision rule (30.09) becomes

$$\begin{aligned} &\text{If} \quad \Lambda \geqslant \Lambda^*, \quad \text{the signal is present;} \\ &\text{If} \quad \Lambda^* > \Lambda > \Lambda_*, \quad \text{no decision is made;} \\ &\text{If} \quad \Lambda \leqslant \Lambda_*, \quad \text{the signal is absent.} \end{aligned} \tag{30.14}$$

Using these rules, it is not hard to build automatic decision circuits. Thus, an optimum receiver which also makes decisions must first calculate the likelihood ratio Λ and then deliver it to the input of a circuit which operates according to the rule (30.12) or (30.14). We note that instead of Λ, we can use any monotonically increasing function of Λ (e.g., $\ln \Lambda$); this often leads to simplifications in the design of the optimum receiver. The threshold Λ_* in formula (30.12) is usually set by requiring that the false alarm probability should equal a certain value (which is often very small, e.g., $F = 10^{-3}$, $F = 10^{-5}$ or $F = 10^{-10}$).

In conclusion, we discuss some of the terminology used in the literature. By the *Neyman-Pearson observer* is meant an observer who, on the basis of the data received during a given time interval T, decides whether the signal $m(t)$ is present, by using a rule which maximizes the probability of correct detection D for a fixed false alarm probability F. It is proved in mathematical statistics that the Neyman-Pearson observer makes his decision by using just the "single-threshold" decision rule (30.12), where the threshold Λ_* is determined from the fixed value of F. Any other decision rule leads to a smaller value of D (for fixed F and T).

The *ideal observer* (due to Siegert) makes the decision which maximizes the probability W given by formula (30.11), for a fixed observation time T. The decision is also made by using the rule (30.12), but the value of the threshold is now chosen to be

$$\Lambda_* = \frac{P(0)}{P(m)}.$$

The *sequential observer* (due to Wald) analyzes the data which arrives continuously at the receiver input. The sequential observer is allowed to reserve his decision until new data arrives, so that his decision rule is of the form (30.14). However, the mathematical theory of the sequential observer is characterized by great complexity, and hence, from now on we shall use only the decision rule (30.12), with one threshold, interpreting it in the spirit of the Neyman-Pearson observer.

A deeper approach to the statistical theory of reception is furnished by the modern theory of games and statistical decisions. This approach has been applied to the theory of optimum receivers by D. Van Meter and D. Middleton. In Appendix I, we discuss some matters which are related to this subject.

31. Simple Detection of a Signal in a Background of Correlated Normal Noise

According to the classification made in Sec. 29, simple detection consists in detecting a completely known signal in the presence of noise. In this case, the useful signal $m(t)$ is either absent or else is a well-defined function of time. As for the noise $n(t)$, in our theory of optimum receivers, we shall assume that it is a stationary random process of the normal (i.e., Gaussian) type, with zero mean value

$$\overline{n(t)} = 0, \tag{31.01}$$

and with an arbitrary correlation function

$$R_n(\tau) = \overline{n(t)n(t - \tau)}, \tag{31.02}$$

which completely determines the statistical properties of the noise (see Chap. 9). The fact that the noise is a normal process makes it comparatively easy for us to calculate various probabilities connected with the noise, by making use of the Gaussian distribution. The stationarity of the noise is not very important in general considerations; however, in most cases, it is only when the noise is stationary that one succeeds in pursuing the problem to the point where it yields results which can be effectively used in practice.

By assuming the noise to have the above properties, we can take account of many kinds of noise of practical interest, in particular, noise in the receiver itself and radar noise due to clutter echoes (see Chaps. 9 and 11).

We begin our discussion of simple detection with the case where we know the input process $f(t)$ only for the discrete times

$$t_h = t_1 + (h - 1)\,\Delta t \qquad (h = 1, 2, \ldots, H). \tag{31.03}$$

We shall denote the values $f(t_h)$ by f_h, and call them the *sample values* of the input process (or *elements* of the input sequence). Similarly, we introduce the sample values of the useful signal and of the noise, by using the formulas

$$m_h = m(t_h), \qquad n_h = n(t_h). \tag{31.04}$$

It is obvious that the formula

$$f(t) = m(t) + n(t) \tag{31.05}$$

implies

$$f_h = m_h + n_h. \tag{31.06}$$

Thus, if we have made H "samplings" during the observation time, the correlation matrix of the noise has the elements

$$R_{gh} = \overline{n_g n_h} = R_n(|g - h|\,\Delta t) \qquad (g, h = 1, 2, \ldots, H). \tag{31.07}$$

This matrix has the following property: The elements of largest absolute value $R_n(0)$ stand along the main diagonal, and the element standing h columns to the left or to the right of the main diagonal equals $R_n(h\,\Delta t)$. The inverse matrix Q_{gh} satisfies the relation

$$\sum_{j=1}^{H} R_{gj} Q_{jh} = \delta_{gh}, \tag{31.08}$$

where δ_{gh} is the Kronecker delta, which equals 1 for $g = h$ and 0 for $g \neq h$. The elements of this matrix are given by the formula

$$Q_{gh} = \frac{\operatorname{cof}(R_{hg})}{\det \|R_{gh}\|}. \tag{31.09}$$

where $\det \|R_{gh}\|$ is the determinant of the correlation matrix $\|R_{gh}\|$, and $\operatorname{cof}(R_{gh})$ is the cofactor of the element R_{gh}. The inverse matrix $\|Q_{gh}\|$, like the correlation matrix $\|R_{gh}\|$, is symmetric, i.e.,

$$Q_{gh} = Q_{hg}, \qquad R_{gh} = R_{hg}, \tag{31.10}$$

but in general its elements depend on g and h, and not just on $|g - h|$.

We now find the likelihood ratio (29.10). Assuming that the noise $n(t)$ is normal, we can immediately write the multidimensional probability density for the sample values $n_1, n_2, \ldots, n_H$ in the form [cf. formula (59.13)]

$$p(n) = p(n_1, n_2, \ldots, n_H)$$
$$= \frac{1}{\sqrt{(2\pi)^H \det \|R_{gh}\|}} \exp\left\{-\frac{1}{2}\sum_{g,h=1}^{H} Q_{gh} n_g n_h\right\}. \tag{31.11}$$

This is an H-dimensional Gaussian distribution. The probability density of the quantities $f_1, f_2, \ldots, f_H$ in the absence of the signal m, i.e., when $f_h = n_h$, is equal to

$$p_0(f) = p(f) = \frac{1}{\sqrt{(2\pi)^H \det \|R_{gh}\|}} \exp\left\{-\frac{1}{2}\sum_{g,h=1}^{H} Q_{gh} f_g f_h\right\}. \tag{31.12}$$

The probability density for the same quantities in the presence of the signal, i.e., when $n_h = f_h - m_h$, is equal to

$$p_m(f) = p(f - m)$$
$$= \frac{1}{\sqrt{(2\pi)^H \det \|R_{gh}\|}} \exp\left\{-\frac{1}{2}\sum_{g,h=1}^{H} Q_{gh}(f_g - m_g)(f_h - m_h)\right\}. \tag{31.13}$$

Thus, the likelihood ratio, which equals

$$\Lambda = \frac{p_m(f)}{p_0(f)} = \frac{p(f - m)}{p(f)}, \tag{31.14}$$

takes the following form for the Gaussian distribution (31.11):

$$\Lambda = \exp\left\{\sum_{g,h=1}^{H} Q_{gh} f_g m_h - \frac{1}{2}\sum_{g,h=1}^{H} Q_{gh} m_g m_h\right\}. \tag{31.15}$$

If we introduce the notation

$$\varphi = \sum_{g,h=1}^{H} Q_{gh} f_g m_h, \tag{31.16}$$

$$\mu = \sum_{g,h=1}^{H} Q_{gh} m_g m_h, \qquad \nu = \sum_{g,h=1}^{H} Q_{gh} n_g m_h, \tag{31.17}$$

then the likelihood ratio becomes

$$\Lambda = e^{\varphi - \frac{1}{2}\mu}, \tag{31.18}$$

where only the quantity φ depends on the input sequence f_h, and Λ is a monotonically increasing function of φ. Therefore, instead of the quantity Λ itself, the optimum receiver can form the simpler quantity φ, and base its decision on the value of φ. Accordingly, the optimum decision rule is the following:

$$\begin{aligned} &\text{If} \quad \varphi \geqslant \varphi_*, \quad \text{decide that } f = m + n; \\ &\text{If} \quad \varphi < \varphi_*, \quad \text{decide that } f = n, \end{aligned} \tag{31.19}$$

where φ_* is the decision threshold.

We now examine the quantity φ more closely. It can be written as

$$\varphi = \sum_{g,h=1}^{H} Q_{gh} f_g m_h = \sum_{g=1}^{H} k_g f_g, \tag{31.20}$$

where the coefficients k_g are given by

$$k_g = \sum_{h=1}^{H} Q_{gh} m_h \qquad (g = 1, 2, \ldots, H). \tag{31.21}$$

Formula (31.21) shows that the operation of forming φ from f is linear, i.e., *the optimum receiver for simple detection in the presence of normal noise is a linear receiver*, where the coefficients k_g depend both on the form of the signal (on the sample values m_h) and on the correlation properties of the noise (on the elements Q_{gh} of the inverse of the correlation matrix).

One usually knows the correlation function of the noise, and hence, the noise correlation matrix $\| R_{gh} \|$. When $\| R_{gh} \|$ has a large number of elements, the problem of finding the inverse matrix $\| Q_{gh} \|$ is quite formidable. Therefore, for practical calculations of the coefficients k_g, we can use the equations

$$\sum_{g=1}^{H} R_{gh} k_g = m_h \qquad (h = 1, 2, \ldots, H) \tag{31.22}$$

instead, which are easily obtained from (31.21). Formulas (31.22) and (31.21) coincide with formulas (26.25) and (26.26) if we set $c = 1$ in the latter, i.e., the equations (31.21) define the optimum linear filter for detecting a sequence of known form in the presence of the sequence n_h, which has the character of noise. Thus, we see that the optimum receiver for detecting a known signal in a background of *normal* noise consists of the optimum linear filter considered in Part 1, Sec. 26, followed by a decision circuit which oeprates according to the rule (31.19). In this way, we have established the relationship between the theory of optimum linear filters (presented in Part 1) and the statistical theory of optimum receivers. In what follows, we shall see that this relationship is not just limited to the present example but is quite far-reaching.

In Part 1, we showed that the action of the optimum linear filter for signals of known form can be characterized by the signal-to-noise (power) ratio at the output of the filter. It is not hard to see, by using (26.21), (26.22) and (26.23), that this parameter, previously denoted by ρ, is equal to

$$\rho = \frac{\mu^2}{\nu^2} = \frac{\left(\sum_h k_h m_h\right)^2}{\sum_{g,h} k_g k_h R_{gh}} = \sum_g k_g m_g = \sum_{g,h} Q_{gh} m_g m_h = \mu, \tag{31.23}$$

and, in particular, for white noise [i.e., uncorrelated noise for which $R_{gh} = R_n(0)\,\delta_{gh}$], we have

$$\mu = \frac{\sum_{h=1}^{H} m_h^2}{R_n(0)}, \qquad R_n(0) = \overline{n_h^2}. \tag{31.24}$$

Formula (27.15) gives a simple spectral interpretation of the parameter μ, i.e.,

$$\mu = \frac{1}{2\pi}\int_{-\pi/\Delta t}^{\pi/\Delta t} \frac{|M(\omega)|^2}{S_n(\omega)}\,d\omega, \tag{31.25}$$

where $S_n(\omega)$ is the spectral density of the noise. In the case of white noise, this expression becomes

$$\mu = \frac{E}{S_n}, \qquad E = \Delta t \sum_{h=1}^{H} m_h^2, \tag{31.26}$$

where E is the total energy of the useful signal, and S_n is the spectral density of the noise. Formula (31.26) is easily obtained from (31.24) by using the relation

$$S_n = R_n(0)\,\Delta t, \tag{31.27}$$

which follows from the general expression (27.02) for the spectral density, when $R_n(\tau) = 0$ for $\tau \neq 0$. Letting $\Delta t \to 0$ in the above formulas, it is easy to make the transition from sequences to continuous processes. We shall not give the corresponding expressions, since they have already been frequently encountered (see Secs. 16, 17, 26 and 27).

In the theory of optimum linear filters, the meaning of the parameter μ is not completely clear. It is obvious that the larger μ, the better the quality of detection, but it is only in the statistical theory of reception that the parameter μ acquires a clear-cut meaning. In particular, we can now relate the parameter μ to the probability of correct detection [cf. formula (31.18)].

The optimum receiver for detecting a completely known signal operates according to the rule (31.19). The false alarm probability and the probability of correct detection are determined by the threshold φ_* and by the probability density of the quantity φ. The quantity φ, being a linear combination of the (jointly) normal random variables $f_1, f_2, \ldots, f_H$, has itself a normal distribution. We now find the parameters of this distribution.

If we receive only noise, then

$$\bar{\varphi} = \bar{\nu} = \sum_{g,h} Q_{gh}\bar{n}_g m_h = 0, \tag{31.28}$$

because of formula (31.01). The variance of the random variable φ equals

$$\overline{\varphi^2} = \overline{\nu^2} = \sum_{g,h}\sum_{j,l} Q_{gh}Q_{jl}\overline{n_g n_j}m_h m_l = \sum_{g,h}\sum_{j,l} Q_{gh}Q_{jl}R_{gj}m_h m_l$$
$$= \sum_{g,h} Q_{gh}m_g m_h = \mu. \tag{31.29}$$

If we have both the useful signal and noise at the receiver input, then

$$\bar{\varphi} = \sum_{g,h} Q_{gh}\bar{f}_g m_h = \sum_{g,h} Q_{gh}m_g m_h = \mu, \tag{31.30}$$

and the variance of φ equals

$$\overline{(\varphi - \bar{\varphi})^2} = \overline{\nu^2} = \mu. \tag{31.31}$$

Thus, in the absence of the useful signal, the probability density of the quantity φ is

$$p_0(\varphi) = \frac{1}{\sqrt{2\pi\mu}}\, e^{-\varphi^2/2\mu}, \tag{31.32}$$

while in its presence, we have

$$p_m(\varphi) = \frac{1}{\sqrt{2\pi\mu}}\, e^{-(\varphi-\mu)^2/2\mu}. \tag{31.33}$$

The false alarm probability F equals the probability that the quantity φ exceeds the threshold φ_* in the presence of noise alone:

$$F = \int_{\varphi_*}^{\infty} p_0(\varphi)\, d\varphi = \frac{1}{\sqrt{2\pi}}\int_{z_*}^{\infty} e^{-z^2/2}\, dz \qquad \left(z_* = \frac{\varphi_*}{\sqrt{\mu}}\right). \tag{31.34}$$

The solid line in Fig. 26 shows the dependence of the normalized threshold z_* on the false alarm probability F.

Similarly, the probability of correct detection (or simply, the *detection probability*) equals

$$D = \int_{\varphi_*}^{\infty} p_m(\varphi)\, d\varphi = \frac{1}{\sqrt{2\pi}}\int_{y_*}^{\infty} e^{-z^2/2}\, dz \qquad (y_* = z_* - \sqrt{\mu}). \tag{31.35}$$

Given the probabilities F and D, we can find the required signal-to-noise ratio μ from the formula

$$\mu = (z_* - y_*)^2 \quad \text{for} \quad D \geqslant F, \tag{31.36}$$

where z_* and y_* are given by formulas (31.34) and (31.35), respectively. Eliminating the parameter z_* from (31.34) and (31.35), we obtain a function

$$D = D(F, \mu), \tag{31.37}$$

which is called the *operating characteristic* of the optimum receiver for detection[2] (in this case, *simple* detection). The function $D(F, \mu)$ satisfies the relations

$$D(0, \mu) = 0, \qquad D(1, \mu) = 1 \tag{31.38}$$

and

$$\left(\frac{\partial D}{\partial F}\right)_{\mu=\text{const}} = \Lambda_*. \tag{31.39}$$

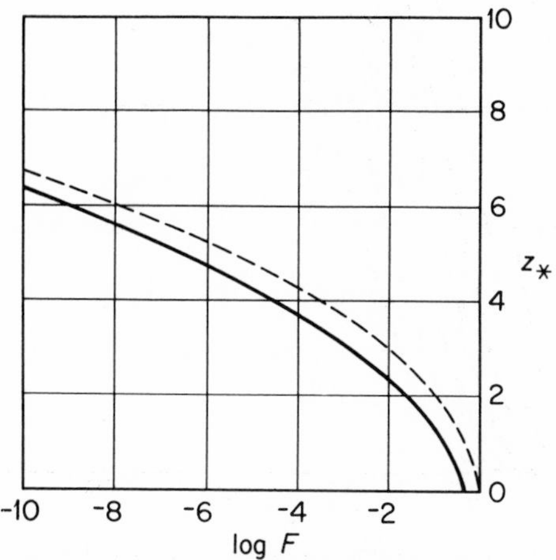

FIG. 26. Dependence of the threshold on the false alarm probability.[3]
Solid curve, for a completely known signal.
Dashed curve, for a signal of unknown phase.

Formula (31.39) holds for all optimum detecting receivers, and often simplifies the calculation of the probability D. The simplest way to derive (31.39) is to differentiate (31.34) and (31.35):

$$\frac{\partial F}{\partial \varphi_*} = -p_0(\varphi_*), \qquad \frac{\partial D}{\partial \varphi_*} = -p_m(\varphi_*). \tag{31.40}$$

It follows from (31.40) that

$$\left(\frac{\partial D}{\partial F}\right)_{\mu=\text{const}} = \frac{p_m(\varphi_*)}{p_0(\varphi_*)}. \tag{31.41}$$

Then, bearing in mind that the likelihood ratio equals

$$\Lambda = \frac{p_m(\varphi)}{p_0(\varphi)}, \tag{31.42}$$

---

[2] The operating characteristics (for detection) will usually be displayed as curves of D vs. μ for constant F; however, they might just as well be displayed as curves of D vs. F for constant μ. (*Translator*)

[3] See footnote 2 on p. 46.

we obtain (31.39). In Fig. 27, we show the dependence of D on μ for fixed values of F, and in Fig. 28 we show the same curves (solid lines), where now the abscissa is marked off in decibels.

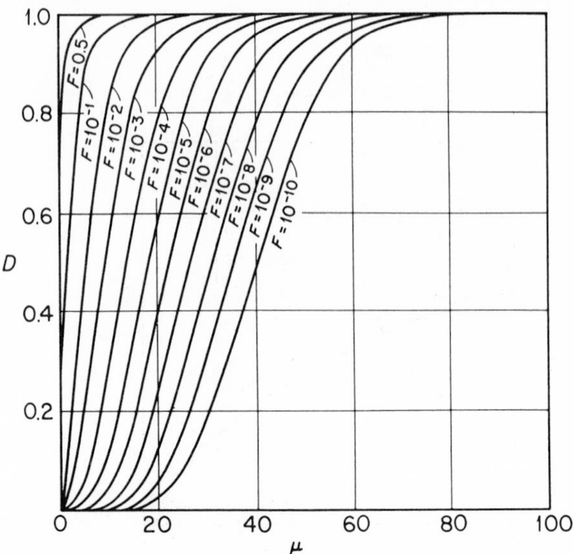

FIG. 27. Operating characteristics for simple detection.

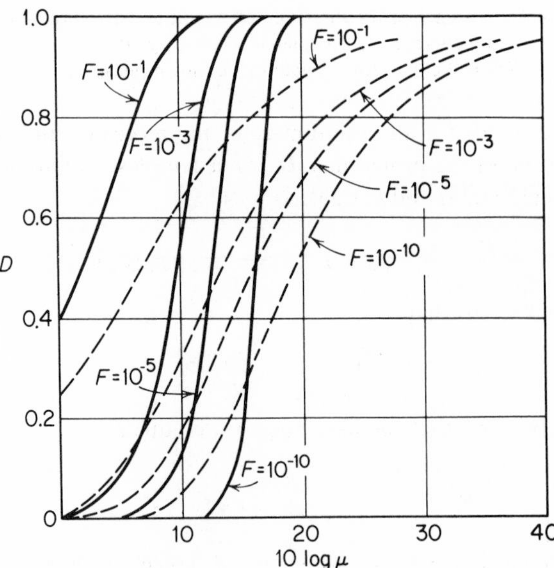

FIG. 28. Comparison of the operating characteristics for detection of a completely known signal (solid curves) and of a signal with unknown amplitude (dashed curves).

If the quantity φ on which we base our decision (31.19) is obtained by using a linear filter which is not optimum, then to achieve the same value of D for a given value of F, we have to provide larger values of the parameter μ. In this case, the false alarm probability can be found from the formula

$$F = \frac{1}{\sqrt{2\pi\sigma^2}} \int_{\varphi_*}^{\infty} e^{-\varphi^2/2\sigma^2}\, d\varphi = \frac{1}{\sqrt{2\pi}} \int_{z_*}^{\infty} e^{-z^2/2}\, dz \qquad \left(z_* = \frac{\varphi_*}{\sigma}\right), \tag{31.43}$$

where

$$\overline{\nu^2} = \sigma^2 \tag{31.44}$$

is the variance of the noise at the output of the given linear filter. Similarly, the detection probability is

$$\begin{aligned} D &= \frac{1}{\sqrt{2\pi\sigma^2}} \int_{\varphi_*}^{\infty} e^{-(\varphi-\bar{\varphi})^2/2\sigma^2}\, d\varphi \\ &= \frac{1}{\sqrt{2\pi}} \int_{y_*}^{\infty} e^{-z^2/2}\, dz \qquad \left(y_* = z_* - \frac{\bar{\varphi}}{\sigma}\right), \end{aligned} \tag{31.45}$$

where $\bar{\varphi}$ is the mean value of the useful signal at the output, and

$$\sigma^2 = \overline{\varphi^2} - (\bar{\varphi})^2 = \overline{\nu^2} \tag{31.46}$$

is its variance.

32. Detection of a Signal with Unknown Amplitude

In the preceding section, we studied detection of a completely known signal. Usually, however, certain parameters of the signal are unknown, so that the optimum receiver has to operate according to formula (29.23) and then make its decision by using the rule (30.12). In the present section, and in subsequent sections of this chapter, we shall study the most elementary cases of *composite* detection.

Thus, let the useful signal be known to within a constant factor G, which we shall henceforth call the *amplitude*. We write the useful signal in the form

$$m(t, G) = Gs(t), \tag{32.01}$$

where $s(t)$ is a known function of time. As in the case of simple detection, we consider discrete sample values, taken during the observation time, and denote the hth sample value of the useful signal $m(t, G)$ at the time t_h by

$$m_h = m(t_h) = Gs_h. \tag{32.02}$$

According to formulas (29.24) and (31.18), the likelihood ratio $\Lambda(G)$ in the presence of normal noise is equal to

$$\Lambda(G) = p_m(G)e^{\varphi(G)-\frac{1}{2}\mu(G)}, \tag{32.03}$$

where $\varphi(G)$ and $\mu(G)$ are given by the expressions (31.16) and (31.17), and $p_m(G)$ is the probability density of the amplitude G. Substituting the values m_h given by formula (32.02) into the expressions for $\varphi(G)$ and $\mu(G)$, we obtain

$$\varphi(G) = G\varphi, \qquad \mu(G) = G^2\mu, \tag{32.04}$$

where φ and μ are defined by the formulas

$$\varphi = \varphi(1) = \sum_{g,h=1}^{H} Q_{gh} f_g s_h, \qquad \mu = \mu(1) = \sum_{g,h=1}^{H} Q_{gh} s_g s_h. \tag{32.05}$$

The average likelihood ratio, which determines the form of the optimum receiver, equals

$$\Lambda = \int \Lambda(G)\, dG = \int p_m(G) e^{G\varphi - (G^2\mu/2)}\, dG. \tag{32.06}$$

Since in (32.06) only the quantity φ depends on the received signal, and since Λ is a monotonically increasing function of φ, we can use the size of φ to decide whether or not the useful signal is present. Assuming that the parameter G can take both positive and negative values, we write the decision rule in the following form:

$$\begin{aligned} &\text{If} \quad |\varphi| \geqslant \varphi_*, \quad \text{decide that } f = m + n; \\ &\text{If} \quad |\varphi| < \varphi_*, \quad \text{decide that } f = n. \end{aligned} \tag{32.07}$$

We now find the false alarm probability F and the detection probability D in the case where the random amplitude has a normal distribution,[4] i.e., where

$$p_m(G) = \frac{1}{\sqrt{2\pi}} e^{-G^2/2}, \tag{32.08}$$

where we have normalized the amplitude G in such a way that

$$\overline{G} = 0, \qquad \overline{G^2} = 1. \tag{32.09}$$

In the absence of the useful signal, the random variable φ has the distribution (31.32), and in the presence of the useful signal, φ is also a normal random variable, with the moments

$$\bar{\varphi} = G\mu, \qquad \overline{(\varphi - \bar{\varphi})^2} = \mu \tag{32.10}$$

(here, we average over the noise, for fixed G), and with the distribution

$$p_m(\varphi, G) = \frac{1}{\sqrt{2\pi\mu}} e^{-(\varphi - G\mu)^2/2\mu}. \tag{32.11}$$

---

[4] The normal law (32.08) greatly simplifies the calculation of D, which justifies its use in this section. In later sections, we shall assume that the random amplitude G has a Rayleigh distribution (34.10) [see, however, formula (49.10)].

The distribution of φ in the presence of the useful signal is obtained by averaging the quantity (32.11) with respect to the random parameter G. The result is

$$\begin{aligned} p_m(\varphi) &= \int p_m(G) p_m(\varphi, G)\, dG \\ &= \frac{1}{2\pi\sqrt{\mu}} \int_{-\infty}^{\infty} e^{-(G^2/2)-(\varphi - G\mu)^2/2\mu}\, dG \\ &= \frac{1}{\sqrt{2\pi\mu(1+\mu)}} e^{-\varphi^2/2\mu(1+\mu)} \frac{1}{\sqrt{2\pi}} \int_{-\infty}^{\infty} e^{-z^2/2}\, dz \\ &= \frac{1}{\sqrt{2\pi\mu(1+\mu)}} e^{-\varphi^2/2\mu(1+\mu)}. \end{aligned} \tag{32.12}$$

Then, taking into account the fact that the useful signal may have either positive or negative amplitudes, we can write the expression

$$\begin{aligned} D &= 2 \int_{\varphi_*}^{\infty} p_m(\varphi)\, d\varphi \\ &= \frac{2}{\sqrt{2\pi}} \int_{y_*}^{\infty} e^{-z^2/2}\, dz \qquad \left(y_* = \frac{\varphi_*}{\sqrt{\mu(1+\mu)}}\right), \end{aligned} \tag{32.13}$$

for D, the total detection probability, and the expression

$$F = 2 \int_{\varphi_*}^{\infty} p_0(\varphi)\, d\varphi = \frac{2}{\sqrt{2\pi}} \int_{z_*}^{\infty} e^{-z^2/2}\, dz \qquad \left(z_* = \frac{\varphi_*}{\sqrt{\mu}}\right), \tag{32.14}$$

for the false alarm probability F. It follows that for given F and D, the signal-to-noise ratio can be calculated by the formula

$$\mu = \left(\frac{z_*}{y_*}\right)^2 - 1. \tag{32.15}$$

In Fig. 28, the dashed curves indicate the operating characteristics for detection of a signal with an unknown, normally distributed amplitude. A comparison of the curves for the completely known signal with the curves for the signal with unknown amplitude shows that reliable detection ($D \gtrsim \frac{1}{2}$) is more readily achieved when the amplitude of the signal is known, and conversely that unreliable detection ($D \lesssim \frac{1}{2}$) is more readily achieved when the amplitude is unknown. This result is quite understandable from a physical point of view. When μ is small, the amplitude of the signal with unknown amplitude will sometimes be large (due to its fluctuations), thereby leading to correct detection more readily than in the case of a fixed amplitude. On the other hand, when μ is large, the amplitude of the signal with unknown amplitude will sometimes be small (due to its fluctuations), thereby leading to false dismissal more readily than in the case of a fixed amplitude. In what follows, we shall frequently encounter similar effects.

33. Detection of a Signal with Unknown Phase

Next, we consider the detection of an r-f signal with unknown phase θ, assuming that the amplitude of the signal and all its other parameters are known. We write the useful signal in the form

$$m(t, \theta) = e(t) \cos [\omega_0 t - \psi(t) - \theta], \tag{33.01}$$

where $e(t)$ is its envelope, ω_0 is the carrier frequency, and $\psi(t)$ is its (slowly varying) supplementary phase, caused by frequency or phase modulation. In the present case, the sample values of the useful signal are

$$m_h(\theta) = e_h \cos (\omega_0 t_h - \psi_h - \theta), \tag{33.02}$$

and the likelihood ratio $\Lambda(\theta)$ can be written in the form

$$\Lambda(\theta) = p_m(\theta) e^{\varphi(\theta) - \frac{1}{2}\mu(\theta)}, \tag{33.03}$$

where

$$\varphi(\theta) = \sum_{g,h=1}^{H} Q_{gh} f_g m_h = \sum_{g,h=1}^{H} Q_{gh} f_g e_h \cos (\omega_0 t_h - \psi_h - \theta), \tag{33.04}$$

$$\begin{aligned} \mu(\theta) &= \sum_{g,h=1}^{H} Q_{gh} m_g m_h \\ &= \sum_{g,h=1}^{H} Q_{gh} e_g e_h \cos (\omega_0 t_g - \psi_g - \theta) \cos (\omega_0 t_h - \psi_h - \theta). \end{aligned} \tag{33.05}$$

We now modify these formulas somewhat, writing the quantity φ in the form

$$\begin{aligned} \varphi &= \cos \theta \sum_{g,h} Q_{gh} f_g e_h \cos (\omega_0 t_h - \psi_h) \\ &\quad + \sin \theta \sum_{g,h} Q_{gh} f_g e_h \sin (\omega_0 t_h - \psi_h) \\ &= x \cos \theta + y \sin \theta = \mathscr{E} \cos (\Phi - \theta), \end{aligned} \tag{33.06}$$

where we have introduced the notation

$$\begin{aligned} x &= \mathscr{E} \cos \Phi = \sum_{g,h} Q_{gh} f_g e_h \cos (\omega_0 t_h - \psi_h), \\ y &= \mathscr{E} \sin \Phi = \sum_{g,h} Q_{gh} f_g e_h \sin (\omega_0 t_h - \psi_h), \\ \mathscr{E} &= \sqrt{x^2 + y^2}, \qquad \tan \Phi = \frac{y}{x}. \end{aligned} \tag{33.07}$$

The quantity μ equals

$$\mu = \frac{1}{2} \sum_{g,h} Q_{gh} e_g e_h \cos [\omega_0(t_g - t_h) - (\psi_g - \psi_h)]$$
$$+ \frac{1}{2} \sum_{g,h} Q_{gh} e_g e_h \cos [\omega_0(t_g + t_h) - (\psi_g + \psi_h) - 2\theta], \tag{33.08}$$

where the second sum can usually be neglected compared to the first sum. In fact, the second sum contains rapidly oscillating terms which largely cancel one another out, whereas in the first sum, all the terms with $g = h$ (for example) are positive, and for a large number of sample values give a result which greatly exceeds the second sum. Therefore, we shall henceforth use the expression

$$\mu = \frac{1}{2} \sum_{g,h} Q_{gh} e_g e_h \cos [\omega_0(t_g - t_h) - (\psi_g - \psi_h)], \tag{33.09}$$

which no longer depends on the unknown phase θ.

To calculate the likelihood ratio Λ, we assume that the unknown r-f phase θ is uniformly distributed from 0 to 2π, so that

$$p_m(\theta) = \frac{1}{2\pi} \quad \text{for} \quad 0 \leqslant \theta < 2\pi. \tag{33.10}$$

Then

$$\Lambda = \int \Lambda(\theta)\, d\theta = \frac{1}{2\pi} \int_0^{2\pi} e^{\mathscr{E} \cos (\Phi - \theta) - (\mu/2)}\, d\theta = e^{-\mu/2} I_0(\mathscr{E}), \tag{33.11}$$

where $I_0(\mathscr{E})$ is the modified Bessel function of the first kind of order zero, defined by the formula

$$I_0(\mathscr{E}) = \frac{1}{2\pi} \int_0^{2\pi} e^{\mathscr{E} \cos \chi}\, d\chi. \tag{33.12}$$

The function $I_0(\mathscr{E})$ is a monotonically increasing function of its argument, and therefore we can base our decision on the quantity $\mathscr{E}$. Thus, the optimum decision rule is the following:

$$\begin{aligned} &\text{If} \quad \mathscr{E} \geqslant \mathscr{E}_*, \quad \text{decide that } f = m + n; \\ &\text{If} \quad \mathscr{E} < \mathscr{E}_*, \quad \text{decide that } f = n, \end{aligned} \tag{33.13}$$

where $\mathscr{E}_*$ is the decision threshold.

We now examine more closely the meaning of the quantity $\mathscr{E}$. According to (33.07),

$$\mathscr{E} = \sqrt{x^2 + y^2}, \tag{33.14}$$

where x and y are the quantities obtained at the output of two *quadrature* circuits, i.e., two circuits which are 90° out of phase with respect to each other. The first circuit is the optimum linear filter for detecting the useful signal $m(t, 0)$, i.e., the signal with phase $\theta = 0$, and the second circuit is the optimum linear filter for detecting the signal $m(t, \pi/2)$ with phase $\theta = \pi/2$. Therefore, $\mathscr{E}$ is the envelope of the output of an optimum linear filter for detecting a completely known signal.

As shown in Sec. 27, the transfer function of the filter forming the quantity (31.20) is equal to

$$K(\omega) = e^{-i\omega t_0} \frac{M^*(\omega)}{S_n(\omega)}, \tag{33.15}$$

where $M(\omega)$ is the amplitude spectrum of the signal $m(t)$. In the present case, the transfer functions of the filters forming the quantities x and y appearing in (33.07) are equal to

$$\begin{aligned} K_x(\omega) &= e^{-i\omega t_0} \frac{M^*(\omega, 0)}{S_n(\omega)}, \\ K_y(\omega) &= e^{-i\omega t_0} \frac{M^*(\omega, \pi/2)}{S_n(\omega)}, \end{aligned} \tag{33.16}$$

where $M(\omega, \theta)$ is the amplitude spectrum of the useful signal (33.01), which depends on the unknown phase θ. It was noted in Sec. 27 that in detecting a completely known signal, one does not require the whole function at the output of the filter (33.15), but only the quantity φ, i.e., its value at the time t_0. Thus, at the output of the filters (33.16), we obtain r-f signals of the form

$$\begin{aligned} x(t) &= \mathscr{E}(t) \cos [\omega_0 t - \Psi(t)], \\ y(t) &= \mathscr{E}(t) \sin [\omega_0 t - \Psi(t)], \end{aligned} \tag{33.17}$$

where $\Psi(t)$ is the slowly varying phase and

$$\mathscr{E}(t) = \sqrt{x^2(t) + y^2(t)} \tag{33.18}$$

is the envelope; at time $t = t_0$, these expressions reduce to the quantities x, y and $\mathscr{E}$ figuring in the formulas (33.07):

$$x = x(t_0), \qquad y = y(t_0), \qquad \mathscr{E} = \mathscr{E}(t_0). \tag{33.19}$$

The quantity $\mathscr{E}$ can also be obtained by using a single r-f filter, e.g., a filter with the transfer function $K_x(\omega)$ or $K_y(\omega)$, then detecting the r-f signal [e.g., one of the signals (33.17)] at the output of this filter,[5] and finally setting $\mathscr{E} = \mathscr{E}(t_0)$. Thus, when the phase of the useful signal (33.01) is unknown, we can obtain the optimum receiver by combining a detector with the optimum linear filter for extracting the signal when it has any fixed phase. What matters here is the value of the envelope at a definite time t_0.

[5] As is well known, this is equivalent to calculating $\mathscr{E}(t)$ by using formula (33.18).

It should be noted that instead of the envelope $\mathscr{E}$, the optimum receiver can form any monotonically increasing function of $\mathscr{E}$, for example $\mathscr{E}^2$, i.e., the receiver can act either as a half-wave linear detector or as a quadratic detector. Here we encounter the following phenomenon: Although the signal-to-noise ratio at the output of the half-wave linear detector, the quadratic detector, and other detectors, is different (cf. Sec. 18), the probability of correctly observing the presence of the signal for a given false alarm probability is the same, regardless of the characteristics of the detector, and hence, regardless of the post-detection signal-to-noise ratio, which, unlike the parameter μ, has no probabilistic significance.

We now calculate the false alarm probability F and the detection probability D. These probabilities are determined by the decision threshold $\mathscr{E}_*$ and by the distribution of the quantity $\mathscr{E}$. In the absence of the useful signal, the quantities x and y equal x_n and y_n, where

$$x_n = \sum_{g,h=1}^{H} Q_{gh} n_g e_h \cos(\omega_0 t_h - \psi_h),$$
$$y_n = \sum_{g,h=1}^{H} Q_{gh} n_g e_h \sin(\omega_0 t_h - \psi_h), \tag{33.20}$$

and where the moments of the normal random variables x_n and y_n are equal to

$$\overline{x_n} = \overline{y_n} = 0,$$
$$\overline{x_n y_n} = \sum_{g,h=1}^{H} Q_{gh} e_g e_h \cos(\omega_0 t_g - \psi_g) \sin(\omega_0 t_h - \psi_h) = 0, \tag{33.21}$$
$$\overline{x_n^2} = \overline{y_n^2} = \sum_{g,h=1}^{H} Q_{gh} e_g e_h \cos(\omega_0 t_g - \psi_g) \cos(\omega_0 t_h - \psi_h) = \mu.$$

Here, as in going from (33.08) to (33.09), we neglect "oscillating sums." First, we find the distribution of the quantity

$$E_n = \sqrt{x_n^2 + y_n^2}, \tag{33.22}$$

where x_n and y_n are normal random variables with moments

$$\overline{x_n} = \overline{y_n} = 0, \qquad \overline{x_n y_n} = 0, \qquad \overline{x_n^2} = \overline{y_n^2} = \sigma^2. \tag{33.23}$$

This is the quantity formed at the output of the quadrature circuits of nonoptimum filters in the absence of the useful signal. For optimum filters, $\sigma^2 = \mu$ and we return to the formulas (33.21).

Because of the independence of the normal random variables x_n and y_n, their two-dimensional probability density is

$$p(x_n, y_n) = \frac{1}{2\pi\sigma^2} e^{-(x_n^2+y_n^2)/2}, \tag{33.24}$$

i.e., $p(x_n, y_n)$ is the product of two one-dimensional Gaussian distributions. Going from Cartesian coordinates x_n, y_n to polar coordinates E_n, ψ by using the formulas

$$\begin{gathered} x_n = E_n \cos\psi, \qquad y_n = E_n \sin\psi, \\ dx_n dy_n = E_n dE_n\, d\psi, \end{gathered} \tag{33.25}$$

we obtain the probability density

$$p_0(E_n, \psi) = \frac{E_n}{2\pi\sigma^2} e^{-E_n^2/2\sigma^2}, \tag{33.26}$$

which shows that the random variables E_n and ψ are independent. The quantity E_n has the so-called *Rayleigh distribution*

$$p_0(E_n) = \frac{E_n}{\sigma^2} e^{-E_n^2/2\sigma^2}, \tag{33.27}$$

while the phase ψ is uniformly distributed in the interval $(0, 2\pi)$.

Next, using (33.27), we find the false alarm probability F, which is the probability that the quantity E_n exceeds the decision threshold $\mathscr{E}_*$:

$$\begin{aligned} F &= \int_{\mathscr{E}_*}^{\infty} \frac{E_n}{\sigma^2} e^{-E_n^2/2\sigma^2}\, dE_n = \int_{z_*}^{\infty} z e^{-z^2/2}\, dz \\ &= e^{-z_*^2/2} \qquad \left(z_* = \frac{E_*}{\sigma}\right). \end{aligned} \tag{33.28}$$

Therefore, the normalized decision threshold z_* and the probability F are related by the simple formula

$$z_* = \sqrt{-2 \ln F}, \tag{33.29}$$

which is plotted as the dashed curve in Fig. 26.

In the presence of the useful signal, the quantities x and y equal

$$x = x_m + x_n, \qquad y = y_m + y_n, \tag{33.30}$$

where

$$x_m = \mu \cos\theta, \qquad y_m = \mu \sin\theta. \tag{33.31}$$

In this case, the envelope has a so-called *Rice distribution* (or *modified Rayleigh distribution*), which we now find, assuming that x_n, y_n are normal as before, with the moments (33.23), and that x_m, y_m equal

$$x_m = \bar{\varphi} \cos\theta, \qquad y = \bar{\varphi} \sin\theta, \tag{33.32}$$

where, for the optimum linear operation described by (33.04), the mean value $\bar{\varphi} = \mu$. Here, we have to make a distinction between the envelope E_n and the phase ψ, corresponding to the noise, and the envelope $\mathscr{E}$ and the phase $\chi = \Phi - \theta$, corresponding to the sum of signal plus noise. We have

$$\begin{aligned}\mathscr{E} &= \sqrt{(x_m + x_n)^2 + (y_m + y_n)^2} \\ &= \sqrt{(\bar{\varphi} \cos \theta + E_n \cos \psi)^2 + (\bar{\varphi} \sin \theta + E_n \sin \psi)^2}\end{aligned} \tag{33.33}$$

or

$$\mathscr{E} = \sqrt{(\bar{\varphi})^2 + 2\bar{\varphi} E_n \cos \Psi + E_n^2} \qquad (\Psi = \psi - \theta), \tag{33.34}$$

and therefore $\mathscr{E}$ is a function of the constant quantity $\bar{\varphi}$ and the random variables E_n and Ψ.

Thus, to find the probability density $p_m(\mathscr{E})$ in the presence of the useful signal, we can use the formula

$$p_m(\mathscr{E})\, d\mathscr{E} = \frac{1}{2\pi\sigma^2} \iint_{(\mathscr{E},\, \mathscr{E} + d\mathscr{E})} E_n\, e^{-E_n^2/2\sigma^2}\, dE_n\, d\Psi, \tag{33.35}$$

where the integration is over the indicated range of the quantity (33.34). We now go from the polar coordinates E_n and Ψ to the rectangular coordinates

$$\xi = E_n \cos \Psi, \qquad \eta = E_n \sin \Psi, \tag{33.36}$$

obtaining

$$p_m(\mathscr{E})\, d\mathscr{E} = \frac{1}{2\pi\sigma^2} \iint_{(\mathscr{E},\, \mathscr{E} + d\mathscr{E})} e^{-(\xi^2 + \eta^2)/2\sigma^2}\, d\xi\, d\eta. \tag{33.37}$$

Then, we go over to new polar coordinates $\mathscr{E}$ and χ by using the formulas

$$\bar{\varphi} + \xi = \mathscr{E} \cos \chi, \qquad \eta = \mathscr{E} \sin \chi. \tag{33.38}$$

Because of the relation

$$E_n^2 = \xi^2 + \eta^2 = (\bar{\varphi})^2 - 2\bar{\varphi}\mathscr{E} \cos \chi + \mathscr{E}^2, \tag{33.39}$$

we obtain

$$p_m(\mathscr{E})\, d\mathscr{E} = \frac{\mathscr{E}\, d\mathscr{E}}{\sigma^2}\, e^{-[(\bar{\varphi})^2 + \mathscr{E}^2]/2\sigma^2}\, \frac{1}{2\pi} \int_0^{2\pi} e^{(\bar{\varphi}\mathscr{E}/\sigma^2) \cos \chi}\, d\chi, \tag{33.40}$$

or finally

$$p_m(\mathscr{E}) = \frac{\mathscr{E}}{\sigma^2}\, e^{-[(\bar{\varphi})^2 + \mathscr{E}^2]/2\sigma^2} I_0\!\left(\frac{\bar{\varphi}\mathscr{E}}{\sigma^2}\right). \tag{33.41}$$

In the absence of the useful signal ($\bar{\varphi} = 0$), formula (33.41) reduces to (33.27). In the presence of the useful signal, if the optimum linear filter is used, so that $\bar{\varphi} = \sigma^2 = \mu$, (33.41) simplifies to

$$p_m(\mathscr{E}) = \frac{\mathscr{E}}{\mu}\, e^{-(\mu^2 + \mathscr{E}^2)/2\mu} I_0(\mathscr{E}). \tag{33.42}$$

In the general case, the detection probability D equals

$$D = \int_{\mathscr{E}_*}^{\infty} \frac{\mathscr{E}}{\sigma^2} e^{-[(\bar{\varphi})^2+\mathscr{E}^2]/2\sigma^2} I_0\left(\frac{\bar{\varphi}\mathscr{E}}{\sigma^2}\right) d\mathscr{E}. \tag{33.43}$$

Introducing the dimensionless variables

$$z = \frac{\mathscr{E}}{\sigma}, \qquad \rho = \left(\frac{\bar{\varphi}}{\sigma}\right)^2, \tag{33.44}$$

and using (33.41),[6] we obtain

$$p_m(z) = ze^{-(\rho+z^2)/2} I_0(\sqrt{\rho}\, z), \tag{33.45}$$

which satisfies the identity

$$\int_0^{\infty} p_m(z)\, dz = \int_0^{\infty} ze^{-(\rho+z^2)/2} I_0(\sqrt{\rho}\, z)\, dz = 1. \tag{33.46}$$

Thus, the probabilities F and D are equal to

$$\begin{aligned} F &= e^{-z_*^2/2} \qquad \left(z_* = \frac{\mathscr{E}_*}{\sigma}\right), \\ D &= \int_{z_*}^{\infty} ze^{-(\rho+z^2)/2} I_0(\sqrt{\rho}\, z)\, dz, \end{aligned} \tag{33.47}$$

[cf. formula (33.28)]. For the optimum receiver, we have

$$\begin{aligned} F &= e^{-z_*^2/2} \qquad \left(z_* = \frac{\mathscr{E}_*}{\sqrt{\mu}}\right), \\ D &= \int_{z_*}^{\infty} ze^{-(\mu+z^2)/2} I_0(\sqrt{\mu}\, z)\, dz, \end{aligned} \tag{33.48}$$

where we have used the relation $\sigma^2 = \rho = \mu$.

Tables of the integrals (33.47) have been prepared by S. A. Navolotskaya,[7] but these tables are not adequate for calculating D when ρ or μ is large. This deficiency is remedied by the asymptotic formula

$$D = \int_{z_*}^{\infty} ze^{-(\mu+z^2)/2} I_0(\sqrt{\mu}\, z)\, dz = \frac{1}{\sqrt{2\pi}} \int_{y_*}^{\infty} e^{-y^2/2}\, dy, \tag{33.49}$$

---

[6] In going from the variable $\mathscr{E}$ to the new variable z, we obtain a *new* function $p_m(z)$, related to the old function $p_m(\mathscr{E})$ by the formula

$$p_m(\mathscr{E})d\mathscr{E} = p_m(z)dz.$$

[7] S. A. Navolotskaya, Таблицы функции распределения Райса (*Tables of the Rice distribution function*), unpublished.

obtained by V. I. Bunimovich,[8] where

$$y_* = z_* - \sqrt{\mu} - \eta, \tag{33.50}$$

and

$$\eta = \frac{1}{2\sqrt{\mu}} - \frac{z_* - \sqrt{\mu}}{(2\sqrt{\mu})^2} + \cdots \tag{33.51}$$

A simplified derivation of this formula will be given in Sec. 38. We note that for $\eta = 0$, the expression (33.49) reduces formally to formula (31.35) for simple detection.

In Fig. 29, we plot the results of calculating D by using tables of the Rice distribution (solid curves) and by using formula (33.49) with $\eta = 1/2\sqrt{\mu}$ (dashed curves) and with $\eta = 0$ (dotted curves). We see that using the first term of the asymptotic expression (33.51) already gives quite an accurate approximation, which is more accurate than setting $\eta = 0$. As $\mu \to \infty$, both approximate formulas approach the exact expressions.

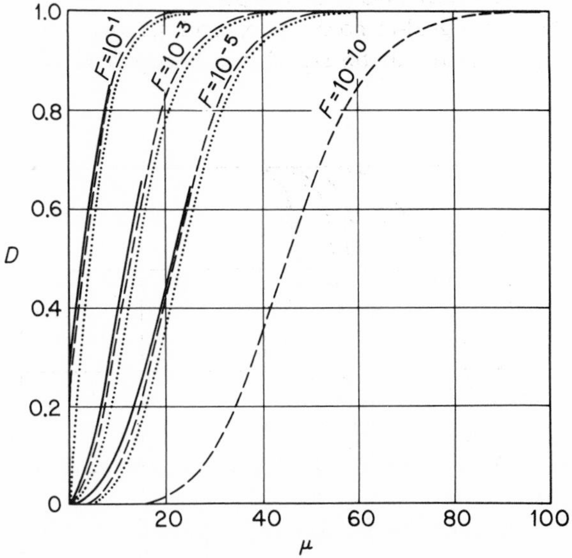

FIG. 29. Operating characteristics for detection of a signal with unknown phase.
Solid curves, using tables of the Rice distribution;
Dashed curves, using Bunimovich's formula, with $\eta = 1/2\sqrt{\mu}$;
Dotted curves, using Bunimovich's formula, with $\eta = 0$.

[8] V. I. Bunimovich, Приближённое выражение вероятности правильного обнаружения при оптимальном приёме сигнала с неизвестной фазой (*An approximate expression for the probability of correct detection in optimum reception of a signal with unknown phase*), Radiotekh. i Elektron., **3**, 552 (1958).

In Sec. 18, we showed that after a mixture of a signal plus strong noise goes through a detector, the signal-to-noise ratio is decreased. Thus, we might assume that as a result of going through the detector which is unavoidable in the case where the phase is unknown, the probability of observing the presence of the signal will be decreased. This assumption turns out to be justified. In Fig. 30, we compare simple detection (the solid curves) with detection of a signal with unknown phase (the dashed curves). The figure shows that for given values of F and D, a somewhat larger signal-to-noise ratio is needed to detect the signal with unknown phase. Moreover, in Sec. 18, it was also shown that after a mixture of a signal plus *weak* noise through a detector, the signal-to-noise ratio is increased. However, this increase is not connected with any actual gain in the ability to observe the presence of the useful signal. This fact only serves to illustrate Woodward's remarks (see Sec. 28) to the effect that the signal-to-noise ratio is often only indirectly related to the actual observability of useful signals.

Nevertheless, as we have seen, the parameter μ comes to the fore quite naturally in the statistical theory of reception. This parameter plays the role of an effective signal-to-noise ratio, and actually characterizes the possibility of detecting the useful signal in a background of normal noise.

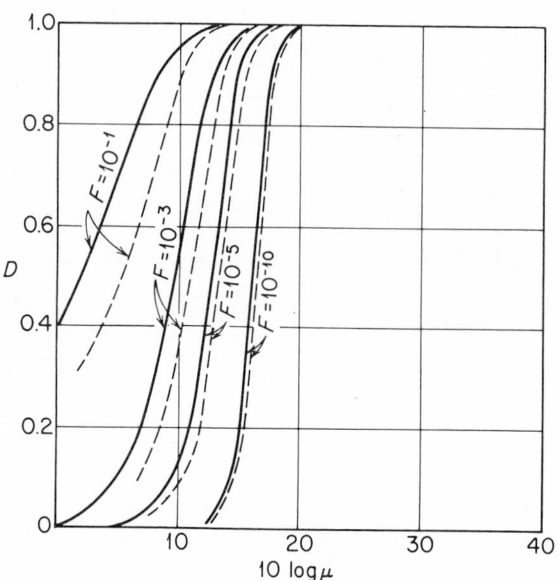

FIG. 30. Comparison of the operating characteristics for detection of a completely known signal (solid curves) and of a signal with unknown phase (dashed curves).

In particular, by using μ, we have been able to compare detection of a completely known signal with detection of a signal with unknown amplitude or unknown phase, and thanks to the uniform definition of μ in all these cases, we have been able to understand the influence of the unknown parameters on the detectability of the signal.

34. Detection of a Signal with Unknown Phase and Unknown Amplitude

In many problems, two parameters are unknown, i.e., the r-f phase θ and the amplitude (envelope) G of the signal. For example, a radar signal reflected from a target has an unknown phase and also fluctuates. If the observation time is small compared to the "fluctuation time," then the unknown parameters θ and G can be regarded as constant.

Thus, we write the useful signal in the form

$$m(t, G, \theta) = Ge(t)\cos[\omega_0 t - \psi(t) - \theta], \tag{34.01}$$

with sample values equal to

$$m_h(G, \theta) = Ge_h \cos(\omega_0 t_h - \psi_h - \theta). \tag{34.02}$$

The likelihood ratio $\Lambda(G, \theta)$ is given by the expression

$$\Lambda(G, \theta) = p_m(G, \theta)e^{\varphi(G,\theta)-\frac{1}{2}\mu(G,\theta)}, \tag{34.03}$$

where

$$\begin{aligned} \varphi &= G\sum_{g,h} Q_{gh} f_g e_h \cos(\omega_0 t_h - \psi_h - \theta) \\ &= G\mathscr{E}\cos(\Phi - \theta), \\ \mathscr{E}\cos\Phi &= \sum_{g,h} Q_{gh} f_g e_h \cos(\omega_0 t_h - \psi_h), \\ \mathscr{E}\sin\Phi &= \sum_{g,h} Q_{gh} f_g e_h \sin(\omega_0 t_h - \psi_h), \end{aligned} \tag{34.04}$$

and

$$\mu(G, \theta) \doteq \frac{G^2}{2}\sum_{g,h} Q_{gh} e_g e_h \cos[\omega_0(t_g - t_h) - (\psi_g - \psi_h)] = G^2\mu. \tag{34.05}$$

Here, μ is defined by formula (33.09).

Next, we find the likelihood ratio $\Lambda(G)$, assuming that the phase is uniformly distributed from 0 to 2π:

$$p_m(G, \theta) = \frac{1}{2\pi} p_m(G). \tag{34.06}$$

Thus, we obtain

$$\Lambda(G) = \int_0^{2\pi} \Lambda(G, \theta)\, d\theta = p_m(G) e^{-G^2\mu/2} I_0(G\mathscr{E}), \tag{34.07}$$

and the likelihood ratio Λ equals

$$\Lambda = \int \Lambda(G)\, dG. \tag{34.08}$$

Formulas (34.07) and (34.08) show that Λ is a monotonically increasing function of $\mathscr{E}$. Therefore, we can use the quantity $\mathscr{E}$ to decide whether or not the useful signal is present. Hence, the optimum decision rule will be the same as for the case of unknown phase or the case of unknown amplitude:

$$\begin{aligned} &\text{If} \quad \mathscr{E} \geqslant \mathscr{E}_*, \quad \text{decide that } f = m + n; \\ &\text{If} \quad \mathscr{E} < \mathscr{E}_*, \quad \text{decide that } f = n, \end{aligned} \tag{34.09}$$

where $\mathscr{E}_*$ is the decision threshold.

In what follows, we shall need the quantity Λ for the case where the amplitude has a Rayleigh distribution

$$p_m(G) = G e^{-G^2/2}, \tag{34.10}$$

where we have normalized the envelope $G \geqslant 0$ in such a way that

$$\overline{G^2} = 2, \qquad \bar{G} = \sqrt{\pi}/2. \tag{34.11}$$

Then we have

$$\Lambda = \int_0^\infty G e^{-(1+\mu)G^2/2} I_0(G\mathscr{E})\, dG. \tag{34.12}$$

Introducing the new variable

$$z = G\sqrt{1 + \mu}, \tag{34.13}$$

we transform the integral (34.12) into the form

$$\Lambda = \frac{1}{1 + \mu} \int_0^\infty z e^{-z^2/2} I_0\left(\frac{\mathscr{E} z}{\sqrt{1 + \mu}}\right) dz. \tag{34.14}$$

Multiplying and dividing this expression by $\exp\{\mathscr{E}^2/2(1 + \mu)\}$, we obtain

$$\Lambda = \frac{1}{1 + \mu} e^{\mathscr{E}^2/2(1+\mu)} \int_0^\infty z e^{-\{[E^2/(1+\mu)]+z^2\}/2} I_0\left(\frac{\mathscr{E} z}{\sqrt{1 + \mu}}\right) dz. \tag{34.15}$$

The integral in (34.15) equals 1, because of the identity (33.46), and hence we have finally

$$\Lambda = \frac{1}{1 + \mu} e^{\mathscr{E}^2/2(1+\mu)}. \tag{34.16}$$

We now find F and D. In the absence of the useful signal, the quantity $\mathscr{E}$ has a Rayleigh distribution, and therefore, the false alarm probability equals

$$F = e^{-z_*^2/2} \quad \left(z_* = \frac{\mathscr{E}_*}{\sqrt{\mu}}\right). \tag{34.17}$$

In the presence of the useful signal and for fixed G, we have

$$\varphi = G\mu + \nu, \qquad \bar{\varphi} = G\mu, \qquad \overline{\nu^2} = \mu, \tag{34.18}$$

and the probability density of the quantity $\mathscr{E}$, in the presence of a signal of amplitude G, is equal to

$$p_m(\mathscr{E}, G) = \frac{\mathscr{E}}{\mu} e^{-(G^2\mu^2+\mathscr{E}^2)/2\mu} I_0(G\mathscr{E}) \tag{34.19}$$

[cf. formula (33.42)]. Thus, for fixed G, the probability of correct detection is

$$D(G) = \int_{\mathscr{E}_*}^{\infty} p_m(\mathscr{E}, G)\, d\mathscr{E} = \int_{z_*}^{\infty} z e^{-(G^2\mu+z^2)/2} I_0(G\sqrt{\mu}z)\, dz. \tag{34.20}$$

The total probability of correct detection can be written as follows:

$$\begin{aligned} D &= \int p_m(G) D(G)\, dG \\ &= \int_0^{\infty} G e^{-G^2/2}\, dG \int_{z_*}^{\infty} z e^{-(G^2\mu+z^2)/2} I_0(G\sqrt{\mu}z)\, dz \\ &= \int_{z_*}^{\infty} z e^{-z^2/2}\, dz \int_0^{\infty} G e^{-(1+\mu)G^2/2} I_0(G\sqrt{\mu}z)\, dG. \end{aligned} \tag{34.21}$$

Calculating the inner integral in the same way as in going from (34.12) to (34.16), we finally obtain

$$\begin{aligned} D &= \int_{z_*}^{\infty} z e^{-z^2/2} \frac{1}{1+\mu} e^{\mu z^2/2(1+\mu)}\, dz = \frac{1}{1+\mu} \int_{z_*}^{\infty} z e^{-z^2/2(1+\mu)}\, dz \\ &= e^{-z_*^2/2(1+\mu)} = e^{-y_*^2/2}, \end{aligned} \tag{34.22}$$

where

$$y_* = \frac{z_*}{\sqrt{1+\mu}}. \tag{34.23}$$

For given F and D, the quantity μ can be calculated from the formula

$$\mu = \left(\frac{z_*}{y_*}\right)^2 - 1 = \frac{\ln F}{\ln D} - 1. \tag{34.24}$$

Thus, in the present case, the probabilities F and D are connected by the relation

$$D = F^{1/(1+\mu)}, \tag{34.25}$$

the simplicity of which is explained by the fact that with the envelope and phase distributions chosen above for the useful signal, we obtain normal random variables at the output of the quadrature filters (cf. Sec. 33). In fact, the formulas (34.04) can be written in the form (33.07), with $x = x_n$ and $y = y_n$ in the absence of the useful signal, where x_n and y_n are given by (33.20) and have the moments (33.21). In the presence of the useful signal, we have

$$x = x_m + x_n, \qquad y = y_m + y_n, \tag{34.26}$$

where the random variables x_m and y_m are equal to

$$x_m = G\mu \cos\theta, \qquad y_m = G\mu \sin\theta. \tag{34.27}$$

Because of formulas (34.06) and (34.10), x_m and y_m are normal random variables with moments

$$\overline{x_m} = \overline{y_m} = 0, \qquad \overline{x_m^2} = \overline{y_m^2} = \mu^2, \qquad \overline{x_m y_m} = 0; \tag{34.28}$$

moreover, x_m and y_m are independent of x_n and y_n. Therefore, the sums (34.26) are also normal and have the moments

$$\bar{x} = \bar{y} = 0, \qquad \overline{x^2} = \overline{y^2} = \mu^2 + \mu, \qquad \overline{xy} = 0. \tag{34.29}$$

Thus, in the present problem, the appearance of the signal does not change the distribution law of the quantity $\mathscr{E}$, but only changes the parameter in the distribution from μ to $\mu(1 + \mu)$. Therefore, formula (34.17)

$$F = e^{-\mathscr{E}_*^2/2\mu} \tag{34.30}$$

immediately implies formula (34.22)

$$D = e^{-\mathscr{E}_*^2/2\mu(1+\mu)}, \tag{34.31}$$

from which we obtain the relation (34.25). It is also easy to derive formula (34.31) from (31.39) and (34.16); we leave this to the reader. Moreover, we recommend that the reader use this last method to calculate D in the other cases as well, and that he find D and F for the case where nonoptimum linear operations are performed on the input data.

We note that whether or not the amplitude of the signal is known, the optimum receiver for detecting the signal has to perform the same operations on the received data. However, the detection probabilities are quite different in the two cases. In Fig. 31, the dashed curves indicate the operating characteristics of the optimum receiver for detecting a signal with unknown phase and unknown amplitude, while the solid curves give the corresponding curves for detecting a signal with unknown phase and known amplitude. We see again (cf. the end of Sec. 32) that when the phase is unknown, unreliable detection of the signal with unknown amplitude is easier, while reliable detection is harder.

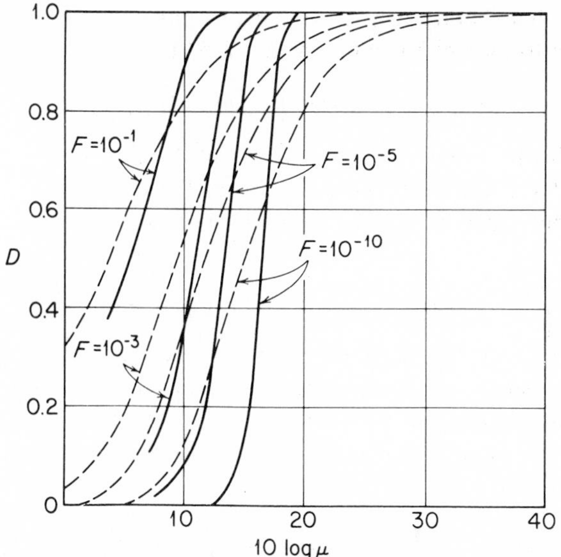

FIG. 31. Comparison of the operating characteristics for detection of a signal with unknown phase (solid curves) and a signal with unknown phase and amplitude (dashed curves).

35. Detection of Random Signals[9]

If sampling is used, then the problem of detecting a random signal with a given correlation function in a background of random noise reduces to the problem of detecting one random sequence in the presence of another random sequence. We shall assume that both the useful signal and the noise are stationary normal random processes with zero mean values ($\overline{m_h} = \overline{n_h} = 0$) and given correlation functions, $R^m_{gh} = R_m(|g - h|\,\Delta t)$ for the useful signal and $R^n_{gh} = R_n(|g - h|\,\Delta t)$ for the noise. Then, our problem can be posed as follows: *Decide whether the received sequence $f_1, \ldots, f_H$ is a mixture of the useful signal and the noise ($f_h = m_h + n_h$) or whether it is pure noise ($f_h = n_h$).* According to the classification of Sec. 28, this is composite detection of a useful signal with the H unknown parameters

$$m_1, \ldots, m_H. \tag{35.01}$$

The likelihood ratio for fixed values of $m_1, \ldots, m_H$ equals

$$\Lambda(m_1, \ldots, m_H) = p_m(m_1, \ldots, m_H)\,\frac{P_{m_1,\cdots,m_H}(f)}{P_{0,\cdots,0}(f)}, \tag{35.02}$$

where $p_m(m_1, \ldots, m_H)$ is the probability density of the quantities (35.01).

[9] I.e., detection of one random process (the useful signal) in the presence of another random process (the noise), when the two processes have given correlation properties.

To find the likelihood ratio Λ, we have to integrate the expression (35.02) with respect to the unknown parameters (35.01):

$$\Lambda = \int \cdots \int \Lambda(m_1, \ldots, m_H)\, dm_1 \ldots dm_H. \tag{35.03}$$

However, in the present case, we can find Λ more simply: According to formula (31.11), the probability density of the quantities $f_1, \ldots, f_H$, given that the input signal reduces to noise alone ($f_h = n_h$), equals

$$p_0(f) = \frac{1}{\sqrt{(2\pi)^H \det \|R^n_{gh}\|}} \exp\left\{-\frac{1}{2}\sum_{g,h=1}^{H} Q^n_{gh} f_g f_h\right\}, \tag{35.04}$$

where the Q^n_{gh} are the elements of the matrix which is the inverse of the correlation matrix $\|R^n_{gh}\|$ (whose determinant is denoted by $\det \|R^n_{gh}\|$). On the other hand, the probability density of the quantities $f_1, \ldots, f_H$, given that the input signal consists of the useful signal plus noise ($f_h = m_h + n_h$), equals

$$p_m(f) = \frac{1}{\sqrt{(2\pi)^H \det \|R^f_{gh}\|}} \exp\left\{-\frac{1}{2}\sum_{g,h=1}^{H} Q^f_{gh} f_g f_h\right\}, \tag{35.05}$$

where R^f_{gh} is the correlation function of the sum $f = m + n$, and the Q^f_{gh} are the elements of the matrix which is the inverse of the matrix $\|R^f_{gh}\|$. If we assume that the useful signal m and the noise n are independent (so that $\overline{m_g n_h} = 0$), then

$$R^f_{gh} = R^m_{gh} + R^n_{gh}. \tag{35.06}$$

It follows from (35.04) and (35.05) that the likelihood ratio is

$$\Lambda = \frac{p_m(f)}{p_0(f)} = \sqrt{\frac{\det \|R^n_{gh}\|}{\det \|R^f_{gh}\|}}\, e^{S/2}, \tag{35.07}$$

where

$$S = \sum_{g,h=1}^{H} (Q^n_{gh} - Q^f_{gh}) f_g f_h = \sum_{g,h=1}^{H} K_{gh} f_g f_h \tag{35.08}$$

and

$$K_{gh} = Q^n_{gh} - Q^f_{gh}. \tag{35.09}$$

Since Λ is a monotonically increasing function of S, we can base our decision on the value of S. Formula (35.08) shows that the optimum receiver for detection of a noise-like signal is a nonlinear device which forms the quadratic function (35.08). The optimum decision rule has the following form:

$$\begin{aligned} &\text{If} \quad S \geqslant S_*, \quad \text{decide that } f = m + n; \\ &\text{If} \quad S < S_*, \quad \text{decide that } f = n, \end{aligned} \tag{35.10}$$

where S_* is the decision threshold.

We now consider some special cases of the optimum receiver:

1. *Detection of an uncorrelated sequence in the presence of another uncorrelated sequence.* In this case, the elements of the correlation matrices of the noise and the useful signal satisfy the relations

$$R^n_{gh} = \overline{n^2}\delta_{gh}, \qquad R^m_{gh} = \overline{m^2}\delta_{gh}, \tag{35.11}$$

where δ_{gh} is the Kronecker delta. Then, the quantity S equals

$$S = \frac{\overline{m^2}}{\overline{n^2}(\overline{m^2} + \overline{n^2})} \sum_{h=1}^{H} f_h^2. \tag{35.12}$$

Thus, the optimum receiver has to form the sum of the squares of the sample values of the input signal. Using formula (31.27), we arrive at the expression

$$S = \frac{S_m}{S_m(S_m + S_n)} \Delta t \sum_{h=1}^{H} f_h^2. \tag{35.13}$$

2. *Detection of a correlated sequence in the presence of a "strong" uncorrelated sequence.* In this case, the correlation matrices have the form

$$R^n_{gh} = \overline{n^2}\delta_{gh}, \qquad R^f_{gh} = \overline{n^2}\delta_{gh} + R^m_{gh} = \overline{n^2}\left(\delta_{gh} + \frac{R^m_{gh}}{\overline{n^2}}\right). \tag{35.14}$$

Assuming that $\overline{n^2} \gg \overline{m^2}$, we can write the approximate expression

$$Q^f_{gh} = \frac{1}{\overline{n^2}}\left(\delta_{gh} - \frac{R^m_{gh}}{\overline{n^2}}\right) \tag{35.15}$$

for the elements of the inverse matrix, which satisfy the relation

$$\sum_{=1}^{H} R^f_{gj} Q^f_{jh} = \delta_{gh}. \tag{35.16}$$

The error in (35.15) is of order $(\overline{m^2}/\overline{n^2})^2$. To this approximation, we obtain the expression

$$S = \frac{1}{(\overline{n^2})^2} \sum_{g,h=1}^{H} R^m_{gh} f_g f_h. \tag{35.17}$$

If we set $R^m_{gh} = \overline{m^2}\,\delta_{gh}$ in (35.17), then we obtain formula (35.12), where the factor $\overline{m^2} + \overline{n^2}$ in the denominator is replaced by $\overline{n^2}$.

3. *Detection of a random sequence in the presence of a strongly correlated (i.e., slowly varying) sequence.* In this case, the correlation matrices have the form

$$\overline{m_g m_h} = R^m_{gh}, \qquad \overline{n_g n_h} = R^n_{gh} \sim R_n(0). \tag{35.18}$$

Then, the elements of the inverse matrix Q^n_{gh} are large and the general formula (35.08) can be written as

$$S = \sum_{g, h=1}^{H} Q^n_{gh} f_g f_h. \tag{35.19}$$

Suppose now that the matrix R^n_{gh} has the form

$$R^n_{gh} = R_n(0) r^{|g-h|} \qquad (-1 < r < 1). \tag{35.20}$$

Then, the elements of the inverse matrix are

$$\begin{aligned} Q^n_{11} = Q^n_{HH} &= \frac{1}{R_n(0)} \frac{1}{1 - r^2}, \\ Q^n_{gg} &= \frac{1}{R_n(0)} \frac{1 + r^2}{1 - r^2} \qquad (1 < g < H), \\ Q^n_{g, g+1} = Q^n_{g+1, g} &= \frac{1}{R_n(0)} \frac{-r}{1 - r^2} \qquad (1 \leqslant g \leqslant H - 1), \end{aligned} \tag{35.21}$$

while the rest are zero. The formulas (35.21) can be obtained by calculating the inverse matrix according to the general rule (31.09), but the simplest way to verify these formulas is just to substitute them into the relation (31.08). In fact, it follows from (35.21) that the general element of the inverse matrix is

$$Q^n_{gh} = \frac{1}{R_n(0)(1 - r^2)} \{[1 + r^2(1 - \delta_{1h} - \delta_{Hh})]\, \delta_{gh} - r(\delta_{g, h-1} + \delta_{g, h+1})\}, \tag{35.22}$$

and then substituting (35.22) and (35.20) into (31.08), we obtain

$$\begin{aligned} \sum_j R^n_{gj} Q^n_{jh} &= \frac{1}{1 - r^2} \sum_j r^{|g-j|} \{[1 + r^2(1 - \delta_{1h} - \delta_{Hh})]\, \delta_{jh} \\ &\qquad - r(\delta_{j, h-1} + \delta_{j, h+1})\} \\ &= \frac{1}{1 - r^2} \{r^{|g-h|}[1 + r^2(1 - \delta_{1h} - \delta_{Hh})] \\ &\qquad - r^{|g-h+1|+1}(1 - \delta_{1h}) - r^{|g-h-1|+1}(1 - \delta_{Hh})\}, \end{aligned} \tag{35.23}$$

which for $g > h$ and $g < h$ gives

$$\sum R^n_{gj} Q^n_{jh} = 0, \tag{35.24}$$

and for $g = h$ gives

$$\sum_j R^n_{gj} Q^n_{jh} = \frac{1}{1 - r^2}(1 - r^2) = 1. \tag{35.25}$$

We note that, like the direct matrix (35.20), the inverse matrix (35.21) is symmetric. However, unlike the elements of the direct matrix, the elements of the inverse matrix depend on g and h, and not just on $|g - h|$. Nevertheless, the expressions

$$Q^n_{gh} = Q_n(|g - h|\,\Delta t),$$

$$Q_n(0) = \frac{1}{R_n(0)}\frac{1 + r^2}{1 - r^2}, \qquad Q_n(\Delta t) = -\frac{1}{R_n(0)}\frac{r}{1 - r^2}, \tag{35.26}$$

$$Q_n(2\,\Delta t) = Q_n(3\,\Delta t) = \cdots = 0$$

give an incorrect result only for $g = h = 1$ and $g = h = H$. Thus, the fact that the elements Q^n_{gh} of the inverse matrix depend on the indices g and h separately is an "edge effect," associated with the ends of the observation interval.

Returning to formula (35.19) and assuming that $r \sim 1$, we obtain

$$S = \frac{1}{(1 - r^2)R_n(0)}[(f_1 - f_2)^2 + (f_2 - f_3)^2 + \cdots + (f_{H-1} - f_H)^2], \tag{35.27}$$

i.e., the optimum way to treat the data is to add up the squares of consecutive differences.

We now find the false alarm probability F and the detection probability D. We shall assume not only that the number of sample values H is large but also that a large number of these sample values are statistically independent. Then, it is natural to use the central limit theorem of probability theory, so that the quantity (35.08) can be regarded as having a normal distribution.

When the useful signal is absent, the mean value of the random variable S equals

$$\begin{aligned} a_0 = \bar{S} &= \sum_{g,h} (Q^n_{gh} - Q^f_{gh})\overline{n_g n_h} = \sum_{g,h} (Q^n_{gh} - Q^f_{gh})R^n_{gh} \\ &= H - \sum_{g,h} Q^f_{gh}R^f_{gh} + \sum_{g,h} Q^f_{gh}R^m_{gh} = \sum_{g,h} Q^f_{gh}R^m_{gh}, \end{aligned} \tag{35.28}$$

and when the useful signal is present (at the receiver input), the mean value of S equals

$$\begin{aligned} a_1 = \bar{S} &= \sum_{g,h} (Q^n_{gh} - Q^f_{gh})R^f_{gh} \\ &= \sum_{g,h} Q^n_{gh}R^n_{gh} + \sum_{g,h} Q^n_{gh}R^m_{gh} - \sum_{g,h} Q^f_{gh}R_{gh} \\ &= \sum_{g,h} Q^n_{gh}R^m_{gh}. \end{aligned} \tag{35.29}$$

Using the formula (58.11)

$$\overline{n_g n_h n_k n_l} = R^n_{gh} R^n_{kl} + R^n_{gk} R^n_{hl} + R^n_{gl} R^n_{hk}, \tag{35.30}$$

we find that the variance of the random variable S equals

$$\begin{aligned} b_0 = \overline{S^2} - a_0^2 &= \sum_{g,h} \sum_{k,l} (Q^n_{gh} - Q^f_{gh})(Q^n_{kl} - Q^f_{kl})(\overline{n_g n_h n_k n_l} - R^n_{gh} R^n_{kl}) \\ &= 2 \sum_{g,h} \sum_{k,l} (Q^n_{gh} - Q^f_{gh})(Q^n_{kl} - Q^f_{kl}) R^n_{gk} R^n_{hl} \\ &= 2 \sum_{g,h} \sum_{k,l} Q^f_{gh} Q^f_{kl} R^m_{gk} R^m_{hl}, \end{aligned} \tag{35.31}$$

in the absence of the useful signal, and

$$\begin{aligned} b_1 = \overline{S^2} - a_1^2 &= 2 \sum_{g,h} \sum_{k,l} (Q^n_{gh} - Q^f_{gh})(Q^n_{kl} - Q^f_{kl}) R^f_{gk} R^f_{hl} \\ &= 2 \sum_{g,h} \sum_{k,l} Q^n_{gh} Q^n_{kl} R^m_{gk} R^m_{hl}, \end{aligned} \tag{35.32}$$

in the presence of the useful signal.

Thus, if the useful signal is absent, the probability density of the random variable S is

$$p_0(S) = \frac{1}{\sqrt{2\pi b_0}} e^{-(S-a_0)^2/2b_0}, \tag{35.33}$$

and if the useful signal is present, the probability density is

$$p_1(S) = \frac{1}{\sqrt{2\pi b_1}} e^{-(S-a_1)^2/2b_1}. \tag{35.34}$$

It follows that the false alarm probability equals

$$F = \int_{S_*}^{\infty} p_0(S)\, dS = \frac{1}{\sqrt{2\pi}} \int_{z_*}^{\infty} e^{-z^2/2}\, dz \quad \left(z_* = \frac{S_* - a_0}{\sqrt{b_0}}\right), \tag{35.35}$$

while the detection probability equals

$$D = \int_{S_*}^{\infty} p_1(S)\, dS = \frac{1}{\sqrt{2\pi}} \int_{y_*}^{\infty} e^{-z^2/2}\, dz \quad \left(y_* = \frac{S_* - a_1}{\sqrt{b_1}}\right). \tag{35.36}$$

In making calculations based on formulas (35.35) and (35.36), it should be kept in mind that for the given number of sample values H (which is assumed to be quite large and to contain quite a large number of practically independent random variables m_h and n_h), the normal distributions (35.33) and (35.44) are good approximations to the exact distributions near their "centers" ($S \sim a_0$, $S \sim a_1$), but the accuracy of the approximations falls off as $(S - a_0)^2$ and $(S - a_1)^2$ increase. Therefore, in calculating both small values of F and D, as well as values of F and D near unity, the formulas (35.35) and (35.36) give rather crude results, as a rule. More accurate calculations can be made, at least for uncorrelated sequences, by using the χ^2 (chi-square) distribution (cf. Secs. 38 and 45).

If the signal is weak (more precisely, if $b_1 \sim b_0$), then instead of making direct calculations by using formulas (35.35) and (35.36), we can use the operating characteristics for simple detection, if we define μ, the effective value of the signal-to-noise ratio for this problem, by formula (31.36), so that

$$\mu = (z_* - y_*)^2 = \frac{(a_1 - a_0)^2}{b_0}, \tag{35.37}$$

where this relation is valid only for small μ.

The problem just studied, i.e., detecting a random signal in the background of a "contaminating" random process, leads to the "quadratic" optimum receiver (35.08). Therefore, this problem cannot be solved within the theory of optimum linear filters, unlike the problem of detecting a signal *of fixed form*, which was essentially solved in Part 1 and was only made more precise in the preceding sections.

In Appendix III, the reader will find an analysis of some paradoxes which arise in connection with the problems considered in this chapter.

6

DETECTION OF SIGNAL TRAINS

36. Coherent and Incoherent Signal Trains. Correlated Noise in Radar Problems

In this chapter, we investigate the detection of signal trains.[1] This is a problem of particular interest in radar applications, where each object usually produces at the receiver input a group of signals (e.g., a pulse train), the form of which will be specified below. Of course, if it is required to detect a signal train, then we can construct the optimum device for detecting the signals separately and base our decisions on each signal. However, it is more natural and effective to construct a receiver that responds to the whole train, and the present chapter is devoted to a study of such receivers.

The operation of a radar transmitter involves the radiation of a periodic sequence of signals (e.g., pulses). By a *coherent sequence* of transmitted signals ("search signals"), we mean a sequence of signals of the form

$$m_\varkappa(t, \theta) = e_\varkappa(t) \cos [\omega_0 t - \psi_\varkappa(t) - \theta] \qquad (\varkappa = 0, \pm 1, \pm 2, \ldots), \quad (36.01)$$

where ω_0 is the carrier frequency, $e_\varkappa(t)$ and $\psi_\varkappa(t)$ are the envelope and (slowly varying) phase of the $\varkappa$th transmitted signal, and θ is the r-f phase, which is the same for all the signals. By an *incoherent sequence* of transmitted signals, we mean a sequence of the form

$$m_\varkappa(t, \theta_\varkappa) = e_\varkappa(t) \cos [\omega_0 t - \psi_\varkappa(t) - \theta_\varkappa] \qquad (\varkappa = 0, \pm 1, \pm 2, \ldots), \quad (36.02)$$

[1] I.e., *groups* or *packets* (Russian: пачки) of signals. (*Translator*)

where the quantities ω_0, $e_\varkappa(t)$ and $\psi_\varkappa(t)$ have the same meaning as for the coherent sequence (36.01), but where $\theta_\varkappa$ is now the phase of the $\varkappa$th signal, and all the $\theta_\varkappa$ are assumed to be unknown quantities, in fact independent random variables. In what follows, we shall assume for simplicity that identical, periodically repeated signals are transmitted, i.e., we shall assume that

$$e_\varkappa(t) = e[t - (\varkappa - 1)T], \qquad \psi_\varkappa(t) = \psi[t - (\varkappa - 1)T], \tag{36.03}$$

where T is the repetition period.

It should be noted that a coherent sequence of signals usually means a sequence which, together with the conditions (36.01) and (36.03), satisfies the extra condition

$$\omega_0 T = 2\pi N, \tag{36.04}$$

where N is an integer (which is usually large). This condition assures that each transmitted signal has the same initial phase. It can also be assumed that the condition (36.04) is not satisfied, but that $\omega_0[t - (\varkappa - 1)T]$ appears in formula (36.01) instead of $\omega_0 t$, i.e., that the r-f phase obeys a condition of the type (36.03).

The signal trains which appear at the receiver input are formed as follows: First, we assume that the reflecting object does not move. Then, due to the rotation of the beam of the transmitting antenna, a comparatively small number of signals are incident on the given object during each spatial span, where this number L depends on the directivity pattern (beamwidth) of the transmitting antenna and its rate of rotation. After being reflected from the object, the L signals are then incident on the receiving antenna, thereby giving rise to a signal train at the receiver input.

If the reflecting object moves, then during the reflection, the signal suffers some additional modulation; in particular, if the target moves as a whole, it produces a frequency shift in the signal, due to the Doppler effect (see Sec. 68). In fact, the Doppler effect changes the frequency ω into the frequency

$$\omega' = \omega - \zeta, \qquad \zeta = \frac{2v_r}{c}\,\omega, \tag{36.05}$$

where v_r is the radial component of the velocity of the reflecting object,[2] and c is the velocity of light. Formula (36.05) is applicable for nonrelativistic velocities, i.e., for small values of the ratio v_r/c. If the transmitted signal is sufficiently narrow-band, then in the expression for ζ, we can replace ω by the carrier frequency ω_0. In this case, we can assume that as a result of the reflection, the spectrum of the signal does not change its shape, but is

[2] If the transmitting and receiving antennas are at different locations, then v_r must be taken to be the component of the velocity in the direction of the bisector of the angle AOB shown in Fig. 61 of Sec. 70.

only shifted as a whole by an amount ζ, depending on the velocity of the reflecting object and the carrier frequency.[3]

Under these conditions, a *received* coherent signal train can be written in the form

$$m_\varkappa(t, \theta) = e_\varkappa(t) \cos [(\omega_0 - \zeta)t - \psi_\varkappa(t) - \theta] \qquad (\varkappa = 1, 2, \ldots, L), \tag{36.06}$$

while a received incoherent signal train can be written in the form

$$m_\varkappa(t, \theta_\varkappa) = e_\varkappa(t) \cos [(\omega_0 - \zeta)t - \psi_\varkappa(t) - \theta_\varkappa] \qquad (\varkappa = 1, 2, \ldots, L), \tag{36.07}$$

where $\zeta = 2v_r\omega_0/c$ is the shift of the carrier frequency of the reflected signal; here $e_\varkappa(t)$ and $\psi_\varkappa(t)$ are the envelope and the phase of the $\varkappa$th reflected signal, determined by the transmitted signal, the distance to the object, and the reflecting properties of the object. We observe that in formulas (36.06) and (36.07), the functions $e_\varkappa(t)$, $\psi_\varkappa(t)$ and the constants θ, $\theta_\varkappa$ differ from the corresponding quantities in formulas (36.01) and (36.02) for the *transmitted* signals. However, for our subsequent purposes, formulas (36.06) and (36.07) are all that matter, where for a given object at a given distance, the functions $e_\varkappa(t)$ and $\psi_\varkappa(t)$ can be regarded as known.

By idealizing the properties of real antennas, we shall assume that the directivity (gain) pattern of the antenna is constant within its "main beam," and that no transmission or reception takes place outside this beam. Because of this assumption, the conditions (36.03) for transmitted signals imply similar conditions for the functions $e_\varkappa(t)$ and $\psi_\varkappa(t)$ in formulas (36.06) and (36.07) for the received train of L signals. If this assumption is not made, then the analysis becomes much more complicated.

It should be noted that in practice one often talks about a coherent or incoherent method of detection, rather than a coherent or incoherent sequence of transmitted signals. In coherent detection, we do not necessarily require that the transmitted r-f signals be coherent [i.e., that they have the same phase θ, as in formula (36.01)]; instead, it is sufficient to know the change in phase from signal to signal. Then, taking account of these phase changes in handling the received data (cf. p. 108), we obtain essentially the same results as if the sequence (36.01) were transmitted and reception took place without "adjusting" the phases (which is now an unnecessary operation). Therefore, we shall henceforth use the terms "coherent reception of a signal train" and "reception (or detection) of a coherent train" as if they

[3] In Appendix IV, we derive the exact formulas and show that not only the carrier frequency changes as a result of the Doppler effect, but also the envelope $e_\varkappa(t)$ and the supplementary phase $\psi_\varkappa(t)$ of each signal. In what follows, however, we confine ourselves to cases where the change in $e_\varkappa(t)$ and $\psi_\varkappa(t)$ can be neglected.

were equivalent. Similarly, we shall speak of a receiver detecting an incoherent signal train (36.02), when we have in mind an incoherent receiver which does not use the phases $\theta_\varkappa$ of the transmitted signals.

In addition to the regular changes in time of $m_\varkappa(t, \theta)$ and $m_\varkappa(t, \theta_\varkappa)$ caused by motion of the target as a whole, the envelope and phase of the reflected signal undergo random changes in time. These fluctuations or "target scintillations," as they are sometimes called, are caused by small changes in orientation of the reflecting body. However, in the present chapter, we shall only study detection of the signal trains (36.06) and (36.07), deferring consideration of "scintillating targets" until the next chapter.

The problem in which we are interested is the detection of signal trains in the presence of both receiver noise and *clutter*. By *clutter*, we mean noise obtained as a result of reflection of electromagnetic waves from raindrops, mist, vegetation, and other spatially distributed objects. A detailed study of signals reflected from randomly located particles will be given in Chap. 11, where it is shown that in the theory of optimum receivers, clutter can be regarded as a stationary random process of the normal (Gaussian) type. The normal character of the noise is due to the fact that it is a superposition of a large number of independent or almost independent terms, coming from individual scattering particles (or from groups of scattering particles). In Chap. 11, we shall find the correlation function of the noise due to these "chaotic" reflections, taking into account the fact that all the reflecting particles move about chaotically inside a "scattering cloud," thereby producing Doppler shifts in the reflected signal.

For a coherent train of narrow-band signals with a spectrum which is symmetric with respect to the carrier frequency, the autocorrelation function of the noise due to chaotic reflections equals

$$R_n(\tau) = R_m(\tau)r(\tau). \tag{36.08}$$

Here, the function $R_m(\tau)$ is simply the autocorrelation function of the periodic sequence of transmitted pulses, and is a periodic function of τ, i.e.,

$$R_m(\tau) = R_m(\tau \pm kT) \qquad (k = 1, 2, \ldots), \tag{36.09}$$

where T is the repetition period, while $r(\tau)$ is a slowly varying function, satisfying the condition

$$r(0) = 1. \tag{36.10}$$

The meaning of formula (36.08) is quite simple: If we assume that all the particles in the scattering cloud are fixed, then during the first repetition period, the noise $n(t)$ caused by the randomly located particles will be a superposition of signals of "standard" form, which are replicas of the transmitted signals and which occur at random moments of time. Therefore, the noise autocorrelation function $R_n(\tau)$ equals (to within a constant factor, which we omit) the autocorrelation function $R_m(\tau)$ of the periodic transmitted signal train, where both $R_n(\tau)$ and $R_m(\tau)$ are periodic functions of τ (with period T). However, the particles in the scattering cloud are actually moving. If we assume that the cloud as a whole is fixed and that the particles only move around inside it, then after the time interval T, the positions of the particles will be somewhat different (i.e., the configuration will change slowly), and as a result, the correlation function $R_n(\tau)$ will slowly go to zero as $|\tau| \to \infty$. It is just this fact which is taken into account by the presence of the factor $r(\tau)$ in (36.08).

If the transmitted sequence is a coherent train of rectangular pulses of duration $T_0 \ll T$, then the function (36.08) gives a periodic sequence of "triangular r-f correlation pulses" (cf. Sec. 20). The function $r(\tau)$ can usually be regarded as constant during time intervals of order T_0, so that $r(\tau)$ is a kind of "pulse-to-pulse" or "period-to-period" correlation coefficient, characterizing the statistical relation between the values of $n(t)$ at the times $t, t \pm T, t \pm 2T$, etc. If the cloud of scattering particles is illuminated by an incoherent train of identical pulses, then, as shown in Sec. 67, the autocorrelation function of the noise due to the clutter equals

$$\begin{aligned} R_n(\tau) &= R_m(\tau) \quad \text{for} \quad -T_0 < \tau < T_0, \\ R_n(\tau) &= 0 \qquad\qquad \text{for all other } \tau. \end{aligned} \tag{36.11}$$

We also obtain the correlation function (36.11) in the case of a *coherent* signal train, if the clutter, i.e., the noise due to the "chaotic" reflections, changes so rapidly in time that the values $r(T), r(2T), \ldots$, can be regarded as zero. However, these two cases correspond to two entirely different statistical situations: In fact, if incoherent signals are reflected by slowly moving scatterers, the noise amplitudes in the different repetition periods are strongly correlated, and the noise itself is not normally distributed. On the other hand, if coherent signals are reflected by rapidly moving scatterers, we obtain normally distributed noise, which has the more familiar appearance of noise, and whose values in different repetition periods are independent. In the theory of detection of an incoherent signal train (developed below), it is assumed that the noise is normal and that it has no period-to-period correlation. This assumption automatically excludes the general case of clutter, and takes into account only receiver noise itself and the case where the clutter is quite "noise-like."

If we write the total noise $n(t)$ as a sum

$$n(t) = n_1(t) + n_2(t), \tag{36.12}$$

where $n_1(t)$ is the clutter and $n_2(t)$ is the receiver noise, then, due to the independence of the random processes $n_1(t)$ and $n_2(t)$, we have

$$R_n(\tau) = R_{n_1}(\tau) + R_{n_2}(\tau), \tag{36.13}$$

where $R_{n_1}(\tau)$ can be written in the form (36.08), as before, and $R_{n_2}(\tau)$ is a function which rapidly falls off to zero as τ is increased. Even if $n_2(\tau)$ is due to "pure" white noise, it acquires some time correlation in passing through linear circuits, but in any event, $n_2(t)$ cannot have any correlation which extends between repetition periods. Therefore, we have

$$R_n(\tau) = R_m(\tau) + R_{n_2}(\tau) \quad \text{for} \quad |\tau| < \frac{T}{2},$$
$$R_n(\tau) = R_m(\tau) r_1(\tau) \quad \text{for} \quad |\tau| > \frac{T}{2}. \tag{36.14}$$

By analogy with formula (36.08), we can write the function $R_n(\tau)$ as

$$R_n(\tau) = R_p(\tau) r(\tau), \tag{36.15}$$

where the function

$$R_p(\tau) = R_m(\tau) + R_{n_2}(\tau) \quad \text{for} \quad |\tau| < \frac{T}{2} \tag{36.16}$$

is continued periodically according to the rule

$$R_p(\tau) = R_p(\tau \pm kT) \qquad (k = 1, 2, \ldots), \tag{36.17}$$

and the function $r(\tau)$ is defined as

$$r(\tau) = 1 \quad \text{for} \quad |\tau| < \frac{T}{2}$$
$$r(\tau) = \frac{r_1(\tau)}{1 + [R_{n_2}(\tau)/R_m(\tau)]} = \frac{R_m(\tau) r_1(\tau)}{R_m(\tau) + R_{n_2}(\tau)} \quad \text{for} \quad |\tau| > \frac{T}{2}. \tag{36.18}$$

From this last formula, we see that we can formally incorporate the receiver noise as clutter if we increase the noise intensity from $R_m(0)$ to $R_p(0) = R_m(0) + R_{n_2}(0)$ and decrease the period-to-period correlation [since then $r(\tau) < r_1(\tau)$ appears instead of $r_1(\tau)$]. Therefore, the results which will be obtained below for the detection of signal trains in a background of clutter have a more general character and are also applicable in the presence of receiver noise.

It should be noted that "pure" noise [i.e., the noise $n_2(t)$ alone] can be formally regarded as noise due to clutter, with the correlation coefficient $r(\tau) = 0$ for $|\tau| > T/2$. However, if we use formula (36.18) to represent the "mixed" noise (36.12) as noise due to clutter alone, then when $R_m \sim R_{n_2}$, we can only obtain results which are qualitatively correct, since the function $r(\tau)$ will no longer be slowly varying; in particular, when the signals are pulses of duration T_0, the function $r(\tau)$ can change appreciably in a time of order T_0.

37. Detection of an Incoherent Signal Train in a Background of Normal Noise

This section is devoted to the optimum detection of an incoherent signal train[4] in a background of normal noise, which is correlated at most over one repetition period and is uncorrelated from period to period. As remarked in the last section, when the problem is stated in this way, we take into account only the receiver noise, since the noise due to clutter satisfies these conditions only in a very special case.

Suppose that during the observation time we sample the signal HL times, where H is the number of samplings made in one repetition period (the sample points have the same positions in each period) and L is the number of periods. We denote the sample values within one period by the indices g and h, where

$$g, h = 1, 2, \ldots, H, \tag{37.01}$$

and the sample values from different periods by the indices $\varkappa$ and λ, where

$$\varkappa, \lambda = 1, 2, \ldots, L. \tag{37.02}$$

Thus, we let $m_{g\varkappa}$, $n_{g\varkappa}$ and $f_{g\varkappa}$ denote the gth sample value of the useful signal, the noise and the received signal, respectively, made in the $\varkappa$th repetition period, and we assume that $\overline{n_{g\varkappa}} = 0$. The correlation function of the noise, which is correlated only within one repetition period and is uncorrelated from period to period, can be written in the form

$$\overline{n_{g\varkappa} n_{h\lambda}} = R_{gh} \delta_{\lambda\varkappa}. \tag{37.03}$$

In the present case, the useful signal depends on L parameters θ_1, θ_2, $\ldots$, θ_L, where the phases $\theta_\varkappa$ are independent and uniformly distributed from 0 to 2π:

$$p_m(\theta_\varkappa) = \frac{1}{2\pi}, \qquad 0 \leqslant \theta_\varkappa < 2\pi. \tag{37.04}$$

In view of the periodicity of the functions $e_\varkappa(t)$ and $\psi_\varkappa(t)$, the sample values of the useful signal with index h from the $\varkappa$th period can be written in the form

$$m_{h\varkappa}(\theta_\varkappa) = e_h \cos\,[(\omega_0 - \zeta)t_{h\varkappa} - \psi_h - \theta_\varkappa]. \tag{37.05}$$

The sampling times $t_{h\varkappa}$ are equal to

$$t_{h\varkappa} = t_h + (\varkappa - 1)T, \qquad t_h = t_1 + (h - 1)\,\Delta t, \tag{37.06}$$

where, in the case of rectangular pulses (of duration T_0), $e_h \neq 0$ only if

$$0 < h\,\Delta t < T_0, \qquad T_0 \ll T. \tag{37.07}$$

---

[4] Again we note that by detection of an incoherent signal train is meant detection by using an incoherent method of reception (see Sec. 36).

Moreover, we assume that

$$\zeta T_0 \ll 1, \qquad \zeta T \gtrsim 1, \tag{37.08}$$

i.e., we neglect the phase change due to the Doppler effect within the duration of one pulse, at the same time that we take into account the phase change during one repetition period.[5] Then, we can write an incoherent train of identical pulses in the form

$$m_{h\varkappa}(\theta_\varkappa) = e_h \cos(\omega_0 t_h - \psi_h - \vartheta_\varkappa), \tag{37.09}$$

where

$$\vartheta_\varkappa = \theta_\varkappa + (\varkappa - 1)\,\Delta\vartheta - \omega_0(\varkappa - 1)T, \qquad \Delta\vartheta = \zeta T. \tag{37.10}$$

The same expression can also be written in the case of signals of any other form which satisfy the conditions (37.06), provided that the correlation time of the transmitted signal replaces the quantity T_0 in formula (37.08).

According to formula (31.18), because of the independence of the phases $\theta_\varkappa$ of the separate signals (or equivalently, of the phases $\vartheta_\varkappa$), the likelihood ratio $\Lambda(\vartheta_1, \ldots, \vartheta_L)$ equals

$$\Lambda(\vartheta_1, \ldots, \vartheta_L) = \frac{1}{(2\pi)^L} e^{\varphi(\vartheta_1,\ldots,\vartheta_L) - \frac{1}{2}\mu(\vartheta_1,\ldots,\vartheta_2)}, \tag{37.11}$$

where

$$\varphi(\vartheta_1, \ldots, \vartheta_L) = \sum_\varkappa \sum_{g,h} Q_{gh} f_{g\varkappa} e_h \cos(\omega_0 t_h - \psi_h - \vartheta_\varkappa) \tag{37.12}$$

and

$$\mu(\vartheta_1, \ldots, \vartheta_L) = \sum_\varkappa \sum_{g,h} Q_{gh} m_{g\varkappa} m_{h\varkappa}. \tag{37.13}$$

The quantity (37.12) can be written in the form

$$\varphi(\vartheta_1, \ldots, \vartheta_L) = \sum_\varkappa \varphi_\varkappa(\vartheta_\varkappa) = \sum_\varkappa \mathscr{E}_\varkappa \cos(\Phi_\varkappa - \vartheta_\varkappa), \tag{37.14}$$

where

$$\varphi_\varkappa(\vartheta_\varkappa) = \sum_{g,h} Q_{gh} f_{g\varkappa} e_h \cos(\omega_0 t_h - \psi_h - \vartheta_\varkappa) = \mathscr{E}_\varkappa \cos(\Phi_\varkappa - \vartheta_\varkappa),$$

$$x_\varkappa = \mathscr{E}_\varkappa \cos\Phi_\varkappa = \sum_{g,h} Q_{gh} f_{g\varkappa} e_h \cos(\omega_0 t_h - \psi_h), \tag{37.15}$$

$$y_\varkappa = \mathscr{E}_\varkappa \sin\Phi_\varkappa = \sum_{g,h} Q_{gh} f_{g\varkappa} e_h \sin(\omega_0 t_h - \psi_h).$$

---

[5] We note that when a pulse is reflected from an extended object, the pulse duration is increased. This increase can be neglected if the dimensions of the object are small compared to cT_0, where c is the velocity of light, and we shall assume that this condition is met. In considering signal trains, it is also tacitly assumed that the condition $v_r LT \ll cT_0$ is met. This last condition essentially means that the position of the reflecting object with respect to the radar does not change appreciably in the time LT during which it is observed. This condition and the conditions (37.08), involving the Doppler effect, are compatible.

It can be seen that the quantities $\mathscr{E}_\varkappa$ and $\Phi_\varkappa$ represent envelopes and phases for the quantities $\varphi_\varkappa(\vartheta_\varkappa)$ obtained as a result of optimum handling of the data received during the $\varkappa$th repetition period.

As we saw in Sec. 33, the quantity

$$\mu_\varkappa = \sum_{g,h} Q_{gh} m_{g\varkappa} m_{h\varkappa} \tag{37.16}$$

is the signal-to-noise ratio at the output of the optimum linear device during one repetition period. As shown there [cf. formula (33.09)], $\mu_\varkappa$ is practically independent of the unknown phase $\vartheta_\varkappa$. Therefore, the quantity (37.13) which equals

$$\mu = \sum_{\varkappa=1}^{L} \mu_\varkappa, \tag{37.17}$$

and which is the effective signal-to-noise ratio for an incoherent train of L signals, does not depend on the phases $\vartheta_1, \ldots, \vartheta_L$.

To detect the incoherent train, we need the likelihood ratio

$$\Lambda = \int_0^{2\pi} \cdots \int_0^{2\pi} \Lambda(\vartheta_1, \ldots, \vartheta_L)\, d\vartheta_1 \ldots d\vartheta_L = e^{-\mu/2} \prod_{\varkappa=1}^{L} I_0(\mathscr{E}_\varkappa)$$
$$= e^{-\mu/2} \exp\left\{ \prod_{\varkappa=1}^{L} \ln I_0(\mathscr{E}_\varkappa) \right\}. \tag{37.18}$$

In the present case, it is convenient to base our decision on the quantity

$$S = \sum_{\varkappa=1}^{L} \ln I_0(\mathscr{E}_\varkappa), \tag{37.19}$$

using the following decision rule:

$$\begin{aligned} &\text{If} \quad S \geqslant S_*, \quad \text{decide that } f = m + n; \\ &\text{If} \quad S < S_*, \quad \text{decide that } f = n, \end{aligned} \tag{37.20}$$

where S_* is the decision threshold.

For strong signals ($\mathscr{E}_\varkappa \gg 1$) and weak signals ($\mathscr{E}_\varkappa \ll 1$), formula (37.19) becomes simpler. Applying the asymptotic formulas

$$I_0(x) \sim \frac{e^x}{\sqrt{2\pi x}}, \qquad \ln I_0(x) \sim x \qquad (\text{for } x \gg 1) \tag{37.21}$$

for strong signals, we obtain

$$S = \sum_{\varkappa=1}^{L} \mathscr{E}_\varkappa. \tag{37.22}$$

For weak signals, we apply the approximate formulas

$$I_0(x) = 1 + \frac{x^2}{4} + \cdots \sim e^{x^2/4}, \qquad \ln I_0(x) \sim \frac{x^2}{4} \quad (\text{for } x \ll 1), \quad (37.23)$$

obtaining

$$S = \frac{1}{4} \sum_{\varkappa=1}^{L} \mathscr{E}_{\varkappa}^2. \quad (37.24)$$

Thus, the optimum receiver for detecting an incoherent signal train consists of an optimum linear device (filter), which processes the data in every repetition period, followed by a nonlinear element (detector) with transfer characteristic $\ln I_0(\mathscr{E})$, a summing device ("accumulator") and a decision circuit. As shown by formulas (37.22) and (37.24), the nonlinear device reduces to a "linear" detector for strong signals, and to a quadratic detector for weak signals.

Comparing, the decision rule for an incoherent signal train with the decision rule for a single signal with unknown phase, we see that in the first case, the detector has to have the transfer characteristic $\ln I_0$, whereas in the second case, its transfer characteristic can be arbitrary. We note that the superiority of the linear detector for strong signal trains and of the quadratic detector for weak signal trains is completely consistent with the results obtained in Sec. 18 for a single signal.

38. Operating Characteristics of a Receiver Detecting an Incoherent Train

In this section, we calculate the probabilities F and D for a receiver which detects an incoherent signal train. Since, according to formula (37.09), all the signals in the train have the same strength, the expression (37.17) takes the form

$$\mu = L\rho, \quad \text{where} \quad \rho = \mu_1 = \ldots = \mu_L. \quad (38.01)$$

We now define the quantity $\mathscr{E}$ by the formula

$$\mathscr{E}^2 = \sum_{\varkappa=1}^{L} \mathscr{E}_{\varkappa}^2 = \sum_{\varkappa=1}^{L} (x_{\varkappa}^2 + y_{\varkappa}^2), \quad (38.02)$$

and use $\mathscr{E}$ to make our decision; according to formula (37.24), this gives the optimum results for weak signals. In the absence of the signal, the probability density of the quantity $\mathscr{E}$ equals

$$p_{0L}(\mathscr{E}) = \frac{\mathscr{E}^{2L-1} e^{-\mathscr{E}^2/2\rho}}{2^{L-1}\rho^L(L-1)!}, \quad (38.03)$$

while in the presence of L incoherent signals, the probability density equals

$$\begin{aligned} p_{mL}(\mathscr{E}) &= \frac{\mathscr{E}^{2L-1}e^{-(L\rho/2)-(\mathscr{E}^2/2\rho)}I_{L-1}(\sqrt{L}\mathscr{E})}{\rho^L(\sqrt{L}\mathscr{E})^{L-1}} \\ &= \frac{\mathscr{E}^L}{\rho^L}\, e^{-(L\rho^2+\mathscr{E}^2)/2\rho}\, \frac{I_{L-1}(\sqrt{L}\mathscr{E})}{L^{(L-1)/2}}, \end{aligned} \tag{38.04}$$

where $I_{L-1}(x)$ is the modified Bessel function of the first kind of order $L - 1$. For small values of x, we have the approximation

$$I_{L-1}(x) \sim \frac{(x/2)^{L-1}}{(L-1)!}. \tag{38.05}$$

We now derive formula (38.04), and incidentally, formula (38.03). First of all, we note that for $L = 1$, (38.04) becomes

$$p_{m1}(\mathscr{E}) = \frac{\mathscr{E}}{\rho}\, e^{-(\rho^2+\mathscr{E}^2)/2\rho} I_0(\mathscr{E}), \tag{38.06}$$

i.e., coincides with the Rice distribution (33.41). Therefore, formula (38.04) is valid for $L = 1$. Next, we assume that formula (38.04) has been proved for some number L and prove it for $L + 1$. Denoting the argument of the function $p_{m,\,L+1}$ by $\tilde{\mathscr{E}}$, we have

$$\tilde{\mathscr{E}}^2 = \mathscr{E}^2 + \mathscr{E}_{L+1}^2. \tag{38.07}$$

The random variables $\tilde{\mathscr{E}}^2$ [defined by formula (38.02)] and $\mathscr{E}_{L+1}^2$ are obviously independent, and hence the function $p_{m,\,L+1}(\mathscr{E})$ can be calculated by the formula

$$\begin{aligned} p_{m,\,L+1}(\tilde{\mathscr{E}})\, d\tilde{\mathscr{E}} &= \iint_{(\tilde{\mathscr{E}},\tilde{\mathscr{E}}+d\tilde{\mathscr{E}})} p_{mL}(\mathscr{E}) p_{m1}(\mathscr{E}_{L+1})\, d\mathscr{E}\, d\mathscr{E}_{L+1} \\ &= \tilde{\mathscr{E}}\, d\tilde{\mathscr{E}} \int_0^{\pi/2} p_{mL}(\tilde{\mathscr{E}}\cos\beta) p_{m1}(\tilde{\mathscr{E}}\sin\beta)\, d\beta. \end{aligned} \tag{38.08}$$

Here, we have introduced polar coordinates by the formulas

$$\mathscr{E} = \tilde{\mathscr{E}}\cos\beta, \qquad \mathscr{E}_{L+1} = \tilde{\mathscr{E}}\sin\beta, \qquad d\mathscr{E}\, d\mathscr{E}_{L+1} = \tilde{\mathscr{E}}\, d\tilde{\mathscr{E}}\, d\beta, \tag{38.09}$$

and the integration with respect to β extends from 0 to $\pi/2$, since the quantities $\mathscr{E}$ and $\mathscr{E}_{L+1}$ in (38.09) do not take negative values.

The explicit form of (38.08) is

$$\begin{aligned} p_{m,\,L+1}(\mathscr{E}) &= \frac{\mathscr{E}^{L+2}}{\rho^{L+1}}\, e^{-[(L+1)\rho^2+\mathscr{E}^2]/2\rho}\, \frac{1}{L^{(L-1)/2}} \\ &\times \int_0^{\pi/2} I_{L-1}(\sqrt{L}\mathscr{E}\cos\beta) I_0(\mathscr{E}\sin\beta) \cos^L\beta \sin\beta\, d\beta. \end{aligned} \tag{38.10}$$

According to Sonine's second finite integral,[6] we have

$$\frac{1}{L^{(L-1)/2}} \int_0^{\pi/2} I_{L-1}(\sqrt{L}\mathscr{E} \cos \beta) I_0(\mathscr{E} \sin \beta) \cos^L \beta \sin \beta \, d\beta = \frac{I_L(\sqrt{L+1}\mathscr{E})}{\mathscr{E}(L+1)^{L/2}}, \tag{38.11}$$

and therefore formula (38.10) gives

$$p_{m,L+1}(\mathscr{E}) = \frac{\mathscr{E}^{L+1}}{\rho^{L+1}} e^{-[(L+1)\rho^2+\mathscr{E}^2]/2\rho} \frac{I_L(\sqrt{L+1}\mathscr{E})}{(L+1)^{L/2}}, \tag{38.12}$$

as was to be proved. Thus, we have established formula (38.04) by induction.

If we introduce the quantity $z = \mathscr{E}/\sqrt{\rho}$, then the distribution (38.04) can also be written in the form

$$p_{mL}(z) = \frac{z^L}{(L\rho)^{(L-1)/2}} e^{-(L\rho+z^2)/2} I_{L-1}(\sqrt{L\rho}\, z) \tag{38.13}$$

(cf. footnote 6 on p. 170). If the linear processing of the data received during each period is not optimum, then formula (38.13) remains valid, but z and ρ are given by (33.44), where, according to (33.23), σ^2 is the noise power at the output of the quadrature filters which process the data during each repetition period, and $\bar{\varphi} = \sqrt{x_m^2 + y_m^2}$ is the useful signal at the output of these filters [cf. (33.32)]. We can easily prove this statement by induction, starting from formula (33.41) or (33.45), and repeating the argument just given. Thus, using nonoptimum linear filters in the receiver is equivalent to lowering the parameter ρ (the effective signal-to-noise ratio for each repetition period), i.e., to increasing the noise level. Even though the value of this parameter becomes less than its optimum value, given by (37.16) and (38.01), the distribution of the random variable z does not change.

If we set $\rho = 0$ in formula (38.13) and use the expression (38.05), then we obtain the probability density of the quantity z in the absence of the useful signal:

$$p_{0L}(z) = \frac{z^{2L-1}}{2^{L-1}(L-1)!} e^{-z^2/2}. \tag{38.14}$$

[Going from the variable z to the variable $\mathscr{E}$, we obtain formula (38.03).] The probability density (38.14) corresponds to the χ^2 (*chi-square*) *distribution*. Introducing the quantity

$$Z = \frac{z^2}{2}, \tag{38.15}$$

we find that it has the probability density

$$p_{0L}(Z) = \frac{Z^{L-1}}{(L-1)!} e^{-Z}. \tag{38.16}$$

[6] G. N. Watson, *A Treatise on the Theory of Bessel Functions*, Second Edition, Macmillan, New York (1945), p. 376.

Detailed tables of the integrals

$$\frac{1}{2^{L-1}(L-1)!}\int_{z^*}^{\infty} z^{2L-1}\, e^{-z^2/2}\, dz$$
$$= \frac{1}{(L-1)!}\int_{Z_*}^{\infty} Z^{L-1} e^{-Z}\, dZ \qquad (Z_* = z_*^2/2) \tag{38.17}$$

are in existence.

The false alarm probability and the detection probability can be calculated by the formulas

$$F = \int_{\mathscr{E}_*}^{\infty} p_{0L}(\mathscr{E})\, d\mathscr{E}$$
$$= \frac{1}{2^L(L-1)!}\int_{z_*}^{\infty} z^{2L-1} e^{-z^2/2}\, dz \qquad \left(z_* = \frac{\mathscr{E}_*}{\sqrt{\rho}}\right) \tag{38.18}$$

and

$$D = \int_{\mathscr{E}_*}^{\infty} p_{mL}(\mathscr{E})\, d\mathscr{E}$$
$$= \frac{e^{-L\rho/2}}{(L\rho)^{(L-1)/2}}\int_{z_*}^{\infty} z^L e^{-z^2/2} I_{L-1}(\sqrt{L\rho}\, z)\, dz, \tag{38.19}$$

where $\mathscr{E}_*$ is the threshold value of the quantity $\mathscr{E}$. According to what was said above, for nonoptimum processing of the data within each repetition period, we have to set $z_* = \mathscr{E}_*/\sigma$.

The calculation of F for a given value of z_* (or Z_*) can be easily accomplished by using tables of the χ^2 distribution compiled by E. E. Slutski[7] or, in the case of very small F, by J. Pachares.[8] However, calculation of the detection probability by using formula (38.19) is very laborious, since the corresponding integrals are not tabulated for $L > 1$. Therefore, we have to calculate the detection probability by using approximate formulas. Thus, for example, in the integral appearing in (38.19), we can replace the function I_{L-1} by a power series [the first term of which is given by formula (38.05)] and then integrate term by term. However, the expression obtained in this way is suitable in practice only for calculations of small values of D (more precisely, when $D \sim F$).

For larger values of D, we can use the asymptotic formula

$$I_{L-1}(x) = \frac{e^x}{\sqrt{2\pi x}}, \tag{38.20}$$

---

[7] E. E. Slutski, Таблицы для вычисления неполной Г-функции и функции вероятности χ^2 (*Tables for calculation of the incomplete gamma function and the χ^2 distribution*), Izd. Akad. Nauk SSSR, Moscow (1950).

[8] J. Pachares, *A Table of bias levels useful in radar detection problems*, IRE Trans. on Inform. Theory, **IT-4**, 38 (1958).

and then (38.04) becomes

$$p_{mL}(\mathscr{E}) = \frac{1}{\sqrt{2\pi\rho}}\left(1 + \frac{x}{\sqrt{\mu}}\right)^{L-1/2} e^{-x^2/2} \qquad \left(x = \frac{\mathscr{E}}{\sqrt{\rho}} - \sqrt{\mu}\right) \tag{38.21}$$

or

$$p_{mL}(\mathscr{E}) = \frac{1}{\sqrt{2\pi\rho}} e^{-y^2/2}, \tag{38.22}$$

where

$$y = x - \eta, \qquad \eta = \frac{L - \frac{1}{2}}{\sqrt{\mu}} + \cdots \tag{38.23}$$

[To calculate the terms of order $1/\mu$, denoted by the dots in formula (38.23), the asymptotic formula (38.20) has to be made more precise.] Finally, we obtain the following asymptotic expression for the probability of correctly detecting the incoherent signal train:

$$D = \frac{1}{\sqrt{2\pi}} \int_{y_*}^{\infty} e^{-y^2/2}\, dy, \tag{38.24}$$

where

$$y_* = z_* - \sqrt{\mu} - \eta, \qquad \eta = \frac{L - \frac{1}{2}}{\sqrt{\mu}}. \tag{38.25}$$

For $L = 1$, this expression goes into Bunimovich's formula (see the end of Sec. 33).

We now reduce the integral (38.19) to an integral of the form (38.24), by another method, i.e., by regarding the quantity $\mathscr{E}^2$ as being normal, which in any event is justified as $L \to \infty$, by the central limit theorem of probability theory. We begin by finding the mean value and the variance of the quantity (38.02). To do so, we calculate the integral

$$\begin{aligned} \overline{\mathscr{E}^{2k}} &= \int_0^\infty \mathscr{E}^{2k} p_{mL}(\mathscr{E})\, d\mathscr{E} \\ &= \frac{e^{-L\rho/2}}{L^{(L-1)/2}\rho^L} \int_0^\infty \mathscr{E}^{L+2k} e^{-\mathscr{E}^2/2\rho} I_{L-1}(\sqrt{L}\,\mathscr{E})\, d\mathscr{E}. \end{aligned} \tag{38.26}$$

Using Weber's first exponential integral in generalized form,[9] i.e.,

$$\begin{aligned} &\int_0^\infty t^{\mu-1} e^{-p^2t^2} J_\nu(at)\, dt \\ &\quad = \frac{\Gamma[(\mu + \nu)/2]}{\Gamma(\nu + 1)} \frac{(a/2p)^\nu}{2p^\mu} e^{-a^2/4p^2} {}_1F_1\!\left(\frac{\nu - \mu}{2} + 1; \nu + 1; \frac{a^2}{4p^2}\right), \end{aligned} \tag{38.27}$$

[9] G. N. Watson, *op. cit.*, p. 394.

we obtain the expression

$$\overline{\mathscr{E}^{2k}} = \frac{\Gamma(L+k)}{\Gamma(L)}(2\rho)^k {}_1F_1\left(-k; L; -\frac{L\rho}{2}\right), \tag{38.28}$$

where

$$\begin{aligned} {}_1F_1(-k; L; x) = 1 + \frac{-k}{L}\frac{x}{1!} + \frac{-k(-k+1)}{L(L+1)}\frac{x^2}{2!} \\ + \frac{-k(-k+1)(-k+2)}{L(L+1)(L+2)}\frac{x^3}{3!} + \cdots \end{aligned} \tag{38.29}$$

is a confluent hypergeometric series, in which only the first $k + 1$ terms are nonzero. From this we find

$$\begin{aligned} \overline{\mathscr{E}^2} &= 2L\rho\left(1 + \frac{\rho}{2}\right), \\ \overline{\mathscr{E}^4} &= 4L(L+1)\rho^2\left[1 + \rho + \frac{L\rho^2}{4(L+1)}\right], \\ \overline{\mathscr{E}^4} - (\overline{\mathscr{E}^2})^2 &= 4L\rho^2(1+\rho), \end{aligned} \tag{38.30}$$

so that the mean value and the variance of the random variable

$$Z = \frac{\mathscr{E}^2}{2\rho} = \frac{z^2}{2} \tag{38.31}$$

turn out to be

$$\overline{Z} = L\left(1 + \frac{\rho}{2}\right), \qquad \overline{Z^2} - (\overline{Z})^2 = L(1+\rho). \tag{38.32}$$

For $\rho = 0$, we have

$$\overline{Z} = L, \qquad \overline{Z^2} - (\overline{Z})^2 = L, \tag{38.33}$$

so that the mean value and variance of the quantity $2Z$ correspond to a chi-square distribution. Finally, assuming that the quantity Z is a normal random variable, we can write the following approximate expression for the detection probability:

$$D = \frac{1}{\sqrt{2\pi}}\int_b^\infty e^{-y^2/2}\,dy, \quad \text{where} \quad b = \frac{Z_* - L[1 + (\rho/2)]}{\sqrt{L(1+\rho)}}. \tag{38.34}$$

The false alarm probability as a function of the normalized threshold $Z_* = \mathscr{E}_*^2/2\rho$ can be calculated by using formula (38.17) and tables of the χ^2 distribution. Thus, in Fig. 32 we show the dependence of the normalized threshold Z_* on the false alarm probability F for various values of L.

The detection probability can be calculated by using the approximate formulas (38.24) and (38.34). Here, as L increases, the accuracy of formula (38.24) gets worse, while the accuracy of formula (38.34) improves. This can be explained by the fact that the asymptotic expression (38.20) used in deriving (38.24) has correction terms which increase as L increases, whereas the normal distribution used in writing (38.24) becomes more and more

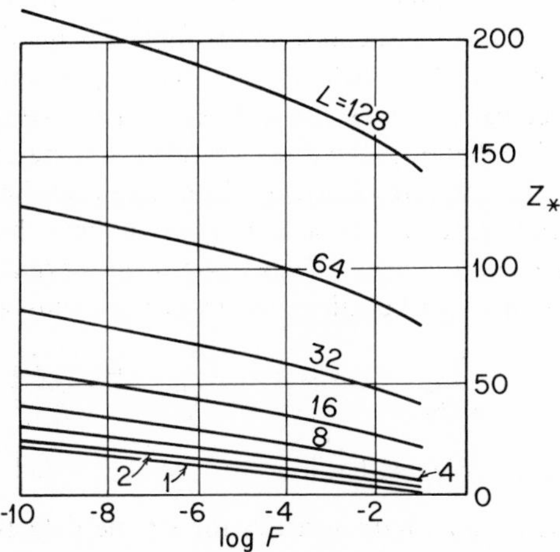

FIG. 32. Dependence of the threshold on the false alarm probability for different numbers of signals in an incoherent train.

accurate as $L \to \infty$, because of the central limit theorem of probability theory. In Figs. 33 to 36, we show the operating characteristics[10] for detection of an incoherent signal train, constructed by using both of the above formulas. Because of the appearance of the extra parameter L, we draw the operating characteristics by plotting L as the abscissa (in logarithmic units), while along the axis of ordinates, we plot the signal-to-noise ratio ρ for one repetition period (the lower curves) and the signal-to-noise ratio $\mu = L\rho$ for the whole signal train (the upper curves). The probabilities F and D corresponding to each curve are fixed. Moreover, the upper and lower curves intersect for $L = 1$, since then $\mu = \rho$.

Figs. 33(a) to 36(a) show on an enlarged scale the dependence of μ on L for fixed F and D. The solid curves correspond to formula (38.34), and the dashed curves correspond to formula (38.24). As a rule, the solid curves and the dashed curves are either very close together over the whole range, or else they come close together for a certain interval of values of L. The curves in Figs. 33(b) to 36(b), which we consider to be more exact, were obtained by interpolation between the dashed and solid curves in Figs. 33(a)

[10] Even though these curves now involve the extra parameter L, they are still called *operating characteristics*. (*Translator*)

to 36(a), where preference was given to the dashed curves for small values of L, and to the solid curves for larger values of L. The approximate accuracy of the resulting curves [Figs. 33(b) to 36(b)] is 0.5 db.

The upper curves in Figs. 33(b) to 36(b) allow us to estimate how much the total energy of the signal has to be increased in order to achieve given probabilities F and D as we increase the number of signals in the train (the noise level is assumed to be constant). The corresponding increment in the total energy can be called *losses due to incoherence when the signal is "split up."* If the train is coherent, then there are no such losses, and the operating characteristics of the train are uniquely determined by the total energy.[11]

To obtain a crude idea of the situation, we assume that in the presence of the noise alone, the quantity $\mathscr{E}^2$ also obeys the normal law. Then, the false alarm probability can be calculated from the formula

$$F = \frac{1}{\sqrt{2\pi}} \int_a^\infty e^{-z^2/2}\, dz \qquad \left(a = \frac{Z_* - L}{\sqrt{L}}\right) \tag{38.35}$$

[cf. formula (38.33)]. We see that if $\rho \ll 1$, so that $\sqrt{L(1 + \rho)} \sim \sqrt{L}$, then we can use the operating characteristics for simple detection, if we assume that the effective signal-to-noise ratio equals

$$\mu_{\text{eff}} = (b - a)^2 = \frac{L\rho^2}{4} = \frac{\mu^2}{4L} \tag{38.36}$$

[cf. formula (31.36) and the end of Sec. 35]. Formula (38.36) shows that if the signal-to-noise ratio at the input of the quadratic detector is small, then the "accumulated" output of the detector has a signal-to-noise ratio which is proportional to the number of repetition periods of the useful signal and to the *square* of the signal-to-noise ratio at the detector input. Here, we once more encounter the suppression of a weak signal by strong noise (an effect with which we are already familiar; cf. Secs. 18 and 33) as a result of the detection (or equivalent data processing) required in the case of a signal with unknown initial phase.

The formula (38.36) implies the approximate relations

$$\mu = 2\sqrt{L\mu_{\text{eff}}} \qquad \rho = 2\sqrt{\mu_{\text{eff}}/L}, \tag{38.37}$$

which give the slope of the curves in Figs. 33 to 36 for large L and small ρ. On the other hand, for large ρ, the parameter μ (for fixed F and D) depends only weakly on L, and the losses due to "incoherent splitting up of the signal" are small. In fact, these losses do increase with L, but the formulas (38.37) correspond to a faster increase of the losses.

---

[11] As already remarked, coherence or incoherence of a train essentially means coherence or incoherence in the way it is handled at the receiver (see p. 186 and the footnote on p. 190).

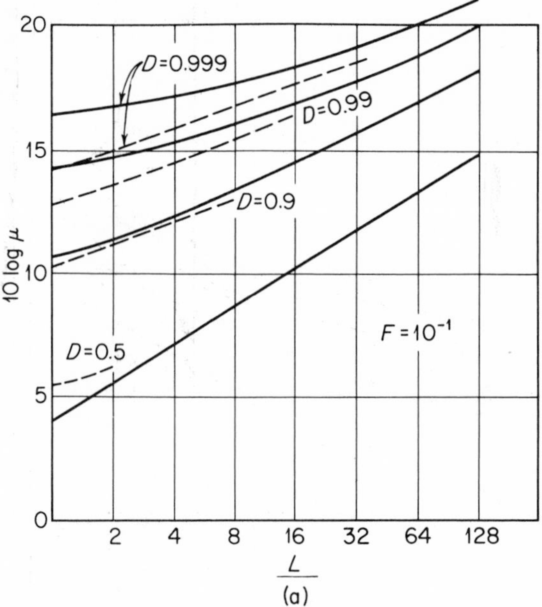

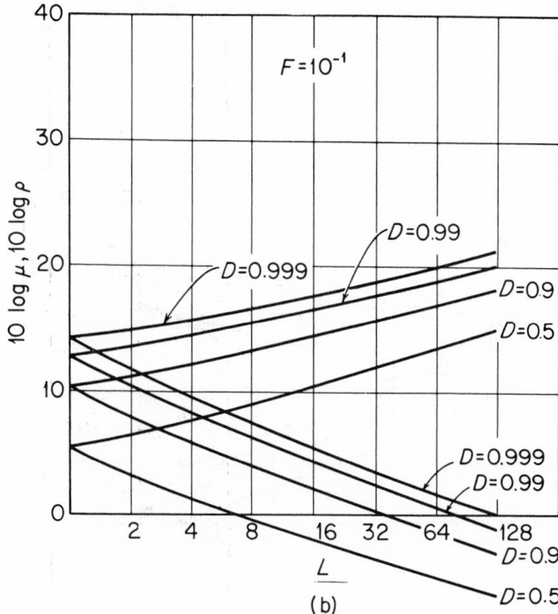

FIG. 33. Operating characteristics for detection of an incoherent signal train for $F = 10^{-1}$.

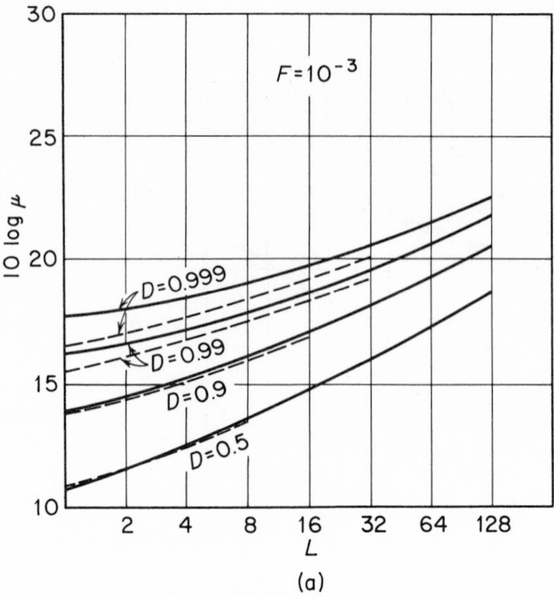

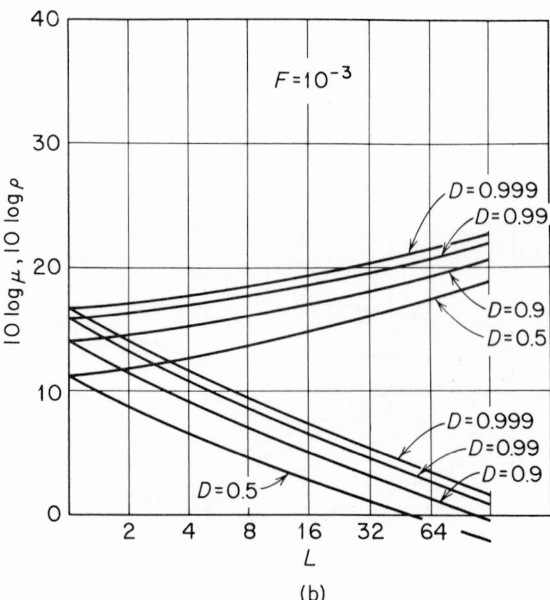

FIG. 34. Operating characteristics for detection of an incoherent signal train for $F = 10^{-3}$.

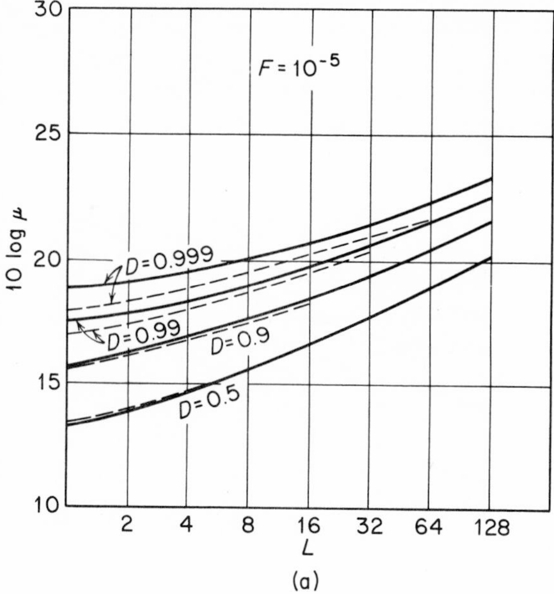

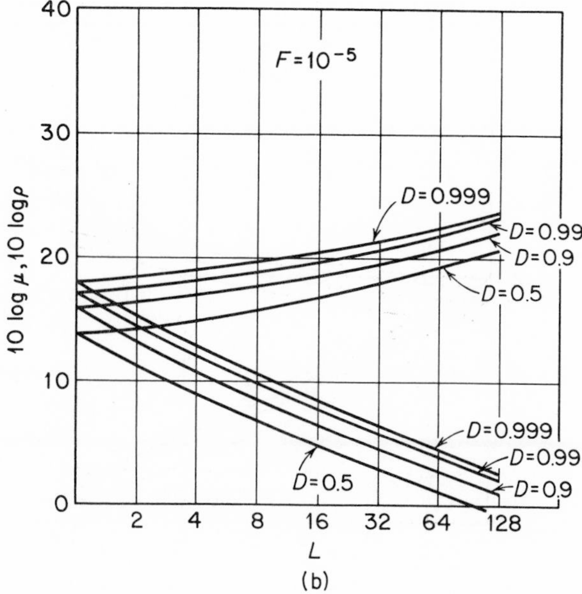

FIG. 35. Operating characteristics for detection of an incoherent signal train for $F = 10^{-5}$.

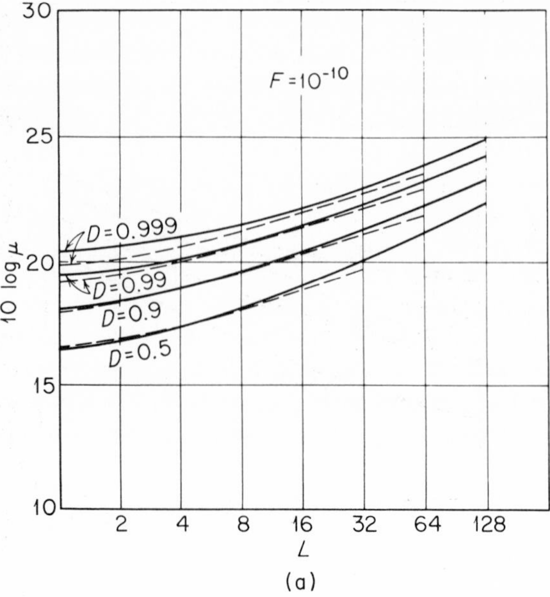

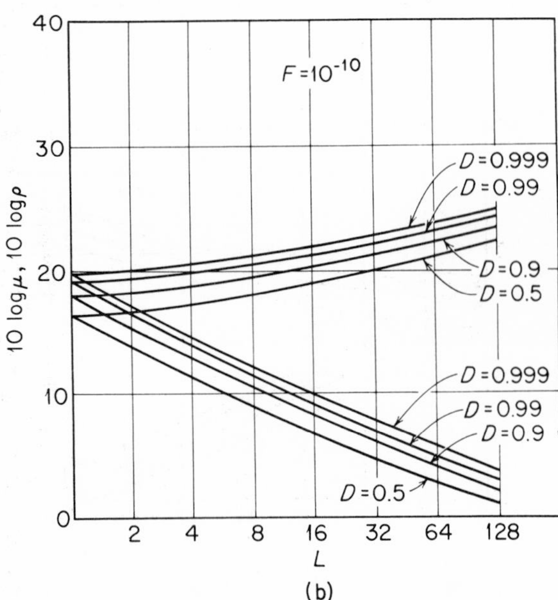

Fig. 36. Operating characteristics for detection of an incoherent signal train for $F = 10^{-10}$.

It must be kept in mind that replacing the distribution laws (38.03) and (38.04) by normal laws (for a given sufficiently large value of L) gives satisfactory results only in the "central" part of the distribution curve, but not in its "tails." Since the calculation of small values of F and D (and also values of F and D near 1) involves the use of just these very "tails" of the distribution curve, the exact functions (38.03) and (38.04) have to be used in making such calculations, while, for example, the approximate relation (38.36) is valid only for values of F and D which are not very small.

In conclusion, we note that although the optimum detector is a linear detector for strong signals and a quadratic detector for weak signals, the transfer characteristic of the detector is actually of no great importance. In fact, in the article by Y. V. Polyak and V. S. Kelzon,[12] it is shown that a linear detector leads to operating characteristics which differ from those of the quadratic detector, for given L, F and D, by less than 1 db (in signal-to-noise ratio).

39. Detection of a Coherent Train in a Background of Correlated Normal Noise

In this section, we consider the optimum receiver performing simple and composite detection of a coherent signal train in a background of receiver noise and clutter. We shall assume that the frequency shift of the signal reflected from the target is known, and that the initial phase of the carrier is known in the case of simple detection, but unknown in the case of composite detection.

When the train of transmitted signals is coherent, the total noise (consisting of receiver noise and clutter) is correlated both within one repetition period and from one period to the next [see formulas (36.08) and (36.15)]. Taking into account formula (36.08) and the remarks at the end of Sec. 36, we can write

$$\overline{n_{g\varkappa}n_{h\lambda}} = R_{gh}r_{\varkappa\lambda}. \tag{39.01}$$

The inverse of the matrix $\|R_{gh}r_{\varkappa\lambda}\|$ has elements $Q_{gh}q_{\varkappa\lambda}$, where $\|Q_{gh}\|$ and $\|q_{\varkappa\lambda}\|$ are the inverses of the matrices $\|R_{gh}\|$ and $\|r_{\varkappa\lambda}\|$, respectively. In fact, from the relations

$$\sum_j R_{gj}Q_{jh} = \delta_{gh}, \tag{39.02}$$

$$\sum_\sigma r_{\varkappa\sigma}q_{\sigma\lambda} = \delta_{\varkappa\lambda}, \tag{39.03}$$

---

[12] Y. V. Polyak and V. S. Kelzon, К теории обнаружения периодических импульсных сигналов в гауссовом шуме при некогерентом накоплении (*On the theory of detection of periodic pulse signals in Gaussian noise, with incoherent addition*), Radiotekh. i Elektron., **3**, 764 (1958).

we obtain

$$\sum_j \sum_\sigma R_{gj} r_{\varkappa\sigma} Q_{jh} q_{\sigma\lambda} = \sum_j R_{gj} Q_{jh} \sum_\sigma r_{\varkappa\sigma} q_{\sigma\lambda} = \delta_{gh} \delta_{\varkappa\lambda}. \tag{39.04}$$

The sample value of the useful signal at the time $t_{h\lambda}$ in the λth period can be written as follows:

$$m_{h\lambda} = e_h \cos [(\omega_0 - \zeta) t_{h\lambda} - \psi_h - \theta]. \tag{39.05}$$

Using formulas (37.06), (37.07) and (37.08), we can write[13]

$$m_{h\lambda} = e_h \cos (\omega_0 t_h - \psi_h - \vartheta_\lambda), \tag{39.06}$$

where

$$\vartheta_\lambda = \theta + (\lambda - 1)\,\Delta\vartheta, \qquad \Delta\vartheta = \zeta T. \tag{39.07}$$

In the case of simple observation, the likelihood ratio Λ is given by the expression (31.18), where now the quantity φ equals

$$\begin{aligned} \varphi &= \sum_{\varkappa,\lambda} \sum_{g,h} Q_{gh} q_{\varkappa\lambda} f_{g\varkappa} m_{h\lambda} \\ &= \sum_{\varkappa,\lambda} q_{\varkappa\lambda} \sum_{g,h} Q_{gh} f_{g\varkappa} e_h \cos (\omega_0 t_h - \psi_h - \vartheta_\lambda) \\ &= \sum_\varkappa a_\varkappa \sum_g A_g f_{g\varkappa} + \sum_\varkappa b_\varkappa \sum_g B_g f_{g\varkappa}. \end{aligned} \tag{39.08}$$

Here, we have introduced the following notation: The coefficients A_g and B_g equal

$$\begin{aligned} A_g &= \sum_h Q_{gh} e_h \cos (\omega_0 t_h - \psi_h), \\ B_g &= \sum_h Q_{gh} e_h \sin (\omega_0 t_h - \psi_h), \end{aligned} \tag{39.09}$$

while the coefficients $a_\varkappa$ and $b_\varkappa$ are defined by the formulas

$$a_\varkappa = \sum_\lambda q_{\varkappa\lambda} \cos \vartheta_\lambda, \qquad b_\varkappa = \sum_\lambda q_{\varkappa\lambda} \sin \vartheta_\lambda. \tag{39.10}$$

Thus, φ can be written as

$$\varphi = \sum_\varkappa (a_\varkappa x_\varkappa + b_\varkappa y_\varkappa), \tag{39.11}$$

where the quantities

$$\begin{aligned} x_\varkappa &= \sum_g A_g f_{g\varkappa} = \sum_{g,h} Q_{gh} f_{g\varkappa} e_h \cos (\omega_0 t_h - \psi_h), \\ y_\varkappa &= \sum_g B_g f_{g\varkappa} = \sum_{g,h} Q_{gh} f_{g\varkappa} e_h \sin (\omega_0 t_h - \psi_h) \end{aligned} \tag{39.12}$$

can be interpreted as the output signals of two linear filters which process in the optimum way the data received during the $\varkappa$th period. Such filters have already been considered in Part 1 (cf. also Sec. 33). Then, the data

[13] See also formula (36.04) and the remark following it. (*Translator*)

processing during all L repetition periods is carried out by using the formula (39.11), where the coefficients $a_\varkappa$ and $b_\varkappa$ are defined by the formulas (39.10).

The quantity μ in the expression for the likelihood ratio can be represented in the following form:

$$\begin{aligned}\mu &= \sum_{\varkappa,\lambda} q_{\varkappa\lambda} \sum_{g,h} Q_{gh} e_g e_h \cos \omega_0(t_g - \psi_g - \vartheta_\varkappa) \cos (\omega_0 t_h - \psi_h - \vartheta_\lambda) \\ &= \frac{1}{2} \sum_{\varkappa,\lambda} q_{\varkappa\lambda} \sum_{g,h} Q_{gh} e_g e_h \cos [\omega_0(t_g - t_h) - (\psi_g - \psi_h) - (\vartheta_\varkappa - \vartheta_\lambda)],\end{aligned} \tag{39.13}$$

where we have neglected the sum containing

$$\cos [\omega_0(t_g + t_h) - (\psi_g + \psi_h) - (\vartheta_\varkappa + \vartheta_\lambda)],$$

which is usually quite permissible because of its small size (the smallness is due to the fact that the terms in this sum oscillate rapidly). Alternatively, we can write

$$\mu = \rho \sum_{\varkappa,\lambda} q_{\varkappa\lambda} \cos (\vartheta_\varkappa - \vartheta_\lambda), \tag{39.14}$$

where the quantity

$$\rho = \frac{1}{2} \sum_{g,h} Q_{gh} e_g e_h \cos [\omega_0(t_g - t_h) - (\psi_g - \psi_h)] \tag{39.15}$$

equals μ in the case of one repetition period ($L = 1$) [cf. formula (33.09)]. According to Sec. 33, ρ is the signal-to-noise ratio for each repetition period when the information in the period is handled in the optimum way.

The optimum receiver for simple detection of a coherent train operates according to a rule similar to (31.19). It is not hard to see that in this case, the operating characteristics for detection of L coherent signals are the same as the operating characteristics for simple detection of a single signal with the parameter μ, defined by formula (39.14).

If the initial phase θ of the train is unknown, then to find the optimum way of handling the data, we have to consider the likelihood ratio

$$\Lambda = \int_0^{2\pi} \Lambda(\theta)\, d\theta = e^{-\mu/2} I_0(\mathscr{E}). \tag{39.16}$$

Here, we have used the fact that φ can be written as

$$\begin{aligned}\varphi &= \sum_{\varkappa,\lambda} q_{\varkappa\lambda} x_\varkappa \cos \vartheta_\lambda + \sum_{\varkappa,\lambda} q_{\varkappa\lambda} y_\varkappa \sin \vartheta_\lambda \\ &= \cos\theta \sum_{\varkappa,\lambda} q_{\varkappa\lambda} \{x_\varkappa \cos [(\lambda - 1)\,\Delta\vartheta] + y_\varkappa \sin [(\lambda - 1)\,\Delta\vartheta]\} \\ &\quad + \sin\theta \sum_{\varkappa,\lambda} q_{\varkappa\lambda} \{-x_\varkappa \sin [(\lambda - 1)\,\Delta\vartheta] + y_\varkappa \cos [(\lambda - 1)\,\Delta\vartheta]\}\end{aligned} \tag{39.17}$$

or

$$\varphi = \mathscr{E} \cos (\Phi - \theta), \tag{39.18}$$

where the quantities $\mathscr{E}$ and Φ are defined by the formulas

$$\begin{aligned}\mathscr{E}\cos\Phi &= \sum_{\varkappa,\lambda} q_{\varkappa\lambda}\{x_\varkappa \cos[(\lambda-1)\,\Delta\vartheta] + y_\varkappa \sin[(\lambda-1)\,\Delta\vartheta]\},\\ \mathscr{E}\sin\Phi &= \sum_{\varkappa,\lambda} q_{\varkappa\lambda}\{-x_\varkappa \sin[(\lambda-1)\,\Delta\vartheta] + y_\varkappa \cos[(\lambda-1)\,\Delta\vartheta]\}.\end{aligned} \tag{39.19}$$

Clearly, in this case, the optimum decision can be made by the rule (33.13), and the operating characteristics for detection are the same as in the case of a single signal with unknown phase, if the parameter μ is defined by formula (39.14).

The quantity $\mathscr{E}$ appearing in formula (39.16) will be important in our subsequent work. Its square can be written in the form

$$\begin{aligned}\mathscr{E}^2 &= \sum_{\varkappa,\lambda}\{\alpha_\varkappa\alpha_\lambda \cos[(\varkappa-\lambda)\,\Delta\vartheta] + \beta_\varkappa\beta_\lambda\cos[(\varkappa-\lambda)\,\Delta\vartheta]\\ &\qquad\qquad - 2\alpha_\varkappa\beta_\lambda \sin[(\varkappa-\lambda)\,\Delta\vartheta]\}\\ &= \left|\sum_\varkappa(\alpha_\varkappa + i\beta_\varkappa)e^{-i\varkappa\Delta\vartheta}\right|^2,\end{aligned} \tag{39.20}$$

where

$$\alpha_\varkappa = \sum_\lambda q_{\varkappa\lambda}x_\lambda, \qquad \beta_\varkappa = \sum q_{\varkappa\lambda}y_\lambda. \tag{39.21}$$

We shall analyze these formulas in the next section.

40. Optimum Detection of a Coherent Train for Different Target Velocities

The likelihood ratio Λ obtained above depends on the phase shift $\Delta\vartheta = \zeta T$ caused by the motion of the target, i.e., Λ depends on the product of the frequency shift ζ and the repetition period T. Depending on the value of $\Delta\vartheta$, we obtain different ways of handling the received signal. If the phase shift equals

$$\Delta\vartheta = 0,\ \pm 2\pi,\ \pm 4\pi,\ \ldots, \tag{40.01}$$

then the target velocity is said to be "blind." For such a velocity, we have

$$\mathscr{E}^2 = \left(\sum_\varkappa \alpha_\varkappa\right)^2 + \left(\sum_\varkappa \beta_\varkappa\right)^2 = \left(\sum_{\varkappa,\lambda} q_{\varkappa\lambda}x_\lambda\right)^2 + \left(\sum_{\varkappa,\lambda} q_{\varkappa\lambda}y_\lambda\right)^2. \tag{40.02}$$

If the phase shift equals

$$\Delta\vartheta = \pm\pi,\ \pm 3\pi,\ \pm 5\pi,\ \ldots, \tag{40.03}$$

then

$$\begin{aligned}\mathscr{E}^2 &= \left[\sum_\varkappa (-1)^{\varkappa+1}\alpha_\varkappa\right]^2 + \left[\sum_\varkappa (-1)^{\varkappa+1}\beta_\varkappa\right]^2\\ &= \left[\sum_{\varkappa,\lambda} q_{\varkappa\lambda}(-1)^{\varkappa+1}x_\lambda\right]^2 + \left[\sum_{\varkappa,\lambda} q_{\varkappa\lambda}(-1)^{\varkappa+1}y_\lambda\right]^2.\end{aligned} \tag{40.04}$$

We now consider formulas (40.02) and (40.04) in more detail in the case where the "period-to-period" correlation coefficient equals $r(\tau) = e^{-u|\tau|}$, so that the elements of the matrix $\|r_{\varkappa\lambda}\|$ have the form

$$r_{\varkappa\lambda} = e^{-u|\varkappa-\lambda|T} = r^{|\varkappa-\lambda|}. \qquad (r = e^{-uT}.) \tag{40.05}$$

Then, the inverse matrix $\|q_{\varkappa\lambda}\|$ equals [cf. formula (35.20) et seq.]

$$\|q_{\varkappa\lambda}\| = \frac{1}{1-r^2}\begin{Vmatrix} 1 & -r & 0 & \cdots & 0 & 0 \\ -r & 1+r^2 & -r & \cdots & 0 & 0 \\ 0 & -r & 1+r^2 & \cdots & 0 & 0 \\ \cdot & \cdot & \cdot & \cdots & \cdot & \cdot \\ 0 & 0 & 0 & \cdots & 1+r^2 & -r \\ 0 & 0 & 0 & \cdots & -r & 1 \end{Vmatrix}. \tag{40.06}$$

According to (39.21), we have

$$\alpha_1 = \frac{x_1 - rx_2}{1-r^2}, \qquad \alpha_2 = \frac{-rx_1 + (1+r^2)x_2 - rx_3}{1-r^2}, \ \ldots \tag{40.07}$$

and similarly for the quantities $\beta_\varkappa$. We also examine the quantity μ, which is the signal-to-noise ratio at the output of the optimum receiver, when the signal parameters are known. In fact, the signal appearing at the output of the optimum receiver can be written as $\varphi = \mu + \nu$, where

$$\bar{\varphi} = \mu, \qquad \overline{\nu^2} = \mu, \qquad \frac{(\bar{\varphi})^2}{\overline{\nu^2}} = \mu \tag{40.08}$$

(cf. Sec. 31). According to formula (39.14), the quantity μ depends on $\Delta\vartheta$ (but not on θ). If the correlation coefficient is defined by (40.05), then, using (39.14), we obtain

$$\mu = \rho\,\frac{L(1 - 2r\cos\Delta\vartheta + r^2) - 2r(r - \cos\Delta\vartheta)}{1-r^2}. \tag{40.09}$$

For "blind" velocities [see formula (40.01)], the quantity (40.02) equals

$$\mathscr{E}^2 = \left\{\frac{x_1 + (1-r)\sum_{\varkappa=2}^{L-1} x_\varkappa + x_L}{1+r}\right\}^2 + \left\{\frac{y_1 + (1-r)\sum_{\varkappa=2}^{L-1} y_\varkappa + y_L}{1+r}\right\}^2, \tag{40.10}$$

where

$$\mu = \rho\,\frac{L(1-r) + 2r}{1+r}. \tag{40.11}$$

We now consider two limiting cases:

(a) If there is no clutter, and the signal is extracted only from a background of "white" noise, then $r = 0$ and

$$\mathscr{E}^2 = \Big(\sum_{\varkappa} x_{\varkappa}\Big)^2 + \Big(\sum_{\varkappa} y_{\varkappa}\Big)^2. \tag{40.12}$$

Thus, the optimum receiver has to add up coherently the results of two quadrature channels and then form the envelope $\mathscr{E}$ of the corresponding sums. The optimum receiver can also be implemented by combining a matched filter and an envelope detector (cf. Secs. 20 and 33). In this case, the output signal-to-noise ratio equals

$$\mu = L\rho, \tag{40.13}$$

i.e., is directly proportional to the number of signals in the train.

(b) If the noise is due mainly to clutter, and if it can be considered constant during the observation time, then $r \sim 1$, and

$$\mathscr{E}^2 = \left(\frac{x_1 + x_L}{2}\right)^2 + \left(\frac{y_1 + y_L}{2}\right)^2. \tag{40.14}$$

In this case, the optimum receiver has to add only the results obtained when the input signal is processed in the optimum way during the first and the last repetition periods (in each quadrature channel). Then, the signal-to-noise ratio equals

$$\mu = \rho, \tag{40.15}$$

i.e., for strongly correlated noise and "blind" velocities, coherent addition does not lead to any improvement in signal detectability. This is explained by the fact that the noise is increased to the same extent as the signal.

Next, we consider the case of the phase shifts (40.03). In this case, the likelihood ratio Λ is a function of the quantity

$$\mathscr{E}^2 = \left\{\frac{x_1 + (1+r)\sum_{\varkappa=2}^{L-1}(-1)^{\varkappa+1}x_{\varkappa} + (-1)^{L+1}x_L}{1-r}\right\}^2 + \left\{\frac{y_1 + (1+r)\sum_{\varkappa=2}^{L-1}(-1)^{\varkappa+1}y_{\varkappa} + (-1)^{L+1}y_L}{1-r}\right\}^2, \tag{40.16}$$

where

$$\mu = \rho\,\frac{L(1+r) - 2r}{1-r}. \tag{40.17}$$

Again, we examine the two limiting cases:

(a) For noise of the "white" type ($r = 0$), we have

$$\mathscr{E}^2 = \Big[\sum_{\varkappa} (-1)^{\varkappa+1} x_{\varkappa}\Big]^2 + \Big[\sum_{\varkappa} (-1)^{\varkappa+1} y_{\varkappa}\Big]^2, \tag{40.18}$$

i.e., we obtain coherent addition which takes account of the alternating phases of the useful signal. Here, the effective signal-to-noise ratio for the train equals

$$\mu = L\rho. \tag{40.19}$$

(b) For clutter, when $r \sim 1$, we obtain

$$\mathscr{E}^2 = \left\{\frac{x_1 + 2\sum\limits_{\varkappa=2}^{L-1} (-1)^{\varkappa+1} x_{\varkappa} + (-1)^{L+1} x_L}{1 - r}\right\}^2 + \left\{\frac{y_1 + 2\sum\limits_{\varkappa=2}^{L-1} (-1)^{\varkappa+1} y_{\varkappa} + (-1)^{L+1} y_L}{1 - r}\right\}^2. \tag{40.20}$$

In particular,

$$\mathscr{E}^2 = \left(\frac{x_1 - x_2}{1 - r}\right)^2 + \left(\frac{y_1 - y_2}{1 - r}\right)^2 \tag{40.21}$$

for $L = 2$, and

$$\mathscr{E}^2 = \left(\frac{x_1 - 2x_2 + x_3}{1 - r}\right)^2 + \left(\frac{y_1 - 2y_2 + y_3}{1 - r}\right)^2 \tag{40.22}$$

for $L = 3$. Thus, the optimum receiver has to form *differences*, the first difference in the case $L = 2$, the second difference in the case $L = 3$, and a more complicated combination of differences when L is larger. Hence, we have arrived at a familiar method for suppressing noise due to clutter, i.e., "pulse-to-pulse subtraction." In this limiting case, the signal-to-noise ratio equals

$$\mu = \rho\,\frac{2(L - 1)}{1 - r}, \tag{40.23}$$

so that $\mu \to \infty$ as $r \to 1$, i.e., the closer to unity the pulse-to-pulse correlation coefficient r, the more the subtraction frees the receiver from the effects of clutter. The signal detectability rises sharply as $r \to 1$.

It is quite difficult to investigate intermediate values of $\Delta\vartheta$ when there are a large number of repetition periods. However, it is comparatively easy to do so when there are just two periods. The next section is devoted to this problem.

41. Detection of a Coherent Signal Train For Two Repetition Periods and For Both Known and Unknown Frequency Shifts

When there are two repetition periods ($L = 2$), the direct and inverse correlation matrices $\|r_{\varkappa\lambda}\|$ and $\|q_{\varkappa\lambda}\|$ are obviously equal to

$$\|r_{\varkappa\lambda}\| = \begin{Vmatrix} 1 & r \\ r & 1 \end{Vmatrix}, \qquad \|q_{\varkappa\lambda}\| = \frac{1}{1-r^2}\begin{Vmatrix} 1 & -r \\ -r & 1 \end{Vmatrix}. \tag{41.01}$$

Setting $L = 2$ in (39.14) and (39.16), we find that in the case of two repetition periods, the likelihood ratio is

$$\Lambda = e^{-\rho(1-r\cos\Delta\vartheta)/(1-r^2)} I_0(\mathscr{E}), \tag{41.02}$$

where the quantity $\mathscr{E}$ equals

$$\begin{aligned}\mathscr{E}^2 &= \frac{1}{(1-r^2)^2}[(1 - 2r\cos\Delta\vartheta + r^2)(x_1^2 + x_2^2 + y_1^2 + y_2^2) \\ &\quad + (2\cos\Delta\vartheta - 2r + r^2\cos\Delta\vartheta)(x_1x_2 + y_1y_2) \\ &\quad - 2\sin\Delta\vartheta(1 - r^2)(x_2y_1 - x_1y_2)] \\ &= \frac{1}{(1-r^2)^2}[\{x_1 - r(x_1\cos\Delta\vartheta + y_1\sin\Delta\vartheta) - rx_2 + x_2\cos\Delta\vartheta \\ &\quad + y_2\sin\Delta\vartheta\}^2 + \{y_1 - r(y_1\cos\Delta\vartheta - x_1\sin\Delta\vartheta) \\ &\quad - ry_2 + y_2\cos\Delta\vartheta - x_2\sin\Delta\vartheta\}^2].\end{aligned} \tag{41.03}$$

As we have already shown, for $\Delta\vartheta = 0, \pm 2\pi, \pm 4\pi, \ldots$, we obtain the formula

$$\mathscr{E}^2 = \frac{1}{(1+r)^2}[(x_1 + x_2)^2 + (y_1 + y_2)^2], \tag{41.04}$$

which corresponds to addition of consecutive periods and gives a signal-to-noise ratio for the train which equals

$$\mu = \frac{2\rho}{1+r}. \tag{41.05}$$

For $\Delta\vartheta = \pm\pi, \pm 3\pi, \pm 5\pi, \ldots$, we obtain the expression

$$\mathscr{E}^2 = \frac{1}{(1-r)^2}[(x_1 - x_2)^2 + (y_1 - y_2)^2], \tag{41.06}$$

which corresponds to subtraction of consecutive periods, where now

$$\mu = \frac{2\rho}{1-r}. \tag{41.07}$$

For uncorrelated noise ($r \sim 0$) and an arbitrary phase difference $\Delta\vartheta$, formula (41.03) becomes

$$\begin{aligned}\mathscr{E}^2 &= x_1^2 + y_1^2 + x_2^2 + y_2^2 + 2\cos\Delta\vartheta(x_1x_2 + y_1y_2) \\ &\quad - 2\sin\Delta\vartheta(x_2y_1 - x_1y_2) \\ &= |x_1 + iy_1 + (x_2 + iy_2)e^{-i\Delta\vartheta}|^2,\end{aligned} \tag{41.08}$$

so that the optimum receiver has to perform coherent addition of the signal, taking into account the phase difference $\Delta\vartheta$. Here, the signal-to-noise ratio of the train is

$$\mu = 2\rho. \tag{41.09}$$

On the other hand, if the noise is strongly correlated ($r \sim 1$), while the phase shift $\Delta\vartheta$ is arbitrary but not equal to $0, \pm 2\pi, \pm 4\pi, \ldots$, i.e., if the velocity is not "blind" (see Sec. 40), then the general formula (41.03) becomes

$$\mathscr{E}^2 = \frac{2(1 - \cos\Delta\vartheta)}{(1 - r^2)^2}[(x_1 - x_2)^2 + (y_1 - y_2)^2]. \tag{41.10}$$

Thus, we have again arrived at a subtraction scheme, where the signal-to-noise ratio equals

$$\mu = \rho\frac{1 - \cos\Delta\vartheta}{1 - r}. \tag{41.11}$$

In Fig. 37, we show the form of the optimum receiver for detecting strong correlated noise. The receiver has to perform the following operations: (1) Optimum processing of the received function $f(t)$ during each repetition period, by using the quadrature filters A and B as described by the formulas

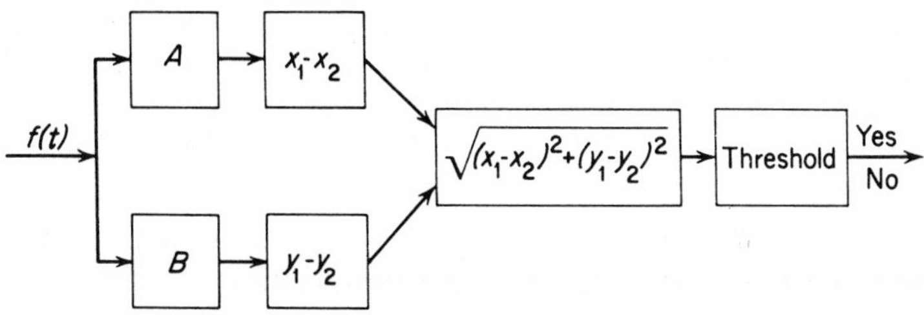

FIG. 37. Block diagram of the optimum receiver for strongly correlated noise.

(39.12); (2) optimum pulse-to-pulse processing, i.e., subtraction in both quadrature channels; (3) formation of the envelope $\sqrt{(x_1 - x_2)^2 + (y_1 - y_2)^2}$, its square, or any other monotonically increasing function of this quantity; (4) making the decision.

For $L = 3, 4, \ldots$, the optimum receivers become more complicated, and the mathematical operations which have to be performed on the input signal depend (even for $r_{\varkappa\lambda} \to 1$) on $\Delta\vartheta$, on the closeness of the various coefficients $r_{\varkappa\lambda}$ to unity, etc. The implementation of such receivers not only involves more complicated circuitry, but it also requires that we have more complete information about the signal and the noise in every specific case.

Quite often, the frequency shift of the reflected useful signal is unknown. In this case, to find the optimum receiver for detection, we have to perform additional averaging (integration) of the likelihood ratio over the unknown frequency (or phase) shift of the useful signal, produced by the Doppler effect. For a train consisting of two coherent signals, it is more convenient to perform this averaging in a somewhat different way, i.e., with respect to the phase of each signal. Thus, we write the sample values of the useful signal as

$$m_{h\lambda} = e_h \cos(\omega_0 t_h - \psi_h - \vartheta_\lambda), \tag{41.12}$$

where we assume that the phases

$$\vartheta_1 = \theta, \qquad \vartheta_2 = \theta + \zeta T = \theta + \Delta\vartheta \tag{41.13}$$

are uniformly distributed from 0 to 2π. The likelihood ratio

$$\Lambda(\vartheta_1, \vartheta_2) = \frac{1}{(2\pi)^2} e^{\varphi(\vartheta_1,\vartheta_2) - \frac{1}{2}\mu(\vartheta_1,\vartheta_2)}. \tag{41.14}$$

is determined by the quantities $\varphi(\vartheta_1, \vartheta_2)$ and $\mu(\vartheta_1, \vartheta_2)$, which, according to formulas (39.14) and (39.11), are expressed in terms of ϑ_1 and ϑ_2 as follows:

$$-\frac{1}{2}\mu(\vartheta_1, \vartheta_2) = -\frac{\rho}{1 - r^2} + \frac{\rho r(\cos\vartheta_1 \cos\vartheta_2 + \sin\vartheta_1 \sin\vartheta_2)}{1 - r^2}, \tag{41.15}$$

$$\varphi(\vartheta_1, \vartheta_2) = \frac{(x_1 - rx_2)\cos\vartheta_1 + (y_1 - ry_2)\sin\vartheta_1}{1 - r^2} + \frac{(x_2 - rx_1)\cos\vartheta_2 + (y_2 - ry_1)\sin\vartheta_2}{1 - r^2}. \tag{41.16}$$

We now show that after integrating with respect to ϑ_1 and ϑ_2, the likelihood ratio (for $r \sim 1$) will depend only on the quantity

$$\mathscr{E} = \sqrt{(x_1 - x_2)^2 + (y_1 - y_2)^2}, \tag{41.17}$$

which characterizes the useful signal. In fact, integrating (41.14) with respect to ϑ_1 and ϑ_2, we obtain

$$\Lambda = e^{-\rho/(1-r^2)} \sum_{k=-\infty}^{\infty} e^{-ik(\Phi_2 - \Phi_1)} I_k\left(\frac{\rho r}{1 - r^2}\right) I_k\left(\frac{\mathscr{E}_1}{1 - r^2}\right) I_k\left(\frac{\mathscr{E}_2}{1 - r^2}\right), \tag{41.18}$$

where

$$\begin{aligned} \mathscr{E}_1 \cos \Phi_1 &= x_1 - rx_2, & \mathscr{E}_2 \cos \Phi_2 &= x_2 - rx_1, \\ \mathscr{E}_1 \sin \Phi_1 &= y_1 - ry_2, & \mathscr{E}_2 \sin \Phi_2 &= y_2 - ry_1. \end{aligned} \tag{41.19}$$

Formula (41.18) is derived as follows: First we integrate $\Lambda(\vartheta_1, \vartheta_2)$ with respect to ϑ_2, obtaining

$$\begin{aligned} \frac{1}{(2\pi)^2} \int_0^{2\pi} \Lambda(\vartheta_1, \vartheta_2)\, d\vartheta_2 = \frac{1}{2\pi} I_0(Z) \exp \bigg\{ &- \frac{\rho}{1 - r^2} \\ &+ \frac{(x_1 - rx_2) \cos \vartheta_1 + (y_1 - ry_2) \sin \vartheta_1}{1 - r^2} \bigg\}, \end{aligned} \tag{41.20}$$

where

$$\begin{aligned} Z &= \frac{1}{1 - r^2} \sqrt{(\rho r \cos \vartheta_1 + x_2 - rx_1)^2 + (\rho r \sin \vartheta_1 + y_2 - ry_1)^2} \\ &= \frac{1}{1 - r^2} \sqrt{\rho^2 r^2 + 2\rho r \mathscr{E}_2 \cos (\vartheta_1 - \Phi_2) + \mathscr{E}_2^2}. \end{aligned} \tag{41.21}$$

Next, we apply the addition theorem for Bessel functions,[14] in the form

$$I_0(Z) = \sum_{k=-\infty}^{\infty} e^{ik(\vartheta_1 - \Phi_2)} I_k\left(\frac{\rho r}{1 - r^2}\right) I_k\left(\frac{\mathscr{E}_2}{1 - r^2}\right). \tag{41.22}$$

Finally, using the relation

$$\begin{aligned} I_k\left(\frac{\mathscr{E}_1}{1 - r^2}\right) = \frac{1}{2\pi} \int_0^{2\pi} \exp \bigg\{ &ik(\vartheta_1 - \Phi_1) \\ &+ \frac{\mathscr{E}_1}{1 - r^2} \cos (\vartheta_1 - \Phi_1) \bigg\}\, d\vartheta_1, \end{aligned} \tag{41.23}$$

we obtain the series (41.18), after integrating with respect to ϑ_1.

For strongly correlated noise ($r \sim 1$), we have

$$\mathscr{E}_1 = \mathscr{E}_2 = \mathscr{E}, \quad \Phi_2 - \Phi_1 = \pi, \quad e^{-ik(\Phi_2 - \Phi_1)} = (-1)^k, \tag{41.24}$$

so that the likelihood ratio (41.18) reduces to

$$\Lambda = e^{-\mu_0} \sum_{k=-\infty}^{\infty} (-1)^k I_k(\mu_0) I_k^2\left(\frac{\mathscr{E}}{1 - r^2}\right), \tag{41.25}$$

where

$$\mu_0 = \frac{\rho}{1 - r^2} \sim \frac{\rho r}{1 - r^2}, \tag{41.26}$$

and $\mathscr{E}$ is given by formula (41.17).

---

[14] G. N. Watson, *op. cit.*, p. 359.

Thus, for $r \sim 1$, the optimum receiver for detection of signals with unknown Doppler frequency has the same form (see Fig. 37) as in the case of a known but arbitrary phase shift $\Delta\vartheta$, which does not equal any of the values (40.01). This result is almost obvious physically, since the "blind" velocities, for which the subtraction scheme is not applicable, have a very small statistical weight and hence disappear when we average over $\Delta\vartheta$.

42. The Probabilities F and D for Pulse-to-Pulse Subtraction

We now find the false alarm probability F and the detection probability D for a receiver forming the quantity

$$\mathscr{E} = \sqrt{(x_1 - x_2)^2 + (y_1 - y_2)^2} \tag{42.01}$$

and making its decision according to the following rule:

$$\begin{aligned} &\text{If} \quad \mathscr{E} \geqslant \mathscr{E}_*, \quad \text{decide that } f = m + n; \\ &\text{If} \quad \mathscr{E} < \mathscr{E}, \quad \text{decide that } f = n, \end{aligned} \tag{42.02}$$

where $\mathscr{E}_*$ is some decision threshold. It was proved above that such a receiver is optimum for any frequency shift if the noise is strongly correlated ($r \sim 1$), and for any kind of noise correlation, if $\Delta\vartheta = \pm\pi, \pm 3\pi, \ldots$. If in formula (39.12) we write $f_{g\varkappa}$ as a sum $m_{g\varkappa} + n_{g\varkappa}$, then the quantities $x_\varkappa$ and $y_\varkappa$ take the form

$$x_\varkappa = x_{m\varkappa} + x_{n\varkappa}, \qquad y_\varkappa = y_{m\varkappa} + y_{n\varkappa}, \tag{42.03}$$

where

$$x_{m\varkappa} = \sum_g A_g m_{g\varkappa}, \qquad y_{m\varkappa} = \sum_g B_g m_{g\varkappa} \tag{42.04}$$

and

$$x_{n\varkappa} = \sum_g A_g n_{g\varkappa}, \qquad y_{n\varkappa} = \sum_g B_g n_{g\varkappa}. \tag{42.05}$$

It follows from (39.06), (39.09), (39.12) and (39.14) that

$$x_{m\varkappa} = \rho \cos \vartheta_\varkappa, \qquad y_{m\varkappa} = -\rho \sin \vartheta_\varkappa. \tag{42.06}$$

The random variables $x_{n\varkappa}$ and $y_{n\varkappa}$ are normal, with moments

$$\begin{aligned} &\overline{x_{n\varkappa}} = \overline{y_{n\varkappa}} = 0, \qquad \overline{x_{n\varkappa} y_{n\lambda}} = 0, \\ &\overline{x_{n\varkappa} x_{n\lambda}} = \overline{y_{n\varkappa} y_{n\lambda}} = \rho r_{\varkappa\lambda}, \end{aligned} \tag{42.07}$$

where $\varkappa$ and λ take the values 1 and 2.

In the absence of the useful signal, the quantity $\mathscr{E}$ equals

$$\mathscr{E} = \sqrt{\xi^2 + \eta^2}, \quad \text{where} \quad \xi = x_{n1} - x_{n2}, \qquad \eta = y_{n1} - y_{n2}. \tag{42.08}$$

According to formula (42.07), the random variables ξ and η are normal, with moments

$$\bar{\xi} = \bar{\eta} = 0, \qquad \overline{\xi\eta} = 0, \qquad \overline{\xi^2} = \overline{\eta^2} = 2\rho(1 - r). \tag{42.09}$$

Therefore, the envelope $\mathscr{E}$ has the Rayleigh distribution

$$p_0(\mathscr{E}) = \frac{\mathscr{E}}{2\rho(1 - r)} e^{-\mathscr{E}^2/4\rho(1-r)} \tag{42.10}$$

[cf. formula (33.27)], and the false alarm probability equals

$$F = \int_{\mathscr{E}_*}^{\infty} p_0(\mathscr{E})\, d\mathscr{E} = e^{-z_*^2/2} \qquad \left(z_* = \frac{\mathscr{E}_*}{\sqrt{2\rho(1 - r)}}\right). \tag{42.11}$$

In the presence of the useful signal, we have

$$\mathscr{E} = \sqrt{\xi^2 + \eta^2},$$

$$\xi = \rho(\cos\vartheta_1 - \cos\vartheta_2) + x_{n1} - x_{n2} = \rho'\sin\vartheta + x_{n1} - x_{n2}, \tag{42.12}$$

$$\eta = \rho(\sin\vartheta_1 - \sin\vartheta_2) + y_{n1} - y_{n2} = \rho'\cos\vartheta + y_{n1} - y_{n2},$$

where we have introduced the notation

$$\rho' = 2\rho \sin\frac{\Delta\vartheta}{2} \tag{42.13}$$

$$\vartheta = \frac{\vartheta_1 + \vartheta_2}{2}, \qquad \Delta\vartheta = \vartheta_2 - \vartheta_1. \tag{42.14}$$

It is clear from (42.12) that in the presence of a useful signal with fixed phase shift $\Delta\vartheta$, the quantity $\mathscr{E}$ has the Rice distribution (33.41), with parameters

$$\bar{\varphi} = \rho', \qquad \sigma^2 = 2\rho(1 - r).$$

Therefore, we have

$$p_m(\mathscr{E}) = \frac{\mathscr{E}}{2\rho(1 - r)} e^{-(\rho'^2 + \mathscr{E}^2)/4\rho(1-r)} I_0\left(\frac{\rho'\mathscr{E}}{2\rho(1 - r)}\right). \tag{42.15}$$

If we let

$$\mu = \rho\frac{1 - \cos\Delta\vartheta}{1 - r} = 2\mu_0(1 - \cos\Delta\vartheta), \tag{42.16}$$

where

$$\mu_0 = \frac{\rho}{2(1 - r)}, \tag{42.17}$$

then, in the presence of both signal and noise at the input, we can write the distribution of the envelope $\mathscr{E}$ as

$$p_m(\mathscr{E}) = \frac{\mathscr{E}}{2\rho(1 - r)} e^{-(\mu/2) - [\mathscr{E}^2/4\rho(1-r)]} I_0\left(\frac{\sqrt{\mu}\,\mathscr{E}}{\sqrt{2\rho(1 - r)}}\right). \tag{42.18}$$

Then, the detection probability for the fixed phase shift $\Delta\vartheta$ equals

$$\begin{aligned} D(\Delta\vartheta) &= \int_{\mathscr{E}_*}^{\infty} p_m(\mathscr{E})\, d\mathscr{E} \\ &= \int_{z_*}^{\infty} z e^{-(\mu+z^2)/2} I_0(\sqrt{\mu}\, z)\, dz \qquad \left(z_* = \frac{\mathscr{E}_*}{\sqrt{2\rho(1-r)}}\right). \end{aligned} \tag{42.19}$$

The quantity μ defined by the formula (42.16) is the signal-to-noise ratio at the subtractor output for fixed $\Delta\vartheta$. In fact, formulas (42.08), (42.09) and (42.12) give

$$\begin{gathered} \xi = \xi_m + \xi_n, \qquad \eta = \eta_m + \eta_n, \\ \xi_n = x_{n1} - x_{n2}, \qquad \eta_n = y_{n1} - y_{n2}, \qquad \overline{\xi_n^2} = \overline{\eta_n^2} = 2\rho(1-r), \\ \xi_m = \rho' \sin\vartheta, \qquad \eta_m = \rho' \cos\vartheta, \\ \overline{\xi_m^2} = \overline{\eta_m^2} = \tfrac{1}{2}\rho'^2 = \rho^2(1 - \cos\Delta\vartheta), \end{gathered} \tag{42.20}$$

where $\overline{\xi_m^2} = \overline{\eta_m^2}$ is averaged over the phase ϑ. Therefore, the signal-to-noise (power) ratio equals

$$\mu = \frac{\overline{\xi_m^2}}{\overline{\xi_n^2}} = \frac{\rho(1 - \cos\Delta\vartheta)}{1 - r}. \tag{42.21}$$

The total probability of correct detection (for any Doppler phase shifts) is obtained by averaging $D(\Delta\vartheta)$ with respect to $\Delta\vartheta$. Assuming for simplicity that all values of $\Delta\vartheta$ are equally probable, we obtain

$$D = \frac{1}{2\pi}\int_0^{2\pi} D(\Delta\vartheta)\, d\,\Delta\vartheta = \frac{1}{\pi}\int_0^{2\pi} D(\Delta\vartheta)\, d\,\Delta\vartheta. \tag{42.22}$$

The quantity D depends on the parameter μ_0 defined by (42.17), as well as on the threshold $\mathscr{E}_*$, which is connected with the false alarm probability. The parameter μ_0 is the signal-to-noise ratio at the subtractor output for arbitrary $\Delta\vartheta$. To see this, we note that for arbitrary $\Delta\vartheta$, the phases ϑ_1 and ϑ_2 are statistically independent, so that, using the notation (42.20), we obtain

$$\begin{aligned} \overline{\xi_m^2} &= \rho^2\overline{(\cos\vartheta_1 - \cos\vartheta_2)^2} = \rho^2, \\ \overline{\eta_m^2} &= \rho^2\overline{(\sin\vartheta_1 - \sin\vartheta_2)^2} = \rho^2. \end{aligned} \tag{42.23}$$

Thus, in this case, the signal-to-noise ratio equals

$$\mu_0 = \frac{\overline{\xi_m^2}}{\overline{\xi_n^2}} = \frac{\rho}{2(1-r)}. \tag{42.24}$$

In Fig. 38, the solid curves show the dependence of $D(\Delta\vartheta)$ on μ, where μ is given by formula (42.16). These curves do not differ from the corresponding curves for optimum detection of a single pulse with unknown r-f phase in a background of normal noise, except that here the effective signal-to-noise ratio at the subtractor output is plotted as abscissa. We observe that for given $\Delta\vartheta$ and r, it is not hard to calculate the corresponding signal-to-noise ratio for one repetition period (after optimum processing of the data within the period), by using the formula

$$\rho = \mu \frac{1 - r}{1 - \cos \Delta\vartheta}. \tag{42.25}$$

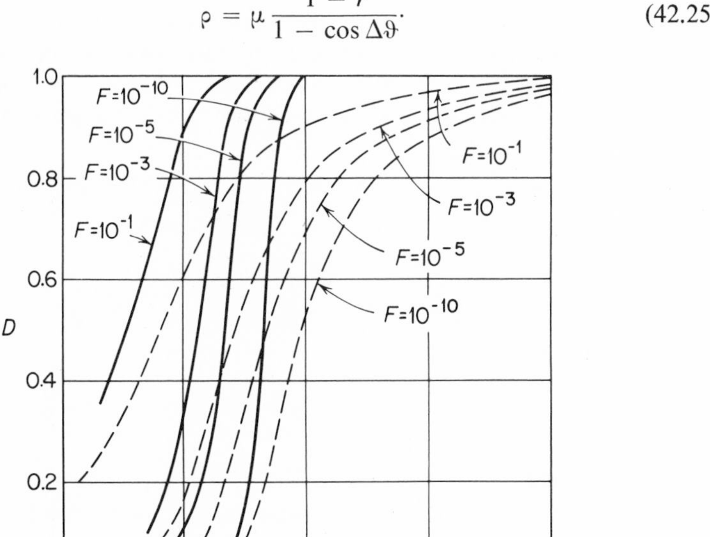

FIG. 38. Comparison of single-channel and double-channel schemes for pulse-to-pulse subtraction, for known $\Delta\vartheta$. Solid curves, single channel; Dashed curves, double channel.

In Fig. 39, we show how D, the total probability of detection (for arbitrary $\Delta\vartheta$), depends on μ_0. We see that when μ_0 is increased, the detection probability approaches 1 very slowly (much more slowly, for example, than in Fig. 38). This is explained by the fact that even for very large μ_0 (for $\mu_0 = 20$ db, say), detection of targets with velocities near the blind velocities is not reliable. It is interesting to note that when $\cos \Delta\vartheta = \frac{1}{2}$, i.e., when

$$\cos \Delta\vartheta = \pm \frac{\pi}{3}, \pm 2\pi \pm \frac{\pi}{3}, \ldots,$$

we have

$$\mu = \frac{\rho}{2(1 - r)} = \mu_0, \tag{42.26}$$

and then the units in Figs. 38 and 39 coincide.

So far, we have been considering the optimum radar receiver when both receiver noise and clutter are present. It is useful to compare the theoretical results which we have obtained with the performance of simpler schemes, in particular, with coherent compensation of clutter using a single channel. We first discuss the optimum handling of the received signal during one period. In the optimum system, as compared with the coherent system, the transfer function is given by formula (33.15), whereas the transfer function of the coherent receiver usually has a shape which is close to being rectangular. The gain in signal-to-noise ratio in the optimum system, as compared with the system with a rectangular transfer function, was examined in Sec. 21.

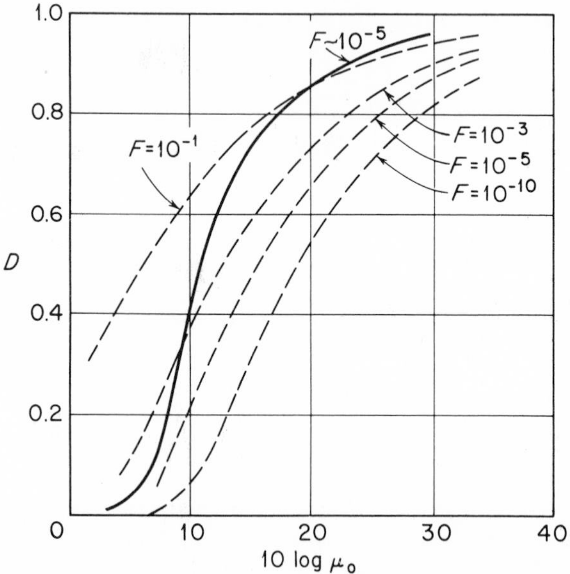

FIG. 39. Comparison of single-channel and double-channel schemes for pulse-to-pulse subtraction, for unknown $\Delta\vartheta$. Solid curves, single channel; Dashed curves, double channel.

This gain can be made indefinitely large by using a sufficiently wide-band Urkowitz filter, but then the receiver noise begins to play an important role, and in fact, the relation between the receiver noise power and the power of the noise due to clutter determines the proper bandwidth for the Urkowitz filter. It must also be borne in mind that if the product of the filter bandwidth $\Delta\omega$ and the pulse duration T_0 satisfies the condition $\Delta\omega T_0 \leqslant 4$, then the Urkowitz filter and the "rectangular" filter give approximately the same output signal-to-noise ratio (see Fig. 25).

If the processing of the received data in each repetition period is non-optimum, then this leads to a decrease in the value of ρ, but it does not prevent us from using the theory of the optimum receiver, as far as processing the signal from pulse to pulse is concerned. If we use a simplified, "single-channel" version of the coherent method for compensating clutter, i.e., if we use only the quantity

$$\xi = x_1 - x_2 \tag{42.27}$$

to decide whether or not the target is present, then we do not make full use of all the available information. For example, if $\Delta\vartheta = \pi$ and if the initial phase $\theta = \pi/2$, the useful signal will not be detected, since it will appear instead in the absent channel forming $\eta = y_1 - y_2$.

We now find the false alarm probability F_1 and the detection probability D_1 for a single-channel coherent receiver, which operates according to the following decision rule:

$$\begin{aligned} &\text{If} \quad |\xi| \geqslant \xi_*, \quad \text{decide that } f = m + n; \\ &\text{If} \quad |\xi| < \xi_*, \quad \text{decide that } f = n, \end{aligned} \tag{42.28}$$

where ξ_* is the decision threshold.

In the absence of the useful signal, the distribution of the quantity ξ is given by the formula

$$p_0(\xi) = \frac{1}{\sqrt{4\pi\rho(1-r)}} e^{-\xi^2/4\rho(1-r)}, \tag{42.29}$$

and the false alarm probability F_1 equals

$$\begin{aligned} F_1 &= 2\int_{\xi_*}^{\infty} p_0(\xi)\, d\xi \\ &= \frac{2}{\sqrt{2\pi}} \int_{z_*}^{\infty} e^{-z^2/2}\, dz \qquad \left(z_* = \frac{\xi_*}{\sqrt{2\rho(1-r)}}\right). \end{aligned} \tag{42.30}$$

In the presence of a signal with known phase shift $\Delta\vartheta$, the distribution of ξ is given by the formula

$$\begin{aligned} p_m(z, \Delta\vartheta) &= \frac{1}{2\pi} \int_0^{2\pi} p_m(z, \Delta\vartheta, \vartheta)\, d\vartheta \\ &= \frac{1}{(2\pi)^{3/2}} \int_0^{2\pi} e^{-(z-\sqrt{\mu}\cos\vartheta^2)/2}\, d\vartheta \qquad \left(z = \frac{\xi}{\sqrt{2\rho(1-r)}}\right). \end{aligned} \tag{42.31}$$

It follows that the detection probability $D_1(\Delta\vartheta)$ for known $\Delta\vartheta$ equals

$$\begin{aligned} D_1(\Delta\vartheta) &= \frac{2}{(2\pi)^{3/2}} \int_0^{2\pi} d\vartheta \int_{z_*}^{\infty} e^{-(z-\sqrt{\mu}\cos\vartheta)^2/2}\, dz \\ &= \frac{2}{\pi} \int_0^{\pi} d\vartheta \frac{1}{\sqrt{2\pi}} \int_{z_* - \sqrt{\mu}\cos\vartheta}^{\infty} e^{-z^2/2}\, dz, \end{aligned} \tag{42.32}$$

and that the detection probability for unknown $\Delta\vartheta$ is

$$D_1 = \frac{1}{\pi}\int_0^{\pi} D_1(\Delta\vartheta)\, d\,\Delta\vartheta. \tag{42.33}$$

In Fig. 38, the dashed curves show the dependence of $D_1(\Delta\vartheta)$ on the parameter μ, which, as before, is defined by formula (42.16). We see that for "single-channel" compensation, the probability $D_1(\Delta\vartheta)$ is considerably less than the probability corresponding to compensation in two quadrature channels. In particular, for $\mu \sim 15$ db, we have $D(\Delta\vartheta) \sim 2D_1(\Delta\vartheta)$, and for larger values of μ, the function $D_1(\Delta\vartheta)$ approaches 1 very slowly. This is due to the fact that there are useful signals with "blind" phases ($\vartheta = 0$, $\pm 2\pi, \ldots$) which go completely undetected in the case of the single-channel scheme; useful signals with values of ϑ near these blind phases can be observed only with difficulty, thereby causing $D_1(\Delta\vartheta)$ to approach 1 slowly as $\mu \to \infty$. We see the same behavior in Fig. 39, where we compare the operating characteristics for single-channel and double-channel (optimum) detection in the case where the frequency shift is unknown. It should be noted that because of difficulties in using (42.32) and (42.33) to make calculations, the operating characteristics of the single-channel receiver shown in Figs. 38 and 39 have been rather crudely computed, and we do not claim that they are very accurate.

In conclusion, we note that single-channel coherent radar receivers, which compensate for noise due to clutter, usually contain additional nonlinear elements, and as a result, the theoretical results just obtained have to be applied with care.

7

RADAR DETECTION OF SCINTILLATING TARGETS

43. Fluctuations of the Useful Signal

One of the interesting problems of statistical reception theory is the problem of radar detection of a "scintillating target," i.e., detection of a useful signal with random amplitude and phase, or a train of such signals. The origin of this problem is as follows: An object reflecting radar signals usually has a complex shape, and when its orientation changes slightly, the useful signal reflected by it fluctuates at the receiver input. In fact, the signal reflected by a complex object is due to the superposition of the fields from many "specular points," which are more or less randomly located with respect to the radar.[1] Therefore, the signal fluctuations obey a normal law, whose parameters are determined by the reflecting object, by the character of its motion and by the transmitted signal.

The assumption that the fluctuations of the useful signal are normally distributed seems quite natural and is ordinarily made in carrying out calculations, although in many cases this assumption is only qualitatively valid. However, by combining the theoretical results on signals with fixed amplitude and phase and the results on signals undergoing normal fluctuations, we get a rather complete theoretical picture of the overall problem of radar detection.

According to the classification of Chap. 5, detection of fluctuating signals comes under the heading of composite detection, since there are unknown random parameters, i.e., the amplitude and phase of each signal in the train.

---

[1] The concept of specular points is explained in Appendix V.

In this chapter, we shall investigate the optimum receiver for detecting a scintillating target by using a coherent or an incoherent signal train in the presence of correlated noise.

We represent the process at the receiver input in the form

$$f(t) = m(t) + n(t), \tag{43.01}$$

where the useful signal $m(t)$ is a train of L signals

$$m_\varkappa(t) = G_\varkappa e_\varkappa(t) \cos [\omega_0 t - \psi_\varkappa(t) - \vartheta_\varkappa] \qquad (\varkappa = 1, 2, \ldots, L), \tag{43.02}$$

and $n(t)$ is the noise, which is a normal (Gaussian) random process. As in Chap. 6, the given functions $e_\varkappa(t)$ and $\psi_\varkappa(t)$ are the envelope and supplementary phase determined by the $\varkappa$th transmitted signal and by the distance to the target, ω_0 is the carrier frequency, while $G_\varkappa$ and $\psi_\varkappa$ are the random amplitude (envelope) and phase of the $\varkappa$th signal of the received train. We assume that $G_\varkappa$ and $\vartheta_\varkappa$ are constant for each signal, but that in general $G_\varkappa$ and $\vartheta_\varkappa$ change in going to the next signal of the train, because of the motion of the target.

Assuming as before that the radar transmits a sequence of identical signals, which repeat themselves after a time interval T (the repetition period), and idealizing the properties of the antenna (cf. p. 186), we can write

$$e_\varkappa(t) = e[t - (\varkappa - 1)T], \qquad \psi_\varkappa(t) = \psi[t - (\varkappa - 1)T]. \tag{43.03}$$

Therefore, going from the continuous time t to discrete sample values of the various functions at the times

$$\begin{aligned} t_{g\varkappa} &= t_1 + (g - 1)\,\Delta t + (\varkappa - 1)T = t_g + (\varkappa - 1)T, \\ t_g &= t_1 + (g - 1)\,\Delta t \qquad (g = 1, 2, \ldots, H;\ \varkappa = 1, 2, \ldots, L), \end{aligned} \tag{43.04}$$

we have

$$e_\varkappa(t_{g\varkappa}) = e(t_g) = e_g, \qquad \psi_\varkappa(t_{g\varkappa}) = \psi(t_g) = \psi_g, \tag{43.05}$$

so that the value of the useful signal at the time $t_{g\varkappa}$ equals

$$m_{g\varkappa} = G_\varkappa e_g \cos (\omega_0 t_g - \psi_g - \vartheta_\varkappa) \tag{43.06}$$

[cf. formula (37.09)]. Without loss of generality, we can assume that

$$\overline{G_\varkappa^2} = 2. \tag{43.07}$$

The random phase of the $\varkappa$th signal in a coherent train can be written in the form

$$\vartheta_\varkappa = (\varkappa - 1)\,\Delta\vartheta + \gamma_\varkappa \qquad (\varkappa = 1, 2, \ldots, L), \tag{43.08}$$

where the first term is due to the uniform motion of the target, and the second term is due to its scintillation.

Next, we consider the statistical properties of the scintillation, i.e., of the random variables $G_\varkappa$ and $\vartheta_\varkappa$, or of the related quantities

$$u_\varkappa = G_\varkappa \cos \gamma_\varkappa, \qquad v_\varkappa = G_\varkappa \sin \gamma_\varkappa. \tag{43.09}$$

Assuming that the target scintillation is a random process, we can introduce the correlation coefficients

$$\begin{aligned} r_{\varkappa\lambda}^{(1)} &= r_{\lambda\varkappa}^{(1)} = \overline{u_\varkappa u_\lambda} = \overline{v_\varkappa v_\lambda}, \\ r_{\varkappa\lambda}^{(2)} &= -r_{\lambda\varkappa}^{(2)} = \overline{u_\varkappa v_\lambda} = -\overline{u_\lambda v_\varkappa}, \end{aligned} \tag{43.10}$$

(cf. Sec. 60), depending only on the difference $\varkappa - \lambda$ and satisfying the relations

$$r_{\varkappa\varkappa}^{(1)} = 1, \qquad r_{\varkappa\varkappa}^{(2)} = 0. \tag{43.11}$$

The first of the relations (43.11) follows from formula (43.07), and the second is obvious at once. Introducing the complex random variables

$$w_\varkappa = u_\varkappa - iv_\varkappa = G_\varkappa e^{-i\gamma_\varkappa}, \qquad w_\varkappa^* = u_\varkappa + iv_\varkappa = G_\varkappa e^{i\gamma_\varkappa}, \tag{43.12}$$

we have

$$\overline{w_\varkappa^* w_\lambda} = 2r_{\varkappa\lambda}^m, \quad \text{where} \quad r_{\varkappa\lambda}^m = r_{\varkappa\lambda}^{(1)} - ir_{\varkappa\lambda}^{(2)} = (r_{\lambda\varkappa}^m)^*, \tag{43.13}$$

so that the complex numbers $r_{\varkappa\lambda}^m$ form a Hermitian matrix. (The asterisk denotes the complex conjugate.) Letting $q_{\varkappa\lambda}^m$ denote the elements of the inverse matrix, we can write the probability distribution of the quantities $w_\varkappa$ and $w_\varkappa^*$ in the form

$$p(w_1, w_1^*, \ldots, w_L, w_L^*) = \frac{1}{(4\pi)^L \det \|r_{\varkappa\lambda}^m\|} \exp\left\{-\frac{1}{2} \sum_{\varkappa,\lambda=1}^{L} q_{\varkappa\lambda}^m w_\varkappa w_\lambda^*\right\}. \tag{43.14}$$

(cf. Sec. 59).

In the preceding chapter, we assumed that the noise $n(t)$ is a stationary random process, with moments

$$\overline{n_{g\varkappa}} = 0, \quad \overline{n_{g\varkappa} n_{h\lambda}} = R_{gh} r_{\varkappa\lambda} \; (g, h = 1, \ldots, H; \; \varkappa, \lambda = 1, \ldots, L), \tag{43.15}$$

where $R_{gh} = R_p(|g - h| \Delta t)$ is the correlation function within each period and $r_{\varkappa\lambda} = r(|\varkappa - \lambda| T)$ is the "period-to-period" correlation coefficient. However, formula (43.15) cannot be considered sufficiently general, when studying the detection of a "scintillating target" by using a coherent signal train. In fact, according to (43.10) and (43.13), the target scintillation is characterized by two correlation coefficients $r_{\varkappa\lambda}^{(1)}$ and $r_{\varkappa\lambda}^{(2)}$, or by one complex correlation coefficient $r_{\varkappa\lambda}^m$, whereas in formula (43.15), the statistical properties of the noise are characterized by only one real coefficient $r_{\varkappa\lambda}$. However, it is obvious from a physical point of view that the noise due to "chaotic" reflections from many scattering centers must have period-to-period fluctuations of the same character as the signal reflected from a scintillating target. Therefore, in this chapter, for a coherent train we shall use the more general expression

$$\overline{n_{g\varkappa}n_{h\lambda}} = \text{Re}\,\{R_{gh}r_{\varkappa\lambda}e^{i(\varkappa-\lambda)\,\Delta\psi}\}, \tag{43.16}$$

derived at the end of Sec. 69. Here, $\|R_{gh}\|$ and $\|r_{\varkappa\lambda}\|$ are complex (Hermitian) matrices, corresponding to the correlation within a single period and from period to period, respectively, and $\Delta\psi$ is the phase increment corresponding to the motion of the scattering centers as a whole.

It is easy to see that for an incoherent train, formulas (43.15) and (43.16) become the same, since for such a train we can put

$$r_{\varkappa\lambda} = 0 \quad \text{for} \quad \varkappa \neq \lambda, \qquad r_{\varkappa\varkappa} = 1, \tag{43.17}$$

i.e., we can assume that the noise has no correlation from period to period, and then R_{gh} in (43.15) has the same meaning as Re $\{R_{gh}\}$ in formula (43.16). In fact, the receiver noise itself never has any correlation from period-to-period, and for an incoherent train, the correlation of the noise due to clutter vanishes, due to the independence of the phases of the transmitted signals (cf. Chap. 6). However, for incoherent trains, the clutter loses its normal character, with the exception of "rapidly varying" noise (see the end of Sec. 67). Therefore, in studying the detection of an incoherent train, we have in mind mainly noise like the receiver noise itself.

As we shall see below, the period-to-period processing of incoherent signal trains is more uniform, and less effective, than in the case of coherent trains.

44. The Likelihood Ratio for an Incoherent Signal Train

A train of L incoherent signals arriving at the receiver from a "scintillating target" can be represented in the form (43.02), but unlike a coherent train, for which formula (43.08) holds, the phases $\vartheta_1, \ldots, \vartheta_L$ are independent, since the transmitted signals have random phases which are not used at the receiver, i.e., which are regarded as being unknown. As for the amplitudes $G_\varkappa$, they are in general statistically related to each other. If the $G_\varkappa$ are normalized as in formula (43.07), then the one-dimensional probability density is

$$p(G_\varkappa) = G_\varkappa e^{-G_\varkappa^2/2}, \tag{44.01}$$

while the two-dimensional probability density is given by formula (60.19).

The likelihood ratio, which defines the operation of the optimum detecting receiver, is obtained by integrating the function

$$\Lambda(G_1, \ldots, G_L; \vartheta_1, \ldots, \vartheta_L) = p_m(G_1, \ldots, G_L; \vartheta_1, \ldots, \vartheta_L)e^{\varphi-\frac{1}{2}\mu} \tag{44.02}$$

over all possible values of $G_\varkappa$ and $\vartheta_\varkappa$. Here

$$p_m(G_1, \ldots, G_L; \vartheta_1, \ldots, \vartheta_L) = \frac{1}{(2\pi)^L}\,p_m(G_1, \ldots, G_L) \tag{44.03}$$

is the probability density of the random variables $G_\varkappa$ and $\vartheta_\varkappa$. In view of formula (43.17), we have

$$\varphi = \sum_{\varkappa} G_\varkappa \sum_{g,h} Q_{gh} f_{g\varkappa} e_h \cos(\omega_0 t_h - \psi_h - \vartheta_\varkappa),$$
$$\mu = \sum_{\varkappa} G_\varkappa^2 \sum_{g,h} Q_{gh} e_g e_h \cos[\omega_0(t_g - t_h) - (\psi_g - \psi_h)] = \rho \sum_{\varkappa} G_\varkappa^2, \tag{44.04}$$

where the Q_{gh} are the elements of the inverse of the matrix $\|R_{gh}\|$, and

$$\rho = \frac{1}{2} \sum_{g,h} Q_{gh} e_g e_h \cos[\omega_0(t_g - t_h) - (\psi_g - \psi_h)] \tag{44.05}$$

is the effective signal-to-noise ratio for one repetition period (with $G_\varkappa = 1$), introduced in Sec. 39.

Integrating the function (44.02) with respect to all the phases $\vartheta_\varkappa$ (which are independent random variables) leads to the likelihood ratio

$$\Lambda(G_1, \ldots, G_L) = p_m(G_1, \ldots, G_L) e^{-\mu/2} \prod_{\varkappa=1}^{L} I_0(G_\varkappa \mathscr{E}_\varkappa), \tag{44.06}$$

where the quantities

$$\mathscr{E}_\varkappa = \sqrt{x_\varkappa^2 + y_\varkappa^2},$$
$$x_\varkappa = \sum_{g,h} Q_{gh} f_{g\varkappa} e_h \cos(\omega_0 t_h - \psi_h), \tag{44.07}$$
$$y_\varkappa = \sum_{g,h} Q_{gh} f_{g\varkappa} e_h \sin(\omega_0 t_h - \psi_h)$$

have already been introduced above [see the formulas (37.15)]. Further averaging with respect to $G_\varkappa$ gives

$$\Lambda = \int_0^\infty G_1 \exp\left\{-\frac{(1+\rho)G_1^2}{2}\right\} I_0(G_1 \mathscr{E}_1)\, dG_1$$
$$= \frac{1}{1+\rho} \exp\left\{\frac{\mathscr{E}_1^2}{2(1+\rho)}\right\} \tag{44.08}$$

for $L = 1$, a result we have already obtained in Sec. 34 [see formula (34.16)].

For $L = 2$, using formula (60.19), we obtain the integral

$$\Lambda = \frac{1}{1-p^2} \int_0^\infty \int_0^\infty G_1 G_2 \exp\left\{-\frac{1}{2}\left(\rho + \frac{1}{1-p^2}\right)(G_1^2 + G_2^2)\right\}$$
$$\times I_0(G_1 \mathscr{E}_1) I_0(G_2 \mathscr{E}_2) I_0\left(\frac{p G_1 G_2}{1+p^2}\right) dG_1\, dG_2, \tag{44.09}$$

where

$$p = |r_{12}^m|. \tag{44.10}$$

Twice applying Weber's second exponential integral[2] to formula (44.09), we obtain

$$\Lambda = Q \exp\left\{\frac{Q}{2}[1 + \rho(1 - p^2)](\mathscr{E}_1^2 + \mathscr{E}_2^2)\right\} I_0(pQ\mathscr{E}_1\mathscr{E}_2), \tag{44.11}$$

where

$$Q = \frac{1}{1 + 2\rho + \rho^2(1 - p^2)}. \tag{44.12}$$

The study of a train consisting of three or more signals leads to serious difficulties, if the law describing the scintillation is arbitrary. Therefore, for $L \geqslant 3$, we consider only limiting cases, corresponding to independent (or rapid) and completely correlated (slow or identical) scintillations. If the scintillations are independent, all the $G_\varkappa$ are independent random variables, and then formulas (44.06) and (44.08) give

$$\Lambda = \frac{1}{(1 + \rho)^L} \exp\left\{\frac{1}{2(1 + \rho)} \sum_\varkappa \mathscr{E}_\varkappa^2\right\}. \tag{44.13}$$

On the other hand, for completely correlated scintillations, all the $G_\varkappa$ are equal, and hence

$$\Lambda = \int_0^\infty G \exp\left\{-\frac{(1 + L\rho)G^2}{2}\right\} \prod_\varkappa I_0(G\mathscr{E}_\varkappa)\, dG. \tag{44.14}$$

If we use the approximation

$$I_0(x) \sim e^{x^2/4}, \tag{44.15}$$

which is valid for small values of the argument x, then we can evaluate the integral (44.14), obtaining

$$\Lambda = \frac{1}{1 + L\rho - \frac{1}{2}\sum_\varkappa \mathscr{E}_\varkappa^2}. \tag{44.16}$$

Formula (44.13) shows that the optimum receiver for detecting a rapidly scintillating target must form the quantity $\mathscr{E}$ defined by the formula

$$\mathscr{E}^2 = \sum_{\varkappa=1}^{L} \mathscr{E}_\varkappa^2 = \sum_{\varkappa=1}^{L} (x_\varkappa^2 + y_\varkappa^2), \tag{44.17}$$

i.e., the receiver must first process the input signal in the optimum way within each period (cf. Secs. 33 and 38), and then sum the results obtained after using a quadratic detector. If the scintillation occurs more slowly, then, as can be seen from (44.11) and (44.16), the likelihood ratio can be expressed in terms of the quantity (44.17) for small $\mathscr{E}_\varkappa$, i.e., for small values

[2] G. N. Watson, *op. cit.*, p. 395.

of the parameter (44.05). The same result is obtained in the absence of scintillation, when the signals in the train have fixed amplitude (cf. Sec. 37). The need to process the data during many repetition periods is greatest when ρ is small, since then a reliable decision cannot be made by using the data from a single period; for this reason, we shall study the receiver which forms the quantity (44.17).

It follows from (44.11) and (44.14) that for intense, strongly correlated signals, optimum summation should take place after a *linear* detector. In fact, for $p \sim 1$ and $Q\mathscr{E}_1\mathscr{E}_2 \gg 1$, formula (44.11) becomes

$$\Lambda = \sqrt{\frac{Q}{2\pi\mathscr{E}_1\mathscr{E}_2}} \exp\left\{\frac{Q}{2}(\mathscr{E}_1 + \mathscr{E}_2)^2\right\}, \tag{44.18}$$

where we have used the asymptotic expression (37.21). Here, the factor before the exponential influences the value of Λ only slightly. Similarly, if we use (37.21) to replace the functions $I_0(G\mathscr{E}_\varkappa)$ in the integral (44.14), we find that the likelihood ratio Λ depends mainly on the quantity

$$S = \sum_{\varkappa=1}^{L} \mathscr{E}_\varkappa, \tag{44.19}$$

which is obtained by summation after linear detection, i.e., by so-called "linear summation" (as opposed to "quadratic summation").

In the next section, we shall calculate the probabilities F and D for a receiver which forms the quantity (44.17), i.e., which performs quadratic summation, and then bases its decision on the following rule:

$$\begin{aligned} &\text{If} \quad \mathscr{E} \geqslant \mathscr{E}_*, \quad \text{decide that } f = m + n; \\ &\text{If} \quad \mathscr{E} < \mathscr{E}_*, \quad \text{decide that } f = n, \end{aligned} \tag{44.20}$$

where $\mathscr{E}_*$ is the decision threshold.

45. Operating Characteristics of a Receiver Performing Quadratic Summation

If the useful signal is absent, then the normal random variables $x_\varkappa$ and $y_\varkappa$ reduce to the random variables $x_{n\varkappa}$ and $y_{n\varkappa}$ defined by (42.05). Since the noise has no correlation from period to period, all $2L$ random variables $x_{n\varkappa}$ and $y_{n\varkappa}$ are independent, with moments

$$\overline{x_{n\varkappa}} = \overline{y_{n\varkappa}} = 0, \quad \overline{x_{n\varkappa}^2} = \overline{y_{n\varkappa}^2} = \rho \qquad (\varkappa = 1, 2, \ldots, L). \tag{45.01}$$

Thus, the quantity $z = \mathscr{E}/\sqrt{\rho}$ has a χ^2 distribution with $2L$ degrees of freedom (cf. Sec. 38), i.e.,

$$p_{0L}(z) = \frac{z^{2L-1}}{2^{L-1}(L-1)!} e^{-z^2/2}, \tag{45.02}$$

and the false alarm probability equals

$$F = \int_{z_*}^{\infty} p_{0L}(z)\,dz = \frac{1}{2^{L-1}(L-1)!}\int_{z_*}^{\infty} z^{2L-1}e^{-z^2/2}dz \qquad \left(z_* = \frac{\mathscr{E}_*}{\sqrt{\rho}}\right). \tag{45.03}$$

In the presence of the useful signal, we have to replace ρ by $\rho(1+\rho)$ in (45.01), as is apparent from (34.28) and (34.29). For uncorrelated (rapid) scintillations, when all the $G_\varkappa$ are independent, formula (45.02) is still applicable if we replace $z = \mathscr{E}/\sqrt{\rho}$ by $z = \mathscr{E}/\sqrt{\rho(1+\rho)}$, and then the detection probability is

$$D = \frac{1}{2^{L-1}(L-1)!}\int_{z_*/\sqrt{1+\rho}}^{\infty} z^{2L-1}e^{-z^2/2}\,dz. \tag{45.04}$$

For completely correlated (slow) scintillations, all the $G_\varkappa$ are equal, i.e., all the signals in the train have the same amplitude G. For fixed G, the quantity $z = \mathscr{E}/\sqrt{\rho}$ has the probability density

$$p_L(G, z) = \frac{z^L}{(L\rho G^2)^{(L-1)/2}}e^{-(L\rho G^2+z^2)/2}I_{L-1}(\sqrt{L\rho}\,Gz), \tag{45.05}$$

obtained from formula (38.13) by replacing ρ by ρG^2 [cf. formulas (38.01) and (44.04)]. Thus, the required probability density of the quantity z is

$$p_{mL}(z) = \int_0^{\infty} Ge^{-G^2/2}p_L(G, z)\,dG = \frac{z^{2L-1}}{2^{L-1}(L-1)!}\frac{e^{-z^2/2}}{1+L\rho}\,{}_1F_1(1; L; qz^2/2), \tag{45.06}$$

with

$$q = \frac{L\rho}{1+L\rho},$$

and

$${}_1F_1(1; L; x) = \sum_{n=0}^{\infty}\frac{(L-1)!}{(L-1+n)!}x^n = \frac{(L-1)!}{x^{L-1}}\left\{e^x - \sum_{n=0}^{L-2}\frac{x^n}{n!}\right\},$$

where we have used Weber's first exponential integral in generalized form.[3] This function can also be written as

$$p_{mL}(z) = \frac{ze^{-z^2/2(1+L\rho)}}{(1+L\rho)q^{L-1}}\frac{1}{2^{L-2}(L-2)!}\int_0^{\sqrt{q}\,z} t^{2L-3}e^{-t^2/2}\,dt, \tag{45.07}$$

and calculated by using tables of the χ^2 distribution. The equivalence of (45.06) and (45.07) is not hard to prove by integrating by parts.

[3] G. N. Watson, *op. cit.*, p. 393.

The probability of correct detection can be obtained from (45.07) as follows, again by integrating by parts:

$$D = \int_{z_*}^{\infty} p_{mL}(z)\,dz = \frac{1}{2^{L-2}(L-2)!}\int_{z_*}^{\infty} z^{2L-3}e^{-z^2/2}\,dz$$
$$+ \frac{e^{-z_*^2/2(1+L\rho)}}{q^{L-1}}\,\frac{1}{2^{L-2}(L-2)!}\int_0^{\sqrt{q}\,z_*} z^{2L-3}e^{-z^2/2}\,dz. \tag{45.08}$$

For $L = 1$, formulas (45.03) and (45.04) lead to the expressions

$$F = e^{-z_*^2/2}, \qquad D = e^{-z_*^2/2(1+\rho)} = F^{1/(1+\rho)}, \tag{45.09}$$

which we have already derived in Sec. 34. For $L \geqslant 2$, quadratic summation of signals from a scintillating target leads to different results, depending on whether the target is rapidly or slowly scintillating. For a train consisting of two signals ($L = 2$), we can calculate D for any value of the coefficient (44.10), i.e., for any correlation of the scintillations. We now show how this is done.

Using formula (60.22), we find that the two-dimensional probability density of the quantities $\mathscr{E}_1$ and $\mathscr{E}_2$ equals

$$p(\mathscr{E}_1, \mathscr{E}_2) = \frac{\mathscr{E}_1\mathscr{E}_2}{\rho^2(1+\rho)^2(1-r^2)}$$
$$\times \exp\left\{-\frac{\mathscr{E}_1^2+\mathscr{E}_2^2}{2\rho(1+\rho)(1-r^2)}\right\} I_0\left(\frac{r\mathscr{E}_1\mathscr{E}_2}{\rho(1+\rho)(1-r^2)}\right), \tag{45.10}$$

where

$$r = \frac{\rho p}{1+\rho}, \tag{45.11}$$

is the correlation coefficient of the mixture of signal plus noise. Formula (45.10) can be derived as follows: For a train of two coherent signals, we have the relations

$$\mathscr{E}_\varkappa = \sqrt{x_\varkappa^2 + y_\varkappa^2}, \qquad \overline{x_\varkappa} = \overline{y_\varkappa} = 0, \qquad \overline{x_\varkappa^2} = \overline{y_\varkappa^2} = \rho(1+\rho),$$
$$\overline{x_1x_2} = \overline{y_1y_2} = \rho^2 p\cos\delta, \qquad \overline{x_1y_2} = -\overline{x_2y_1} = \rho^2 p\sin\delta, \tag{45.12}$$

which follow from the complex formula (47.17), derived below, if we set

$$r_{12}^m = pe^{i\varepsilon}, \qquad \delta = \varepsilon + \Delta\vartheta, \tag{45.13}$$

where $\Delta\vartheta$ is the phase shift due to the motion of the target. It is clear that for a coherent train, x_1, x_2, y_1 and y_2 are normal random variables, and hence, writing

$$x_\varkappa = \mathscr{E}_\varkappa\cos\Phi_\varkappa, \qquad y_\varkappa = \mathscr{E}_\varkappa\sin\Phi_\varkappa, \tag{45.14}$$

we can use formula (60.16), which in this case becomes

$$p(x_1, y_1, x_2, y_2) = \frac{1}{(2\pi)^2(1 - r^2)} \times \exp\left\{-\frac{\mathscr{E}_1^2 + \mathscr{E}_2^2 - 2r\mathscr{E}_1\mathscr{E}_2 \cos(\Phi_2 - \Phi_1 + \varepsilon + \Delta\vartheta)}{2(1 - r^2)}\right\}. \tag{45.15}$$

If we now consider all possible values of $\Delta\vartheta$ to be equally likely, and integrate first over $\Delta\vartheta$ and then over either of the phases $\Phi_\varkappa$, we obtain formula (45.10) [cf. also formulas (60.20) to (60.22)]. On the other hand, a train of two coherent signals, where $\Delta\vartheta$ is arbitrary in formula (43.08), is essentially an incoherent train. This justifies the use of formula (45.10) in the present case.

In the case of two signals, the probability density of the quantity $\mathscr{E}$ is

$$p(\mathscr{E}) = \mathscr{E} \int_0^{\pi/2} p(\mathscr{E} \cos \beta, \mathscr{E} \sin \beta)\, d\beta \tag{45.16}$$

[cf. formula (38.08)]. Substituting the expression (45.10) for the function $p(\mathscr{E}_1, \mathscr{E}_2) = p(\mathscr{E} \cos \beta, \mathscr{E} \sin \beta)$ into (45.16), we obtain the probability density

$$p(z) = \frac{z^3}{(1 + \rho)^2(1 - r^2)} \exp\left\{-\frac{z^2}{2(1 + \rho)(1 - r^2)}\right\} \times \int_0^{\pi/2} I_0\left(\frac{rz^2 \cos \beta \sin \beta}{(1 + \rho)(1 - r^2)}\right) \cos \beta \sin \beta\, d\beta \tag{45.17}$$

for the quantity $z = \mathscr{E}/\sqrt{\rho}$. Using Sonine's first finite integral,[4] we can reduce (45.17) to the form

$$p(z) = \frac{z}{r(1 + \rho)} \exp\left\{-\frac{z^2}{2(1 + \rho)(1 - r^2)}\right\} \sinh \frac{rz^2}{2(1 + \rho)(1 - r^2)}. \tag{45.18}$$

Then, the detection probability equals

$$D = \int_{z_*}^{\infty} p(z)\, dz = \exp\left\{-\frac{z_*^2}{2(1 + \rho)(1 - r^2)}\right\} \times \left[\cosh \frac{rz_*^2}{2(1 + \rho)(1 - r^2)} + \frac{1}{r} \sinh \frac{rz_*^2}{2(1 + \rho)(1 - r^2)}\right]. \tag{45.19}$$

For $r = p = 0$, (45.19) gives

$$D = \exp\left\{-\frac{z_*^2}{2(1 + \rho)}\right\}\left[1 + \frac{z_*^2}{2(1 + \rho)}\right], \tag{45.20}$$

which agrees with (45.04) when $L = 2$. Setting $p = 1$, we obtain

$$D = \frac{1}{2\rho}\left[(1 + 2\rho) \exp\left\{-\frac{z_*^2}{2(1 + 2\rho)}\right\} - \exp\left\{-\frac{z_*^2}{2}\right\}\right], \tag{45.21}$$

which agrees with (45.08) when $L = 2$.

---

[4] G. N. Watson, *op. cit.*, p. 373.

We note that similar formulas are obtained if the input signal (data) is subjected to an *arbitrary* linear transformation and then passed through a quadratic detector, after which summation over the pulses is carried out. Although it is assumed above that the linear data processing is optimum, if it is nonoptimum, the only effect is to decrease the value of ρ, the signal-to-noise ratio for one repetition period. However, this causes no difficulty as far as subsequent transformations of the mixture of signal plus noise are concerned. In fact, these transformations are just the same as those that follow optimum linear data processing, except that we now have a different (i.e., smaller) value of ρ (cf. Secs. 38 and 42).

In Fig. 40, we show the dependence of L, the number of signals in the train, on the parameter ρ, for a given false alarm probability $F = 10^{-10}$ and for given detection probabilities $D = 0.5$ and $D = 0.9$. The solid curves in Fig. 40(a) correspond to rapid (independent) target scintillations and those in Fig. 40(b) correspond to slow (identical) target scintillations. The dashed curves in Figs. 40(a) and 40(b) correspond to a target which produces a signal train with a constant (nonfluctuating) amplitude; these curves, which are the same in both figures, allow us to estimate the extent to which the energy of each signal has to be increased in order to guarantee detection of a scintillating target for the same values of L, F and D. We see that for rapid fluctuations, the required increase in energy is small, and that it becomes smaller as L is increased and D is decreased. In fact, for large L, the appearance of a series of signals with small energy is very improbable, and, according to the law of large numbers, the larger L, the less the energy of the whole train will experience random fluctuations about its mean value. However, if L is small ($L < 5$, say), then the fact already mentioned above (see Secs. 32 and 34) makes itself felt, i.e., the closer the required detection probability is to unity, the larger the increase of ρ required for reliable detection ($D = 0.5$) of the fluctuating useful signal.

In comparing a constant signal train with a fluctuating signal train, it must be kept in mind that according to formulas (44.04) and (43.07), for a single fluctuating signal, we have

$$\mu = \rho G_1^2, \qquad \bar{\mu} = 2\rho, \tag{45.22}$$

whereas $\mu = \rho$ for a single constant signal. Therefore, in order to have the solid and dashed curves approach each other as $L \to \infty$, we have plotted the following parameter as abscissa in Fig. 40(a):

$$\begin{aligned} \rho' &= \rho \quad \text{for fluctuating signals}, \\ \rho' &= \tfrac{1}{2}\rho \quad \text{for constant signals}; \end{aligned} \tag{45.23}$$

for uniformity, the same has been done in Figs. 40(b), 41(a) and 41(b).

Figure 40(b) shows that to detect a slowly scintillating target with probability $D \geqslant 0.5$ by using a train of L signals requires a definite increase in ρ', as compared with a constant target, just as in the case of detection of a single fluctuating signal (see Sec. 34). The required increase in ρ' in decibels is practically independent of L and increases sharply as D approaches unity.

In Fig. 41, we show the dependence of D, the probability of correct detection, on ρ', for a train of two signals and for $F = 10^{-10}$ and $F = 10^{-5}$; curves corresponding to various values of ρ, the correlation coefficient of the scintillations, are shown. We see that for large ρ', the detection probability depends on the correlation coefficient p, whereas for $\rho' < 10$ db, this dependence practically vanishes. We also observe that by assuming that the scintillations are uncorrelated ($p = 0$) and completely correlated ($p = 1$), we can find the boundaries within which the receiver operating

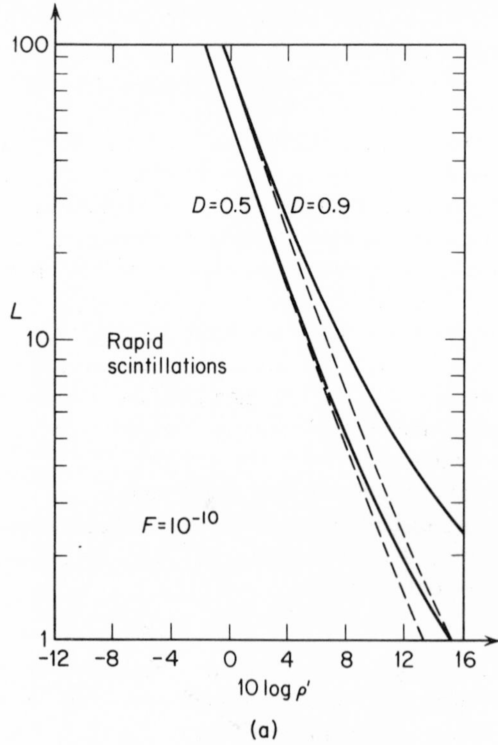

FIG. 40. Operating characteristics (L vs. $10 \log \rho'$) of a receiver detecting a scintillating target by using an incoherent signal train. (a) Rapid (uncorrelated) scintillations. *On opposite page:* (b) Slow (strongly correlated) scintillations. The dashed curves, which are the same in both figures, show the operating characteristics for detection of a constant target.

characteristics (i.e., those for intermediate values of p) are to be found. We have borrowed Figs. 40 and 41 from a paper by M. Schwartz,[5] which explains their "nonstandard" form.[6] Finally, it should be noted that in the literature, by the signal-to-noise ratio is often meant the parameter ρ' defined by (45.23).

46. Various Approximations for Problems Involving Detection of Incoherent Trains

Using the formulas obtained in the preceding sections, we can carry out a variety of calculations pertaining to incoherent radar systems. The simplest results are obtained if we consider the problem of detecting a

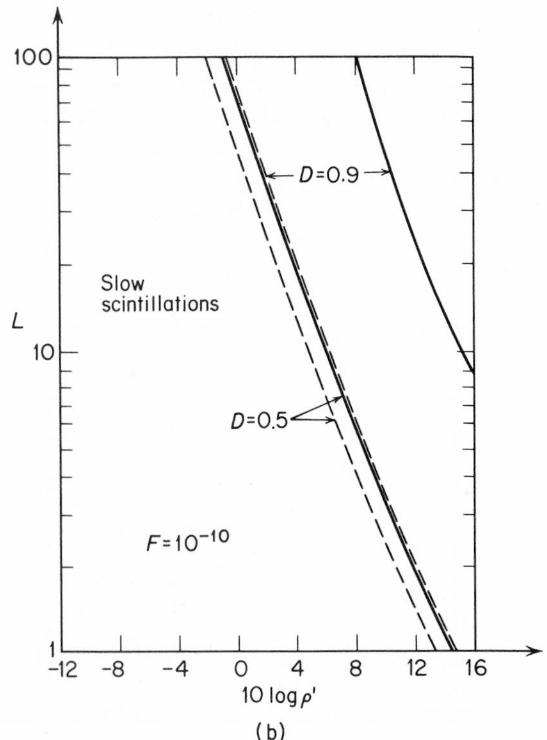

(b)

[5] M. Schwartz, *Effects of signal fluctuation on the detection of pulse signals in noise*, IRE Trans. on Inform. Theory, **IT-2**, 66 (1956).

[6] The receiver "operating characteristics" for signal trains which are plotted elsewhere in this book display ρ or μ (in decibels) vs. L for constant F and D. (*Translator*)

rapidly scintillating target by using the quantity

$$Z = \frac{z^2}{2} = \frac{\mathscr{E}^2}{2\rho} = \frac{1}{2\rho}\sum_{\varkappa}\mathscr{E}_{\varkappa}^2 = \frac{1}{2\rho}\sum_{\varkappa}(x_{\varkappa}^2 + y_{\varkappa}^2). \tag{46.01}$$

The quantity $2Z$ has a χ^2 distribution with $2L$ degrees of freedom, both in the presence and in the absence of the signal, where we recall that L is the number of repetition periods, i.e., the number of pulses or other signals, which are being used to detect the target. It is clear that as L is increased, the distribution of the quantity Z approaches a normal distribution, because of the central limit theorem of probability theory. If for finite values of L, we use the normal distribution to approximate the distribution of Z (the validity of this approximation can be checked in detail later by making more exact calculations), then, as a rule, we obtain very simple relations, from which we can readily get insight into the problem.

As an example, we consider the following problem: What is the optimum number L of transmitted signals for detecting a rapidly scintillating target, if the total energy of all the signals is fixed? In other words, what is the optimum number L of repetition periods over which the given energy should be distributed in order to best detect the target? Since the parameter ρ is proportional to the energy of the useful signal for one repetition period, the total energy of the train is proportional to the quantity

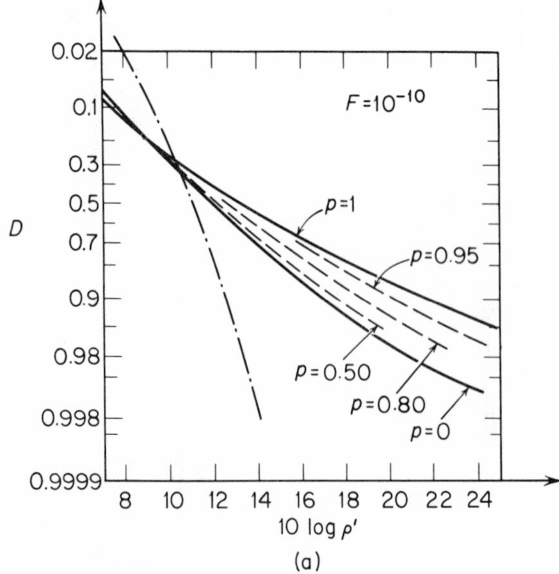

FIG. 41. Operating characteristics (D vs. $10 \log \rho'$) for two incoherent signals for different values of p, the correlation coefficient of the scintillations. (a) $F = 10^{-10}$ (the unlabelled curve corresponds to a constant target). *On opposite page:* (b) $F = 10^{-5}$.

$$\mu = L\rho, \tag{46.02}$$

which is fixed, by the hypothesis of the problem, since the noise level is constant. We are also given the false alarm probability F, and we have to find the value L for which the detection probability D is a maximum. Since D is obviously a monotonically increasing function of μ, we can pose the problem somewhat differently: *Given F and D, find the value of L for which the required value of μ is a minimum.*

The normal approximation to the distribution (45.02) is determined by the first and second moments of the random variable Z. In the absence of the signal, we have

$$\overline{Z} = L, \qquad \overline{Z^2} - (\overline{Z})^2 = L, \tag{46.03}$$

where the first formula follows from (45.01), and the second follows from identities

$$\overline{x_\varkappa^2 x_\lambda^2} = \overline{y_\varkappa^2 y_\lambda^2} = \rho^2 \qquad \text{for } \varkappa \neq \lambda,$$
$$\overline{x_\varkappa^2 y_\lambda^2} = \rho^2, \qquad \overline{x_\varkappa^4} = \overline{y_\varkappa^4} = 3\rho^2, \tag{46.04}$$

which are essentially special cases of (35.30). Thus, we have

$$\overline{Z^2} = L(L + 1), \tag{46.05}$$

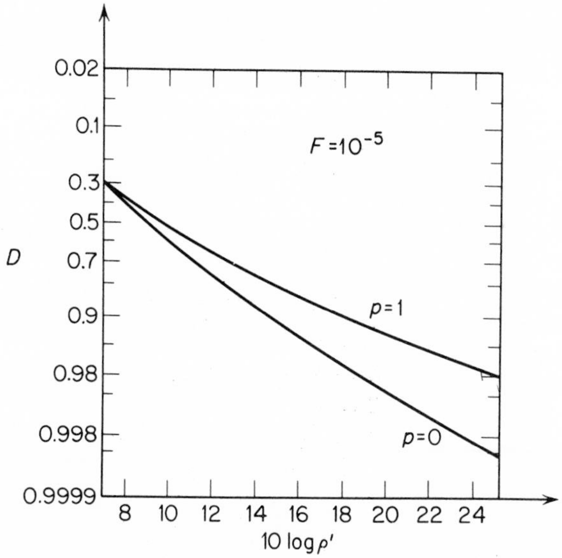

(b)

which gives the second of the formulas (46.03). Therefore, in the absence of the useful signal, the distribution of Z equals

$$p_0(Z) = \frac{1}{\sqrt{2\pi L}} \exp\left\{-\frac{(Z-L)^2}{2L}\right\}, \tag{46.06}$$

so that the false alarm probability equals

$$F = \frac{1}{\sqrt{2\pi}} \int_a^\infty e^{-s^2/2}\, ds \qquad \left(a = \frac{Z_* - L}{\sqrt{L}}\right). \tag{46.07}$$

In the presence of the useful signal, we have to change ρ to $\rho(1 + \rho)$ in (46.04), so that the formulas (46.03) become

$$\overline{Z} = L(1+\rho), \qquad \overline{Z^2} - (\overline{Z})^2 = L(1+\rho)^2, \tag{46.08}$$

and instead of the distribution (46.07), we obtain

$$p_m(Z) = \frac{1}{\sqrt{2\pi L}(1+\rho)} \exp\left\{-\frac{[Z - L(1+\rho)]^2}{2L(1+\rho)^2}\right\}. \tag{46.09}$$

Thus, the detection probability equals

$$D = \frac{1}{\sqrt{2\pi}} \int_b^\infty e^{-s^2/2}\, ds \qquad \left(b = \frac{1}{\sqrt{L}}\left[\frac{Z_*}{1+\rho} - L\right]\right). \tag{46.10}$$

Specifying F and D corresponds to specifying the limits of integration a and b. However, according to (46.02), a and b satisfy the relation

$$b = \frac{a - \rho\sqrt{L}}{1+\rho} = \frac{a - (\mu/\sqrt{L})}{1 + (\mu/L)}, \tag{46.11}$$

so that

$$\mu = \frac{a - b}{(b/L) + (1/\sqrt{L})}, \tag{46.12}$$

which gives the dependence of μ on F, D and L. The minimum of μ is achieved when we have

$$-\frac{\partial}{\partial L}\left(\frac{b}{L} + \frac{1}{\sqrt{L}}\right) = \frac{b}{L^2} + \frac{1}{2L^{3/2}} = 0, \tag{46.13}$$

or

$$\sqrt{L} = -2b. \tag{46.14}$$

Thus, we see that an extremum is obtained only for $b < 0$, i.e., for $D > \frac{1}{2}$; from now on, we shall assume that this condition is met. The corresponding value of L is

$$L = 4b^2, \tag{46.15}$$

and it is easily verified that L does in fact correspond to the minimum of the quantity (46.12). This minimum value is

$$\mu_{\min} = -4b(a - b). \tag{46.16}$$

For example, if

$$D = 1 - F, \qquad a = -b, \tag{46.17}$$

we have

$$\mu_{\min} = 8a^2 = 2L. \tag{46.18}$$

In the above argument, we have assumed that L is a continuous parameter; actually, of course, in formulas (46.14) and (46.15), we have to take the nearest integer.

It can easily be seen why the function $\mu = \mu(L)$ has a minimum. It is clear that reliable detection of a scintillating target by using one signal requires larger values of μ, since there is always the danger that the useful signal will be received with a small amplitude (cf. Sec. 32). In fact, formula (46.12) shows that μ increases as L decreases, although (46.12) is not really applicable for small L. Moreover, the larger L, the smaller the probability that all the signals in a train of L independent signals will have small amplitudes. Therefore, as L increases, the quantity μ at first decreases. However, when the total energy is too drastically "split up" among the separate signals, then μ begins to increase again, and according to (46.12), we have

$$\mu \sim (a - b)\sqrt{L} \quad \text{as} \quad L \to \infty. \tag{46.19}$$

This is explained by the fact that when L is large enough, the quantity $\rho = \mu/L$ becomes small for each signal in the train, and then the phenomenon of suppression of weak signals by strong noise (cf. Secs. 18, 33 and 38) begins to make itself felt. This weak-signal suppression effect is characteristic of *incoherent* radar systems, in which signals with random phases are first detected and only added up afterwards.

If $b \to 0$ (and hence $D \to \frac{1}{2}$), then, according to formula (46.15), the optimum value of L goes to zero and our whole argument (which is valid only for large L) becomes dubious. For $b > 0$, i.e., for $D < \frac{1}{2}$, equation (46.14) has no roots at all, so that at least for large L, the quantity μ is a monotonically increasing function of L. In this case, the value $L = 1$ is optimum, since, according to Sec. 34, unreliable detection of a scintillating target (with probability $D < \frac{1}{2}$) by using one signal requires comparatively small values of μ.

For sufficiently large L ($L > 50$, say), the exactness of the distribution (46.06) becomes "nonuniform," i.e., the error of formula (46.06) compared with the exact formula (45.02) becomes larger as $|Z - L|$ increases. This is immediately apparent from the fact that according to the exact formula, we must have

$$p_0(Z) = 0 \qquad \text{for} \quad Z < 0, \tag{46.20}$$

whereas, for negative Z, the normal approximation (46.05) leads to nonzero (although small) values of $p_0(Z)$. Therefore, the calculation of very small values of F and values of D very close to unity, by using formulas (46.07) and (46.10) leads to quite crude results. A similar situation has already been noted in Sec. 35.

In Figs. 42 to 45, we show the dependence of μ and ρ on L for fixed values of F and D, calculated by using formulas (45.03) and (45.04) and tables of the χ^2 distribution. We see that the dependence of μ on L agrees qualitatively with the results obtained by using the normal distribution, but quantitative agreement does not always occur.

According to formulas (38.30) and (38.32), for a signal train with constant (nonfluctuating) amplitude, we have

$$\begin{aligned} \bar{Z} &= L(1 + \tfrac{1}{2}\rho), \\ \overline{Z^2} &= L[L + 1 + (L + 1)\rho + \tfrac{1}{4}L\rho^2], \\ \overline{Z^2} - (\bar{Z})^2 &= L(1 + \rho) \sim L(1 + \tfrac{1}{2}\rho)^2 \quad \text{for} \quad \rho \ll 1. \end{aligned} \tag{46.21}$$

Comparing (46.08) and (46.21), we see that the two formulas agree as $\rho \to 0$ if we express them in terms of the parameter ρ' defined by formula (45.23). This agreement is explained by the fact that the solid and the dashed curves in Fig. 40(a) approach each other as $L \to \infty$ and $\rho' \to 0$, a fact we have already discussed in the preceding section.

For a signal train with constant amplitude, the limits of integration a and b in formulas (46.07) and (46.10) equal

$$a = \frac{Z_* - L}{\sqrt{L}}, \qquad b = \frac{Z_* - L[1 + (\rho/2)]}{\sqrt{L(1 + \rho)}}. \tag{46.22}$$

Eliminating the quantity $\mu = L\rho$ from (46.22), we obtain the expression

$$\mu = 2[b^2 + a\sqrt{L} - b\sqrt{b^2 + 2a\sqrt{L} + L}], \tag{46.23}$$

which, unlike (46.12), is a monotonically increasing function of L. Thus, when the amplitude is constant, it is best to concentrate all the energy into one signal, i.e., "incoherent splitting up" of the total energy always leads to losses (cf. Sec. 38 and Figs. 33 to 36). We note that formula (46.23) gives the most accurate results if we do not regard the quantity a as being constant, but rather calculate it by using the first of the formulas (46.22). This is the way in which the solid curves in Figs. 33 to 36 were calculated.

We conclude this section by considering the case of an incoherent signal train reflected by a slowly scintillating target. In this case, all the signals have the same *random* amplitude G, which is distributed according to the

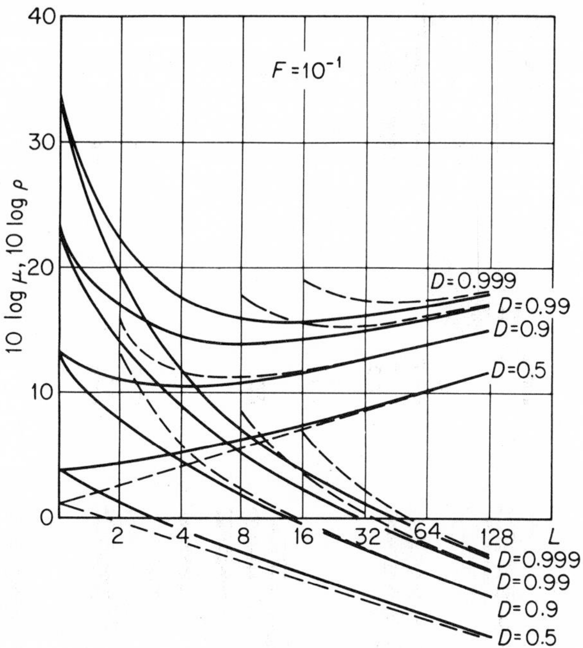

FIG. 42. Operating characteristics for detection of a rapidly scintillating target by using an incoherent signal train, for $F = 10^{-1}$. The solid curves are calculated by the exact distribution, and the dashed curves by the normal distribution.[7]

Rayleigh law (44.01). For a fixed value of G, the expressions (46.21) are replaced by

$$\bar{Z} = L(1 + \tfrac{1}{2}\rho G^2),$$
$$\overline{Z^2} = L[L + 1 + (L + 1)\rho G^2 + \tfrac{1}{4}L\rho^2 G^4]. \tag{46.24}$$

Then, performing additional averaging over G by using the relations

$$\overline{G^2} = 2, \qquad \overline{G^4} = 8, \tag{46.25}$$

we obtain

$$\bar{Z} = L(1 + \rho), \qquad \overline{Z^2} - (\bar{Z})^2 = L(1 + 2\rho + L\rho^2), \tag{46.26}$$

which differ from the corresponding expressions (46.08) by the fact that the

---

[7] This last remark applies to Figs. 43, 44 and 45 as well.

variance of the quantity Z now contains a term proportional to L^2. We can also derive (46.26) by starting from the distribution function (45.07). These formulas show that for large L, the distribution $p_m(Z)$ is comparatively "broad," and hence, we cannot even make approximate calculations of the probability D by using the normal distribution.

However, to calculate the detection probability D, we can use another approximation, which is suggested immediately by Fig. 40(b), i.e., we note that if ρ' is changed in a certain proportion (by 1 db for $D = 0.5$ and by 9 db for $D = 0.9$), then the corresponding solid and broken curves practically coincide. Because of this fact, it is not hard to obtain the operating

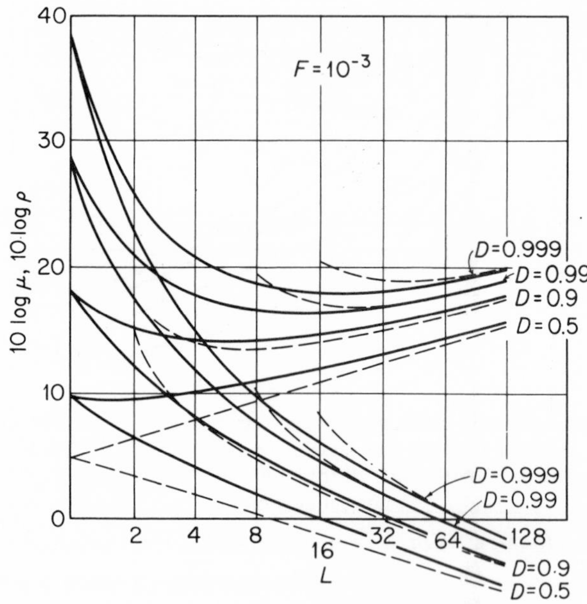

FIG. 43. Operating characteristics for detection of a rapidly scintillating target by using an incoherent signal train, for $F = 10^{-3}$.

characteristics for detection of a slowly scintillating target by starting from Figs. 33 to 36. The required shifts of the curves in Figs. 33 to 36 along the axis of ordinates, i.e., the unknown changes in ρ and μ, are easily found by determining the shift of the points corresponding to $L = 1$ by using Fig. 31, which refers to one signal with unknown amplitude and phase.

This prescription for approximately constructing the operating characteristics for detection of a slowly scintillating target is based essentially on the fact that the losses due to "incoherent splitting up" of the total energy are practically the same for a slowly scintillating target and for a constant target. To verify the prescription, we can use the approximate formula

$$D = \frac{e^{-z_*^2/2(1+L\rho)}}{q^{L-1}} = \left(\frac{1+\mu}{\mu}\right)^{L-1} e^{-Z_*/(1+\mu)}, \tag{46.27}$$

which follows from the exact expression (45.08), provided that the parameter $q = \mu/(1 + \mu)$ is close to unity. If this is the case, then the first term in the right-hand side of (45.08) can be replaced by zero, while in the second term we can take the range of integration to extend from 0 to ∞, thereby

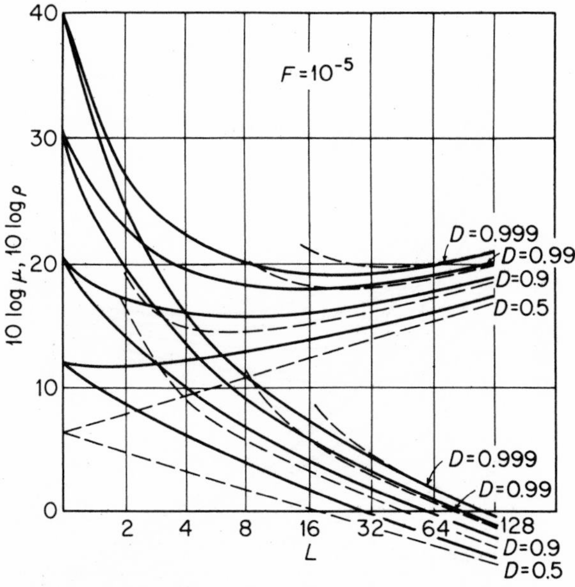

FIG. 44. Operating characteristics for detection of a rapidly scintillating target by using an incoherent signal train, for $F = 10^{-5}$.

obtaining formula (46.27), whose absolute error is in order of magnitude equal to F, the false alarm probability. Taking the logarithm of (46.27) and using the approximate expression

$$\ln \frac{\mu}{1+\mu} = \ln\left(1 - \frac{1}{1+\mu}\right) = -\frac{1}{1+\mu}, \tag{46.28}$$

we obtain the simple formula

$$\mu = \frac{Z_* - L + 1}{\ln(1/D)} - 1, \tag{46.29}$$

which, combined with (46.07), becomes simply

$$\mu = \frac{1 + a\sqrt{L}}{\ln (1/D)} - 1. \tag{46.30}$$

It is clear from (46.30) that μ is a monotonically increasing function of L, so that "splitting up" the energy always leads to losses, just as in the case of a constant target. Formula (46.29) is very convenient for making quantitative calculations.

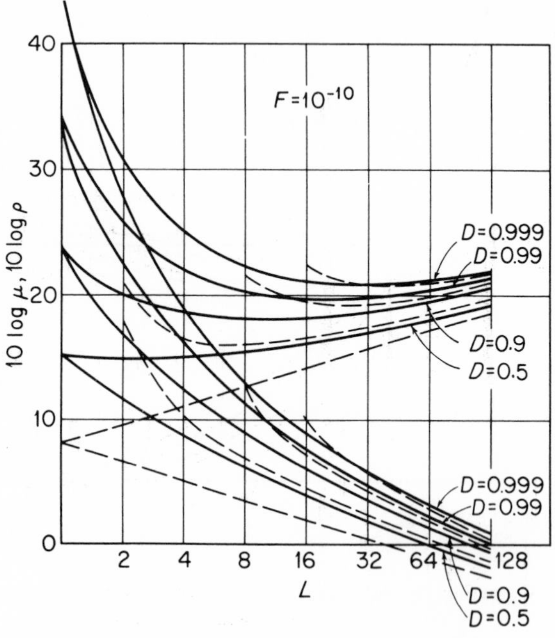

FIG. 45. Operating characteristics for detection of a rapidly scintillating target by using an incoherent signal train, for $F = 10^{-10}$.

In Figs. 46 to 49, the solid curves show the operating characteristics for detection of a slowly scintillating target, calculated by using (46.29), while the dashed curves show the operating characteristics constructed by using the prescription described above. We see that both methods give approximately the same results.

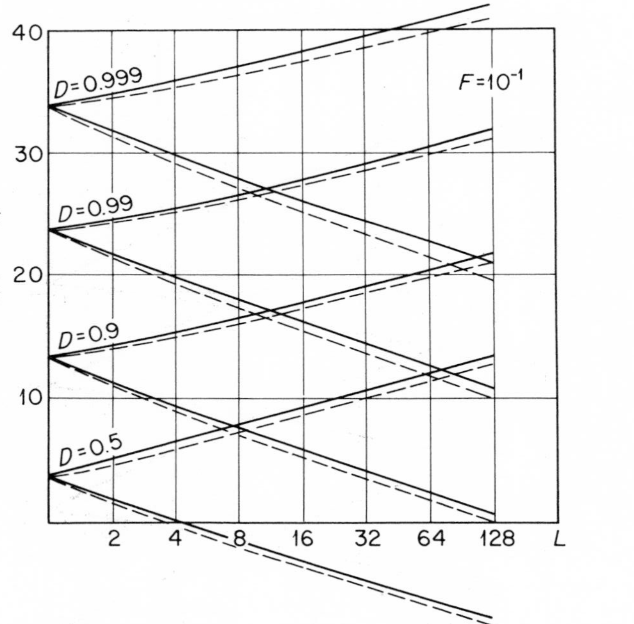

FIG. 46. Operating characteristics for detection of a slowly scintillating target by using an incoherent signal train, for $F = 10^{-1}$. The solid curves are obtained from formula (46.29), and dashed curves from Figs. 33(b) and 31.

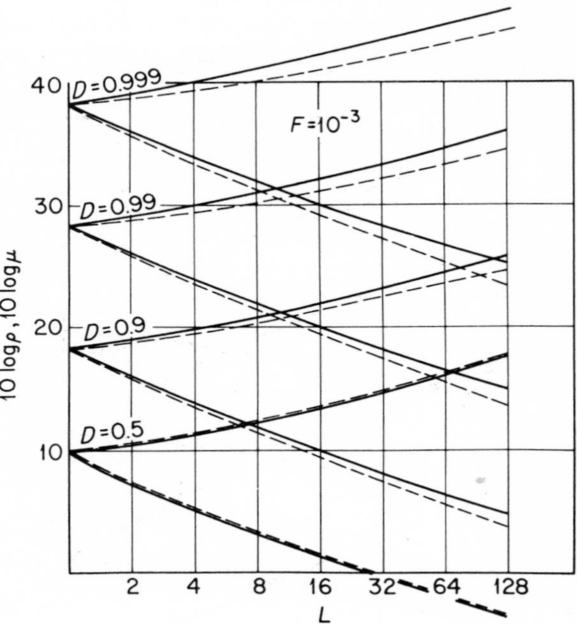

FIG. 47. Operating characteristics for detection of a slowly scintillating target by using an incoherent signal train, for $F = 10^{-3}$. The dashed curves are obtained from Figs. 34(b) and 31.

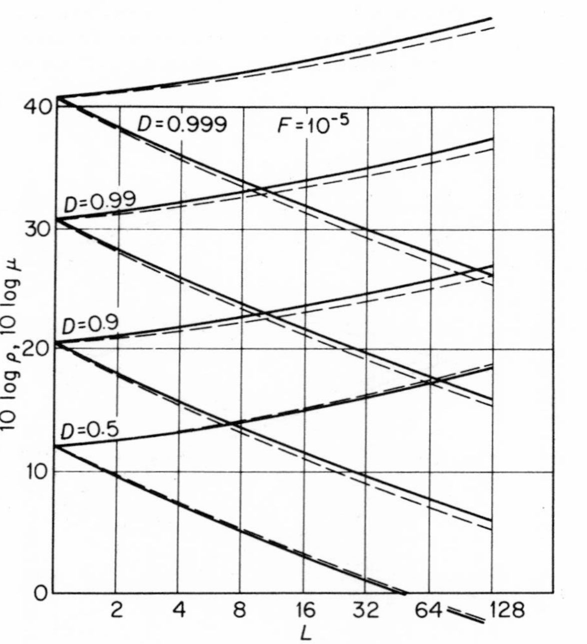

FIG. 48. Operating characteristics for detection of a slowly scintillating target by using an incoherent signal train, for $F = 10^{-5}$. The dashed curves are obtained from Figs. 35(b) and 31.

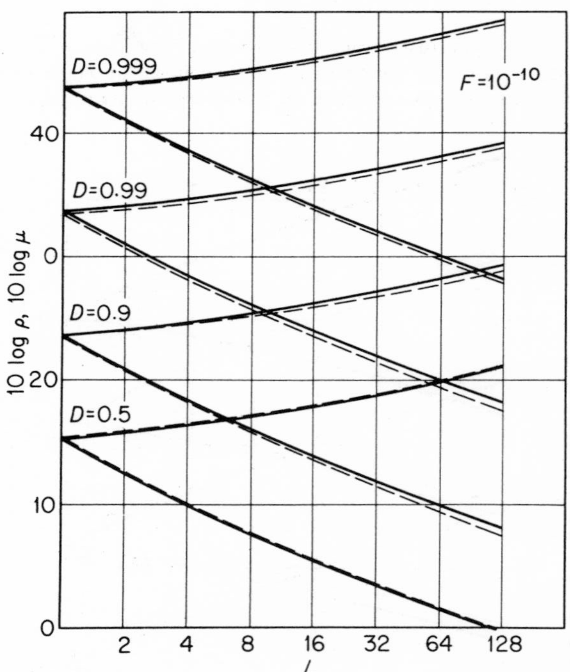

FIG. 49. Operating characteristics for detection of a slowly scintillating target by using an incoherent signal train, for $F = 10^{-10}$. The dashed curves are obtained from Figs. 36(b) and 31.

47. The Likelihood Ratio for a Coherent Signal Train

We now turn to the problem of the optimum receiver for detecting a scintillating target by using a *coherent* signal train. We recall that in this case, the noise has correlation from period to period as described by formula (43.16). As in Sec. 59, we introduce complex random variables $N_{g\varkappa}$, corresponding to the noise and satisfying the relations

$$n_{g\varkappa} = \text{Re } N_{g\varkappa}, \tag{47.01}$$

$$\overline{N_{g\varkappa}} = 0, \qquad \overline{N^*_{g\varkappa} N_{h\lambda}} = 2R_{gh} r_{\varkappa\lambda} e^{i(\varkappa-\lambda)\,\Delta\psi}. \tag{47.02}$$

If by analogy, we write

$$\begin{aligned} M_{g\varkappa} &= M_g w_\varkappa \, e^{-i(\varkappa-1)\Delta\vartheta}, \\ M_g &= e_g \, e^{i(\omega_0 t_g - \psi_g)}, \end{aligned} \tag{47.03}$$

then, according to (43.06), (43.08) and (43.12), we have

$$m_{g\varkappa} = \text{Re } M_{g\varkappa}. \tag{47.04}$$

Now let $\|Q_{gh}\|$ and $\|q_{\varkappa\lambda}\|$ denote the inverses of the matrices $\|R_{gh}\|$ and $\|r_{\varkappa\lambda}\|$, respectively. Then, it is not hard to show that the matrices

$$\|Q_{gh} q_{\varkappa\lambda} e^{i(\varkappa-\lambda)\,\Delta\psi}\| \quad \text{and} \quad \|R_{gh} r_{\varkappa\lambda} e^{i(\varkappa-\lambda)\,\Delta\psi}\| \tag{47.05}$$

are inverses of each other, since the following relation holds:

$$\begin{aligned} \sum_j \sum_\sigma R_{gj} Q_{jh} r_{\varkappa\sigma} q_{\sigma\lambda} e^{i(\varkappa-\sigma+\sigma-\lambda)\,\Delta\psi} &= e^{i(\varkappa-\lambda)\,\Delta\psi}\, \delta_{gh}\, \delta_{\varkappa\lambda} \\ &= \delta_{gh}\, \delta_{\varkappa\lambda}. \end{aligned} \tag{47.06}$$

Since the complex random variables $N_{g\varkappa}$ are assumed to be normal, their probability density is

$$P(N_{11}, N^*_{11}, \ldots, N_{HL}, N^*_{HL}) = \frac{\exp\left\{-\dfrac{1}{2} \sum\limits_{\varkappa,\lambda} \sum\limits_{g,h} Q_{gh} q_{\varkappa\lambda} e^{i(\varkappa-\lambda)\,\Delta\psi} N_{g\varkappa} N^*_{h\lambda}\right\}}{(4\pi)^{HL} \det \|R_{gh} r_{\varkappa\lambda} e^{i(\varkappa-\lambda)\,\Delta\psi}\|}. \tag{47.07}$$

If we introduce the complex random variables

$$F_{g\varkappa} = M_{g\varkappa} + N_{g\varkappa}, \quad \text{where} \quad f_{g\varkappa} = \text{Re } F_{g\varkappa}, \tag{47.08}$$

then the likelihood ratio $\Lambda(w_1, w_1^*, \ldots, w_L, w_L^*)$ equals

$$\begin{aligned} \Lambda(w_1, w_1^*, \ldots, w_L, w_L^*) &= p(w_1, w_1^*, \ldots, w_L, w_L^*) \\ &\times \frac{P(F_{11} - M_{11}, F^*_{11} - M^*_{11}, \ldots, F_{HL} - M_{HL}, F^*_{HL} - M^*_{HL})}{P(F_{11}, F^*_{11}, \ldots, F_{HL}, F^*_{HL})}, \end{aligned} \tag{47.09}$$

where the function P is given by (47.07), and the function p is given by (43.14). The operation of the optimum detecting receiver is determined by the likelihood ratio

$$\Lambda = \int\int \cdots \int\int \Lambda(w_1, w_1^*, \ldots, w_L, w_L^*)\, dw_1\, dw_1^* \ldots dw_L\, dw_L^*, \quad (47.10)$$

where the integration is over all possible values of w_L. Although the integral (47.10) can be calculated by the same method as used to calculate the integral (59.15) in Sec. 59, and then leads to formula (47.25), in this section we shall use another method to calculate Λ, which leads more quickly to the desired result. Here, we only call the reader's attention to the fact that formula (47.09) can be written in more detail as

$$\Lambda(w_1, w_1^*, \ldots, w_L, w_L^*) = p(w_1, w_1^*, \ldots, w_L, w_L^*)e^{\varphi - \frac{1}{2}\mu}, \quad (47.11)$$

where

$$\begin{aligned} \varphi &= \frac{1}{2}\sum_{\varkappa,\lambda}\sum_{g,h} Q_{gh}q_{\varkappa\lambda}e^{i(\varkappa-\lambda)\Delta\psi}(F_{g\varkappa}M_{h\lambda}^* + F_{h\lambda}^* M_{g\varkappa}) \\ &= \operatorname{Re}\left\{\sum_{\varkappa,\lambda} q_{\varkappa\lambda}e^{i(\varkappa-\lambda)\Delta\psi}F_\varkappa w_\lambda^* e^{i(\lambda-1)\Delta\vartheta}\right\}, \end{aligned} \quad (47.12)$$

$$F_\varkappa = \sum_{g,h} Q_{gh}F_{g\varkappa}M_h^*$$

and

$$\mu = \rho\sum_{\varkappa,\lambda} q_{\varkappa\lambda}e^{i(\varkappa-\lambda)(\Delta\psi-\Delta\vartheta)}w_\varkappa w_\lambda^*, \qquad \rho = \sum_{g,h} Q_{gh}M_g M_h^*. \quad (47.13)$$

Thus, it follows from (47.10) and (47.11) that the way the optimum receiver handles the input data $F_{g\varkappa}$ within one period is to form the quantities

$$F_\varkappa = \sum_{g,h} Q_{gh}F_{g\varkappa}M_h^* = M_\varkappa + N_\varkappa, \quad (47.14)$$

where

$$M_\varkappa = \rho w_\varkappa e^{-i(\varkappa-1)\Delta\vartheta}, \qquad N_\varkappa = \sum_{g,h} Q_{gh}N_{g\varkappa}M_h^*. \quad (47.15)$$

The subsequent treatment of the quantities $F_\varkappa$ depends only on the period-to-period correlation of the noise and of the useful signals. The random variables $F_\varkappa$ are normal, both in the presence of signals and when only noise is present, and in either case we have

$$\overline{F_\varkappa} = 0. \quad (47.16)$$

Formula (47.15) shows that

$$\overline{M_\varkappa^* M_\lambda} = 2\rho^2 r_{\varkappa\lambda}^m e^{i(\varkappa-\lambda)\Delta\vartheta}, \quad (47.17)$$

where the averaging is with respect to the target scintillations, for a fixed value of $\Delta\vartheta$. On the other hand, for the quantities $N_\varkappa$, we have

$$\overline{N_\varkappa^* N_\lambda} = 2 \sum_{g,h} \sum_{j,k} Q_{hg} Q_{jk} R_{gj} r_{\varkappa\lambda} e^{i(\varkappa-\lambda)\Delta\psi} M_h M_k^* \tag{47.18}$$

or

$$\overline{N_\varkappa^* N_\lambda} = 2\rho r_{\varkappa\lambda} e^{i(\varkappa-\lambda)\Delta\psi}, \tag{47.19}$$

where we have used the second of the formulas (47.13).

In the presence of the useful signal, we have

$$\overline{F_\varkappa^* F_\lambda} = 2\rho r_{\varkappa\lambda}^f, \quad \text{where} \quad r_{\varkappa\lambda}^f = \rho r_{\varkappa\lambda}^m e^{i(\varkappa-\lambda)\Delta\vartheta} + r_{\varkappa\lambda} e^{i(\varkappa-\lambda)\Delta\psi}, \tag{47.20}$$

and the corresponding probability density is

$$p_m(F_1, F_1^*, \ldots, F_L, F_L^*) = \frac{1}{(4\pi\rho)^L \det \|r_{\varkappa\lambda}^f\|} \exp\left\{-\frac{1}{2\rho} \sum_{\varkappa,\lambda} q_{\varkappa\lambda}^f F_\varkappa F_\lambda^*\right\}, \tag{47.21}$$

where the $q_{\varkappa\lambda}^f$ are the elements of the inverse of the matrix $\|r_{\varkappa\lambda}^f\|$. If the useful signal is absent, then

$$\overline{F_\varkappa^* F_\lambda} = 2\rho r_{\varkappa\lambda}^n, \quad \text{where} \quad r_{\varkappa\lambda}^n = r_{\varkappa\lambda} e^{i(\varkappa-\lambda)\Delta\psi}, \tag{47.22}$$

and the probability density for the same quantities $F_\varkappa$, $F_\varkappa^*$ is

$$p_0(F_1, F_1^*, \ldots, F_L, F_L^*) = \frac{1}{(4\pi\rho)^L \det \|r_{\varkappa\lambda}^n\|} \exp\left\{-\frac{1}{2\rho} \sum_{\varkappa,\lambda} q_{\varkappa\lambda}^n F_\varkappa F_\lambda^*\right\}, \tag{47.23}$$

where

$$q_{\varkappa\lambda}^n = q_{\varkappa\lambda} e^{i(\varkappa-\lambda)\Delta\psi}. \tag{47.24}$$

If a sequence of values $F_\varkappa$ and $F_\varkappa^*$ is obtained experimentally, then, according to the general theory (cf. Chap. 5), the probability that the useful signal is present is determined by the likelihood ratio

$$\Lambda = \frac{p_m(F_1, F_1^*, \ldots, F_L, F_L^*)}{p_0(F_1, F_1^*, \ldots, F_L, F_L^*)}, \tag{47.25}$$

which in the present case equals

$$\Lambda = \frac{\det \|r_{\varkappa\lambda}^n\|}{\det \|r_{\varkappa\lambda}^f\|} \exp\left\{\frac{1}{2\rho} \sum_{\varkappa,\lambda} (q_{\varkappa\lambda}^n - q_{\varkappa\lambda}^f) F_\varkappa F_\lambda^*\right\}. \tag{47.26}$$

The likelihood ratio (47.26) can be written more compactly as

$$\Lambda = \frac{D^n}{D^f} e^S, \tag{47.27}$$

where the determinants

$$D^n = \det \|r^n_{\varkappa\lambda}\| = \det \|r_{\varkappa\lambda}\|, \qquad D^f = \det \|r^f_{\varkappa\lambda}\| \tag{47.28}$$

depend only on the statistical properties of the signals and the noise, and the quantity

$$S = \frac{1}{2\rho} \sum_{\varkappa,\lambda} (q^n_{\varkappa\lambda} - q^f_{\varkappa\lambda}) F_\varkappa F^*_\varkappa \tag{47.29}$$

depends on the input data to the receiver as well. Therefore, the optimum receiver has to form the quantity S or some other quantity which is a single-valued function of S.

In conclusion, we note that in the original statement of the problem, we assumed that we are given the real quantities $f_{g\varkappa}$, i.e., the sample values of the real function $f(t)$ at the receiver input, and not the complex quantities $F_{g\varkappa}$, i.e., the sample functions of the complex function $F(t)$, which is connected with $f(t)$ by the relation

$$f(t) = \text{Re}\, F(t). \tag{47.30}$$

However, the definition of the function $F(t)$ presents no difficulty, and is particularly simple in the case of "narrow-band" signals, whose bandwidth is small compared to some carrier frequency (a condition which is always met in practice). In this case, $f(t)$ can be written in the form

$$f(t) = E(t) \cos [\omega_0 t - \Psi(t)], \tag{47.31}$$

where $E(t)$ and $\Psi(t)$ are slowly varying functions of time, and then the complex function $F(t)$ equals

$$F(t) \doteq E(t) e^{i[\omega_0 t - \Psi(t)]}. \tag{47.32}$$

In practice, the real function

$$\text{Im}\, F(t) = E(t) \sin [\omega_0 t - \Psi(t)] \tag{47.33}$$

can be formed by delaying the process (47.31) by a quarter of a period ($\pi/2\omega_0$), since during this time the functions $E(t)$ and $\Psi(t)$ do not change appreciably. Thus, in dealing with the complex quantities

$$F_\varkappa = x_\varkappa + i y_\varkappa, \tag{47.34}$$

we assume that the input data is being handled in two channels (in a more general way than in Chap. 6).

Simpler formulas are obtained if we do not strive for generality, but assume that the correlation properties of the noise are given by formula (43.15), in particular, that the reflecting objects have no regular motion.

Then, the quantities $x_\varkappa$ and $y_\varkappa$ in formula (47.34) are given by the expressions

$$x_\varkappa = \sum_g A_g f_{g\varkappa}, \qquad y_\varkappa = \sum_g B_g f_{g\varkappa},$$
$$A_g = \sum_h Q_{gh} e_h \cos(\omega_0 t_h - \psi_h), \tag{47.35}$$
$$B_g = \sum_h Q_{gh} e_h \sin(\omega_0 t_h - \psi_h)$$

which are the same as in the preceding chapter [cf. formulas (39.09) and (39.12)]. All the other results of this section are still valid.

In what follows, we shall use the general definition of the complex quantities $F_\varkappa$ until this leads to formulas that are too complicated. In Sec. 49, we shall use the much simpler formula (43.15).

48. Special Cases of the Optimum Receiver

Formula (47.29), which describes how the optimum receiver processes the input data from period to period, is rather complicated, and hence we now consider the most interesting special cases. We begin with a train consisting of only two signals ($L = 2$). If we write

$$r_{12} = re^{-i\beta}, \qquad r_{12}^m = pe^{-i\varepsilon}, \tag{48.01}$$

we have

$$\|r_{\varkappa\lambda}^n\| = \begin{Vmatrix} 1 & re^{-i\alpha} \\ re^{i\alpha} & 1 \end{Vmatrix}, \qquad \|q_{\varkappa\lambda}^n\| = \frac{1}{D^n}\begin{Vmatrix} 1 & -re^{-i\alpha} \\ -re^{i\alpha} & 1 \end{Vmatrix},$$
$$D^n = 1 - r^2, \qquad \alpha = \beta + \Delta\psi \tag{48.02}$$

and

$$\|r_{\varkappa\lambda}^f\| = \begin{Vmatrix} 1+\rho & re^{-i\alpha} + \rho pe^{-i\delta} \\ re^{i\alpha} + \rho pe^{i\delta} & 1+\rho \end{Vmatrix},$$
$$\|q_{\varkappa\lambda}^f\| = \frac{1}{D^f}\begin{Vmatrix} 1+\rho & -re^{-i\alpha} - \rho pe^{-i\delta} \\ -re^{i\alpha} - \rho pe^{i\delta} & 1+\rho \end{Vmatrix}, \tag{48.03}$$
$$D^f = 1 - r^2 + 2\rho[1 - rp\cos(\delta - \alpha)] + \rho^2(1 - p^2),$$
$$\delta = \varepsilon + \Delta\vartheta.$$

The quantity S equals

$$S = \frac{1}{2\rho D^n D^f}\{[D^f - (1+\rho)D^n][|F_1|^2 + |F_2|^2]$$
$$+ 2\,\mathrm{Re}\,[r(D^n - D^f)F_1F_2^* e^{-i\alpha} + \rho p D^n F_1 F_2^* e^{-i\delta}]\}. \tag{48.04}$$

In the limiting cases, we have the following results:

1. *Uncorrelated scintillations,* $p = 0$. In this case, the terms involving the phase $\delta = \varepsilon + \Delta\vartheta$ drop out of formulas (48.03) and (48.04), and due to the scintillations, the coherence of the train disappears. In particular, there is no need to carry out coherent addition. The expression (48.04) becomes

$$S = \frac{(1 + r^2 + \rho)(|F_1|^2 + |F_2|^2) - 2r(2 + \rho)\,\mathrm{Re}\,\{F_1F_2^* e^{-i\alpha}\}}{2(1 - r^2)(1 - r^2 + 2\rho + \rho^2)}, \tag{48.05}$$

which, in the case of uncorrelated noise ($r = 0$), reduces to

$$S = \frac{|F_1|^2 + |F_2|^2}{2(1 + \rho)}, \tag{48.06}$$

i.e., the optimum receiver must add the signals after a quadratic detector. On the other hand, if the noise is strongly correlated ($r \sim 1, \beta \sim 0$), we have

$$S = \frac{|F_1 - F_2 e^{i\Delta\psi}|^2}{2\rho(1 - r^2)}, \tag{48.07}$$

so that the optimum receiver has to perform "pulse-to-pulse" subtraction, taking into account the phase shift $\Delta\psi$; as a result, the strongly correlated noise is almost completely subtracted out. For $\Delta\psi = 0$, when the reflecting particles do not move as a whole, we have

$$S = \frac{|F_1 - F_2|^2}{2\rho(1 - r^2)} = \frac{(x_1 - x_2)^2 + (y_1 - y_2)^2}{2\rho(1 - r^2)}, \tag{48.08}$$

and the receiver has to perform pulse-to-pulse subtraction in both channels, and then add up the squares of the resulting differences.

2. *Completely correlated scintillations,* $p = 1$ *and* $\varepsilon = 0$. This case is very close to a case considered in Chap. 5, i.e., the receiver for a constant signal train, except that here the amplitude of both signals in the train is random (although constant). The expression (48.04) now becomes

$$S = \frac{|[e^{-i\Delta\vartheta} - re^{-i\alpha}]F_1 + [1 - re^{i(\alpha - \Delta\vartheta)}]F_2|^2}{2(1 - r^2)\{1 - r^2 + 2\rho[1 - r\cos(\Delta\vartheta - \alpha)]\}}. \tag{48.09}$$

For strongly correlated noise ($r \sim 1, \beta \sim 0$), formula (48.09) reduces to (48.07) again, while for uncorrelated noise ($r = 0$), it becomes

$$S = \frac{|F_1 + F_2 e^{i\Delta\vartheta}|^2}{2(1 + 2\rho)}, \tag{48.10}$$

i.e., the optimum way to treat the data is to add the signals coherently, taking into account the phase shift $\Delta\vartheta$.

If the noise correlation coefficient r is arbitrary, while $\alpha = 0$ and $\Delta\vartheta = 0, \pm 2\pi, \pm 4\pi, \ldots$, then

$$S = \frac{|F_1 + F_2|^2}{2(1 + r)(1 + r + 2\rho)}, \tag{48.11}$$

while if $\alpha = 0$ and $\Delta\vartheta = \pm\pi, \pm 3\pi, \ldots$, then

$$S = \frac{|F_1 - F_2|^2}{2(1 - r)(1 - r + 2\rho)}. \tag{48.12}$$

Thus, the optimum receiver for these values of α and $\Delta\vartheta$ must perform coherent summation (i.e., simple addition or subtraction). We note that for $r \sim 1$, formulas (48.08) and (48.12) become equivalent.

3. *Uncorrelated noise*, $r = 0$. Writing $q^2 = 1 - p^2$, we have

$$S = \frac{(1 + \rho q^2)(|F_1|^2 + |F_2|^2) + 2p \operatorname{Re}\{F_1 F_2^* e^{-i\delta}\}}{2(1 + 2\rho + \rho^2 q^2)}. \tag{48.13}$$

This expression is applicable for any correlation between consecutive signals. For uncorrelated and completely correlated scintillations, it reduces to formulas (48.06) and (48.10), respectively.

4. *Strongly correlated noise*, $r \sim 1$ *and* $\beta \sim 0$. In this case, since $D^n = 1 - r^2 \sim 0$, we can neglect the terms in braces in (48.04) which are proportional to D^n; the result is

$$S = \frac{|F_1 - F_2 e^{i\Delta\psi}|^2}{2\rho(1 - r^2)}, \tag{48.14}$$

as in formula (48.07).

Many of the results obtained above can easily be generalized to the case where L, the number of signals in the train, is arbitrary. We confine ourselves to the case of strongly correlated noise ($r^n_{\varkappa\lambda} \sim 1$), where the elements $q^n_{\varkappa\lambda}$ are large and the expression (47.29) can be written in the approximate form

$$S = \frac{1}{2\rho} \sum_{\varkappa, \lambda} q^n_{\varkappa\lambda} F_\varkappa F_\lambda^*. \tag{48.15}$$

If the matrix $\|r^n_{\varkappa\lambda}\|$ is of the form

$$r^n_{\varkappa\lambda} = r^{|\varkappa-\lambda|} e^{i(\varkappa-\lambda)\beta} \qquad (r < 1;\ \varkappa, \lambda = 1, 2, \ldots, L), \tag{48.16}$$

then the elements of the matrix $\|q^n_{\varkappa\lambda}\|$ equal

$$\begin{gathered} q^n_{11} = q^n_{LL} = \frac{1}{1 - r^2}, \qquad q^n_{\varkappa\varkappa} = \frac{1 + r^2}{1 - r^2} \qquad (1 < \varkappa < L), \\ q^n_{\varkappa, \varkappa+1} = (q^n_{\varkappa+1, \varkappa})^* = -\frac{r}{1 - r^2} e^{-i\alpha} \qquad (1 \leqslant \varkappa \leqslant L - 1) \end{gathered} \tag{48.17}$$

(cf. Secs. 35 and 40), while the rest of the $q^n_{\varkappa\lambda}$ are zero. Then, formula (48.15) takes the form

$$S = \frac{1}{2\rho(1-r^2)}[|F_1|^2 + (1+r^2)(|F_2|^2 + \cdots + |F_{L-1}|^2) + |F_L|^2 - 2r\,\mathrm{Re}\,\{(F_1F_2^* + \cdots + F_{L-1}F_L^*)e^{-i\alpha}\}] \tag{48.18}$$

$$\sim \frac{1}{2\rho(1-r^2)}[|F_1 - F_2e^{i\Delta\psi}|^2 + |F_2 - F_3e^{i\Delta\psi}|^2 + \cdots + |F_{L-1} - F_Le^{i\Delta\psi}|^2],$$

since $r \sim 1, \beta \sim 0$. In this case, the optimum receiver has to perform quadratic summation of consecutive differences.

If the correlation coefficient r_λ is given by the formula

$$r_{\varkappa\lambda} = r^{(\varkappa-\lambda)^2}, \tag{48.19}$$

then for $L = 3$ and $\Delta\psi = 0$, we have

$$D^n = (1+r^2)(1-r^2)^3,$$

$$\|q^n_{\varkappa\lambda}\| = \frac{1}{(1+r^2)(1-r^2)^2} \left\| \begin{matrix} 1 & -r(1+r^2) & r^2 \\ -r(1+r^2) & (1+r^2)(1+r^4) & -r(1+r^2) \\ r^2 & -r(1+r^2) & 1 \end{matrix} \right\|, \tag{48.20}$$

and instead of (48.18), we obtain the expression

$$S = \frac{1}{2\rho(1+r^2)(1-r^2)^2}[|F_1|^2 + (1+r^2)(1+r^4)|F_2|^2 + |F_3|^2 - 2r(1+r^2)\,\mathrm{Re}\,\{F_1F_2^* + F_2F_3^*\} + 2r^2\,\mathrm{Re}\,\{F_1F_3^*\}] \tag{48.21}$$

$$\sim \frac{1}{4\rho(1-r^2)^2}|F_1 - 2F_2 + F_3|^2,$$

which contains the second-order difference (we again set $r \sim 1$). It can be shown that the third-order difference appears for $L = 4$, and the fourth-order difference for $L = 5$. Evidently, for arbitrary L, we obtain the difference of order $L - 1$.

It is shown in Chap. 11 that formulas (48.16) and (48.19) determine the behavior (the decay as $|\varkappa - \lambda|$ increases) of the correlation coefficient of the noise due to reflections from randomly moving particles, in the limiting cases of large τ and small τ, respectively (compared to the correlation time of the velocities of the particles). We see that in these limiting cases, we obtain completely different formulas describing the optimum data processing.

The appearance of the second-order difference in formula (48.21) can be understood as follows: We write

$$\xi_\varkappa = \operatorname{Re} N_\varkappa, \quad \overline{\xi_\varkappa} = 0 \qquad (\varkappa = 1, 2, 3), \tag{48.22}$$

and specify the moments of the random variables $\xi_\varkappa$ by the formulas

$$\overline{\xi_\varkappa^2} = 1, \qquad \overline{\xi_1\xi_2} = \overline{\xi_2\xi_3} = r, \qquad \overline{\xi_1\xi_3} = r', \tag{48.23}$$

taking $r = r_{12} = r_{23}$ and $r' = r_{13}$ to be real numbers. We have to set

$$r' = r^2 \tag{48.24}$$

in the case of (48.16), and

$$r' = r^4 \tag{48.25}$$

in the case of (48.19). The relations (48.23) imply the formulas

$$\overline{(\xi_1 - \xi_2)^2} + \overline{(\xi_2 - \xi_3)^2} = 4(1 - r) \tag{48.26}$$

and

$$\overline{(\xi_1 - 2\xi_2 + \xi_3)^2} = 6 - 8r + 2r'. \tag{48.27}$$

For $r' = r^2$, we have

$$\overline{(\xi_1 - 2\xi_2 + \xi_3)^2} = (1 - r)[8 - 2(1 + r)] \sim 4(1 - r) \quad \text{for} \quad r \sim 1, \tag{48.28}$$

so that in this case, forming the square of the second-order difference leads to essentially the same result as summing the squares of the first-order differences. However, if we set $r' = r^4$, we obtain

$$\overline{(\xi_1 - 2\xi_2 + \xi_3)^2} = 2(1 - r)^2(3 + 2r + r^2) \sim 12(1 - r)^2, \tag{48.29}$$

so that for $r \sim 1$, the second-order difference gives a substantial decrease in the noise intensity, as compared with formula (48.26).

49. Operating Characteristics of a Receiver Performing Pulse-to-Pulse Subtraction

The optimum receiver, which gives an affirmative answer to the question of whether the target is present whenever the likelihood ratio exceeds a certain threshold value, is characterized by its false alarm probability F and detection probability D. These probabilities depend both on the threshold and on the effective signal-to-noise ratio. We now indicate how F and D are calculated for a receiver which forms the pulse-to-pulse difference

$$\mathscr{E} = |F_1 - F_2| = \sqrt{(x_1 - x_2)^2 + (y_1 - y_2)^2} \tag{49.01}$$

(cf. Sec. 42), and then bases its decision on the following rule:

$$\begin{aligned} &\text{If} \quad \mathscr{E} \geqslant \mathscr{E}_*, \quad \text{decide that } f = m + n; \\ &\text{If} \quad \mathscr{E} < \mathscr{E}_*, \quad \text{decide that } f = n. \end{aligned} \tag{49.02}$$

As can be seen from formulas (48.08) and (48.12), under certain conditions such a receiver is close to being optimum, at least when $\beta = 0$ and $\Delta\psi = 0$.

The random variable (49.01) has the probability density

$$p(\mathscr{E}) = \frac{\mathscr{E}}{\sigma^2} e^{-\mathscr{E}^2/2\sigma^2}, \tag{49.03}$$

where, according to (47.20), (47.22) and (48.01), for $\Delta\psi = 0$ and real $r = r_{12} = r_{21}$, we obtain

$$\begin{aligned} \sigma^2 &= \tfrac{1}{2}\overline{\mathscr{E}^2} = 2\rho(1 - r), \qquad \text{if the signal is absent,} \\ \sigma^2 &= \tfrac{1}{2}\overline{\mathscr{E}^2} = 2\rho[1 - r + \rho(1 - p\cos\delta)] = 2\rho(1 - r)(1 + \mu), \\ &\qquad \text{if the signal is present.} \end{aligned} \tag{49.04}$$

Here, the quantity

$$\mu = \rho\,\frac{1 - p\cos\delta}{1 - r} \tag{49.05}$$

plays the role of an effective signal-to-noise ratio for the present problem. In fact, $\sigma^2 = \sigma_n^2$ if the useful signal is absent, while $\sigma^2 = \sigma_m^2 + \sigma_n^2$ if it is present, where σ_m^2 is the intensity of the useful signal, and σ_n^2 is the intensity of the noise *after subtraction*. Therefore, it is natural to define

$$\mu = \frac{\sigma_m^2}{\sigma_n^2}, \tag{49.06}$$

from which, using the expressions (49.04), we immediately obtain formula (49.05). If now we calculate F and D, we obtain the usual relation between them, i.e.,

$$D = F^{1/(1+\mu)}, \tag{49.07}$$

which is characteristic of a fluctuating signal in a background of normal noise [cf. Sec. 34 and formula (45.09)].

It will be recalled that the complex quantities $F_\varkappa$ are obtained as a result of processing of the input data within each period, by using two channels which are in quadrature with respect to each other (cf. the end of Sec. 47). Together with the receiver considered above, which forms the "double-channel" difference (49.01), we now consider the simpler receiver which operates according to the following rule:

$$\begin{aligned} &\text{If } \ |\xi| \geqslant \xi_*, \ \text{ decide that } f = m + n; \\ &\text{If } \ |\xi| < \xi_*, \ \text{ decide that } f = m. \end{aligned} \tag{49.08}$$

Here

$$\xi = x_1 - x_2 \tag{49.09}$$

is the "single-channel" difference [cf. formulas (42.27) and (42.28)], whose probability density is

$$p(\xi) = \frac{1}{\sqrt{2\pi}\sigma} e^{-\xi^2/2\sigma^2}, \tag{49.10}$$

where σ^2 is calculated by the formulas (49.04). The probabilities F and D are equal to

$$\begin{aligned} F &= \frac{2}{\sqrt{2\pi}} \int_{z_*}^{\infty} e^{-z^2/2}\, dz \qquad \left(z_* = \frac{\mathscr{E}_*}{\sqrt{2\rho(1-r)}}\right), \\ D &= \frac{2}{\sqrt{2\pi}} \int_{y_*}^{\infty} e^{-z^2/2}\, dz \qquad \left(y_* = \frac{z_*}{\sqrt{1+\mu}}\right). \end{aligned} \tag{49.11}$$

These formulas were obtained in Sec. 32, and they were used to construct the dashed curves in Fig. 28, which therefore give the operating characteristics of a receiver forming the single-channel difference (49.09). If the receiver forms the double-channel difference (49.01), then its operating characteristics (for detection) are given by the dashed curves in Fig. 31. This last figure allows us to compare the detection of a scintillating target with the detection of a constant target by using such a receiver. The advantages of the double-channel receiver, which operates according to formula (49.02), over the single-channel scheme (49.08) can be found by comparing the dashed curves in Figs. 31 and 28.

The preceding results are valid provided that the phase $\delta = \varepsilon + \Delta\vartheta$ has some definite value, i.e., the target moves with a fixed velocity. The parameters μ and D depend on $\Delta\vartheta$, and this dependence disappears only for uncorrelated scintillations ($p = 0$). If the velocity of the target is a random variable, then to calculate D it is necessary to carry out additional averaging with respect to the phase difference $\Delta\vartheta$ (cf. Sec. 42), and this requires the use of numerical methods. Without making numerical calculations, we can only derive from (49.07) the pair of inequalities

$$F^{1/[1+2\mu_0(1+p)]} \leqslant D \leqslant F^{1/[1+2\mu_0(1-p)]}, \tag{49.12}$$

from which we can estimate D quite accurately for small values of p. Here, the parameter

$$\mu_0 = \frac{\rho}{2(1-r)}, \tag{49.13}$$

introduced earlier in Sec. 42, plays the role of a signal-to-noise ratio when the velocity is unknown.

We note that it is only in the case of slow scintillations ($p = 1, \varepsilon = 0$) that the parameter (49.05) equals the parameter

$$\mu = \rho \frac{1 - \cos \Delta\vartheta}{1 - r} \tag{49.14}$$

introduced in Sec. 42 for the case of a constant target [cf. formula (42.16)]. In the opposite case, where $p = 0$, formula (49.05) becomes

$$\mu = \frac{\rho}{1 - r} = 2\mu_0, \tag{49.15}$$

and the ratio of the quantities (49.14) and (49.15) equals $1 - \cos \Delta\vartheta$. This means that for $\Delta\vartheta = \pm\pi, \pm 3\pi, \ldots$, the quantity (49.14) is only twice as large as (49.15), whereas for velocities near the "blind" velocities ($\Delta\vartheta = 0, \pm 2\pi, \pm 4\pi, \ldots$), the quantity (49.14) is many times smaller than (49.15).

These considerations show that because of the blind velocities, it is harder to detect a constant or slowly scintillating target (for an arbitrary value of $\Delta\vartheta$) than to detect a rapidly scintillating target, for which $p = 0$ and there are no blind velocities. Figure 50 illustrates this situation: The solid curve is the operating characteristic for detection of a rapidly scintillating target ($p = 0$, $\mu = 2\mu_0$), constructed by using (49.07) or (49.12), while the dashed curve corresponds to a constant target and is taken from Fig. 39 (where it is given by the solid curve). As a result of the fact that the constant target is not observed for the blind velocities, larger values of μ_0 are needed to detect it (2 to 6 db larger) than to detect a rapidly scintillating target. It is clear that as the correlation coefficient p increases, blind velocities also begin to appear in the case of the scintillating target, so that the probability of detecting it (for a given value of μ_0) decreases and the entire solid curve in Fig. 50 moves to the right.

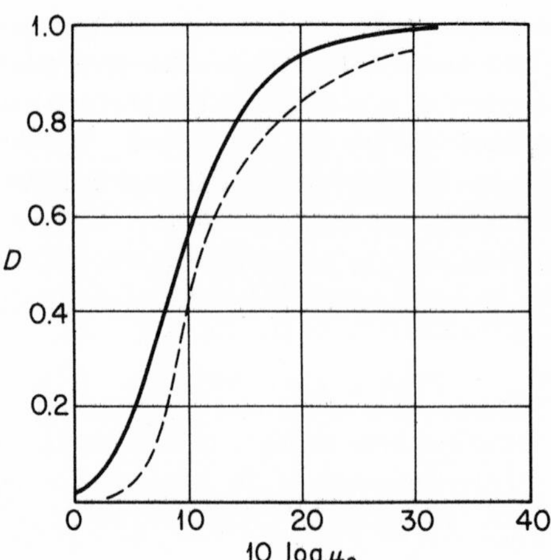

FIG. 50. Operating characteristics for detection, for the case where the receiver forms the "double-channel" difference (49.01); $F = 0.37 \times 10^{-5}$. The solid curve corresponds to a rapidly scintillating target, and the dashed curve to a constant target.

8

MEASUREMENT OF SIGNAL PARAMETERS IN THE PRESENCE OF NOISE

50. Measurement of a Parameter by Using the Maximum A Posteriori Probability

In the preceding chapters, we have considered various cases of detection of a useful signal in a noise background. We now study the problem of *measuring* the parameters of a useful signal in the presence of noise. This problem will be studied within the framework of the statistical theory presented in Chap. 5, but it has a variety of special features. In order not to create spurious difficulties, we first separate the problem of measurement from the problem of detection, by assuming that the useful signal m is already present, i.e., that the a priori probabilities that the useful signal is present and absent are

$$P(m) = 1, \qquad P(0) = 0, \tag{50.01}$$

respectively. The problem now consists in measuring the parameter τ of the signal $m(t, \tau)$. This statement of the problem corresponds to "pure" measurement, in which case formulas (29.28) to (29.30) take the form

$$p_f[m(\tau)] = \frac{\Lambda(\tau)}{\Lambda}, \qquad \Lambda = \int \Lambda(\tau)\, d\tau, \tag{50.02}$$

where

$$\Lambda(\tau) = p_m(\tau) \frac{p_{m(\tau)}(f)}{p_0(f)} \tag{50.03}$$

is the likelihood ratio, which differs from the a posteriori probability density $p_f[m(\tau)]$ only by the factor Λ, which does not depend on τ.

According to Chap. 5, the optimum receiver for measuring the parameter τ must form the a posteriori probability density $p_f[m(\tau)]$ or the likelihood ratio $\Lambda(\tau)$ (which, for "pure" measurement, is an unnormalized probability density). Then, using this probabilistic data, the receiver has to make a decision and indicate some definite value of the parameter τ as the result of the measurement. We can assume that the device making this decision is included in the optimum receiver (cf. Sec. 30). *Thus, it is natural to define the most probable value of τ (i.e., the value of τ for which the probability density $p_f[m(\tau)]$ and the likelihood ratio $\Lambda(\tau)$ take their maximum values) as being the result of the measurement, and to regard this value as the "measured" value of τ.*

We now consider the simplest consequences of this definition. For normal noise, the likelihood ratio equals

$$\Lambda(\tau) = p_m(\tau)\frac{p(f-m)}{p(f)} = p_m(\tau)\frac{\exp\left\{-\frac{1}{2}\sum_{g,h=1}^{H} Q_{gh}[f_g - m_g(\tau)][f_h - m_h(\tau)]\right\}}{\exp\left\{-\frac{1}{2}\sum_{g,h=1}^{H} Q_{gh}f_g f_h\right\}}. \tag{50.04}$$

It is easy to show that in this case, finding the most probable value of τ reduces to a generalization of the method of least squares. In fact, first let the noise be uncorrelated, so that $Q_{gh} = 0$ for $g \neq h$ and all the values Q_{hh} are equal. Then, the maximum of $\Lambda(\tau)$ is achieved [for $p_m(\tau) = \text{const}$] when the expression

$$\varepsilon^2 = \sum_{h=1}^{H} [f_h - m_h(\tau)]^2 \tag{50.05}$$

is a minimum. In the general case, instead of the expression (50.05), we have to use a quadratic form which takes account of the correlation of the noise:

$$\varepsilon^2 = \sum_{g,h} Q_{gh}[f_g - m_g(\tau)][f_h - m_h(\tau)]; \tag{50.06}$$

it is also necessary to take into account the a priori probability distribution $p_m(\tau)$, if $p_m(\tau) \neq \text{const}$. Moreover, if there is another unknown parameter θ, then the likelihood ratio $\Lambda(\tau)$ is calculated by using formula (29.34).

As an example, consider the measurement of the unknown amplitude a of a signal of known form $s(t)$, i.e., let

$$m(t, a) = as(t), \tag{50.07}$$

and suppose that the amplitude a has the normal distribution

$$p_m(a) = \frac{1}{\sqrt{2\pi}\,a_0} e^{-a^2/2a_0^2}. \tag{50.08}$$

If we denote the sample values of the functions $f(t)$, $m(t)$ and $s(t)$ at the times t_h by

$$f_h = f(t_h), \quad m_h = m(t_h), \quad s_h = s(t_h) \qquad (h = 1, \ldots, H), \tag{50.09}$$

and if we assume that the sample values $n_h = n(t_h)$ of the noise are independent at different times and have moments

$$\overline{n_h} = 0, \qquad \overline{n_h^2} = \sigma^2, \tag{50.10}$$

then we can write the probability density of the random variables $n_1, \ldots, n_H$ in the form

$$p(n_1, \ldots, n_H) = \frac{1}{(2\pi)^{H/2}\sigma^H} \exp\left\{-\frac{1}{2\sigma^2}\sum_{h=1}^{H} n_h^2\right\}. \tag{50.11}$$

Therefore, the likelihood ratio $\Lambda(a)$ equals

$$\Lambda(a) = p_m(a) e^{\varphi(a) - \frac{1}{2}\mu(a)} \tag{50.12}$$

[cf. (32.03)], where $\varphi(a)$ and $\mu(a)$ are given by

$$\begin{aligned} \varphi(a) &= \sum_{g,h} Q_{gh} f_g m_h = \frac{a}{\sigma^2}\sum_h f_h s_h, \\ \mu(a) &= \sum_{g,h} Q_{gh} m_g m_h = \frac{a^2}{\sigma^2}\sum_h s_h^2. \end{aligned} \tag{50.13}$$

Using formula (50.08), we can write the likelihood ratio in the form

$$\Lambda(a) = \frac{1}{\sqrt{2\pi}\,a_0} \exp\left\{\frac{a}{\sigma^2}\sum_h f_h s_h - \frac{a^2}{2}\left(\frac{1}{a_0^2} + \frac{1}{\sigma^2}\sum_h s_h^2\right)\right\}. \tag{50.14}$$

We now let $\hat{a}$ denote the most probable value of the parameter a. Then, according to what was said above, the function $\Lambda(a)$ takes its maximum, for $a = \hat{a}$, and therefore $\hat{a}$ can be determined from the equation

$$\frac{\partial \ln \Lambda(a)}{\partial a} = \frac{1}{\sigma^2}\sum_h f_h s_h - a\left(\frac{1}{a_0^2} + \frac{1}{\sigma^2}\sum_h s_h^2\right) = 0, \tag{50.15}$$

from which it follows that

$$\hat{a} = \frac{\sum_h f_h s_h}{\sum_h s_h^2 + (\sigma^2/a_0^2)}. \tag{50.16}$$

An important property of the quantity $\hat{a}$, shown by (50.16), is the fact that $\hat{a}$ is a *linear* function of the input data $f_1, \ldots, f_H$.

In this problem, the parameter

$$\rho = \frac{a_0^2 \sum_h s_h^2}{\sigma^2} \tag{50.17}$$

plays the role of a signal-to-noise ratio. If ρ is large, then formula (50.16) becomes

$$\hat{a} = \frac{\sum_h f_h s_h}{\sum_h s_h^2}, \tag{50.18}$$

so that the most probable value of a does not depend on the parameter a_0 characterizing the a priori probability distribution (50.08). Writing $\Lambda(a)$ in the form

$$\Lambda(a) = \frac{1}{\sqrt{2\pi}\, a_0} \exp\left\{-\frac{(a - \hat{a})^2}{2a_0^2/(1 + \rho)} + \left(\frac{\hat{a}}{a_0}\right)^2 \frac{1 + \rho}{2}\right\}, \tag{50.19}$$

we see that the a posteriori distribution of the quantity a is also Gaussian; the mean value of this distribution is random and equals $\hat{a}$, while its variance does not depend on random variables and equals

$$b = \frac{a_0^2}{1 + \rho}. \tag{50.20}$$

We now examine the statistical properties of the random variable $\hat{a}$. Averaging f_h over the noise, we obtain

$$\overline{f_h} = m_h = a s_h, \tag{50.21}$$

so that

$$\begin{aligned} \bar{\hat{a}} &= \frac{\rho a}{1 + \rho}, \\ \overline{(\hat{a} - \bar{\hat{a}})^2} &= \frac{\rho a_0^2}{(1 + \rho)^2}. \end{aligned} \tag{50.22}$$

It follows that $\hat{a}$ is a normal random variable (for fixed a), whose distribution equals

$$p_a(\hat{a}) = \frac{1 + \rho}{\sqrt{2\pi\rho}\, a_0} \exp\left\{-\frac{[\hat{a} - \{\rho a/(1 + \rho)\}]^2}{2\rho a_0^2/(1 + \rho)^2}\right\}. \tag{50.23}$$

Thus, the quantity $\hat{a}$ has the mathematical expectation $\bar{\hat{a}}$, which is shifted with respect to the true value of the unknown parameter a by the amount

$$\bar{\hat{a}} - a = -\frac{a}{1 + \rho}, \tag{50.24}$$

depending on the parameter a itself. The variance of $\hat{a}$ is given by the second of the formulas (50.22), and does not depend on the parameter a being measured.

Instead of the two variances $\overline{(\hat{a} - \bar{\hat{a}})^2}$ and b, it is convenient to introduce the concept of the mean square measurement error Δ^2, defined by the formula

$$\Delta^2 = \overline{(\hat{a} - a)^2}. \tag{50.25}$$

Using (50.22) and (50.24), we have

$$\begin{aligned} \Delta^2 &= \overline{[(\hat{a} - \bar{\hat{a}}) + (\bar{\hat{a}} - a)]^2} \\ &= \overline{(\hat{a} - \bar{\hat{a}})^2} + (\bar{\hat{a}} - a)^2 = \frac{\rho a_0^2 + a^2}{(1 + \rho)^2}. \end{aligned} \tag{50.26}$$

Formula (50.26) shows that in general the mean square measurement error is greater than the variance $\overline{(\hat{a} - \bar{\hat{a}})^2}$, and is only equal to the variance when it achieves its minimum value (for $a = 0$). Averaging Δ^2 with respect to the random parameter a, we obtain

$$\overline{\Delta^2} = \frac{a_0^2}{1 + \rho} = b, \tag{50.27}$$

i.e., the mean square measurement error, averaged over all possible values of the parameter a, equals the variance (50.20) of the a posteriori distribution.

Next, we consider the a posteriori distribution (50.19) for large and for small values of the signal-to-noise ratio ρ. As $\rho \to \infty$, we have

$$\bar{\hat{a}} = a, \tag{50.28}$$

while the variance

$$\overline{(\hat{a} - \bar{\hat{a}})^2} = \frac{a_0^2}{\rho} = \frac{\sigma^2}{\sum_h s_h^2} \tag{50.29}$$

does not depend on the unknown parameter a or on a_0, i.e., on the a priori distribution (50.08), but only on the noise power σ^2 and the signal energy $\sum_h s_h^2$. For $\rho \gg 1$, the a posteriori distribution is much sharper than the a priori distribution, and in fact its variance is

$$b \sim \frac{a_0^2}{\rho} = \frac{\sigma^2}{\sum_h s_h^2}, \tag{50.30}$$

i.e., equals the variance (50.29) and is also independent of the a priori distribution (50.08). For large ρ, the mean square measurement error defined by (50.26) is

$$\Delta^2 \sim \frac{a_0^2}{\rho}. \tag{50.31}$$

Thus, when $\rho \gg 1$, all three mean square quantities (50.29), (50.30) and (50.31) coincide, and the a posteriori distribution is characterized by the two parameters $\bar{\hat{a}} = a$ and b.

As $\rho \to 0$, we obtain

$$\hat{a} = 0 \tag{50.32}$$

for any value of a, so that

$$\bar{\hat{a}} = 0, \qquad \bar{\hat{a}} - a = -a, \tag{50.33}$$

while the variance of $\hat{a}$ equals

$$\overline{(\hat{a} - \bar{\hat{a}})^2} = 0. \tag{50.34}$$

Moreover, for $\rho \to 0$, the variance of the a posteriori distribution equals

$$b = a_0^2, \tag{50.35}$$

i.e., the a posteriori distribution has the same variance as the a priori distribution. It is easy to see that for small ρ, the whole a posteriori distribution reproduces the a priori distribution practically without change, so that the operation of measurement gives no new information. In this case, the mean square measurement error is

$$\Delta^2 = a^2, \tag{50.36}$$

and its average over a is

$$\overline{\Delta^2} = a_0^2. \tag{50.37}$$

Formulas (50.36) and (50.37) also indicate the poor quality of the measurement.

In principle, it might be possible to use the quantity $\hat{a}$ given by formula (50.18) as the measured value of a (for any value of ρ); as we have already seen, this quantity does not depend on the parameter a_0. Then, if a is fixed and ρ is arbitrary, the distribution of the random variable $\hat{a}$ defined by (50.18) is

$$p_a(\hat{a}) = \frac{1}{\sqrt{2\pi a_0^2/\rho}} \exp\left\{-\frac{(\hat{a} - a)^2}{2a_0^2/\rho}\right\}, \tag{50.38}$$

since the quantity $\hat{a}$ has the mean and variance

$$\begin{gathered} \bar{\hat{a}} = a, \\ \overline{(\hat{a} - a)^2} = \overline{\left(\frac{\sum_h n_h s_h}{\sum_h s_h^2}\right)^2} = \frac{\sigma^2}{\sum_h s_h^2} = \frac{a_0^2}{\rho}. \end{gathered} \tag{50.39}$$

The defect of the quantity $\hat{a}$ defined by formula (50.18), for arbitrary ρ, is that as $\rho \to 0$, the variance $\overline{(\hat{a} - a)^2}$ grows indefinitely. Moreover, the variance given by (50.39) is greater than the "average" variance given by (50.27). Thus, in what follows, we shall assume that all measurements are made by using maximum a posteriori probability, since the advantages of other methods of measurement in no way compensate for their drawbacks.

51. Extraction of a Random Signal from a Noise Background

In this section, we analyze the simplest case involving measurement of several unknown parameters, i.e., measurement of the elements of a random sequence. Thus, let m_h and n_h be the sample values of two independent normal random processes $m(t)$ and $n(t)$, satisfying the relations

$$\begin{aligned} \overline{m_h} &= 0, \qquad \overline{m_g m_h} = R^m_{gh}, \\ \overline{n_h} &= 0, \qquad \overline{n_g n_h} = R^n_{gh}. \end{aligned} \tag{51.01}$$

Assuming that $m(t)$ is the useful signal and $n(t)$ the noise, we pose the problem of measuring each element m_h in the presence of the noise n_h. The H-dimensional a priori probability density of the useful signal is

$$p(m_1, \ldots, m_H) = \frac{1}{\sqrt{(2\pi)^H \det \|R^m_{gh}\|}} \exp\left\{-\frac{1}{2}\sum_{g,h=1}^{H} Q^m_{gh} m_g m_h\right\}, \tag{51.02}$$

and the H-dimensional a priori probability density of the noise is

$$p(n_1, \ldots, n_H) = \frac{1}{\sqrt{(2\pi)^H \det \|R^n_{gh}\|}} \exp\left(-\frac{1}{2}\sum_{g,h=1}^{H} Q^n_{gh} n_g n_h\right). \tag{51.03}$$

Then, the likelihood ratio can be written in the form

$$\begin{aligned} \Lambda(m_1, \ldots, m_H) &= p(m_1, \ldots, m_H)\frac{p(f_1 - m_1, \ldots, f_H - m_H)}{p(f_1, \ldots, f_H)} \\ &= \frac{1}{\sqrt{(2\pi)^H \det \|R^m_{gh}\|}} \exp\left\{-\frac{1}{2}\sum_{g,h} (Q^n_{gh} + Q^m_{gh}) m_g m_h + \sum_{g,h} Q^n_{gh} f_g m_h\right\}. \end{aligned} \tag{51.04}$$

We now find the most probable values of m_g, which we denote by $\hat{m}_g$ $(g = 1, \ldots, H)$. The quantities $\hat{m}_g$ are the solutions of the equations

$$\frac{\partial \ln \Lambda}{\partial m_g} = 0 \qquad (g = 1, \ldots, H). \tag{51.05}$$

Using the symmetry of the matrices $\|Q^n_{gh}\|$ and $\|Q^m_{gh}\|$, we find that the quantities $\hat{m}_g$ satisfy the equations

$$\sum_j (Q^n_{gj} + Q^m_{gj})\hat{m}_j - \sum_h Q^n_{gh} f_h = 0. \tag{51.06}$$

It follows that

$$\hat{m}_g = \sum_h k_{gh} f_h, \tag{51.07}$$

i.e., the $\hat{m}_g$ are linear combinations of the input data f_h, where the coefficients k_{gh} obey the relations

$$\sum_j (Q^n_{gj} + Q^m_{gj}) k_{jh} = Q^n_{gh}. \tag{51.08}$$

The equations (51.08) can be reduced to the form (26.10) by making some rather tedious calculations. To simplify these calculations, we introduce the following notation for the various matrices involved:

$$\begin{gathered} k = \|k_{gh}\|, \qquad R_f = \|R^f_{gh}\| = \|R^m_{gh} + R^n_{gh}\| = R^m + R^n, \\ R^m = \|R^m_{gh}\|, \qquad R^n = \|R^n_{gh}\|, \\ Q^m = \|Q^m_{gh}\|, \qquad Q^n = \|Q^n_{gh}\|, \qquad Q^f = \|Q^f_{gh}\|, \end{gathered} \tag{51.09}$$

so that

$$Q^n R^n = R^n Q^n = Q^m R^m = R^m Q^m = Q^f R^f = R^f Q^f = E, \tag{51.10}$$

where E is the unit matrix. Then, equation (51.08) can be written as

$$(Q^m + Q^n) k = Q^n. \tag{51.11}$$

Multiplying (51.11) on the left by R^n, we obtain

$$(R^n Q^m + E) k = (R^n + R^m) Q^m k = R^f Q^m k = E. \tag{51.12}$$

This implies

$$Q^m k = Q^f, \tag{51.13}$$

and finally

$$k = R^m Q^f, \qquad k R^f = R^m, \tag{51.14}$$

which agrees with (26.12) and (26.10).

Thus, the operation of extracting a random signal from random noise by using the maximum likelihood ratio is a linear operation, and in fact, it is just the operation of optimum linear filtering of random sequences, presented in Chap. 4 and based on the criterion of the least mean square error. In particular, the quantities (51.07) coincide with the quantities (26.05).

These results establish the connection between the theory of optimum filtering of random sequences and processes (developed in Part 1) and the theory of optimum receivers. This connection could be investigated in more detail, but instead we confine ourselves to these remarks and turn our attention now to more complicated problems involving the measurement of signal parameters in the presence of noise.

52. Measurement of a Signal Parameter in Weak Noise and in Strong Noise

In the two preceding sections, we considered some very simple cases of measurement of signal parameters in the presence of noise. In such cases, the following conditions are satisfied: (1) The measured parameters have Gaussian distributions, and (2) the useful signal depends linearly on the measured parameters. If these conditions are not met, the problem becomes much more complicated. A theoretical investigation of the optimum receiver for making measurements in the presence of noise was first carried out by V. A. Kotelnikov in 1946, and the method proposed by him is very general. In this section, we shall study the problem of measuring a signal parameter, for the most part following Kotelnikov's work, except that we use different notation. Moreover, we shall generalize Kotelnikov's work somewhat, by considering the noise to be correlated.

If in addition to the time t, the useful signal $m(t, \tau)$ depends only on a single parameter τ which is to be measured, then, in the case of normal noise, the likelihood ratio equals

$$\Lambda(\tau) = p_m(\tau)e^{\varphi(\tau)-\frac{1}{2}\mu(\tau)}, \tag{52.01}$$

where $p_m(\tau)$ is the a priori probability density of the parameter τ, and $\varphi(\tau)$ and $\mu(\tau)$ have their usual meanings, i.e.,

$$\varphi(\tau) = \sum_{g,h} Q_{gh} f_g m_h(\tau) \tag{52.02}$$

and

$$\mu(\tau) = \sum_{g,h} Q_{gh} m_g(\tau) m_h(\tau). \tag{52.03}$$

Here $f_g = f(t_g)$ are the sample values of the process at the receiver input, $m_h(\tau) = m(t_h, \tau)$ are the sample values of the useful signal with parameter value τ, and $\| Q_{gh} \|$ is the inverse of the noise correlation matrix, whose elements equal

$$R_{gh} = \overline{n_g n_h} = \overline{n(t_g)n(t_h)}. \tag{52.04}$$

The optimum receiver must form the likelihood ratio $\Lambda(\tau)$ or some monotonically increasing function of $\Lambda(\tau)$ [in what follows, it is convenient to choose this function to be $\ln \Lambda(\tau)$], on the basis of which it gives as its output the value $\hat{\tau}$, i.e., the value of τ corresponding to the maximum likelihood ratio. It is clear that this is the best that can be done by a receiver which is required to give a definite answer in the form of a number, and all that remains is for us to calculate the characteristics of such a receiver.

There are certain difficulties associated with calculating the characteristics of the optimum receiver which measures a signal parameter in the presence of noise. In weak noise, when the measurement errors are small and when

τ, the parameter being measured, has a Gaussian distribution (as in the cases considered above), the quality of the measurement can be characterized by its mean square error (see below). In strong noise, it is convenient to characterize the quality of the measurement by the probability that the error exceeds a certain given value.

We begin with the case of weak noise. It follows from the relation (52.01) that

$$\ln \Lambda(\tau) = \varphi(\tau) - \frac{1}{2}\mu(\tau) + \ln p_m(\tau). \tag{52.05}$$

The quantity τ is a root of the equation

$$\frac{d}{d\tau}\ln \Lambda(\tau) = 0, \tag{52.06}$$

for which the second derivative is negative, i.e.,

$$\frac{d^2}{d\tau^2}\ln \Lambda(\tau) < 0 \quad \text{for} \quad \tau = \hat{\tau}. \tag{52.07}$$

If there are several values of $\hat{\tau}$ satisfying the conditions (52.06) and (52.07), then we have to select the one for which $\Lambda(\hat{\tau})$ is a maximum, since it is assumed that only a single useful signal is present.

For $\tau \sim \hat{\tau}$, we can expand $\ln \Lambda(\tau)$ in a Taylor's series, obtaining

$$\ln \Lambda(\tau) = \ln \Lambda(\hat{\tau}) - \frac{(\tau - \hat{\tau})^2}{2\,\Delta^2} + \cdots, \tag{52.08}$$

where we omit terms of order $(\tau - \hat{\tau})^3$ and higher. The positive quantity Δ^2 is given by the formula

$$\frac{1}{\Delta^2} = -\frac{d^2}{d\hat{\tau}^2}\ln \Lambda(\hat{\tau}) = \frac{1}{2}\mu''(\hat{\tau}) - \varphi''(\tau) - \frac{d^2}{d\hat{\tau}^2}\ln p_m(\hat{\tau}). \tag{52.09}$$

Carrying out the differentiation, we obtain

$$\begin{aligned} \frac{1}{2}\mu''(\tau) &= \sum_{g,h} Q_{gh} m'_g(\tau) m'_h(\tau) + \sum_{g,h} Q_{gh} m_g(\tau) m''_h(\tau), \\ \varphi''(\tau) &= \sum_{g,h} Q_{gh} f_g m''_h(\tau), \end{aligned} \tag{52.10}$$

where we have used the symmetry of the matrix $\| Q_{gh} \|$. Finally, we have

$$\begin{aligned} \frac{1}{\Delta^2} = &\sum_{g,h} Q_{gh} m'_g(\hat{\tau}) m'_h(\hat{\tau}) \\ &- \sum_{g,h} Q_{gh}[f_g - m_g(\hat{\tau})] m''_h(\hat{\tau}) - \frac{d^2}{d\hat{\tau}^2}\ln p_m(\hat{\tau}). \end{aligned} \tag{52.11}$$

Moreover, for $\tau \sim \hat{\tau}$, the likelihood ratio becomes

$$\Lambda(\tau) = \Lambda(\hat{\tau}) e^{-(\tau-\hat{\tau})^2/2\Delta^2}. \tag{52.12}$$

It is interesting to note that in the simple cases considered earlier, the formula (52.12) was exact, and we obtained a Gaussian distribution for any value of $\tau - \hat{\tau}$. In such cases, formula (52.11) becomes simpler, i.e., the second term vanishes $[m_h''(\tau) = 0$, since the useful signal depends linearly on the measured parameter], and the third term is a constant, since the distribution $p_m(\tau)$ is normal and $\ln p_m(\tau)$ is a quadratic function of τ. In the general case, formula (57.12) has limited applicability. However, for sufficiently weak noise, or equivalently, for sufficiently large signal-to-noise ratios, (52.12) gives us practically the whole a posteriori distribution of the quantity τ. This distribution is Gaussian, with mean (and most probable) value $\hat{\tau}$ and variance Δ^2, which in weak noise can be calculated from the formula

$$\Delta^2 = \frac{1}{\sum_{g,h} Q_{gh} m_g'(\hat{\tau}) m_h'(\hat{\tau})}. \tag{52.13}$$

As the noise power is decreased and the signal power is increased, Δ^2 becomes indefinitely small and the Gaussian distribution (52.12) becomes indefinitely "sharp," and hence more exact, since the omitted terms play a smaller and smaller role. The quantity appearing in the denominator of formula (52.13) is always positive [cf. formula (52.26) below] and grows monotonically as the signal amplitude is increased. Therefore, the other terms in the right-hand side of (52.11) can be neglected for sufficiently large signal-to-noise ratios, in the case of the term

$$-\frac{d^2}{d\hat{\tau}^2} \ln p_m(\hat{\tau})$$

because it does not depend on the signal-to-noise ratio, and in the case of the sum

$$\sum_{g,h} Q_{gh}[f_g - m_g(\hat{\tau})] m_h''(\hat{\tau}) \tag{52.14}$$

because under these conditions, the difference $f_g - m_g(\hat{\tau})$ is essentially determined by the noise, and consequently makes a smaller contribution to the quantity $1/\Delta^2$.

Suppose now that the true value of τ is τ_0, so that at the receiver input there appears the function

$$f(t) = m(t, \tau_0) + n(t), \tag{52.15}$$

with sample values

$$f_g = m_g(\tau_0) + n_g. \tag{52.16}$$

Then, what is the relation between the true value τ_0 and the measured value $\hat{\tau}$? In this case, the function (52.02) can be represented in the form

$$\varphi(\tau) = \mu(\tau, \tau_0) + \nu(\tau), \tag{52.17}$$

where

$$\mu(\tau, \tau_0) = \sum_{g,h} Q_{gh} m_g(\tau_0) m_h(\tau) \tag{52.18}$$

and

$$\nu(\tau) = \sum_{g,h} Q_{gh} n_g m_h(\tau). \tag{52.19}$$

It is easily verified that the function (52.18) has the properties

$$\begin{aligned} \mu(\tau, \tau_0) &= \mu(\tau_0, \tau) = \overline{\nu(\tau)\nu(\tau_0)}, \\ \mu(\tau) &= \mu(\tau, \tau) = \overline{\nu^2(\tau)}. \end{aligned} \tag{52.20}$$

For weak noise, the difference $\hat{\tau} - \tau_0$ can be expected to be small. Thus, when $\tau = \hat{\tau}$, in the expression for the derivative

$$\frac{d}{d\tau} \ln \Lambda(\tau) = \frac{\partial \mu(\tau, \tau_0)}{\partial \tau} + \nu'(\tau) - \frac{1}{2}\mu'(\tau) + \frac{d}{d\tau} \ln p_m(\tau), \tag{52.21}$$

we can confine ourselves to the zeroth-order and first-order terms in the Taylor's series of the functions

$$\begin{aligned} \frac{\partial \mu(\tau, \tau_0)}{\partial \tau} &= \sum_{g,h} Q_{gh} m_g(\tau_0) m_h'(\tau) \\ &= \sum_{g,h} Q_{gh} m_g(\tau_0) m_h'(\tau_0) + (\tau - \tau_0) \sum_{g,h} Q_{gh} m_g(\tau_0) m_h''(\tau_0), \\ \frac{1}{2}\mu'(\tau) &= \sum_{g,h} Q_{gh} m_g(\tau) m_h'(\tau) = \sum_{g,h} Q_{gh} m_g(\tau_0) m_h'(\tau_0) \\ &\quad + (\tau - \tau_0)\left[\sum_{g,h} Q_{gh} m_g(\tau_0) m_h''(\tau_0) + \sum_{g,h} Q_{gh} m_g'(\tau_0) m_h'(\tau_0)\right], \\ \frac{d}{d\tau} \ln p_m(\tau) &= \frac{d}{d\tau_0} \ln p_m(\tau_0) + (\tau - \tau_0) \frac{d^2}{d\tau_0^2} \ln p_m(\tau_0), \end{aligned} \tag{52.22}$$

and we can also replace $\nu'(\tau)$ by $\nu'(\tau_0)$. Equating (52.21) to zero for $\tau = \hat{\tau}$, we obtain the expression

$$\hat{\tau} - \tau_0 = \frac{\nu'(\tau_0) + (d/d\tau_0) \ln p_m(\tau_0)}{\sum_{g,h} Q_{gh} m_g'(\tau_0) m_h'(\tau_0) - (d^2/d\tau_0^2) \ln p_m(\tau_0)} \tag{52.23}$$

for the difference $\hat{\tau} - \tau_0$, where

$$\nu'(\tau_0) = \sum_{g,h} Q_{gh} n_g m_h'(\tau_0). \tag{52.24}$$

In the present approximation, the random variable $\hat{\tau}$ is normal, with mean and variance

$$\bar{\hat{\tau}} = \tau_0 + \frac{(d/d\tau_0)\ln p_m(\tau_0)}{\sum_{g,h} Q_{gh} m_g'(\tau_0) m_h'(\tau_0) - (d^2/d\tau_0^2)\ln p_m(\tau_0)},$$

$$\overline{(\hat{\tau} - \bar{\hat{\tau}})^2} = \frac{\sum_{g,h} Q_{gh} m_g'(\tau_0) m_h'(\tau_0)}{\left[\sum_{g,h} Q_{gh} m_g'(\tau_0) m_h'(\tau_0) - (d^2/d\tau_0^2)\ln p_m(\tau_0)\right]^2}, \tag{52.25}$$

since

$$\overline{[\nu'(\tau_0)]^2} = \sum_{g,h} Q_{gh} m_g'(\tau_0) m_h'(\tau_0). \tag{52.26}$$

For sufficiently large signal-to-noise ratios, we can neglect the derivatives of $\ln p_m(\tau_0)$, in comparison with the quantity (52.26). Then we have

$$\bar{\hat{\tau}} = \tau_0, \qquad \overline{(\hat{\tau} - \tau)_0^2} = \Delta^2, \tag{52.27}$$

where the quantity

$$\Delta^2 = \Delta^2(\tau_0) = \frac{1}{\sum_{g,h} Q_{gh} m_g'(\tau_0) m_h'(\tau_0)} \tag{52.28}$$

is practically the same as the quantity (52.13). Then, the conditional distribution of the quantity $\hat{\tau}$ is given by the normal law

$$p_{\tau_0}(\hat{\tau}) = \frac{1}{\sqrt{2\pi}\,\Delta} e^{-(\hat{\tau}-\tau_0)^2/2\Delta^2}, \tag{52.29}$$

with the same variance as in (52.12).

As the signal-to-noise ratio is decreased, the relations derived above become less accurate, and for sufficiently strong noise, they give results which are not even qualitatively correct. For strong noise, it is appropriate to characterize the quality of a measurement by the probability that the value $\hat{\tau}$, which is measured in any way, differs from the true value τ_0 by more than ε in absolute value. This probability equals

$$\begin{aligned} P(|\hat{\tau} - \tau_0| > \varepsilon) &= P(\hat{\tau} > \tau_0 + \varepsilon) + P(\hat{\tau} < \tau_0 - \varepsilon) \\ &= \int P_{\tau_0}(\hat{\tau} > \tau_0 + \varepsilon) p_m(\tau_0)\, d\tau_0 \\ &\quad + \int P_{\tau_0}(\hat{\tau} < \tau_0 - \varepsilon) p_m(\tau_0)\, d\tau_0, \end{aligned} \tag{52.30}$$

where $P_{\tau_0}(\hat{\tau} > \tau_0 + \varepsilon)$ is the probability of the event $\hat{\tau} > \tau_0 + \varepsilon$, given that the true value of the parameter τ equals τ_0. In writing formula (52.30), we have used the expression (29.04) for the total probability. Going over to the variable $\tau = \tau_0 + \varepsilon$ in the first integral and to the variable $\tau = \tau_0 - \varepsilon$ in the second integral, we obtain

$$P(|\hat{\tau} - \tau_0| > \varepsilon) = \int [P_{\tau-\varepsilon}(\hat{\tau} > \tau)p_m(\tau - \varepsilon) + P_{\tau+\varepsilon}(\hat{\tau} < \tau)p_m(\tau + \varepsilon)]\, d\tau. \tag{52.31}$$

From now on, we confine ourselves to the case where the a priori probability distribution $p_m(\tau)$ is rectangular:

$$p_m(\tau) = \frac{1}{T} \quad \text{for} \quad 0 < \tau < T, \qquad p_m(\tau) = 0 \quad \text{for} \quad \tau < 0 \quad \text{and} \quad \tau > T. \tag{52.32}$$

This can always be achieved by making a suitable change of variables. The functions $p_m(\tau)$, $p_m(\tau - \varepsilon)$ and $p_m(\tau + \varepsilon)$ are shown in Fig. 51. If in the integral (52.31), we restrict the range of integration to the interval $\varepsilon < \tau < T - \varepsilon$, then, since the integrand is positive, we can only decrease the value of the integral, and hence

$$P(|\hat{\tau} - \tau_0| > \varepsilon) \geqslant \frac{1}{T}\int_{\varepsilon}^{T-\varepsilon} [P_{\tau-\varepsilon}(\hat{\tau} > \tau) + P_{\tau+\varepsilon}(\hat{\tau} < \tau)]\, d\tau. \tag{52.33}$$

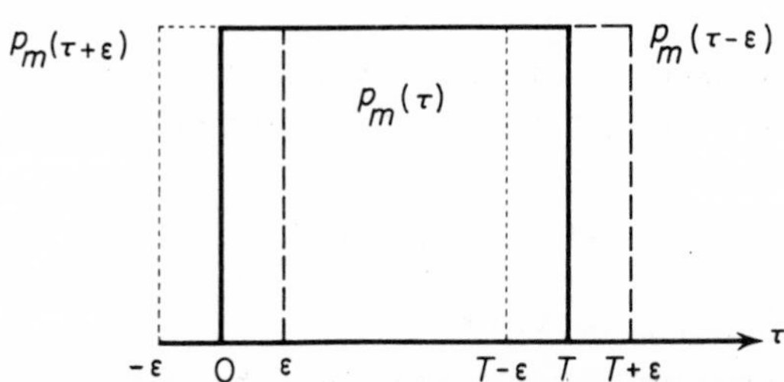

FIG. 51. Rectangular a priori distribution of the parameter τ.

We can derive the following inequality for the integral in (52.33):

$$\tfrac{1}{2}[P_{\tau-\varepsilon}(\hat{\tau} > \tau) + P_{\tau+\varepsilon}(\hat{\tau} < \tau)] \geqslant F[\tfrac{1}{2}\sqrt{\mu_\varepsilon(\tau)}], \tag{52.34}$$

where

$$F(z_*) = \frac{1}{\sqrt{2\pi}}\int_{z_*}^{\infty} e^{-z^2/2}\, dz \tag{52.35}$$

is the false alarm probability for simple detection, corresponding to the normalized threshold z_* [cf. formula (31.34)], and

$$\mu_\varepsilon(\tau) = \sum_{g,h} Q_{gh}[m_g(\tau + \varepsilon) - m_g(\tau - \varepsilon)][m_h(\tau + \varepsilon) - m_h(\tau - \varepsilon)] = \mu(\tau + \varepsilon) + \mu(\tau - \varepsilon) - 2\mu(\tau + \varepsilon, \tau - \varepsilon) \tag{52.36}$$

is the signal-to-noise ratio for the problem of detecting the useful "difference" signal

$$m_\varepsilon(t, \tau) = m(t, \tau + \varepsilon) - m(t, \tau - \varepsilon),$$

with sample values (52.37)

$$m_{\varepsilon h}(\tau) = m_h(\tau + \varepsilon) - m_h(\tau - \varepsilon)$$

in a background of correlated normal noise.

The inequality (52.34) is proved as follows: Suppose that in the presence of noise one of the signals $m(t, \tau + \varepsilon)$ or $m(t, \tau - \varepsilon)$ is received, where the a priori probability of each of the two signals is $\frac{1}{2}$. The optimum receiver for resolving (i.e., distinguishing between) the two mutually exclusive cases

$$f(t) = m(t, \tau + \varepsilon) + n(t), \qquad f(t) = m(t, \tau - \varepsilon) + n(t) \tag{52.38}$$

is essentially the optimum receiver for detecting the difference signal (52.37) in the known difference function

$$\tilde{f}(t) = f(t) - m(t, \tau - \varepsilon). \tag{52.39}$$

This receiver is uniquely determined, for example, by specifying the false alarm probability F or the threshold z_* in formula (52.35), but the detection probability D still depends on the parameter (52.36). The total probability of making the correct decision is given by formula (30.11), and V, the total probability of error when both signals are equally likely, is given by

$$V = 1 - W = \frac{1}{2}(1 - D + F), \tag{52.40}$$

and depends on F.

The derivative

$$\frac{\partial V}{\partial F} = \frac{1}{2}\left(-\frac{\partial D}{\partial F} + 1\right) \quad \text{for} \quad \mu_\varepsilon(\tau) = \text{const} \tag{52.41}$$

vanishes if the condition

$$\frac{\partial D}{\partial F} = \Lambda_* = 1 \tag{52.42}$$

[cf. formula (31.39)]; this can easily be seen to correspond to a minimum of V. Bearing in mind the relation

$$\Lambda_* = e^{\varphi_* - \frac{1}{2}\mu_\varepsilon(\tau)}, \tag{52.43}$$

we see that to achieve the minimum value of V, we have to put

$$\varphi_* = \frac{1}{2}\mu_\varepsilon(\tau), \qquad z_* = \frac{1}{2}\sqrt{\mu_\varepsilon(\tau)} \tag{52.44}$$

in (31.34). Then, formula (31.35) becomes

$$\begin{aligned} D &= \frac{1}{\sqrt{2\pi}} \int_{-\sqrt{\mu_\varepsilon(\tau)}/2}^{\infty} e^{-z^2/2}\, dz \\ &= 1 - \frac{1}{\sqrt{2\pi}} \int_{\sqrt{\mu_\varepsilon(\tau)}/2}^{\infty} e^{-z^2/2}\, dz = 1 - F, \end{aligned} \tag{52.45}$$

so that finally

$$V_{\min} = F[\tfrac{1}{2}\sqrt{\mu_\varepsilon(\tau)}]. \tag{52.46}$$

The left-hand side of the inequality (52.34) equals the total probability of error of a receiver which resolves the signals $m(t, \tau - \varepsilon)$ and $m(t, \tau + \varepsilon)$ by measuring the parameter τ, and deciding that the first signal has been received if $\hat{\tau}$, the measured value of the parameter, is less than τ, and that the second signal has been received if $\hat{\tau} > \tau$. Since such a method for resolving the two signals is nonoptimum, and in any event cannot lead to a probability of error less than (52.46), we finally obtain the inequality (52.34).[1]

Formulas (52.33) and (52.34) lead to the inequality

$$P(|\hat{\tau} - \tau_0| > \varepsilon) \geqslant \frac{2}{T} \int_\varepsilon^{T-\varepsilon} F[\tfrac{1}{2}\sqrt{\mu_\varepsilon(\tau)}]\, d\tau, \tag{52.47}$$

which relates the probability of error for measuring the parameter τ with the false alarm probability for detecting the difference signal (52.37). For sufficiently small ε, we can set

$$m_h(\tau + \varepsilon) - m_h(\tau - \varepsilon) = 2\varepsilon m_h'(\tau), \tag{52.48}$$

so that the quantity (52.36) is approximately equal to

$$\mu_\varepsilon(\tau) = \frac{4\varepsilon^2}{\Delta^2(\tau)}, \qquad \frac{1}{2}\sqrt{\mu_\varepsilon(\tau)} = \frac{\varepsilon}{\Delta(\tau)}, \tag{52.49}$$

where $\Delta^2(\tau)$ is given by (52.28). Therefore, the right-hand side of formula (52.45) equals

$$\begin{aligned} \frac{2}{T} \int_\varepsilon^{T-\varepsilon} F[\tfrac{1}{2}\sqrt{\mu_\varepsilon(\tau)}]\, d\tau &= \frac{2}{T} \int_\varepsilon^{T-\varepsilon} F\left(\frac{\varepsilon}{\Delta(\tau)}\right) d\tau \\ &\sim \frac{2}{T} \int_0^{T} F\left(\frac{\varepsilon}{\Delta(\tau)}\right) d\tau. \end{aligned} \tag{52.50}$$

---

[1] Formula (52.46) corresponds to the so-called *ideal observer*, providing the maximum value of W (and the minimum value of $V = 1 - W$). In Chap. 5 (see end of Sec. 30), we noted that the ideal observer is equivalent to the optimum receiver for detection, with false alarm probability F corresponding to the maximum value of W. A rigorous proof that such an optimum receiver gives the absolute maximum of W can be found in Appendix I.

If the noise is sufficiently weak and if the measurement is based on the maximum likelihood ratio, then by using the distribution (52.29), we find that the conditional probability of error, given the value of τ_0, equals

$$P_{\tau_0}(|\hat{\tau} - \tau_0| > \varepsilon) = \frac{2}{\sqrt{2\pi}\,\Delta(\tau_0)} \int_\varepsilon^\infty e^{-x^2/2\Delta^2(\tau_0)}\,dx$$
$$= \frac{2}{\sqrt{2\pi}} \int_{\varepsilon/\Delta(\tau_0)}^\infty e^{-z^2/2}\,dz = 2F\left(\frac{\varepsilon}{\Delta(\tau_0)}\right), \tag{52.51}$$

and the total probability of error equals

$$P(|\hat{\tau} - \tau_0| > \varepsilon) = \frac{2}{T}\int_0^T F\left(\frac{\varepsilon}{\Delta(\tau_0)}\right)d\tau_0. \tag{52.52}$$

Comparing (52.52) with (52.47) and (52.50), we see that if the measurement is based on the likelihood ratio, then, for small errors ε and weak noise, the inequality sign in (52.47) can be changed to an equality. The receiver making such a measurement is optimum in the sense that it guarantees the minimum probability of error $P(|\hat{\tau} - \tau_0| > \varepsilon)$. In other cases, formula (52.47) gives in general only a lower bound for the measurement error, and the actual probability of error $P(|\hat{\tau} - \tau_0| > \varepsilon)$ can be considerably larger than its minimum value (cf. the end of Sec. 56).

53. Simple Measurement of the Arrival Time of a Signal in Weak Noise

One of the methods most commonly used in radar for measuring the unknown coordinates of a target is to measure the arrival time of a signal reflected from the target. Thus, in this and subsequent sections, we shall consider the problem of measuring the arrival time τ of a signal, assuming that the dependence of the useful signal on τ is given by

$$m(t, \tau) = m(t - \tau), \tag{53.01}$$

where we neglect the possible dependence of the signal amplitude on τ. For simplicity, we also assume that the a priori probability distribution of the parameter τ is rectangular [see formula (52.32)].

The parameter τ introduced in this way has many special features which simplify both the theoretical investigation of measurement possibilities and the practical implementation of the optimum receiver for measurement. In fact, in the present case, formula (52.02) can be written as

$$\varphi(\tau) = \sum_g k_g(\tau) f_g, \tag{53.02}$$

where

$$k_g(\tau) = \sum_h Q_{gh} m_h(\tau) = \sum_h Q_{gh} m(t_h - \tau). \tag{53.03}$$

This last formula is the result of solving the system of linear algebraic equations

$$\sum_h R_{gh}k_h(\tau) = m(t_g - \tau) \qquad (g, h = 1, 2, \ldots, H), \tag{53.04}$$

for the coefficients $k_g(\tau)$, where

$$R_{gh} = R(t_g - t_h) \tag{53.05}$$

for stationary noise.

Thus, we can write the coefficients $k_g(\tau)$ in the form

$$k_g(\tau) = k(\tau - t_g)\,\Delta t, \tag{53.06}$$

and the expression (53.02) becomes

$$\varphi(\tau) = \Delta t \sum_g k(\tau - t_g)f_g, \tag{53.07}$$

which is essentially the same as formula (26.47). If the interval of observation is infinite, then the function $\varphi(\tau)$ can be obtained as the process at the output of a filter with the transfer function (27.10), where the parameter τ plays the role of an actual (physical) time. Essentially the same results are obtained if the observations are made during a finite time interval which contains all the signals from the earliest signal $m(t)$ to the latest signal $m(t - T)$, and which moreover has extra intervals at either end, with length given by the correlation time of the noise (cf. the end of Sec. 27). In other cases, one has to solve the system of equations (53.04), or the corresponding integral equation, but formula (53.07) remains valid, so that $\varphi(\tau)$ can be produced (as a function of time) by some linear filter.

Similarly, the random function $\nu(\tau)$ defined by formula (52.19) can be represented in the form

$$\nu(\tau) = \Delta t \sum_g k(\tau - t_g)n(t_g), \tag{53.08}$$

which can be regarded as the result of passing the noise $n(t)$ through the filter just considered, with impulse response $k(\tau)$. It is easy to see that $\nu(\tau)$ is a stationary random process, whose autocorrelation function

$$\mu(\tau, \tau_0) = \overline{\nu(\tau)\nu(\tau_0)} \tag{53.09}$$

is an even function of the difference $\tau - \tau_0$. Therefore, in the present case, we have

$$\mu(\tau, \tau_0) = \mu(\tau - \tau_0) = \mu(\tau_0 - \tau). \tag{53.10}$$

Moreover, we have the inequality

$$|\mu(\tau - \tau_0)| \leqslant \mu, \tag{53.11}$$

where the parameter $\mu = \mu(0)$ is the effective signal-to-noise ratio (which is independent of τ) already introduced in Sec. 31. The quantity $\mu_\varepsilon(\tau)$ introduced in formula (52.36) is also independent of τ, and can be written simply as

$$\mu_\varepsilon = 2[\mu - \mu(2\varepsilon)]. \tag{53.12}$$

Assuming that the difference $\tau - \tau_0$ is sufficiently small, and bearing in mind that $\mu(\tau - \tau_0)$ is an even function, we can write the expression

$$\mu(\tau - \tau_0) = \mu[1 - \tfrac{1}{2}(\delta\omega)^2(\tau - \tau_0)^2], \tag{53.13}$$

where the parameter $\delta\omega$, which has the dimension of a frequency, is defined by the formula

$$(\delta\omega)^2 = -\frac{\mu''(0)}{\mu(0)} = \frac{1}{\mu}\frac{\partial^2}{\partial\tau\partial\tau_0}\mu(\tau - \tau_0)\Big|_{\tau=\tau_0} \tag{53.14}$$

or, in explicit form, by

$$(\delta\omega)^2 = \frac{\sum\limits_{g,h} Q_{gh}m'(t_g)m'(t_h)}{\sum\limits_{g,h} Q_{gh}m(t_g)m(t_h)}. \tag{53.15}$$

The quantity Δ introduced in Sec. 52 equals

$$\Delta = \frac{1}{\delta\omega\sqrt{\mu}}. \tag{53.16}$$

Δ does not depend on τ and defines the variance of the random variable $\hat{\tau}$, the value of the parameter τ measured by using the maximum likelihood ratio [cf. formulas (52.28) and (52.29)].

We now explain the meaning of the parameter $\delta\omega$. For uncorrelated noise, we have

$$(\delta\omega)^2 = \frac{\sum\limits_h [m'(t_h)]^2}{\sum\limits_h m^2(t_h)} = \frac{\int_{-\pi/\Delta t}^{\pi/\Delta t} \omega^2|M(\omega)|^2\,d\omega}{\int_{-\pi/\Delta t}^{\pi/\Delta t} |M(\omega)|^2\,d\omega}, \tag{53.17}$$

so that $\delta\omega$ is defined by the shape of the useful signal and characterizes the bandwidth occupied by the signal. However, the parameter $\delta\omega$ differs from the bandwidth $\Delta\omega$, defined by formula (3.30). The two parameters often have the same order of magnitude, and then the order of magnitude of $\delta\omega$ is equal to $1/T_0$, where T_0 is the duration of the useful signal [see formulas (53.23) and (53.25) below, for bell-shaped and triangular pulses]. However, in some cases of great practical interest, $\delta\omega$ can be considerably greater than $\Delta\omega$ and $1/T_0$ [see formula (53.29) below].

Since the expressions (52.22) and (53.13) for $\mu(\tau, \tau_0)$ are valid only under the condition

$$\delta\omega(\tau - \tau_0) \sim \delta\omega\, \Delta \ll 1, \tag{53.18}$$

then the formula (53.16) obtained above is valid only under the conditions

$$\mu \gg 1, \qquad \Delta \ll T_0, \tag{53.19}$$

so that what has just been said pertains to exact measurements of the parameter τ in the presence of weak noise. As μ is decreased, the quantity Δ increases, and starting from a certain value of μ, formula (53.16) becomes unsuitable. In fact, we can use the applicability of formulas (52.22) or (53.13) for $|\tau - \tau_0| \sim \Delta$ to define a lower bound for "large" values of the parameter μ, values for which formula (53.16) is still valid. In any case, the applicability of formulas (52.22) or (53.13) is a necessary condition for being able to regard the noise as weak.

If the noise is correlated, then instead of formula (53.17), we have

$$(\delta\omega)^2 = \frac{\displaystyle\int_{-\pi/\Delta t}^{\pi/\Delta t} \frac{\omega^2\, |M(\omega)|^2}{S_n(\omega)}\, d\omega}{\displaystyle\int_{-\pi/\Delta t}^{\pi/\Delta t} \frac{|M(\omega)|^2}{S_n(\omega)}\, d\omega}, \tag{53.20}$$

so that $\delta\omega$ depends on the shape of the noise spectrum. The quantity $\delta\omega$ can be called the "mean square" bandwidth of the useful signal at the input of the optimum linear filter which we considered earlier, in Sec. 27.

Finally, we consider some special cases of measurement of the arrival time τ of a useful signal in a background of uncorrelated (white) noise with constant spectral density S_n, by using the function $f(t)$, which is known for a certain time interval. In this case, the quantity $\delta\omega$ can be calculated from the formula

$$(\delta\omega)^2 = \frac{\displaystyle\int_{-\infty}^{\infty} [m'(t)]^2\, dt}{\displaystyle\int_{-\infty}^{\infty} m^2(t)\, dt}. \tag{53.21}$$

For the bell-shaped (Gaussian) pulse

$$m(t) = ae^{-t^2/2\beta^2} \tag{53.22}$$

(where a and β are constants), we obtain

$$\delta\omega = \frac{1}{\sqrt{2}\beta}, \tag{53.23}$$

while for the triangular pulse

$$m(t) = a\left(1 - \frac{2|t|}{T_0}\right) \quad \text{for} \quad |t| \leqslant \frac{T_0}{2},$$
$$m(t) = 0 \quad \text{for} \quad |t| > \frac{T_0}{2}, \tag{53.24}$$

we have

$$\delta\omega = \frac{2\sqrt{3}}{T_0}. \tag{53.25}$$

For the rectangular pulse

$$m(t) = a \quad \text{for} \quad |t| < \frac{T_0}{2},$$
$$m(t) = 0 \quad \text{for} \quad |t| > \frac{T_0}{2}, \tag{53.26}$$

the quantity $\delta\omega$ turns out to be infinite, since the derivative $m'(t)$ is infinite for $t = \pm T_0/2$. Therefore, the quantity Δ in formula (53.16) is zero. This testifies to the fact that the considerations of Sec. 52 are not applicable to rectangular pulses, since they are too drastic an idealization of actual radar signals, which have steep (but not infinitely steep) sides. In fact, for a rectangular pulse, the function $\mu(\tau - \tau_0)$ equals

$$\mu(\tau - \tau_0) = \mu\left[1 - \frac{|\tau - \tau_0|}{T_0}\right] \quad \text{for} \quad |\tau - \tau_0| \leqslant T_0$$
$$\mu(\tau - \tau_0) = 0 \quad \text{for} \quad |\tau - \tau_0| \geqslant T_0, \quad \text{where} \quad \mu = \frac{a^2 T_0}{S_n} \tag{53.27}$$

(cf. Sec. 20), so that the expansion (53.13) is not valid for such a signal.

To analyze this situation in more detail, we consider the trapezoidal pulse

$$m(t) = a \quad \text{for} \quad |t| \leqslant \frac{T_0}{2},$$
$$m(t) = a\frac{1 + \gamma - (2|t|/T_0)}{\gamma} \quad \text{for} \quad \frac{T_0}{2} \leqslant |t| \leqslant (1 + \gamma)\frac{T_0}{2}, \tag{53.28}$$
$$m(t) = 0 \quad \text{for} \quad |t| \geqslant (1 + \gamma)\frac{T_0}{2}$$

(see Fig. 52), for which

$$\delta\omega = \frac{2}{\sqrt{\gamma[1 + (\gamma/3)]}T_0} \sim \frac{2}{\sqrt{\gamma}T_0} \quad \text{for} \quad \gamma \ll 1. \tag{53.29}$$

Calculating the function $\mu(\tau - \tau_0)$ for the various pulses, we can assess the applicability of the approximate formula (53.13). The bell-shaped pulse (53.22) gives

$$\mu(\tau - \tau_0) = \mu e^{-(\tau-\tau_0)^2/4\beta^2}, \quad \text{where} \quad \mu = \frac{\sqrt{\pi}a^2\beta}{S_n}, \tag{53.30}$$

and the triangular pulse gives

$$\begin{aligned} \mu(\tau - \tau_0) &= \mu\left[1 - 6\frac{(\tau-\tau_0)^2}{T_0^2} + 6\frac{|\tau-\tau_0|^3}{T_0^3}\right] \quad \text{for} \quad |\tau - \tau_0| \leqslant \frac{T_0}{2}, \\ \mu(\tau - \tau_0) &= 2\mu\left[1 - \frac{|\tau-\tau_0|}{T_0}\right]^3 \quad \text{for} \quad \frac{T_0}{2} \leqslant |\tau - \tau_0| \leqslant T_0, \\ \mu(\tau - \tau_0) &= 0 \quad \text{for} \quad |\tau - \tau_0| \geqslant T_0, \quad \text{where} \quad \mu = \frac{a^2T_0}{3S_n}. \end{aligned} \tag{53.31}$$

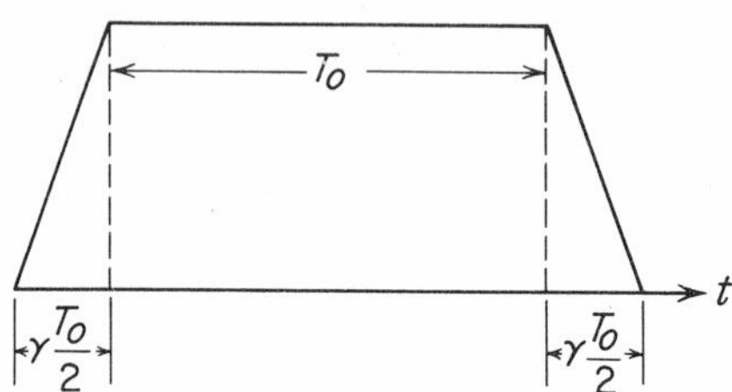

FIG. 52. A trapezoidal pulse.

Thus, the expression (53.13) is valid only under the condition

$$(\tau - \tau_0)^2 \ll 4\beta^2 \tag{53.32}$$

for the bell-shaped pulse, and under the condition

$$|\tau - \tau_0| \ll T_0 \tag{53.33}$$

for the triangular pulse. Since the parameter β defines the effective duration of the bell-shaped pulse, the two conditions (53.32) and (53.33) are essentially equivalent, and reduce to the relations (53.18) and (53.19).

For the trapezoidal pulse (53.28), we obtain

$$\begin{aligned} \mu(\tau - \tau_0) &= \mu\left[1 - \frac{2(\tau-\tau_0)^2}{\gamma[1 + (\gamma/3)]T_0^2} + \frac{4|\tau-\tau_0|^3}{3\gamma^2[1 + (\gamma/3)]T_0^3}\right] \\ &\qquad \text{for} \quad |\tau - \tau_0| \leqslant \gamma\frac{T_0}{2}, \\ \mu(\tau - \tau_0) &= \mu\left[\frac{1 + (\gamma/2)}{1 + (\gamma/3)} - \frac{|\tau-\tau_0|}{[1 + (\gamma/3)]T_0}\right] \\ &\qquad \text{for} \quad \frac{\gamma T_0}{2} \leqslant |\tau - \tau_0| \leqslant T_0, \\ &\qquad \cdots\cdots\cdots\cdots \\ \mu(\tau - \tau_0) &= 0 \quad \text{for} \quad |\tau - \tau_0| \geqslant (1 + \gamma)T_0, \\ &\qquad \text{where} \quad \mu = \frac{[1 + (\gamma/3)]a^2T_0}{S_n}, \end{aligned} \tag{53.34}$$

so that the expression (53.13) is applicable only if

$$|\tau - \tau_0| \ll \frac{\gamma T_0}{2}, \tag{53.35}$$

and for $\gamma T_0/2 \leqslant |\tau - \tau_0| \leqslant T_0$ and $\gamma \ll 1$, the function (53.34) is practically the same as the expression (53.27) for the rectangular pulse.

We can now appraise the possibilities of measuring the arrival time of a trapezoidal pulse with quite steep sides, i.e., with a quite small value of γ. Since, according to formulas (53.16) and (53.29), the error in measuring the arrival time is given by the quantity

$$\Delta = \frac{1}{2}\sqrt{\gamma/\mu}\,T_0 = \frac{\sqrt{S_n\gamma T_0}}{2a} \quad \text{for} \quad \gamma \ll 1, \tag{53.36}$$

we actually have $\Delta \to 0$ as $\gamma \to 0$. However, formula (53.16) is valid only under the condition

$$\Delta = \frac{1}{2}\sqrt{\gamma/\mu}\,T_0 \ll \frac{\gamma T_0}{2}, \tag{53.37}$$

which can be written in the form

$$\mu \gg \frac{1}{\gamma}, \quad \text{or} \quad \frac{a^2}{S_n} \gg \frac{1}{\gamma T_0}. \tag{53.38}$$

Thus, if the edge of the transmitted signal is made steeper, so that the quantity $\delta\omega$ becomes smaller, we need to make the measurement with larger values of the parameter μ (the signal-to-noise ratio) in order to obtain the mean square error (53.36).

It is clear from this example that the use of long signals, satisfying the condition $\delta\omega \gg 1/T_0$ allows us to increase the accuracy of measurement of the arrival time (which determines the target range in radar). However, a too drastic increase of the quantity $\delta\omega$ (for given T_0 and μ) may not lead to the desired increase in accuracy, since formula (53.16) is valid only under certain conditions.

This result is a special case of a proposition proved by V. A. Kotelnikov, by examining various different ways of modulating signals. The smaller the probability of making small errors in the presence of weak noise, "the lower the noise intensity at which the boundary between 'strong' and 'weak' noise occurs, and the formulas which we have derived are not valid for 'strong' noise. In the limit, the methods presented here allow one to reduce to zero the error resulting from the action of 'weak' noise, but at the same time, 'weak' noise comes to mean noise with an intensity which is itself equal to zero. Thus, we cannot succeed in completely nullifying the action of noise by these methods, as might otherwise be expected; we can only obtain a reduction of its effect. This reduction is worthwhile for communication in the presence of noise with sufficiently low intensity, when it is necessary to have very few errors."[2]

54. Composite Measurement of the Arrival Time of a Signal in Weak Noise

In the preceding treatment, we did not take into account the fact that the useful signal $m(t - \tau)$, whose arrival time τ we have to measure, has the character of an r-f signal which can be written in the form

$$m(t - \tau) = e(t - \tau) \cos [\omega_0(t - \tau) - \psi(t - \tau) - \theta], \qquad (54.01)$$

where ω_0 is the carrier frequency, $e(t)$ is the envelope, $\psi(t)$ is the slowly varying (supplementary) phase, and θ is the initial phase. The function

$$\begin{aligned} \varphi(\tau) &= \sum_{g,h} Q_{gh} f_g m_h(\tau) \\ &= \sum_{g,h} Q_{gh} f_g e(t_h - \tau) \cos [\omega_0(t_h - \tau) - \psi(t - \tau) - \theta] \end{aligned} \qquad (54.02)$$

is of the same character, and can be written in the form

$$\varphi(\tau) = \mathscr{E}(\tau) \cos [\omega_0 \tau - \Phi(\tau) + \theta], \qquad (54.03)$$

where

$$\begin{aligned} \mathscr{E}(\tau) \cos \Phi(\tau) &= \sum_{g,h} Q_{gh} f_g e(t_h - \tau) \cos [\omega_0 t_h - \psi(t_h - \tau)], \\ \mathscr{E}(\tau) \sin \Phi(\tau) &= \sum_{g,h} Q_{gh} f_g e(t_h - \tau) \sin [\omega_0 t_h - \psi(t_h - \tau)], \end{aligned} \qquad (54.04)$$

where $\mathscr{E}(\tau)$ and $\Phi(\tau)$ are slowly varying functions (compared to the r-f phase $\omega_0 \tau$).

In principle, the optimum device for precise measurement allows us to measure the arrival time to within a fraction of a carrier period (equal to $2\pi/\omega_0$). This requires that we measure the initial phase θ of the useful signal. However, in the majority of cases, detailed information on the delay associated with the phase θ is unnecessary, so that θ can be regarded as an unknown parameter, which is uniformly distributed from 0 to 2π. Thus, we arrive at a problem of composite measurement of the parameter τ in the presence of a random (unknown) parameter θ. Then, the likelihood ratio $\Lambda(\tau)$ turns out to be

$$\Lambda(\tau) = p_m(\tau) e^{-\mu/2} I_0[\mathscr{E}(\tau)], \qquad (54.05)$$

(cf. Sec. 33). When $p_m(\tau)$ has the rectangular a priori distribution (52.32),

[2] V. A. Kotelnikov, *The Theory of Optimum Noise Immunity*, translated by R. A. Silverman, McGraw-Hill, New York (1959). See p. 89.

and when μ is independent of τ, the optimum receiver for composite measurement has to give as its output the number $\hat{\tau}$ (the measured value of τ) corresponding to the maximum of the function

$$\begin{aligned}\mathscr{E}(\tau) = &\left\{\sum_{g,h} Q_{gh} f_g e(t_h - \tau) \cos [\omega_0 t_h - \psi(t_h - \tau)]\right\}^2 \\ &+ \left\{\sum_{g,h} Q_{gh} f_g e(t_h - \tau) \sin [\omega_0 t_h - \psi(t_h - \tau)]\right\}^2.\end{aligned} \tag{54.06}$$

Suppose now that the given values of f_g are equal to

$$f_g = e(t_g - \tau_0) \cos [\omega_0(t_g - \tau_0) - \psi(t_g - \tau_0) - \theta_0] + n_g, \tag{54.07}$$

where τ_0 is the true arrival time of the useful signal, θ_0 is its phase, and the n_g are the sample values of the noise at the times t_g. Neglecting sums of the rapidly oscillating terms proportional to

$$\begin{aligned}&\cos [\omega_0(t_g + t_h) - \psi(t_g - \tau_0) - \psi(t_h - \tau)], \\ &\sin [\omega_0(t_g + t_h) - \psi(t_g - \tau_0) - \psi(t_h - \tau)]\end{aligned} \tag{54.08}$$

(as in Sec. 33), we can transform (54.06), without omitting any other terms, into the form

$$\begin{aligned}\mathscr{E}^2(\tau) = &\left\{M \cos (\omega_0 \tau_0 - \Psi + \theta_0)\right. \\ &\left.+ \sum_{g,h} Q_{gh} n_g e(t_h - \tau) \cos [\omega_0 t_h - \psi(t_h - \tau)]\right\}^2 \\ &+ \left\{M \sin (\omega_0 \tau_0 - \Psi + \theta_0)\right. \\ &\left.+ \sum_{g,h} Q_{gh} n_g e(t_h - \tau) \sin [\omega_0 t_h - \psi(t_h - \tau)]\right\}^2,\end{aligned} \tag{54.09}$$

where the quantities M and Ψ are defined by the relations

$$\begin{aligned}M \cos \Psi &= \frac{1}{2} \sum_{g,h} Q_{gh} e(t_g - \tau_0) e(t_h - \tau) \\ &\qquad \times \cos [\omega_0(t_g - t_h) - \psi(t_g - \tau_0) + \psi(t_h - \tau)], \\ M \sin \Psi &= \frac{1}{2} \sum_{g,h} Q_{gh} e(t_g - \tau_0) e(t_h - \tau) \\ &\qquad \times \sin [\omega_0(t_g - t_h) - \psi(t_g - \tau_0) + \psi(t_h - \tau)].\end{aligned} \tag{54.10}$$

It is not hard to show (cf. Sec. 53) that $M = M(\tau - \tau_0)$ and $\Psi = \Psi(\tau - \tau_0)$, where M is an even function of $\tau - \tau_0$ and Ψ is an odd function of $\tau - \tau_0$, and moreover that

$$\mu = M(0). \tag{54.11}$$

If the parameter μ is large (i.e., if the noise is sufficiently weak), then the first term in each of the braces in (54.09) is as a rule much larger than the second term (i.e., the sum due to the noise sample values n_g). Therefore, the squares of these latter terms can be neglected in forming the squares of the sums in braces. As a result, we obtain

$$\mathscr{E}^2(\tau) = M^2(\tau - \tau_0) + 2M(\tau - \tau_0)N(\tau, \tau_0), \tag{54.12}$$

where

$$N(\tau, \tau_0) = \sum_{g,h} Q_{gh} n_g e(t_h - \tau) \cos [\omega_0 t_h - \psi(t_h - \tau) - \omega_0\tau_0 + \Psi - \theta_0]. \tag{54.13}$$

If in calculating the square root of the right-hand side of (54.12), we neglect terms of order N^2/M^2 compared to the terms which are retained, i.e., if we make the same approximation as was made in writing formula (54.12) itself, then we obtain

$$\mathscr{E}(\tau) = M(\tau - \tau_0) + N(\tau, \tau_0). \tag{54.14}$$

This can be described by saying that for sufficiently large signal-to-noise ratios, the expression for the envelope $\mathscr{E}(t)$ becomes "linearized," i.e., can be represented as the sum of the useful signal M and the noise N.

To avoid complications, we confine ourselves to the simplest case, where the noise is white, so that

$$Q_{gh} = \frac{1}{R_n(0)}\,\delta_{gh}. \tag{54.15}$$

In this case, the formulas (54.10) give

$$M(\tau - \tau_0) = \frac{1}{2R_n(0)} \sum_h e(t_h - \tau_0)\, e(t_h - \tau), \tag{54.16}$$

if we make the additional assumption that there is no frequency or phase modulation $[\psi(t) \equiv 0]$. From formula (54.13), we easily find that

$$\overline{\left[\frac{\partial N(\tau, \tau_0)}{\partial \tau}\right]^2} = \frac{1}{2R_n(0)} \sum_h [e'(t_h - \tau_0)]^2 \quad \text{for} \quad \tau = \tau_0. \tag{54.17}$$

Using the approximate expression

$$M(\tau - \tau_0) = \mu[1 - \tfrac{1}{2}(\delta\omega)^2(\tau - \tau_0)^2], \tag{54.18}$$

where

$$(\delta\omega)^2 = \frac{\sum\limits_h [e'(t_h - \tau_0)]^2}{\sum\limits_h e^2(t_h - \tau_0)}, \tag{54.19}$$

we obtain, as in Secs. 52 and 53, the expression

$$\Delta = \frac{1}{\delta\omega\sqrt{\mu}} \tag{54.20}$$

where Δ^2 is the variance of the measured value τ; this expression is essentially equivalent to formula (53.16).

In the preceding section, we assumed that the useful signal was a video pulse, e.g., a bell-shaped, triangular or trapezoidal pulse, which does not modulate an r-f carrier. The relations derived above show that if the useful signal is an r-f pulse without phase or frequency modulation, then for large values of μ, measurement of its arrival time reduces to measurement of the arrival time of the video pulse $e(t - \tau)/\sqrt{2}$, where $e(t - \tau)$ is the envelope of the r-f pulse. This extends the results of Sec. 53 to the case of radar measurements of range and azimuth by using the arrival times of r-f pulses.

55. Measurement of the Arrival Time of a Signal in Arbitrary Noise

The inequality (52.47) derived earlier for simple measurement of any parameter, simplifies in the case where τ is the arrival time of the useful signal, since then the quantity μ_ε does not depend on τ and is given by formula (53.12):

$$\mu_\varepsilon = 2[\mu - \mu(2\varepsilon)]. \tag{55.01}$$

In this case, the integral in the right-hand side of (52.47) is trivial, and we obtain

$$P(|\hat{\tau} - \tau_0| > \varepsilon) \geqslant \left(1 - \frac{2\varepsilon}{T}\right)A, \tag{55.02}$$

where

$$A = 2F(\tfrac{1}{2}\sqrt{\mu_\varepsilon}) = \frac{2}{\sqrt{2\pi}}\int_{\sqrt{\mu_\varepsilon}/2}^{\infty} e^{-z^2/2}\,dz \tag{55.03}$$

is twice the minimum probability of error of an ideal receiver resolving two equally likely signals $m(t, \tau + \varepsilon)$ and $m(t, \tau - \varepsilon)$, i.e., detecting the difference signal (52.37).

In Sec. 52, we showed that for small ε and weak noise, the inequality sign in (55.02) can be changed to an equality, in the case of a simple measurement made by using the likelihood ratio. In strong noise, when the signal-to-noise ratio is sufficiently small, $F \sim \frac{1}{2}$ and $A \sim 1$, and clearly we have

$$P(|\tau - \tau_0| > \varepsilon) = 1 - \frac{2\varepsilon}{T}, \tag{55.04}$$

since the probability of obtaining $\hat{\tau}$ in the indicated interval is then given by the a priori distribution (52.32). Therefore, in this limiting case, too, we can take the equality sign in (55.02). However, in intermediate cases, the coefficient A only determines a lower bound for the probability of error of the optimum receiver.

The quantity A, which can be called the *ambiguity coefficient* (or the *unreliability coefficient*), is shown in Fig. 53. As $\mu_\varepsilon \to \infty$, the coefficient

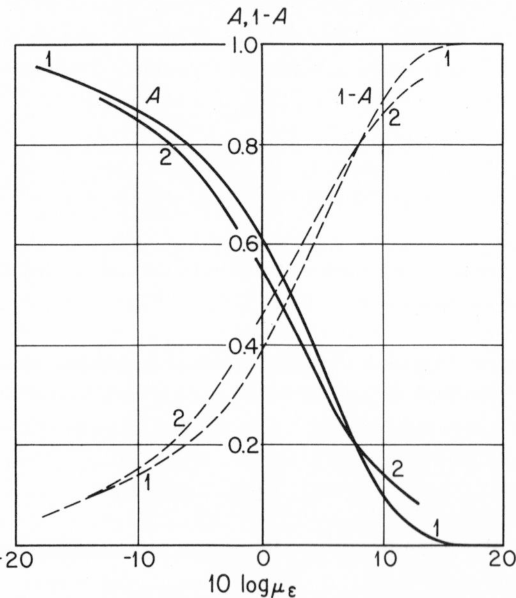

FIG. 53. The ambiguity coefficient A and the quantity $1 - A$ as functions of μ_ε. Curve 1, for a signal with known amplitude; Curve 2, for a signal with a Rayleigh distributed random amplitude.

$A \to 0$, so that probability of error vanishes and the measurement leads to a unique result. As $\mu_\varepsilon \to 0$, the coefficient $A \to 1$, which means that the observed maxima (peaks) of the likelihood ratio $\Lambda(\tau)$, or of the a posteriori distribution $p_f[m(\tau)]$, do not correspond to any signal, but are just peaks of the random noise masking the useful signal.

The coefficient A shown in Fig. 53 can be interpreted in different ways: Suppose that we use the input process $f(t)$ to measure the location of a signal in a white noise background, and suppose that the duration of the signal equals T_0 and that the signal vanishes outside of an interval of length T_0. According to formulas (52.03) and (31.27), we have

$$\mu(\tau - \tau_0) = \frac{1}{R_n(0)} \sum_h m(t_h - \tau_0)\, m(t_h - \tau)$$
$$= \frac{\Delta t}{S_n} \sum_h m(t_h - \tau_0)\, m(t_h - \tau), \tag{55.05}$$

or, as $\Delta t \to 0$,

$$\mu(\tau - \tau_0) = \frac{1}{S_n} \int_{-\infty}^{\infty} m(t - \tau_0)\, m(t - \tau)\, dt. \tag{55.06}$$

Thus, for signals whose total duration is T_0, we have

$$\mu(\tau - \tau_0) = 0 \quad \text{for} \quad |\tau - \tau_0| \geqslant T_0 \tag{55.07}$$

and

$$\mu_\varepsilon = 2\mu \quad \text{for} \quad \varepsilon \geqslant \frac{T_0}{2}. \tag{55.08}$$

By using this last value of μ_ε, we obtain the ambiguity coefficient A in the narrow sense, which we denote by A_0. The quantity A_0 gives the probability of identifying as the useful signal a "false" peak of the likelihood ratio $\Lambda(\tau)$, caused by the noise and having nothing to do with the signal. If $\varepsilon < T_0/2$, then instead of formula (55.05), we have to use the general formula (55.01), which as a rule leads to a smaller value of μ_ε and a larger value of the ambiguity coefficient A. This is caused by adding the probabilities of two kinds of errors, errors caused by identifying a "false" peak as a signal (A_0 gives the probability of such an error) and errors in the exact determination of the signal arrival time even when using a "correct" peak, due to the fact that the noise shifts the peak so that $|\hat{\tau} - \tau_0| > \varepsilon$.

Formula (55.02) can be generalized to the case of composite measurement, where the useful signal depends on an extra parameter θ, which is not measured and takes a continuous range of values. Here, we need to use formula (29.04) for the total probability, i.e.,

$$P(|\hat{\tau} - \tau_0| > \varepsilon) = \int p_m(\theta) P_\theta(|\hat{\tau} - \tau_0| > \varepsilon)\, d\theta, \tag{55.09}$$

where $p_m(\theta)$ is the probability density of the random parameter θ, and $P_\theta(|\hat{\tau} - \tau_0| > \varepsilon)$ is the probability of error in measuring τ, given that θ has a definite value. This latter probability is the same as the probability of error for simple measurement, so that it satisfies formulas (55.02) and (55.03), where in general the parameter μ_ε depends on θ.

If the parameter θ is the phase of the useful signal, then according to Sec. 33, the parameter μ_ε does not depend on θ, so that to measure the arrival time of a signal with unknown phase, we can use formulas (55.02) and (55.03) derived above for the case of simple measurement. The results of Sec. 54 show that for sufficiently weak noise, we should choose the equality sign in formula (55.02), just as in the case of simple measurement.

If the extra parameter is the random amplitude (envelope) G, then

$$\mu_\varepsilon(G) = G^2\mu_\varepsilon, \quad \text{where} \quad \mu_\varepsilon = \mu_\varepsilon(1), \tag{55.10}$$

and (55.09) reduces to the formula

$$\begin{aligned} P(|\hat{\tau} - \tau_0| > \varepsilon) &= \int p_m(G)P_G(|\hat{\tau} - \tau_0| > \varepsilon)\, dG \\ &\geqslant \left(1 - \frac{2\varepsilon}{T}\right)\frac{2}{\sqrt{2\pi}}\int p_m(G)\, dG \int_{|G|\sqrt{\mu_\varepsilon}/2}^{\infty} e^{-z^2/2}\, dz \\ &= \left(1 - \frac{2\varepsilon}{T}\right)\sqrt{\frac{\mu_\varepsilon}{2\pi}}\int p_m(G)\, dG \int_{|G|}^{\infty} e^{-\mu_\varepsilon x^2/8}\, dx. \end{aligned} \tag{55.11}$$

If we assume that the amplitude of the signal has the Rayleigh distribution

$$\begin{aligned} p_m(G) &= Ge^{-G^2/2} \quad \text{for} \quad G \geqslant 0, \\ p_m(G) &= 0 \qquad\qquad \text{for} \quad G < 0 \end{aligned} \tag{55.12}$$

(cf. Sec. 34), then we can transform the double integral as follows:

$$\begin{aligned} &\sqrt{\mu_\varepsilon/2\pi}\int_0^\infty Ge^{-G^2/2}\, dG \int_0^\infty e^{-\mu_\varepsilon x^2/8}\, dx \\ &= \sqrt{\mu_\varepsilon/2\pi}\int_0^\infty e^{-\mu_\varepsilon x^2/8}\, dx \int_0^x Ge^{-G^2/2}\, dG \\ &= \sqrt{\mu_\varepsilon/2\pi}\int_0^\infty [e^{-\mu_\varepsilon x^2/8} - e^{-[1+(\mu_\varepsilon/4)]x^2/2}]\, dx \\ &= 1 - \frac{\sqrt{\mu_\varepsilon/2}}{\sqrt{1 + (\mu_\varepsilon/4)}} = 1 - \frac{1}{\sqrt{1 + (4/\mu_\varepsilon)}}. \end{aligned} \tag{55.13}$$

Thus, we again obtain the inequality (55.02), where now the ambiguity coefficient is

$$A = 1 - \frac{1}{\sqrt{1 + (4/\mu_\varepsilon)}}, \tag{55.14}$$

and characterizes the measurement of the arrival time of a signal with unknown amplitude or even with unknown amplitude and unknown phase.

In Fig. 53, we also show the quantity (55.14) as a function of μ_ε. We see that for large μ_ε, the coefficient A is considerably larger for a signal with random amplitude than for a signal with constant amplitude. It should be noted that in measuring the parameter τ of a signal with a random amplitude which can take arbitrarily small values, even noise of arbitrarily small intensity cannot be regarded as weak in the sense of Secs. 52 to 54. Therefore, as things now stand, quantitative estimates of the accuracy (or rather, the reliability) of the arrival time of a fluctuating signal can only be made by using the coefficient A.

In using the results obtained in this section, it should be kept in mind that the coefficient A does not determine the measurement error itself, but rather a lower bound for the error, since the inequality (55.02) becomes an equality only in limiting cases. This means that if the coefficient A is close to unity, the measurement can give only an indeterminate result, but, on the other hand, it is hard to draw any quantitative conclusions from the smallness of A (from values like $A = 0.1$ or $A = 0.2$). At the end of the next section, we shall examine this problem in more detail.

56. The Problem of Resolving *M* Orthogonal Signals

Above, we investigated the measurement of a continuous parameter in the presence of normal noise. In this section, we study an analogous problem for a *discrete* parameter. This problem is simpler and therefore allows us to obtain a more complete solution, which is interesting in its own right and, moreover, enables us to explain certain matters relating to the measurement of continuous parameters.

Thus, we again suppose that we know in advance that the useful signal is present, but this time we assume that it has an unknown discrete parameter k which we are required to find, and which can take M values

$$k = 1, 2, \ldots, M. \tag{56.01}$$

In other words, it is known that one of the M signals $m_k(t) = m(t, k)$ is present at the receiver input, and we have to ascertain just which of these signals is present in the received function

$$f(t) = m_k(t) + n(t). \tag{56.02}$$

If we are interested in detecting each of the signals $m_k(t)$ separately, then we have to start with the corresponding likelihood ratio Λ_k. If the signals $m_k(t)$ have unknown random phase, then according to Sec. 33, the likelihood ratio Λ_k equals

$$\Lambda_k = p_k e^{-\mu_k/2} I_0(\mathscr{E}_k), \tag{56.03}$$

and if the amplitude of the $m_k(t)$ is also random, with a Rayleigh distribution, then, according to Sec. 34, we have

$$\Lambda_k = \frac{p_k}{1 + \mu_k} e^{-\mathscr{E}_k^2/2(1+\mu_k)}. \tag{56.04}$$

In writing the expressions (56.03) and (56.04), we have used formula (29.38), with certain changes in notation. Here, p_k is the a priori probability of occurrence of the kth signal $m_k(t)$, and μ_k is its effective signal-to-noise ratio. For simplicity, we henceforth assume that all the p_k and μ_k are equal:

$$p_k = \frac{1}{M}, \qquad \mu_k = \mu \qquad (k = 1, 2, \ldots, M). \tag{56.05}$$

The quantity $\mathscr{E}_k$ is the envelope, calculated by formula (33.07); it is essentially $\mathscr{E}_k$ that determines the likelihood ratio Λ_k, which is a monotonic function of $\mathscr{E}_k$ or of the dimensionless parameter

$$z_k = \frac{\mathscr{E}_k}{\sqrt{\mu}}. \tag{56.06}$$

To measure the discrete parameter k, it is natural to form all M likelihood ratios Λ_k and base the decision on the maximum Λ_k (cf. Sec. 50). In this way, we arrive at the scheme of an M-channel receiver, which at the output of the kth channel ($k = 1, 2, \ldots, M$) forms the quantities

$$\varphi_k = \mu + \nu_k \quad \text{or} \quad \varphi_k = \nu_k, \tag{56.07}$$

and $\mathscr{E}_k$, z_k or Λ_k. The second of the formulas (56.05) means that the random variables ν_k have the same statistical properties in all the channels, in particular that

$$\overline{\nu_k} = 0, \qquad \overline{\nu_k^2} = \mu, \tag{56.08}$$

where, in addition, we assume that the quantities ν_k in the different channels are statistically independent:

$$\overline{\nu_k \nu_l} = 0 \quad \text{for} \quad k \neq l. \tag{56.09}$$

We can write the condition (56.09) in more detail as

$$\overline{\nu_k \nu_l} = \sum_{g,h} Q_{gh} m_g(k) m_h(l) = 0 \quad \text{for} \quad k \neq l, \tag{56.10}$$

where $m_g(k)$ is the value of the signal $m(t, k)$ as the time t_g. Using the received values f_g to form the quantity

$$\varphi_l = \sum_{g,h} Q_{gh} f_g m_h(l) \tag{56.11}$$

in the lth channel ($l = 1, 2, \ldots, M$), we have noise alone at the output of the lth channel, i.e.,

$$\varphi_l = \nu_l = \sum_{g,h} Q_{gh} n_g m_h(l), \tag{56.12}$$

provided that

$$f_g = m_g(k) + n_g, \quad \text{where} \quad k \neq l. \tag{56.13}$$

This means that each signal goes through its own channel and gives nothing at the output of the other channels. Therefore, in the literature, the present problem is often called the problem of (*a system of*) *M orthogonal signals.*

The above model can be used (for example) in the problem of a signal with unknown arrival time τ (see Secs. 53 to 55). As an illustration, we choose a pulse of rectangular shape, whose arrival time can only take one of the discrete values

$$\tau = k\,\Delta\tau \qquad (k = 1, 2, \ldots, M). \tag{56.14}$$

If the noise is white and if the condition

$$\Delta\tau \gg T_0 \tag{56.15}$$

is met, where T_0 is the pulse duration, then, because of the relation

$$\sum_h m_h(k)m_h(l) = 0 \quad \text{for} \quad k \neq l, \tag{56.16}$$

we have the problem of M orthogonal signals, with

$$M = \frac{T}{\Delta\tau}, \tag{56.17}$$

where T is the time during which we look for the appearance of the signal.

In the case of signals of arbitrary form, the correlation function

$$\mu(\tau - \tau_0) = \overline{\nu(\tau)\nu(\tau_0)} = \sum_{g,h} Q_{gh} m_g(\tau_0) m_h(\tau) \tag{56.18}$$

goes to zero as $|\tau - \tau_0| \to \infty$. If, when the condition

$$|\tau - \tau_0| \geqslant \Delta\tau \tag{56.19}$$

is met, the function $\mu(\tau - \tau_0)$ takes small values, which can be neglected, then, for the discrete values (56.14), we can again assume that the orthogonality condition (56.10) holds. The problem of M orthogonal signals also has other interpretations and applications. For example, the signals may be separated in frequency rather than in time, as a result of which the condition (56.10) is satisfied.

Consider an M-channel receiver, which decides that the signal $m(t, \hat{k})$ is present if

$$\Lambda_{\hat{k}} > \Lambda_k \quad \text{for all } k = 1, 2, \ldots, M \text{ not equal to } \hat{k}. \tag{56.20}$$

We now calculate the probability that a measurement based on this decision rule is correct, i.e., that the parameter $\hat{k}$ chosen by using the maximum value of Λ_k (or z_k) is the true value k_0. This probability, which we denote by $P(z)$, obviously depends on the value $z = z_{k_0}$. Let $F(z)$ be the false alarm probability in each channel for the threshold z [if such a channel is used to detect each of the signals $m(t, k)$]. Then, because of the independence of the random variables ν_k in the $M - 1$ channels for which $k \neq k_0$, the probability $P(z)$ equals

$$P(z) = [1 - F(z)]^{M-1}. \tag{56.21}$$

If we let $p(z)$ denote the probability density of the quantity z in the k_0th channel, in which the signal $m(t, k_0)$ actually occurs, then the probability P_m of making the correct measurement of k for any value of z equals

$$P_m = \int_0^\infty P(z)p(z)\,dz = \int_0^\infty [1 - F(z)]^{M-1}p(z)\,dz \tag{56.22}$$

or

$$\begin{aligned} P_m &= \sum_{k=0}^{M-1} \binom{M-1}{k}(-1)^k \int_0^\infty F^k(z)p(z)\,dz \\ &= \sum_{k=0}^{M-1} (-1)^k \binom{M-1}{k} \overline{F^k}, \end{aligned} \tag{56.23}$$

where $\binom{M-1}{k}$ is the binomial coefficient

$$\begin{aligned} \binom{M-1}{k} &= \frac{(M-1)!}{k!(M-1-k)!} \\ &= \frac{(M-1)(M-2)\dots(M-2-k)}{k!}. \end{aligned} \tag{56.24}$$

In the case of a signal with unknown phase, where

$$F(z) = e^{-z^2/2}, \qquad p(z) = ze^{-(\mu+z^2)/2}I_0(\sqrt{\mu}z), \tag{56.25}$$

we can use the identity (33.46) to obtain

$$\begin{aligned} \overline{F^k} &= \overline{e^{-kz^2/2}} = \int_0^\infty ze^{-[\mu+(k+1)z^2]/2}I_0(\sqrt{\mu}z)\,dz \\ &= \frac{e^{-k\mu/2(k+1)}}{k+1}\int_0^\infty ze^{-\frac{1}{2}\{[\mu/(k+1)]+z^2\}}I_0[\sqrt{\mu/(k+1)}z]\,dz \\ &= \frac{e^{-k\mu/2(k+1)}}{k+1}. \end{aligned} \tag{56.26}$$

Then, formula (56.23) leads to the expression

$$P_m = \sum_{k=0}^{M-1} (-1)^k \binom{M-1}{k} \frac{e^{-k\mu/2(k+1)}}{k+1}. \tag{56.27}$$

In the case of a fluctuating signal with unknown phase, where

$$F(z) = e^{-z^2/2}, \qquad p(z) = \frac{z^2}{1+\mu}e^{-z^2/2(1+\mu)}, \tag{56.28}$$

we obtain the simpler expression

$$P_m = \sum_{k=0}^{M-1} (-1)^k \binom{M-1}{k} \frac{1}{1+k(1+\mu)}, \tag{56.29}$$

since then

$$\overline{F^k} = \frac{1}{1+\mu}\int_0^\infty ze^{-\frac{1}{2}\{[1/(1+\mu)]+k\}z^2} = \frac{1}{1+k(1+\mu)}. \tag{56.30}$$

For two signals ($M = 2$), formula (56.27) takes the form

$$P_m = 1 - \frac{1}{2}e^{-\mu/4}, \tag{56.31}$$

and formula (56.29) gives

$$P_m = 1 - \frac{1}{2+\mu}. \tag{56.32}$$

For arbitrary M, we have in both cases the limiting relations

$$\lim_{\mu\to\infty} P_m = 1, \qquad \lim_{\mu\to 0} P_m = \frac{1}{M}, \tag{56.33}$$

which, of course, could have been anticipated. The second of these relations is a consequence of the identity

$$\begin{aligned}\sum_{k=0}^{M-1}(-1)^k\binom{M-1}{k}\frac{1}{k+1} &= \sum_{k=0}^{M-1}(-1)^k\binom{M-1}{k}\int_0^1 x^k\,dx \\ &= \int_0^1 dx\sum_{k=0}^{M-1}(-1)^k\binom{M-1}{k}x^k = \int_0^1(1-x)^{M-1}\,dx = \frac{1}{M}.\end{aligned} \tag{56.34}$$

For large M, calculations using formulas (56.27) and (56.29) become formidable. Therefore, it is appropriate to derive asymptotic formulas which are valid for $M \to \infty$. To do so, we approximate the function (56.21) by

$$\begin{aligned} P(z) &= 0 \quad \text{for} \quad z < z_0, \\ P(z) &= 1 \quad \text{for} \quad z > z_0, \end{aligned} \tag{56.35}$$

where z_0 can be defined by the requirement that for $z = z_0$, the exact function (56.21) should equal

$$P(z_0) = [1 - F(z_0)]^{M-1} = \frac{1}{2} \tag{56.36}$$

or

$$F(z_0) = e^{-z_0^2/2} = 1 - 2^{-1/(M-1)}. \tag{56.37}$$

It follows that

$$z_0 = \sqrt{-2\ln[1 - 2^{-1/(M-1)}]}. \tag{56.38}$$

In fact, as M is increased, the transition of the function $P(z)$ from the value $P(z) \sim 0$ to the value $P(z) \sim 1$ becomes progressively sharper, and hence the approximation (56.35) gives increasingly accurate results. Substituting the expression (56.35) into (56.22), we obtain

$$P_m = \int_{z0}^{\infty} p(z)\, dz = D(z_0), \tag{56.39}$$

i.e., the probability of making the correct measurement equals the *probability of correctly detecting a single signal* by using the threshold (56.38), which

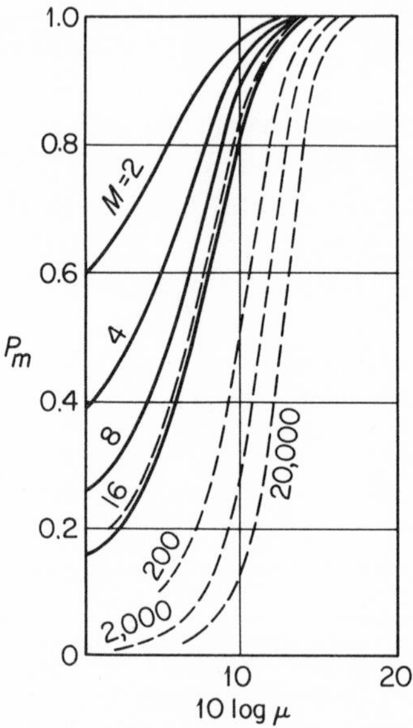

FIG. 54. Dependence of P_m, the probability of correctly resolving one of M signals, on the signal-to-noise ratio in one channel, when the phase of the signals is unknown. The solid curves are calculated by the exact formula (56.27), and the dashed curves by the approximate formula (56.39).

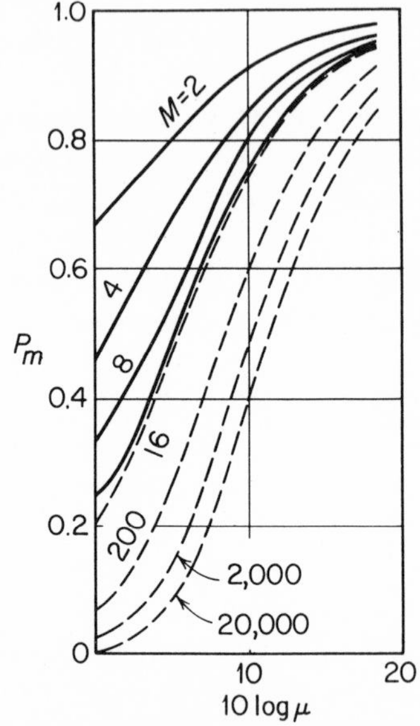

FIG. 55. Dependence of P_m, the probability of correctly resolving one of M signals, on the signal-to-noise ratio in one channel, when the phase and the amplitude of the signals are unknown. The solid curves are calculated by the exact formula (56.29) and the dashed curves by the approximate formula (56.39).

depends on M and satisfies the approximate formula

$$z_0 = \sqrt{2 \ln [(M-1)/\ln 2]} \quad \text{for} \quad M \gg 1. \tag{56.40}$$

In Figs. 54 and 55, we show the dependence of the probability P_m on the signal-to-noise ratio μ, calculated for $M = 2, 4, 8$ and 16 by using the exact formulas (56.27) and (56.29), and for $M = 16$, 200, 2000 and 20,000 by using the approximate formula (56.39). It is clear from the figures that by the time $M = 16$, the calculations made by using the approximate formula give quite satisfactory results. It follows from the above formulas that as μ is increased, the difference $1 - P$ decreases much more rapidly (i.e., exponentially) for signals with constant amplitude than for signals with fluctuating amplitude. Thus "reliable" measurements of a discrete parameter are much more easily carried out for nonfluctuating signals than for fluctuating signals; on the other hand, "unreliable" resolution of signals of constant amplitude requires a larger signal-to-noise ratio.[3] We have already discussed this state of affairs earlier, in our study of detection theory. It is clear from Figs. 54 and 55, and from formulas (56.39) and (56.40), that the required values of μ increase with M, but only rather slowly, since the formulas involve the logarithm of the number of signals M.

In Sec. 55, we derived the inequality (55.02) satisfied by the probability of measuring a continuous parameter τ. The right-hand side of (55.02) involves the probability of error in resolving two signals $m(t, \tau + \varepsilon)$ and $m(t, \tau - \varepsilon)$. For sufficiently large ε, these signals can be regarded as orthogonal, and then, according to formulas (55.02) and (55.08), we obtain

$$P(|\hat{\tau} - \tau_0| > \varepsilon) \geqslant \left(1 - \frac{2\varepsilon}{T}\right)A_0, \tag{56.41}$$

where

$$A_0 = \frac{2}{\sqrt{2\pi}}\int_{\sqrt{2\mu}/2}^{\infty} e^{-z^2/2}\,dz. \tag{56.42}$$

On the other hand, in this section we have shown that when M is very large, it is more difficult to resolve M orthogonal signals than when $M = 2$ or $M = 4$. Therefore, it is clear that when formula (56.17) leads to large values of M, the probability of error $P(|\hat{\tau} - \tau_0| > \varepsilon)$ must be considerably larger than the quantity appearing in the right-hand side of the inequality (56.41).

At the present time, it is only by examining a "system of M orthogonal signals" that one can obtain quantitative (albeit approximate) results on the possibilities of measuring a signal parameter when the parameter can take a wide range of values. It is only when the probability P_m is quite close to unity that one can assume that a rough measurement of the continuous parameter τ is quite reliable and that the given maximum of the likelihood ratio is actually due to a signal, rather than to a random "peak." If we obtain a value of P_m which is quite close to unity when we divide the "a priori" interval $0 < \tau < T$ into M parts, in accordance with formulas (56.14), (56.15) and (56.19), then we can raise the question of further increasing the accuracy of the value of τ, i.e., making a more accurate measurement.

---

[3] If, instead of the parameter μ, the comparison is made by using the parameter μ', which equals $\mu/2$ for the nonfluctuating signal and μ for the fluctuating signal (cf. Sec. 45 and Appendix II), then the probabilities P_m will practically coincide for small μ', as is also apparent from formulas (56.27) and (56.29).

The theoretical possibilities associated with exact measurement of an arbitrary parameter τ were discussed in Sec. 52, and were made concrete in Secs. 53 to 55, in the case of measurement of signal arrival times. If the signal has a constant amplitude and if the noise is sufficiently weak, then the measured value $\hat{\tau}$ is a normal random variable, whose mean value is τ_0, the true value of τ, and whose variance is given by formula (53.16). We can also use the inequality (55.02) and Fig. 53, which must give an approximate value of the error committed in making an "accurate" measurement following a preliminary "rough" measurement, since then the accurate measurement involves a rather small range of τ.

In practice, it is natural to divide the measurement of a signal parameter in the presence of noise into two different operations, i.e., a "rough" measurement and an "accurate" measurement, where the results of the accurate measurement are taken into account only when they agree with those of the rough measurement. We note that often an experimental investigation of the functions $\Lambda(\tau)$, $\varphi(\tau)$ and $\mathscr{E}(\tau)$, for a continuous parameter τ, is only possible when these functions are constructed at the separate points (56.14), obtained by dividing the original interval into a large number of small intervals $\Delta\tau$, where the noise in different intervals is approximately independent. Thus, the problem of M orthogonal signals reflects the properties of actual engineering equipment.

The problem of M orthogonal signals was first stated and solved (with assumptions of a more special nature) by V. A. Kotelnikov.

57. Detection of a Signal with a Discrete Parameter, Combined with Measurement of the Parameter

In the preceding sections, we have considered only "pure" measurement, i.e., we have assumed that it is known in advance that a *single* useful signal is present, with an unknown value of the parameter a, τ or k, which it is required to measure. Ordinarily, however, measurement has to be combined with detection, and as a result we have to study the problem further. Detection of the signals $m_k(t) = m(t, k)$ with a discrete parameter k ($k = 1, 2, \ldots, M$), combined with measurement of the parameter, can be carried out by using various kinds of M-channel receivers. We shall discuss three kinds of receivers, called receivers of type I, type II and type III, respectively.

A receiver *of type I* carries out detection by using the likelihood ratio

$$\Lambda = \sum_{k=1}^{M} \Lambda_k \tag{57.01}$$

and the decision rule

$$\begin{aligned} &\text{If} \quad \Lambda \geqslant \Lambda_*, \quad \text{decide that a signal is present;} \\ &\text{If} \quad \Lambda < \Lambda_*, \quad \text{decide that no signal is present.} \end{aligned} \tag{57.02}$$

Then, if $\Lambda \geqslant \Lambda_*$, it decides that the signal with the maximum Λ_k is present. This receiver needs modification if the signals can occur in pairs (for example).

If the signals $m_k(t)$ have no other unknown parameters, then every channel has to form the quantity

$$\Lambda_k = p_k e^{\varphi_k - \frac{1}{2}\mu_k}, \tag{57.03}$$

where p_k is the probability of occurrence of the kth signal, given that some useful signal is present, and φ_k is defined by formula (56.11). Thus, from a practical point of view, the implementation of a type I receiver is a rather formidable problem, since after linear processing of the input data (which gives φ_k), the receiver has to form the quantities (57.03) and then sum them in accordance with formula (57.01). However, a type I receiver is the *optimum* receiver for detection in the sense of Chap. 5, so that the operating characteristics of all other receivers are inferior to those of the type I receiver. Since calculation of the operating characteristics of a type I receiver involves certain difficulties (see below), the advantages of such a receiver cannot be studied in detail. However, we can regard it as proved that these advantages are not large.

A receiver *of type II* makes a preliminary test of all M channels, using the decision rule

$$\begin{aligned} &\text{If} \quad \Lambda_k \geqslant \lambda_k, \quad \text{decide that the signal } m_k(t) \textit{ may} \text{ be present;} \\ &\text{If} \quad \Lambda_k < \lambda_k, \quad \text{decide that the signal } m_k(t) \text{ is absent,} \end{aligned} \tag{57.04}$$

where λ_k is a threshold for the kth channel of the receiver. If $\Lambda_k < \lambda_k$ in all the channels, then it is decided that no signal is present, but if $\Lambda_k \geqslant \lambda_k$ in at least one channel, it is decided that signals are present. If it is known in advance that there can be no more than one signal, then the signal with the largest Λ_k is chosen as present. If there is no restriction on the number of signals, then the test using (57.04) is "final."[4]

A receiver *of type III* first makes a measurement, i.e., it chooses the largest of the M quantities $\Lambda_1, \Lambda_2, \ldots, \Lambda_M$, and then it tests the selected value of Λ_k by using the following decision rule:

$$\begin{aligned} &\text{If} \quad \Lambda_k \geqslant \lambda_k, \quad \text{decide that the signal } m_k(t) \text{ is present;} \\ &\text{If} \quad \Lambda_k < \lambda_k, \quad \text{decide that no signals are present,} \end{aligned} \tag{57.05}$$

where the λ_k are the same thresholds as in (57.04). This receiver can only be used provided that occurrence of two or more useful signals $m_k(t)$ is excluded *a priori*. If only one signal can occur, then it is easy to see that the receivers of types II and III are equivalent, since they perform the same operations, but in a different order.

---

[4] I.e., it is decided that all the signals for which $\Lambda_k \geqslant \lambda_k$ are present. (*Translator*)

We might say that a type I receiver first carries out detection and then measurement, that a type II receiver carries out detection and measurement in parallel, while a type III receiver first measures the parameter k and then uses detection to verify the presence of a signal with the measured parameter. In practice, it is much simpler to implement receivers of types II and III than a receiver of type I, since instead of the separate Λ_k, we can form any monotonically increasing function of Λ_k in each channel of the receiver.

To investigate the characteristics of the receivers introduced above, we confine ourselves to the case of a system of M orthogonal signals with identical signal-to-noise ratios (see Sec. 56), and we exclude the possibility that two or more signals can occur simultaneously. It is clear that since the signals are equally likely [cf. formulas (56.05) and (56.08)], all the thresholds λ_k in (57.04) and (57.05) should be chosen to be the same, and then the false alarm probabilities and the detection probabilities in all the channels of a type II receiver are the same:

$$F = F_1 = \cdots = F_M, \qquad D = D_1 = \cdots = D_M. \tag{57.06}$$

We now calculate the false alarm probability in a type II receiver. The random variables ν_k in the different channels are independent, because of (56.09), and therefore, according to the multiplication formula for probabilities of independent events, the probability of correct *nondetection* equals

$$1 - F' = (1 - F)^M, \tag{57.07}$$

so that the false alarm probability is

$$F' = 1 - (1 - F)^M. \tag{57.08}$$

The false dismissal probability of a type II receiver is obviously equal to

$$1 - D' = (1 - D)(1 - F)^{M-1}, \tag{57.09}$$

since a type II receiver can detect the signal as a result of a false alarm in one of the $M - 1$ "empty" channels. Thus, the probability of correct detection is

$$D' = 1 - (1 - D)(1 - F)^{M-1}. \tag{57.10}$$

Formulas (57.08) and (57.10) relate the probabilities F' and D' in an M-channel receiver to the probabilities F and D in a single channel, which detects just one signal. It should be noted that F' and D' characterize only the "detecting functions" of the type II receiver and have nothing to do with its "measuring functions." For sufficiently small F, we can use the approximate formulas

$$F' = MF, \qquad D' = D. \tag{57.11}$$

These formulas give a particularly simple result for signals with unknown amplitude and phase (see Sec. 34). In fact, according to formulas (34.25) and (57.11), we have

$$D' = \left(\frac{F'}{M}\right)^{1/(1+\mu)}, \tag{57.12}$$

where μ is the signal-to-noise ratio in each channel. This formula allows us to find explicitly the value of μ which is necessary to provide given values of F' and D':

$$\mu = \frac{\ln(1/F') + \ln M}{\ln(1/D')} - 1. \tag{57.13}$$

In a single-channel detecting receiver, i.e., for $M = 1$, the corresponding value of μ equals

$$\mu' = \frac{(\ln 1/F')}{\ln(1/D')} - 1 \tag{57.14}$$

[cf. formula (34.24)], so that formula (57.13) can be rewritten in the form

$$\mu = \mu' + \frac{\ln M}{\ln(1/D')}. \tag{57.15}$$

We see that the larger the value of M, the larger the value of μ needed to achieve given values of F' and D' in an M-channel receiver, and in fact, the necessary increment in μ is proportional to $\ln M$.

For signals with unknown phase, using formulas (33.48) and (57.11), we obtain

$$z_* = \sqrt{2[\ln(1/F') + \ln M]}, \tag{57.16}$$

where z_* is the normalized decision threshold in the M-channel receiver. Substituting this expression into formula (33.49), where we take $\eta = 0$, we obtain the formula

$$D' = D = \frac{1}{\sqrt{2\pi}} \int_{y_*}^{\infty} e^{-y^2/2}\, dy, \tag{57.17}$$

where

$$y_* = z_* - \sqrt{\mu} = \sqrt{2[\ln(1/F') + \ln M]} - \sqrt{\mu}. \tag{57.18}$$

Solving this last relation for μ, we arrive at the expression

$$\mu = \{\sqrt{2[\ln(1/F') + \ln M]} - y_*\}^2, \tag{57.19}$$

which for $y_* = 0$ (i.e., for $D = \frac{1}{2}$) simplifies to

$$\mu = \mu' + 2\ln M, \tag{57.20}$$

where

$$\mu' = 2\ln\frac{1}{F'} \tag{57.21}$$

is the signal-to-noise ratio leading to the same values of the probabilities F' and $D' = \frac{1}{2}$ in the single-channel detecting receiver described in Sec. 33. Formulas (57.19) and (57.20) again lead to a logarithmic dependence of μ on the number of channels M; the same kind of dependence is obtained for signals with other properties, and also in the case of measurement (see Sec. 56).

With these assumptions, the characteristics of the receivers of types II and III are the same, and therefore all that remains is to investigate receivers of type I. If the signals $m_k(t)$ do not depend on an additional parameter, then in the absence of the signal $m_k(t)$, the likelihood ratio (57.03) equals

$$\Lambda_k = \frac{1}{M} e^{\nu_k - (\mu/2)}. \tag{57.22}$$

Since the random variables ν_k are normal and have moments

$$\overline{\nu_k} = 0, \qquad \overline{\nu_k^2} = \mu, \tag{57.23}$$

it is easy to write the distribution of the ν_k and calculate the expectation

$$\overline{e^{q\nu_k}} = \frac{1}{\sqrt{2\pi\mu}} \int_{-\infty}^{\infty} e^{q\nu - (\nu^2/2\mu)}\, d\nu = e^{q^2\mu/2}, \tag{57.24}$$

where q is any number. From this, it is not hard to find the moments of the random variable (57.22):

$$\overline{\Lambda_k} = \frac{1}{M}, \quad \overline{\Lambda_k^2} = \frac{1}{M^2} e^{\mu}, \quad \overline{\Lambda_k^2} - (\overline{\Lambda_k})^2 = \frac{1}{M^2}(e^{\mu} - 1). \tag{57.25}$$

In the presence of the signal $m_k(t)$, we have $\varphi_k = \mu + \nu_k$ and

$$\Lambda_k = \frac{1}{M} e^{\nu_k + (\mu/2)} \tag{57.26}$$

so that

$$\overline{\Lambda_k} = \frac{1}{M} e^{\mu}, \quad \overline{\Lambda_k^2} = \frac{1}{M^2} e^{3\mu}, \quad \overline{\Lambda_k^2} - (\overline{\Lambda_k})^2 = \frac{1}{M^2} e^{2\mu}(e^{\mu} - 1). \tag{57.27}$$

If we now bear in mind that, according to formula (56.10), the noises ν_k in the different channels of the receiver, where the quantities Λ_k are formed, are statistically independent, i.e.,

$$\overline{\nu_k \nu_l} = 0 \quad \text{for} \quad k \neq l, \tag{57.28}$$

then we obtain

$$a_0 = \overline{\Lambda} = 1, \qquad b_0 = \overline{\Lambda^2} - (\overline{\Lambda})^2 = \frac{1}{M}(e^{\mu} - 1) \tag{57.29}$$

in the absence of the useful signal, and

$$a_1 = \overline{\Lambda} = 1 + \frac{1}{M}(e^{\mu} - 1),$$
$$b_1 = \overline{\Lambda^2} - (\overline{\Lambda})^2 = \frac{1}{M}(e^{\mu} - 1)\left[1 + \frac{1}{M}(e^{2\mu} - 1)\right] \tag{57.30}$$

in the presence of one useful signal.

So far, our argument has been completely rigorous, but it still does not enable us to calculate the false alarm probability F' and the detection probability D', since the distribution of the quantity Λ is unknown, and we only know the moments (57.29) and (57.30). Since Λ is the sum of M independent random variables Λ_k, it is natural to assume that for large M, the distribution of the random variable Λ is approximately Gaussian. Then, we obtain the false alarm probability

$$F' = \frac{1}{\sqrt{2\pi}} \int_{z_*}^{\infty} e^{-z^2/2}\, dz \qquad \left(z_* = \frac{\Lambda_* - a_0}{\sqrt{b_0}}\right), \tag{57.31}$$

and the detection probability

$$D' = \frac{1}{\sqrt{2\pi}} \int_{y_*}^{\infty} e^{-z^2/2}\, dz \qquad \left(y_* = \frac{\Lambda_* - a_1}{\sqrt{b_1}}\right). \tag{57.32}$$

If for simplicity we set $y_* = 0$ and $D' = \frac{1}{2}$, we obtain the relations

$$z_* = \sqrt{\mu'} = \frac{a_1 - a_0}{\sqrt{b_0}} = \sqrt{(e^{\mu} - 1)/M}, \qquad e^{\mu} = M\mu' + 1. \tag{57.33}$$

Here, according to formulas (31.34) and (31.35), μ' denotes the signal-to-noise ratio which provides the same probabilities F' and $D' = \frac{1}{2}$ for simple detection.

The formulas (57.33) lead to the expression

$$\mu = \ln(M\mu' + 1) \sim \ln \mu' + \ln M \qquad \text{for} \quad M\mu' \gg 1. \tag{57.34}$$

Before analyzing this result, we consider the case of signals with unknown phase. Then, the likelihood ratio is

$$\Lambda_k = \frac{1}{M} e^{-\mu/2} I_0(\mathscr{E}_k) \tag{57.35}$$

[cf. formula (56.03)], which, in the absence of the useful signal $m_k(t)$, has the moments

$$\overline{\Lambda_k} = \frac{1}{M}, \qquad \overline{\Lambda_k^2} = \frac{1}{M^2} I_0(\mu),$$
$$\overline{\Lambda_k^2} - (\overline{\Lambda_k})^2 = \frac{1}{M^2}[I_0(\mu) - 1], \tag{57.36}$$

where we have used Weber's first and second exponential integrals,[5] and the fact that the probability density of the random variable $\mathscr{E}_k$ is

$$p(\mathscr{E}_k) = \frac{\mathscr{E}_k}{\mu} e^{-\mathscr{E}_k^2/2\mu} \tag{57.37}$$

(see Sec. 33). Therefore, instead of the expressions (57.29), we obtain

$$a_0 = \overline{\Lambda} = 1, \qquad b_0 = \overline{\Lambda^2} - (\overline{\Lambda})^2 = \frac{1}{M}[I_0(\mu) - 1], \tag{57.38}$$

and, in the presence of one useful signal,

$$a_1 = \overline{\Lambda} = 1 + \frac{1}{M}[I_0(\mu) - 1]. \tag{57.39}$$

As a result, formula (57.33) is changed to

$$z_* = \sqrt{\mu'} = \frac{a_1 - a_0}{\sqrt{b_0}} = \sqrt{[I_0(\mu) - 1]/M}. \tag{57.40}$$

Here, we have used the approximate formula (33.49), which implies that $z_* = \sqrt{\mu'}$ for $\eta = 0$ and $y_* = 0$, where μ' means the signal-to-noise ratio for single-channel detection with the same probabilities F' and $D' = \frac{1}{2}$. The relation between μ and μ' is given by

$$I_0(\mu) = M\mu' + 1, \tag{57.41}$$

and it follows from the inequality

$$I_0(\mu) < e^{\mu} \tag{57.42}$$

that the value of μ in (57.41) will be larger than the value of μ calculated by (57.34). However, it is clear from the asymptotic expression

$$I_0(\mu) = \frac{e^{\mu}}{\sqrt{2\pi\mu}} \tag{57.43}$$

that this difference will be comparatively small when (57.34) leads to large values of μ. Thus, formula (57.34) can also be used to obtain a rough estimate of μ for signals with unknown phase. Comparing formulas, (57.20) and (57.34) for large M, we see once again that a type I receiver is superior to a type II receiver, since for sufficiently large values of $\ln M$, the latter needs twice as large a value of the signal-to-noise ratio to achieve the same values of F' and D'.

The above argument cannot be applied to a signal with a fluctuating amplitude, since it turns out that

$$\overline{\Lambda_k^2} = \infty \quad \text{for} \quad \mu > 1. \tag{57.44}$$

[5] G. N. Watson, *op. cit.*, pp. 393, 395.

In this case, investigation of the asymptotic distribution law of the random variable Λ (as $M \to \infty$) requires a more exact mathematical method. The type I receiver for signals with unknown amplitude and phase is studied in the paper of R. L. Dobrushin,[6] where *for small values of F*, the author obtains formula (57.13), which was derived above for the type II receiver. Thus, under these conditions, the type I receiver has no appreciable advantage over the type II receiver.

---

[6] R. L. Dobrushin, *A statistical problem arising in the theory of detection of signals in the presence of noise in a multi-channel system and leading to stable distribution laws*, Theory Prob. and Its Appl., English edition, **3,** 161 (1958).

Part 3

AUXILIARY TOPICS

9

NORMAL RANDOM VARIABLES AND NORMAL RANDOM PROCESSES

This part of the book contains auxiliary material on the mathematical and physical properties of random variables and random processes representing the noise (and sometimes the useful signals themselves) in the study of optimum filters and optimum receivers. Part 3 is intended to make it easier for the reader to use the rest of the book.

58. Characteristic Functions of Normal (Gaussian) Random Variables

In this chapter, we derive the basic formulas pertaining to normal random variables, which are used throughout the entire book. It is convenient to begin our presentation with the concept of the characteristic function of several random variables.

The (*joint*) *characteristic function* of the H random variables $x_1, \ldots, x_H$ is the function of H auxiliary parameters $u_1, \ldots, u_H$ defined by the relation

$$\chi(u_1, \ldots, u_H) = \overline{e^{i(u_1x_1+\ldots+u_Hx_H)}} \equiv \overline{\exp i \sum_{h=1}^{H} u_h x_h}, \tag{58.01}$$

where the overbar denotes the operation of averaging (i.e., the mathematical expectation). If it is assumed that the H-dimensional probability density of the random variables $x_1, \ldots, x_H$ is $p(x_1, \ldots, x_H)$, then formula (58.01) can be written in the form

$$\chi(u_1, \ldots, u_H) = \int_{-\infty}^{\infty} \cdots \int_{-\infty}^{\infty} e^{i(u_1x_1 + \ldots + u_Hx_H)} \times p(x_1, \ldots, x_H)\, dx_1 \ldots dx_H, \tag{58.02}$$

so that the function χ is the H-dimensional Fourier transform of the function p. The inversion of this transform is given by

$$p(x_1, \ldots, x_H) = \frac{1}{(2\pi)^H} \int_{-\infty}^{\infty} \cdots \int_{-\infty}^{\infty} e^{-i(u_1x_1 + \ldots + u_Hx_H)} \times \chi(u_1, \ldots, u_H)\, dx_1 \ldots dx_H, \tag{58.03}$$

which allows us to calculate the probability density p from a knowledge of the characteristic function χ.

The definition (58.01) implies the following properties of the characteristic function:

$$\begin{aligned} \chi(0, \ldots, 0) &= 1, \\ \frac{\partial \chi}{\partial u_h}(0, \ldots, 0) &= i\overline{x_h}, \\ \frac{\partial^2 \chi}{\partial u_g \partial u_h}(0, \ldots, 0) &= -\overline{x_g x_h}, \\ \frac{\partial^3 \chi}{\partial u_g \partial u_h \partial u_k}(0, \ldots, 0) &= -i\overline{x_g x_h x_k}, \\ \frac{\partial^4 \chi}{\partial u_g \partial u_h \partial u_k \partial u_l}(0, \ldots, 0) &= \overline{x_g x_h x_k x_l}. \end{aligned} \tag{58.04}$$

Thus, the moments of the random variables $x_1, \ldots, x_H$ can be expressed directly in terms of derivatives of their characteristic function, evaluated at the origin of coordinates, i.e., at the point $u_1 = \cdots = u_H = 0$.

From now on, we shall consider only random variables $x_1, \ldots, x_H$ with zero mean values:

$$\overline{x_h} = 0 \qquad (h = 1, \ldots, H). \tag{58.05}$$

This constitutes no loss of generality, since if $\overline{x_h} \neq 0$, we can always introduce new random variables

$$x_h' = x_h - \overline{x_h}, \tag{58.06}$$

which satisfy the condition (58.05), and then transform back to the variables x_h in the final expressions.

The H random variables $x_1, \ldots, x_H$ satisfying (58.05) are said to be *(jointly) normal* or *Gaussian*, if their characteristic function is

$$\chi(u_1, \ldots, u_H) = \exp\left\{-\frac{1}{2} \sum_{g,h=1}^{H} R_{gh} u_g u_h\right\}, \tag{58.07}$$

where the coefficients R_{gh} correspond to a positive definite quadratic form and satisfy the symmetry condition

$$R_{gh} = R_{hg}. \tag{58.08}$$

According to the third of the relations (58.04), the coefficient R_{gh} has the meaning

$$R_{gh} = \overline{x_g x_h}, \tag{58.09}$$

since differentiating the function (58.07) twice gives

$$\begin{aligned} \frac{\partial \chi}{\partial u_g} &= -\chi \sum_k R_{gk} u_k, \\ \frac{\partial^2 \chi}{\partial u_g \partial u_h} &= -\chi\left(R_{gh} - \sum_k R_{gk} u_k \sum_l R_{hl} u_l\right). \end{aligned} \tag{58.10}$$

Using the fourth and fifth of the formulas (58.04), we can also easily derive the relations

$$\begin{aligned} \overline{x_g x_h x_k} &= 0, \\ \overline{x_g x_h x_k x_l} &= R_{gh} R_{kl} + R_{gk} R_{hl} + R_{gl} R_{hk}. \end{aligned} \tag{58.11}$$

The second of these relations was used in Sec. 35.

Above, we tacitly assumed that the random variables $x_1, \ldots, x_H$ are real, i.e., that they take only real values. Sometimes, it is convenient to introduce complex random variables as well. Thus, suppose we have $2H$ real normal random variables $x_1, \ldots, x_H$ and $y_1, \ldots, y_H$, with moments

$$\begin{aligned} \overline{x_g} &= 0, \qquad \overline{y_h} = 0, \\ \overline{x_g x_h} = \overline{y_g y_h} &= R^{(1)}_{gh}, \quad \text{where} \quad R^{(1)}_{gh} = R^{(1)}_{hg}, \\ \overline{x_g y_h} = -\overline{x_g y_h} &= R^{(2)}_{gh}, \quad \text{where} \quad R^{(2)}_{gh} = -R^{(2)}_{hg}. \end{aligned} \tag{58.12}$$

It follows immediately from the definition (58.07) that the characteristic function of these random variables is

$$\begin{aligned} \chi(u_1, \ldots, u_H; v_1, \ldots, v_H) &= \overline{e^{i(u_1 x_1 + \ldots + u_H x_H + v_1 y_1 + \ldots + v_H y_H)}} \\ &= \exp\left\{-\frac{1}{2} \sum_{g,h} [R^{(1)}_{gh}(u_g u_h + v_g v_h) + R^{(2)}_{gh}(u_g v_h - u_h v_g)]\right\}. \end{aligned} \tag{58.13}$$

Instead of $2H$ real random variables, we can introduce H complex random variables z_h, defined by

$$z_h = x_h + iy_h, \quad z_h^* = x_h - iy_h \qquad (h = 1, \ldots, H), \tag{58.14}$$

which then satisfy the relations

$$\begin{aligned} \overline{z_g z_h} &= \overline{x_g x_h} - \overline{y_g y_h} + i(\overline{x_g y_h} + \overline{x_h y_g}) = 0, \quad \overline{z_g^* z_h^*} = 0, \\ \overline{z_g^* z_h} &= \overline{x_g x_h} + \overline{y_g y_h} + i(\overline{x_h y_h} - \overline{x_h y_g}) = 2[R_{gh}^{(1)} + iR_{gh}^{(2)}]. \end{aligned} \tag{58.15}$$

Introducing the complex correlation coefficients

$$R_{gh} = R_{gh}^{(1)} + iR_{gh}^{(2)}, \qquad R_{gh}^* = R_{hg}, \tag{58.16}$$

we can write the relations (58.15) in the form

$$\overline{z_g z_h} = \overline{z_g^* z_h^*} = 0, \qquad \overline{z_g^* z_h} = 2R_{gh}. \tag{58.17}$$

Then, introducing the quantities

$$w_h = u_h + iv_h, \qquad w_h^* = u_h - iv_h, \tag{58.18}$$

we can write the characteristic function (58.13) more compactly as

$$\chi(w_1, w_1^*, \ldots, w_H, w_H^*) = \exp\left\{-\frac{1}{2}\sum_{g,h} R_{gh} w_g w_h^*\right\}, \tag{58.19}$$

where, according to (58.16),

$$\sum_{g,h} R_{gh} w_g w_h^* = \sum_{g,h} [R_{gh}^{(1)}(u_g u_h + v_g v_h) + R_{gh}^{(2)}(u_g v_h - u_h v_g)] \tag{58.20}$$

is a positive definite Hermitian form, which takes real nonnegative values for any u_h and v_h (or w_h). In formula (58.19), we can also regard χ as a function of w_h and w_h^* (rather than of u_h and v_h) defined by the relation

$$\chi(w_1, w_1^*, \ldots, w_H, w_H^*) = \overline{e^{\frac{1}{2}(w_1^* z_1 + w_1 z_1^* + \cdots + w_H^* z_H + \cdots + w_H z_H^*)}}. \tag{58.21}$$

Thus, for example,

$$\frac{\partial^2 \chi}{\partial w_g \partial w_h^*}(0, 0, \ldots, 0, 0) = -\frac{1}{4}\overline{z_g^* z_h} = -\frac{1}{2}R_{gh}, \tag{58.22}$$

which agrees with formula (58.17).

59. Multidimensional Gaussian Distributions

We now calculate the probability density $p(x_1, \ldots, x_H)$ of H normally distributed, real random variables $x_1, \ldots, x_H$. According to formulas (58.03) and (58.07), we have

$$\begin{aligned} p(x_1, \ldots, x_H) &= \frac{1}{(2\pi)^H}\int_{-\infty}^{\infty} \cdots \int_{-\infty}^{\infty} \\ &\times \exp\left\{-i\sum_h u_h x_h - \frac{1}{2}\sum_{g,h} R_{gh} u_g u_h\right\} du_1 \ldots du_H. \end{aligned} \tag{59.01}$$

The integral in (59.01) can easily be evaluated if we go from the variables $u_1, \ldots, u_H$ to new variables $t_1, \ldots, t_H$ by making an orthogonal transformation

$$t_g = \sum_h \alpha_{gh} u_h, \qquad u_h = \sum_g \alpha_{gh} t_g, \qquad \det \|\alpha_{gh}\| = 1 \tag{59.02}$$

such that the quadratic form in the integral (59.01) is transformed to principal axes,[1] and hence becomes

$$\sum_{g,h} R_{gh} u_g u_h = \sum_k \rho_k t_k^2. \tag{59.03}$$

In these variables, we also have

$$\sum_h u_h x_h = \sum_{g,h} \alpha_{gh} t_g x_h = \sum_k \xi_k t_k, \quad \text{where} \quad \xi_k = \sum_h \alpha_{kh} x_h, \tag{59.04}$$

and the multiple integral (59.01) reduces to a product of H single integrals, i.e.,

$$\begin{aligned} p(x_1, \ldots, x_H) &= \frac{1}{(2\pi)^H} \int_{-\infty}^{\infty} \cdots \int_{-\infty}^{\infty} \exp\Big\{-i \sum_k \xi_k t_k \\ &\qquad - \frac{1}{2} \sum_k \rho_k t_k^2\Big\}\, dt_1 \ldots dt_H \\ &= \frac{1}{(2\pi)^H} \prod_{k=1}^{H} \int_{-\infty}^{\infty} e^{-i\xi_k t_k - (\rho_k t_k^2/2)}\, dt_k, \end{aligned} \tag{59.05}$$

each of which can be simply evaluated as

$$\begin{aligned} \int_{-\infty}^{\infty} e^{-i\xi_k t_k - (\rho_k t_k^2/2)}\, dt_k &= e^{-\xi_k^2/2\rho_k} \int_{-\infty}^{\infty} e^{-\frac{1}{2}\rho_k[t_k + i(\xi_k/\rho_k)]^2}\, dt_k \\ &= \frac{1}{\sqrt{\rho_k}} e^{-\xi_k^2/2\rho_k} \int_{-\infty}^{\infty} e^{-x^2/2}\, dx \\ &= \sqrt{2\pi/\rho_k}\, e^{-\xi_k^2/2\rho_k}, \end{aligned} \tag{59.06}$$

so that

$$p(x_1, \ldots, x_H) = \frac{1}{\sqrt{(2\pi)^H \prod_k \rho_k}} \exp\Big\{-\frac{1}{2} \sum_k \frac{\xi_k^2}{\rho_k}\Big\}. \tag{59.07}$$

As is well known from the theory of quadratic forms, the determinant

---

[1] For a discussion of the methods of linear algebra used in this section, see e.g. R. Courant and D. Hilbert, *Methods of Mathematical Physics*, Vol. I, Chap. 1, Interscience Publishers, Inc., New York (1953) or V. I. Smirnov, *Linear Algebra and Group Theory*, translated and edited by R. A. Silverman, McGraw-Hill Book Co., Inc., New York (1961). (*Translator*)

made up of the coefficients of a quad· atic form is invariant under orthogonal transformations like (59.02), so that

$$\det \|R_{gh}\| = \prod_k \rho_k = \rho_1 \cdots \rho_H. \tag{59.08}$$

Moreover, according to formula (59.04), we have

$$\sum_k \frac{\xi_k^2}{\rho_k} = \sum_{g,h} Q_{gh} x_g x_h, \quad \text{where} \quad Q_{gh} = \sum_k \frac{1}{\rho_k} \alpha_{kg}\alpha_{kh}, \tag{59.09}$$

while formula (59.03) gives

$$R_{gh} = \sum_j \rho_j \alpha_{jg} \alpha_{jh}. \tag{59.10}$$

Since the coefficients α_{gh} of the orthogonal transformation (59.02) have to satisfy the relations

$$\sum_k \alpha_{kg}\alpha_{kh} = \sum_l \alpha_{gl}\alpha_{hl} = \delta_{gh}, \tag{59.11}$$

we easily obtain the formula

$$\sum_l R_{gl} Q_{lh} = \sum_{j,k,l} \frac{\rho_j}{\rho_k} \alpha_{jg}\alpha_{jl}\alpha_{kl}\alpha_{kh} = \sum_{j,k} \frac{\rho_j}{\rho_k} \delta_{jk}\alpha_{jg}\alpha_{kh} = \delta_{gh}, \tag{59.12}$$

which shows that the Q_{gh} are the elements of the inverse of the matrix $\|R_{gh}\|$. Therefore, in explicit form, formula (59.07) reads

$$p(x_1, \ldots, x_H) = \frac{1}{\sqrt{(2\pi)^H \det \|R_{gh}\|}} \exp\left\{-\frac{1}{2}\sum_{g,h} Q_{gh} x_g x_h\right\}. \tag{59.13}$$

In the case of complex random variables, we have to bear in mind that, according to (58.14) and (58.18), we have

$$dx_h dy_h = \frac{1}{2} dz_h dz_h^*, \qquad du_h dv_h = \frac{1}{2} dw_h dw_h^*. \tag{59.14}$$

Therefore, defining the probability density for the complex random variables in such a way that

$$p(z_1, z_1^*, \ldots, z_H, z_H^*)\, dz_1\, dz_1^* \ldots dz_H\, dz_H^*$$

is the probability that $z_1, z_1^*, \ldots, z_H, z_H^*$ lie in the corresponding volume element of the $2H$-dimensional space, we obtain

$$\begin{aligned} p(z_1, z_1^*, \ldots, z_H, z_H^*) \\ = \frac{1}{(4\pi)^{2H}} \int\int \cdots \int\int \exp\left\{-\frac{i}{2}\sum_h (w_h^* z_h + w_h z_h^*) - \frac{1}{2}\sum_h R_{gh} w_g w_h^*\right\} \\ \times\, dw_1\, dw_1^* \ldots dw_H\, dw_H^*, \end{aligned} \tag{59.15}$$

instead of (59.01).

Using the unitary transformation

$$t_g = \sum_h \alpha_{gh} w_h, \qquad w_h = \sum_g \alpha^*_{gh} t_g, \tag{59.16}$$

whose coefficients by definition satisfy the relations

$$\sum_k \alpha_{gk}\alpha^*_{hk} = \sum_k \alpha_{kg}\alpha^*_{kh} = \delta_{gh}, \tag{59.17}$$

we can transform the Hermitian matrix $\|R_{gh}\|$ to principal axes, i.e.,

$$\sum_{g,h} R_{gh} w_g w^*_h = \sum_k \rho_k |t_k|^2 \qquad (\rho_k > 0), \tag{59.18}$$

where

$$\sum_h w_h z^*_h = \sum_k \zeta^*_k t_k, \qquad \sum_h w^*_h z_h = \sum_k \zeta_k t^*_k, \qquad \zeta_k = \sum_h \alpha_{kh} z_h. \tag{59.19}$$

Introducing the real variables defined by

$$t_k = r_k + is_k, \qquad \zeta_k = \xi_k + i\eta_k, \tag{59.20}$$

we have

$$\begin{aligned} dt_k dt^*_k &= 2\, dr_k\, ds_k, \qquad |t_k|^2 = r_k^2 + s_k^2, \\ \frac{1}{2}(\zeta^*_k t_k + \zeta_k t^*_k) &= \xi_k r_k + \eta_k s_k. \end{aligned} \tag{59.21}$$

From this, using formula (59.06), we obtain

$$\begin{aligned} \int\!\!\int \exp\left\{-\frac{i}{2}(\zeta^*_k t_k + \zeta_k t^*_k) - \frac{1}{2}\rho_k |t_k|^2\right\} dt_k\, dt^*_k \\ = 2\int_{-\infty}^{\infty} e^{-i\xi_k r_k - (\rho_k r_k^2/2)}\, dr_k \int_{-\infty}^{\infty} e^{-i\eta_k s_k - (\rho_k s_k^2/2)}\, ds_k \\ = \frac{4\pi}{\rho_k} e^{-(\xi_k^2+\eta_k^2)/2\rho_k} = \frac{4\pi}{\rho_k} e^{-|\zeta_k|^2/2\rho_k}, \end{aligned} \tag{59.22}$$

so that

$$p(z_1, z^*_1, \ldots, z_H, z^*_H) = \frac{1}{(4\pi)^H \prod_k \rho_k} \exp\left\{-\frac{1}{2}\sum_k \frac{|\xi_k|^2}{\rho_k}\right\}. \tag{59.23}$$

The relation (59.08) is also valid for unitary transformations, and moreover

$$\sum_k \frac{|\zeta_k|^2}{\rho_k} = \sum_{g,h} Q_{gh} z_g z^*_h, \quad \text{where} \quad Q_{gh} = \sum_k \frac{1}{\rho_k} \alpha_{kg}\alpha^*_{gh}. \tag{59.24}$$

Since

$$R_{gh} = \sum \rho_j \alpha_{jg}\alpha^*_{jh} \quad \text{and} \quad \sum_l R_{gl} Q_{lh} = \delta_{gh}, \tag{59.25}$$

the matrix $\|Q_{gh}\|$ is the inverse of the matrix $\|R_{gh}\|$, and hence the probability density for the H complex normal random variables becomes

$$p(z_1, z_1^*, \ldots, z_H, z_H^*) = \frac{1}{(4\pi)^H \det \|R_{gh}\|} \exp\left\{-\frac{1}{2}\sum_{g,h} Q_{gh} z_g z_h^*\right\}. \quad (59.26)$$

If we use formulas (58.14) and (59.14) to return to the real random variables $x_1, \ldots, x_H$ and $y_1, \ldots, y_H$, and if we write the elements of the Hermitian matrix $\|Q_{gh}\|$ in the form

$$\begin{gathered} Q_{gh} = Q_{gh}^{(1)} + iQ_{gh}^{(2)}, \\ Q_{gh}^{(1)} = Q_{hg}^{(1)}, \qquad Q_{gh}^{(2)} = -Q_{hg}^{(2)}, \end{gathered} \quad (59.27)$$

then the probability density equals

$$\begin{aligned} p(x_1, \ldots, x_H; y_1, \ldots, y_H) &= \frac{1}{(2\pi)^H \det \|R_{gh}\|} \\ &\times \exp\left\{-\frac{1}{2}\sum_{g,h} [Q_{gh}^{(1)}(x_g x_h + y_g y_h) + Q_{gh}^{(2)}(x_g y_h - x_h y_g)]\right\}. \end{aligned} \quad (59.28)$$

Thus, finally, the H-dimensional Gaussian distribution is defined by formula (59.13) for real random variables, and by formula (59.26) for complex random variables.

It should be noted that if we have H real normal random variables $x_1, \ldots, x_H$, then, by introducing H additional real normal random variables $y_1, \ldots, y_H$ satisfying the conditions (58.12), we can always obtain H complex normal random variables of the type just considered. Here, the coefficients $R_{gh}^{(2)}$ can be chosen in various ways. For example, if we assume that $R_{gh}^{(2)} = 0$, then the quantities (58.16) will be real. In Sec. 43, we dealt with the case where the choice of the numbers R_{gh} was suggested by the general formula for the correlation function obtained in Sec. 69 below.

From the point of view of probability theory, the significance of Gaussian random variables lies in the fact that a random variable which is the sum of a sufficiently large number of independent (or weakly dependent) random variables has a distribution close to the Gaussian distribution. In probability theory, conditions are investigated under which the Gaussian distribution (59.13) is a limit distribution (in this sense).

60. Probability Distribution of the Envelope

In Chap. 7, we used a somewhat different notation for complex random variables, i.e., we started from the real random variables

$$u_\varkappa = G_\varkappa \cos \gamma_\varkappa, \qquad v_\varkappa = G_\varkappa \sin \gamma_\varkappa \qquad (\varkappa = 1, \ldots, L), \quad (60.01)$$

which we took to be Gaussian. Here, it is natural to assume that the one-dimensional probability density $p(\gamma_\varkappa)$ and the two-dimensional probability density $p(\gamma_\varkappa, \gamma_\lambda)$ satisfy the relations

$$p(\gamma_\varkappa) = p(\gamma_\varkappa + \vartheta), \qquad p(\gamma_\varkappa, \gamma_\lambda) = p(\gamma_\varkappa + \vartheta, \gamma_\lambda + \vartheta), \tag{60.02}$$

where ϑ is an arbitrary phase angle. These relations mean that when all the phases γ_k are shifted by the same angle ϑ, we arrive at new phases with the same probability distribution. It follows from (60.02) that we have the identities

$$\begin{gathered}\overline{\cos\gamma_\varkappa} = 0, \qquad \overline{\sin\gamma_\varkappa} = 0,\\ \overline{\cos(\gamma_\varkappa + \gamma_\lambda)} = 0, \qquad \overline{\sin(\gamma_\varkappa + \gamma_\lambda)} = 0,\\ \overline{\cos\gamma_\varkappa\cos\gamma_\lambda} = \overline{\sin\gamma_\varkappa\sin\gamma_\lambda},\\ \overline{\cos\gamma_\varkappa\sin\gamma_\lambda} = -\overline{\sin\gamma_\varkappa\cos\gamma_\lambda},\end{gathered} \tag{60.03}$$

which in turn imply that

$$\begin{gathered}\overline{u_\varkappa} = 0, \qquad \overline{v_\varkappa} = 0,\\ \overline{u_\varkappa u_\lambda} = \overline{v_\varkappa v_\lambda} = r^{(1)}_{\varkappa\lambda},\\ \overline{u_\varkappa v_\lambda} = -\overline{u_\lambda v_\varkappa} = r^{(2)}_{\varkappa\lambda},\end{gathered} \tag{60.04}$$

if we make the additional assumption that the quantities $G_\varkappa$ and G_λ (the amplitudes or *envelopes*) are independent of the phases $\gamma_\varkappa$ and γ_λ. If the envelopes $G_\varkappa$ are normalized according to the formula

$$\overline{G^2_\varkappa} = 2, \tag{60.05}$$

then the $r^{(1)}_{\varkappa\lambda}$ are correlation coefficients, since

$$r^{(1)}_{\varkappa\varkappa} = 1. \tag{60.06}$$

The formulas

$$r^{(1)}_{\varkappa\lambda} = r^{(1)}_{\lambda\varkappa}, \qquad r^{(2)}_{\varkappa\lambda} = -r^{(2)}_{\lambda\varkappa}, \qquad r^{(2)}_{\varkappa\varkappa} = 0 \tag{60.07}$$

express other properties of the coefficients $r^{(1)}_{\varkappa\lambda}$ and $r^{(2)}_{\varkappa\lambda}$.

If we introduce the complex random variables

$$w_\varkappa = u_\varkappa - iv_\varkappa = G_\varkappa e^{-i\gamma_\varkappa}, \qquad w^*_\varkappa = u_\varkappa + iv_\varkappa = G_\varkappa e^{i\gamma_\varkappa}, \tag{60.08}$$

then they have the moments

$$\begin{gathered}\overline{w_\varkappa} = \overline{w^*_\varkappa} = 0,\\ \overline{w_\varkappa w_\lambda} = \overline{w^*_\varkappa w^*_\lambda} = 0,\\ \overline{w^*_\varkappa w_\lambda} = 2r^m_{\varkappa\lambda},\end{gathered} \tag{60.09}$$

where the complex correlation coefficient $r^m_{\varkappa\lambda}$ equals

$$r^m_{\varkappa\lambda} = r^{(1)}_{\varkappa\lambda} - ir^{(2)}_{\varkappa\lambda}, \qquad r^m_{\varkappa\lambda} = (r^m_{\lambda\varkappa})^*. \tag{60.10}$$

For $L = 1$, the Hermitian matrix $\|r^m_{\varkappa\lambda}\|$ and its inverse matrix $\|q^m_{\varkappa\lambda}\|$ reduce to the number 1, and the probability density (59.13) becomes

$$p(u_1, v_1) = \frac{1}{2\pi} e^{-(u_1^2+v_1^2)/2} = \frac{1}{2\pi} e^{-G_1^2/2}. \tag{60.11}$$

To go from Cartesian coordinates u_1 and v_1 to polar coordinates G_1 and γ_1, we use the relation

$$du_1\, dv_1 = G_1\, dG_1\, d\gamma_1, \tag{60.12}$$

obtaining

$$p(G_1, \gamma_1) = \frac{G_1}{2\pi} e^{-G_1^2/2}. \tag{60.13}$$

Thus, the one-dimensional probability densities of the quantities G_1 and γ_1 are

$$\begin{aligned} p(\gamma_1) &= \frac{1}{2\pi} \qquad (0 \leqslant \gamma_1 < 2\pi), \\ p(G_1) &= G_1 e^{-G_1^2/2} \qquad (0 \leqslant G_1 < \infty). \end{aligned} \tag{60.14}$$

For $L = 2$, writing $r^m_{12} = pe^{-i\varepsilon}$, we obtain

$$\|r^m_{\varkappa\lambda}\| = \begin{Vmatrix} 1 & pe^{-i\varepsilon} \\ pe^{i\varepsilon} & 1 \end{Vmatrix}, \quad \|q^m_{\varkappa\lambda}\| = \frac{1}{1-p^2} \begin{Vmatrix} 1 & -pe^{-i\varepsilon} \\ -pe^{i\varepsilon} & 1 \end{Vmatrix}, \tag{60.15}$$

from which it follows that

$$\begin{aligned} p(u_1, u_2; v_1, v_2) &= \frac{1}{(2\pi)^2(1-p^2)} \\ &\times \exp - \left\{\frac{G_1^2 + G_2^2 - 2pG_1G_2 \cos(\gamma_1 - \gamma_2 + \varepsilon)}{2(1-p^2)}\right\}. \end{aligned} \tag{60.16}$$

Going over to polar coordinates, we obtain

$$\begin{aligned} p(G_1, G_2; \gamma_1, \gamma_2) &= \frac{G_1G_2}{(2\pi)^2(1-p^2)} \\ &\times \exp\left\{-\frac{G_1^2 + G_2^2 - 2pG_1G_2 \cos(\gamma_1 - \gamma_2 + \varepsilon)}{2(1-p^2)}\right\}. \end{aligned} \tag{60.17}$$

To find the two-dimensional probability density $p(G_1, G_2)$, we have to integrate (60.17) over γ_1 and γ_2. We use the identity

$$\frac{1}{2\pi}\int_0^{2\pi} \exp\left\{\frac{pG_1G_2 \cos(\gamma_1 - \gamma_2 + \varepsilon)}{1-p^2}\right\} d\gamma_1 = I_0\left(\frac{pG_1G_2}{1-p^2}\right), \tag{60.18}$$

to integrate over γ_1, after which integration over γ_2 gives the factor 2π. Finally, we obtain

$$p(G_1, G_2) = \frac{G_1G_2}{1-p^2} \exp\left\{-\frac{G_1^2 + G_2^2}{2(1-p^2)}\right\} I_0\left(\frac{pG_1G_2}{1-p^2}\right). \tag{60.19}$$

If G_1 and G_2 are normalized differently, e.g., if

$$\overline{G_1^2} = \overline{G_2^2} = 2\sigma^2, \tag{60.20}$$

so that

$$\overline{w_1^* w_2} = 2\sigma^2 p e^{-i\varepsilon}, \tag{60.21}$$

then it can easily be shown that formula (60.19) takes the form

$$p(G_1, G_2) = \frac{G_1 G_2}{\sigma^4(1 - p^2)} \exp\left\{-\frac{G_1^2 + G_2^2}{2\sigma^2(1 - p^2)}\right\} I_0\left(\frac{p G_1 G_2}{\sigma^2(1 - p^2)}\right). \tag{60.22}$$

Finally, it should be noted that the derivation of the formulas (60.04) given above is lacking in rigor. In view of the fact that these formulas imply a variety of important consequences, we point out that a rigorous treatment of the problem has to be based on the definition of the envelope and phase of a random process given by V. I. Bunimovich (see his book, cited on p. 34). The way in which the envelope and phase are usually introduced is not quite correct, from a mathematical point of view, and as a result it does not lead to a convincing proof of the formulas (60.04).

61. Thermal Noise and Shot Noise as Examples of Normal Random Processes

Random variables come to the fore when we "sample" random processes, i.e., when we consider the values of various random functions of time at discrete instants. Then, random processes whose sample values have the Gaussian distribution (see Sec. 59), or equivalently, a characteristic function of the form (58.07), are said to be *normal* or *Gaussian.*

In the theory of optimum receivers, it is usually assumed that the noise is a stationary normal random process. In addition, another assumption is often made (from which we have completely freed ourselves in this book) to the effect that the noise is "white," i.e., has a constant power spectral density; such noise, being uncorrelated in time (an "absolutely random" process) can be represented as a random superposition of disturbances (pulses) of zero duration (cf. Secs. 12 and 17). It is important to note that the nature of receiver noise itself, both thermal and shot noise (to be studied in detail below), gives some grounds for this idealization. However, the white noise model leads to certain mathematical difficulties, which do not entirely correspond to physical reality; and what is particularly important, the white noise model does not allow us to take into consideration an interesting kind of noise encountered in radar, i.e., clutter echoes due to "chaotic" reflections (see Chap. 11).

Since noise in the receiver itself has been considered throughout this book, it is appropriate to analyze briefly the physical characteristics of this kind of noise.

Thermal noise arises as a result of the thermal motion of electrical charges in conductors. Due to fluctuations, in every resistance in a state of thermodynamic equilibrium at absolute temperature T, there occurs a random electromotive force $\mathscr{E}(t)$, with spectral density equal to

$$S_{\mathscr{E}}(\omega) = 2RkT, \tag{61.01}$$

where k is Boltzmann's constant and R is the resistance. This relation is applicable to any element of an electrical circuit, where in general R is given by the formula

$$R = \operatorname{Re} Z(\omega), \tag{61.02}$$

and $Z(\omega)$ is the impedance of the given circuit element at the frequency ω.

We observe that for a purely ohmic resistance, which does not depend on the frequency, the fluctuating electromotive force $\mathscr{E}(t)$ is white noise, since its spectral density is constant. Actually, of course, for sufficiently high frequencies, the constancy of $S_{\mathscr{E}}(\omega)$ is always destroyed as a result of residual capacitance and inductance, the skin effect or quantum phenomena. It must also be borne in mind that as the frequency is increased, the quasi-stationary approach to the circuit, and with it formula (61.01), loses its meaning.

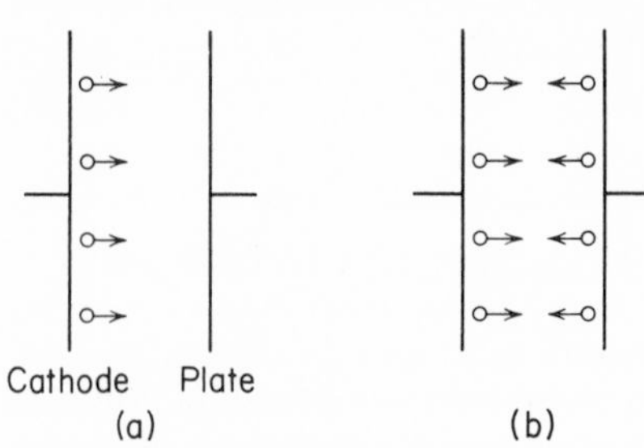

FIG. 56. Electron flow in a diode. (a) An ordinary diode, in which the electrons flow from the cathode to the plate; (b) An "equilibrium diode," in which the electrons move towards each other, and the total plate current is zero.

It turns out that in the case of metallic conductors, formula (61.01) can be applied even when direct or alternating currents flow in the conductors, when, strictly speaking, thermodynamic equilibrium does not occur. The reason for this is that when a current which is not too strong flows in a metallic conductor, the thermal motion of the electrical charges is perturbed only slightly, so that the fluctuations continue to obey formula (61.01).

The *shot effect* in vacuum tubes appears as a result of the discrete structure of the electron flow. Consider, for example, a diode and suppose that the voltage applied to the plate is so large that all the electrons emitted by the cathode arrive at the plate [see Fig. 56(a)]. Then, since the number of electrons emitted by the cathode fluctuates, a random "shot current" $I(t)$ is added to the average plate current J. The current $I(t)$ has spectral density

$$S_I(\omega) = eJ, \tag{61.03}$$

where e is the absolute value of the charge on the electron. We see that the current $I(t)$ due to the shot effect can also be regarded as white noise, since its spectral density does not depend on ω. Actually, if by $I(t)$ we mean the current in the external plate circuit, then formula (61.03) is only applicable if the condition

$$\omega\tau_0 \ll 1 \tag{61.04}$$

is met, where τ_0 is the transit time of an electron in the diode, or the duration of the pulse which appears in the plate circuit when a single electron goes from the cathode to the plate. If $\omega\tau_0 > 1$, there is a sharp cutoff in the spectral density of the shot noise. As a matter of fact, shot noise is the physical realization of the model of a random process which we considered in Sec. 12, since it consists of a superposition of randomly occurring perturbations (pulses) of "standard" form.

Due to the presence of the space-charge in a vacuum tube, only some of the electrons emitted by the cathode arrive at the plate. It turns out that the space-charge reduces the shot effect, so that formula (61.03) for the diode is replaced by

$$S_I(\omega) = \Gamma^2 eJ, \tag{61.05}$$

where Γ^2 is the so-called *space-charge-smoothing factor*, and J is the plate current.

We observe that a vacuum tube is not an equilibrium system. Therefore, formula (61.01) is not applicable to a vacuum tube, and the fluctuations are of an entirely different physical nature, a fact which is reflected in formulas (61.03) and (61.05). However, it is interesting to note that we can conceive of an electrical circuit containing an "equilibrium diode" [see Fig. 56(b)], i.e., a diode whose cathode and plate are at the same temperature and voltage, and are made of the same material capable of emitting electrons. If for simplicity we assume that the external circuit is simply a short circuit between the cathode and the plate, and if we let R denote the internal resistance of the equilibrium diode (with respect to small plate voltages and currents), then the thermal electromotive force $\mathscr{E}(t)$ appearing in the equilibrium diode is related to the fluctuation current $I(t)$ in the diode by the formula

$$\mathscr{E} = RI. \tag{61.06}$$

Hence, according to formula (61.01), we have

$$S_I(\omega) = \frac{2kT}{R}. \tag{61.07}$$

On the other hand, if the charge density is not too high, we can neglect electron collisions in the space between the cathode and the plate, and then the only "random element" in the system shown in Fig. 56(b) is the emission of electrons. If we let J_p denote the current which flows from the cathode to the plate, then, in the equilibrium diode, a current $-J_p$ must flow in the opposite direction, and both of these currents must experience the shot effect. Therefore, in the equilibrium diode, we must have

$$S_I(\omega) = 2eJ_p. \tag{61.08}$$

Then, since the expressions (61.07) and (61.08) for $S_I(\omega)$ must be equal, the resistance of the equilibrium diode has to be

$$R = \frac{kT}{eJ_p}, \tag{61.09}$$

a result which is confirmed by a detailed microscopic study of electron flow in a diode. Thus, in the present case, shot noise and thermal noise are just two different names for the same phenomenon.

In the absence of thermal equilibrium, the spectral density of shot noise is often written in the form

$$S_I(\omega) = \Theta \frac{2kT}{R}, \tag{61.10}$$

where Θ is a coefficient which gives the reduction of the equilibrium thermal noise. It turns out that

$$\Theta = \frac{1}{2} \tag{61.11}$$

in a diode with a retarding plate voltage and a cold plate, and in this case formulas (61.03) and (61.10) are equivalent. In a plane-parallel diode with an accelerating plate voltage and a high space-charge density,[2]

$$\Theta = 0.644, \tag{61.12}$$

and in this case the coefficient Γ^2 in formula (61.05) is small.

Above, we have considered the simplest systems in which thermal noise and shot noise appears. In actual systems, this noise undergoes various transformations. For example, in radio receivers, shot noise and thermal noise are amplified, filtered, etc. In the theory of optimum receivers, we assumed that noise equivalent to all the internal noise of the receiver is somehow applied to the input stage of the receiver, and that this noise can be represented as a random process $n(t)$ with known statistical properties.

Thermal noise and shot noise are classical examples of normal random processes. Such processes remain normal after passing through linear

---

[2] In such a diode, the so-called "three-halves law" is valid, according to which the plate current depends mainly on the plate voltage and is practically independent of the emission current.

systems (frequency filters). This is a simple consequence of the fact that after a linear transformation

$$x'_g = \sum_h a_{gh} x_h \tag{61.13}$$

of the normal random variables x_h, the new random variables x'_g are still normal, i.e., still have a Gaussian distribution. As we have already noted, another example of a normal random process is the radar noise caused by reflection from many randomly moving scatterers (see Chap. 11).

10

MODULATION BY NORMAL RANDOM PROCESSES

62. Amplitude, Frequency and Phase Modulation of a Sine Wave by a Normal Process

There exists a detailed literature on transformations of normal processes in passing through linear and nonlinear devices, and, along these lines, in this book, we have been concerned with various cases of filtering and detection of normal processes in optimum systems. Another way to transform a normal process is to use the process to modulate the output of a sine wave generator. In this way, one obtains a new random process which is not normal in general, but rather represents the result of making a complicated transformation of the original normal process. This topic, i.e., modulation by normal random processes, is the subject matter of the present chapter.

Thus, suppose that we have a source which in the absence of any modulation produces a pure sine wave[1] of frequency ω_0, and suppose that starting from the time $t = 0$, the source is modulated by a normal random process (noise), which we denote by $n(t)$. For simplicity, we normalize the random function $x(t)$ as follows:

$$\overline{x(t)} = 0, \qquad \overline{x^2(t)} = 1. \tag{62.01}$$

Suppose that as a result of the modulation, we obtain the oscillation

$$V(t) = A(t) \cos [\omega_0 t - \Theta(t)], \tag{62.02}$$

[1] The term *sine wave* as used here is synonymous with the term *harmonic oscillation*, and allows for an arbitrary initial phase. (*Translator*)

where $A(t)$ and $\Theta(t)$ are random functions. We assume that the instantaneous value of the amplitude $A(t)$ is determined by the value of $x(t)$ at the same time. For linear amplitude modulation (AM), we have

$$A(t) = A_0[1 + mx(t)], \qquad A_0 = \text{const}, \tag{62.03}$$

while exponential AM, i.e.,

$$A(t) = A_0 e^{mx(t)}, \tag{62.04}$$

is the simplest example of nonlinear AM. We also assume that the random process $x(t)$ changes the instantaneous values of the frequency and phase of the sine wave produced by the source, and that both the frequency modulation (FM) and the phase modulation (PM) are *linear*, so that for $t > 0$, we have

$$\Theta(t) = n\omega_0 y(t) + px(t) + \Theta_0, \tag{62.05}$$

where

$$y(t) = \int_0^t x(s)\, ds. \tag{62.06}$$

The quantities m, n and p in these formulas are called the *indices of amplitude, frequency and phase modulation*, respectively. In the general case, m, n and p can be negative or zero. The quantity $n\omega_0$ is sometimes called the *frequency deviation* (in this case, it is a root mean square deviation).

As a result of the random modulation, the spectrum of the sine wave which was originally (for $t < 0$) concentrated at the frequency ω_0, becomes spread out in frequency, in a way which depends on the spectral density of the random process $x(t)$ and on the modulation indices. Our problem is to calculate the spectral density and the correlation function of the modulated sine wave. Thus, writing

$$X(t) = \frac{V(t)}{A_0} \tag{62.07}$$

for brevity, we shall study the properties of the random functions

$$X(t) = [1 + mx(t)] \cos [\omega_0 t - \Theta(t)] \tag{62.08}$$

(linear AM) and

$$X(t) = e^{mx(t)} \cos [\omega_0 t - \Theta(t)] \tag{62.09}$$

(exponential AM).

The random function $y(t)$ is also normal, since it is obtained by a linear operation (i.e., integration) on $x(t)$. Writing

$$x_\alpha = x(t_\alpha), \qquad y_\alpha = y(t_\alpha), \qquad \Theta_\alpha = \Theta(t_\alpha), \tag{62.10}$$

and using formula (58.07), we can write the characteristic function

$$\chi(u_1, u_2; v_1, v_2) = \overline{e^{i(u_1 x_1 + u_2 x_2 + v_1 y_1 + v_2 y_2)}} \tag{62.11}$$

in the form

$$\chi(u_1, u_2; v_1, v_2) = \exp\{-\tfrac{1}{2}(a_1u_1^2 + a_2u_2^2 + 2e_1u_1u_2 + b_1v_1^2 + b_2v_2^2 + 2e_2v_1v_2 + 2c_1u_1v_1 + 2c_2u_2v_2 + 2d_1u_1v_2 + 2d_2u_2v_1)\}, \tag{62.12}$$

where the coefficients $a_1, \ldots, e_2$ can easily be expressed in terms of the correlation function

$$r(\tau) = r(-\tau) = \overline{x(t)x(t - \tau)}, \tag{62.13}$$

which describes how the process $x(t)$ varies in time. According to formula (58.09), we have

$$a_1 = \overline{x_1^2} = 1, \qquad a_2 = \overline{x_2^2} = 1, \qquad e_1 = \overline{x_1x_2} = r(\tau), \tag{62.14}$$

where

$$\tau = t_1 - t_2. \tag{62.15}$$

Moreover, we have

$$\begin{aligned} b_1 &= \overline{y_1^2} = \int_0^{t_1}\int_0^{t_1} r(s_1 - s_2)\, ds_1\, ds_2, \\ b_2 &= \overline{y_2^2} = \int_0^{t_2}\int_0^{t_2} r(s_1 - s_2)\, ds_1\, ds_2, \\ e_2 &= \overline{y_1y_2} = \int_0^{t_1}\int_0^{t_2} r(s_1 - s_2)\, ds_1\, ds_2, \end{aligned} \tag{62.16}$$

and

$$\begin{aligned} c_1 &= \overline{x_1y_1} = \int_0^{t_1} r(t_1 - s)\, ds, \quad c_2 = \overline{x_2y_2} = \int_0^{t_2} r(t_2 - s)\, ds, \\ d_1 &= \overline{x_1y_2} = \int_0^{t_2} r(t_1 - s)\, ds, \quad d_2 = \overline{x_2y_1} = \int_0^{t_1} r(t_2 - s)\, ds. \end{aligned} \tag{62.17}$$

If, for brevity, we introduce the notation

$$\begin{aligned} g(\tau) &= -g(-\tau) = \int_0^{\tau} r(s)\, ds \\ h(\tau) &= h(-\tau) = \int_0^{\tau}\int_0^{\tau} r(s_1 - s_2)\, ds_1\, ds_2, \end{aligned} \tag{62.18}$$

then

$$\begin{aligned} b_1 + b_2 - 2e_2 &= \overline{(y_1 - y_2)^2} = h(\tau), \\ c_1 - d_1 &= d_2 - c_2 = g(\tau). \end{aligned} \tag{62.19}$$

A knowledge of the characteristic function (62.12) allows us to calculate the correlation function of the modulated sine wave, as we show in the next section.

63. Correlation Function and Spectral Density of a Modulated Sine Wave

Using the formula

$$\cos\alpha\cos\beta = \frac{1}{2}\cos(\alpha - \beta) + \frac{1}{2}\cos(\alpha + \beta), \tag{63.01}$$

we can write

$$\overline{X(t_1)X(t_2)} = R(\tau) + \tilde{R}(t_1, t_2), \qquad \tau = t_1 - t_2, \tag{63.02}$$

so that for linear AM,

$$R(\tau) = \frac{1}{2}\overline{(1 + mx_1)(1 + mx_2)\cos[\omega_0\tau - (\Theta_1 - \Theta_2)]}. \tag{63.03}$$

For brevity, we write the function $R(\tau)$ in the form

$$R(\tau) = \frac{1}{2}\operatorname{Re}\{E(\tau)e^{i\omega_0\tau}\} = \frac{1}{4}[E(\tau)e^{i\omega_0\tau} + E^*(\tau)e^{-i\omega_0\tau}], \tag{63.04}$$

where the auxiliary function $E(\tau)$ is

$$E(\tau) = \overline{e^{-i(\Theta_1-\Theta_2)}} + \overline{m(x_1 + x_2)e^{-i(\Theta_1-\Theta_2)}} + \overline{m^2x_1x_2e^{-i(\Theta_1-\Theta_2)}} \tag{63.05}$$

for linear AM, and

$$E(\tau) = \overline{e^{m(x_1+x_2)-i(\Theta_1-\Theta_2)}} \tag{63.06}$$

for exponential AM.

Since

$$\Theta_1 - \Theta_2 = p(x_1 - x_2) + n\omega_0(y_1 - y_2), \tag{63.07}$$

according to formula (62.11), we have

$$\begin{aligned}
\overline{e^{-i(\Theta_1-\Theta_2)}} &= \chi(-p, p;\ -n\omega_0, n\omega_0),\\
\overline{x_1e^{-i(\Theta_1-\Theta_2)}} &= -i\frac{\partial\chi}{\partial u_1}(-p, p;\ -n\omega_0, n\omega_0),\\
\overline{x_2e^{-i(\Theta_1-\Theta_2)}} &= -i\frac{\partial\chi}{\partial u_2}(-p, p;\ -n\omega_0, n\omega_0),\\
\overline{x_1x_2e^{-i(\Theta_1-\Theta_2)}} &= -\frac{\partial^2\chi}{\partial u_1\partial u_2}(-p, p;\ -n\omega_0, n\omega_0).
\end{aligned} \tag{63.08}$$

Taking into account formulas (62.12) to (62.19), we obtain

$$\begin{aligned}
\overline{e^{-i(\Theta_1-\Theta_2)}} &= \exp\{-\tfrac{1}{2}n^2\omega_0^2h(\tau) - p^2[1 - r(\tau)]\},\\
\overline{x_1e^{-i(\Theta_1-\Theta_2)}} &= -i\{n\omega_0g(\tau) + p[1 - r(\tau)]\}\\
&\quad\times\exp\{-\tfrac{1}{2}n^2\omega_0^2h(\tau) - p^2[1 - r(\tau)]\},\\
\overline{x_2e^{-i(\Theta_1-\Theta_2)}} &= -i\{n\omega_0g(\tau) - p[1 - r(\tau)]\}\\
&\quad\times\exp\{-\tfrac{1}{2}n^2\omega_0^2h(\tau) - p^2[1 - r(\tau)]\},\\
\overline{x_1x_2e^{-i(\Theta_1-\Theta_2)}} &= \{r(\tau) - n^2\omega_0^2g^2(\tau) + p^2[1 - r(\tau)]^2\}\\
&\quad\times\exp\{-\tfrac{1}{2}n^2\omega_0^2h(\tau) - p^2[1 - r(\tau)]\}.
\end{aligned} \tag{63.09}$$

Therefore, for linear AM, the correlation function of the modulated sine wave is given by formula (63.04), where

$$E(\tau) = \{[1 - imn\omega_0 g(\tau)]^2 + m^2 r(\tau) + m^2 p^2 [1 - r(\tau)]^2\} \times \exp\{-\tfrac{1}{2}n^2\omega_0^2 h(\tau) - p^2[1 - r(\tau)]\}. \tag{63.10}$$

Similarly, we have

$$\overline{e^{m(x_1+x_2)-i(\Theta_1-\Theta_2)}} = \chi(-p - im, p - im; -n\omega_0, n\omega_0), \tag{63.11}$$

so that for exponential AM, the function $E(\tau)$ equals

$$E(\tau) = \exp\{-2imn\omega_0 g(\tau) - \tfrac{1}{2}n^2\omega_0^2 h(\tau) + m^2[1 + r(\tau)] - p^2[1 - r(\tau)]\}. \tag{63.12}$$

As for the function

$$\tilde{R}(t_1, t_2) = \frac{1}{2}\overline{(1 + mx_1)(1 + mx_2)\cos[\omega_0(t_1 + t_2) - (\Theta_1 + \Theta_2)]} \tag{63.13}$$

for linear AM, or

$$\tilde{R}(t_1, t_2) = \frac{1}{2}\overline{e^{m(x_1+x_2)}\cos[\omega_0(t_1 + t_2) - (\Theta_1 + \Theta_2)]} \tag{63.14}$$

for exponential AM, which appears in the right-hand side of (63.02), it rapidly converges to zero as t_1 and t_2 are increased. To see this, we first note that $\tilde{R}(t_1, t_2)$ is proportional to the expression

$$\exp\{-\tfrac{1}{2}n^2\omega_0^2(b_1 + b_2 + 2e_2)\}. \tag{63.15}$$

Then, for sufficiently large t_1 and $t_2 \leqslant t_1$, we have the approximate formula

$$b_1 \sim 2t_1\,\delta\tau, \qquad b_2 \sim e_2 \sim 2t_2\,\delta\tau \tag{63.16}$$

(cf. Sec. 66 below), so that

$$\tilde{R} \sim e^{-t/t_0}, \tag{63.17}$$

for large t, where the correlation time is given by the formula

$$\frac{1}{t_0} = 4n^2\omega_0^2\,\delta\tau. \tag{63.18}$$

The function $\tilde{R}(t_1, t_2)$ appears here because the random process $X(t)$ is nonstationary (the modulation began at time $t = 0$). If we neglect transient effects and consider $X(t)$ only for sufficiently large t, then we can write

$$\overline{X(t_1)X(t_2)} = R(\tau). \tag{63.19}$$

We note that the intensity (average power) of the stationary process $X(t)$ is

$$\overline{X^2} = R(0), \tag{63.20}$$

where

$$R(0) = \frac{1}{2}(1 + m^2), \tag{63.21}$$

for linear AM, and

$$R(0) = \frac{1}{2} e^{2m^2} \tag{63.22}$$

for exponential AM.

Using the correlation function $R(\tau)$ just found, it is not hard to calculate the spectral density

$$S(\omega) = \int_{-\infty}^{\infty} e^{-i\omega\tau} R(\tau)\, d\tau \tag{63.23}$$

of the modulated sine wave. Substituting (63.04) into this formula, we can write the spectral density in the form

$$S(\omega) = F(\omega) + F^*(-\omega), \tag{63.24}$$

where

$$\begin{aligned} F(\omega) &= \frac{1}{4}\int_{-\infty}^{\infty} e^{-i(\omega-\omega_0)\tau} E(\tau)\, d\tau, \\ F^*(\omega) &= \frac{1}{4}\int_{-\infty}^{\infty} e^{-i(\omega+\omega_0)\tau} E^*(\tau)\, d\tau. \end{aligned} \tag{63.25}$$

These formulas, together with (63.10) and (63.12), provide a complete solution of the problem of calculating the power spectrum of a modulated sine wave. In using them, it should be noted that instead of $r(\tau)$, the correlation function of the modulating process $x(t)$, we are often given the spectral density $s(\omega)$ of the process $x(t)$, connected with $r(\tau)$ by the relations

$$s(\omega) = \int_{-\infty}^{\infty} e^{-i\omega\tau} r(\tau)\, d\tau \tag{63.26}$$

and

$$r(\tau) = \frac{1}{2\pi}\int_{-\infty}^{\infty} e^{i\omega\tau} s(\omega)\, d\omega. \tag{63.27}$$

Then, starting from the spectral density of the modulating process, we must first calculate the random function $r(\tau)$, using (63.27), next calculate the functions $g(\tau)$ and $h(\tau)$, using (62.18), and finally calculate the desired spectral density $S(\omega)$, using (63.24) and (63.25). In the next section, we shall analyze the most interesting applications of these formulas.

64. Quasi-Sinusoidal Modulation

Below, we shall make extensive use of the delta function, which we have tried to avoid using throughout the book, wherever possible [see, however, formulas (1.13) and (21.04)]. If the correlation function $R(\tau)$ has the form

$$R(\tau) = \sum_k P_k \cos \omega_k \tau, \tag{64.01}$$

then the integral (63.23) leads to the expression

$$S(\omega) = \pi \sum_k P_k[\delta(\omega - \omega_k) + \delta(\omega + \omega_k)], \tag{64.02}$$

which shows that all the intensity of the given process is concentrated at the discrete frequencies $\omega = \pm\omega_k$. For example, in the absence of any modulation $[x(t) \equiv 0]$, we have

$$X(t) = \cos(\omega_0 t - \Theta_0). \tag{64.03}$$

If the phase Θ_0 is random and is uniformly distributed from 0 to 2π, then averaging over Θ_0 gives

$$R(\tau) = \overline{X(t_1)X(t_2)} = \frac{1}{2}\cos\omega_0\tau. \tag{64.04}$$

It follows that

$$S(\omega) = \frac{\pi}{2}[\delta(\omega - \omega_0) + \delta(\omega + \omega_0)], \tag{64.05}$$

so that in the absence of modulation, the intensity is concentrated at $\omega = \pm\omega_0$.

The formulas derived in Sec. 63 give the simplest results in the case of linear AM, when there is no frequency or phase modulation (FM or PM), i.e., when $m \neq 0$ and $n = p = 0$. Then we have

$$F(\omega) = \frac{\pi}{2}\delta(\omega - \omega_0) + \frac{m^2}{4}s(\omega - \omega_0), \tag{64.06}$$

so that the spectrum function $F(\omega)$ appearing in (63.24) consists of the line $\omega = \omega_0$, corresponding to the unmodulated oscillation, and the spectral density $s(\omega)$, "shifted over" to the carrier frequency ω_0. If the spectrum of the modulating process is concentrated in a very narrow frequency band near the frequency ω_1, then we can write

$$s(\omega) = \pi[\delta(\omega - \omega_1) + \delta(\omega + \omega_1)], \tag{64.07}$$

and the corresponding correlation function equals

$$r(\tau) = \cos\omega_1\tau. \tag{64.08}$$

In this case, the modulating process is an oscillation with a definite frequency ω_1, but with a random amplitude and phase. We shall call this kind of modulation *quasi-sinusoidal*, since it differs from ordinary sinusoidal modulation (see below).

For quasi-sinusoidal AM, formula (64.06) takes the form

$$F(\omega) = \frac{\pi}{2}\left[\delta(\omega - \omega_0) + \frac{m^2}{4}\delta(\omega - \omega_0 - \omega_1) + \frac{m^2}{4}\delta(\omega - \omega_0 + \omega_1)\right]. \tag{64.09}$$

The spectral density corresponding to (64.06) and (64.09) can easily be derived by an elementary argument.

For quasi-sinusoidal PM ($p \neq 0$, $m = n = 0$), the function $F(\omega)$ equals

$$F(\omega) = \frac{1}{4} e^{-p^2} \int_{-\infty}^{\infty} e^{-i(\omega-\omega_0)\tau + p^2 \cos \omega_1 \tau} \, d\tau. \tag{64.10}$$

The function $\exp \{p^2 \cos \omega_1 \tau\}$ is periodic, with period $2\pi/\omega_1$, and hence can be expanded in a Fourier series

$$\begin{aligned} e^{p^2 \cos \omega_1 \tau} &= I_0(p^2) + 2 \sum_{k=1}^{\infty} I_k(p^2) \cos k\omega_1 \tau \\ &= \sum_{k=-\infty}^{\infty} I_k(p^2) e^{ik\omega_1 \tau}, \end{aligned} \tag{64.11}$$

where I_k is the modified Bessel function of the first kind of order k, defined by the formula

$$\begin{aligned} I_k(x) &= \frac{1}{\pi} \int_0^{\pi} e^{x \cos \varphi} \cos k\varphi \, d\varphi \\ &= \frac{\omega_1}{\pi} \int_0^{\pi/\omega_1} e^{x \cos \omega_1 \tau} \cos k\omega_1 \tau \, d\tau. \end{aligned} \tag{64.12}$$

It follows that

$$\begin{aligned} F(\omega) = \frac{\pi}{2} e^{-p^2} \Big\{ & I_0(p^2) \delta(\omega - \omega_0) \\ & + \sum_{k=1}^{\infty} I_k(p^2) [\delta(\omega - \omega_0 + k\omega_1) + \delta(\omega - \omega_0 - k\omega_1)] \Big\}, \end{aligned} \tag{64.13}$$

i.e., in the case of quasi-sinusoidal PM, the spectrum is discrete as in the case of ordinary sinusoidal PM, but the intensity associated with each frequency is expressed in terms of the coefficient of phase modulation in a somewhat different way.

To give an elementary derivation of formula (64.13), we proceed as follows: Let

$$x(t) = a \cos (\omega_1 t - \vartheta), \tag{64.14}$$

where a and ϑ are constants. Then we have

$$\begin{aligned} X(t) &= \cos [\omega_0 t - pa \cos (\omega_1 t - \vartheta) - \Theta_0] = J_0(pa) \cos (\omega_0 t - \Theta_0) \\ &+ \sum_{k=1}^{\infty} J_k(pa) \left\{ \cos \left[(\omega_0 + k\omega_1) t - k\left(\frac{\pi}{2} + \vartheta\right) - \Theta_0 \right] \right. \\ &+ \left. (-1)^k \cos \left[(\omega_0 - k\omega_1) t + k\left(\frac{\pi}{2} + \vartheta\right) - \Theta_0 \right] \right\}. \end{aligned} \tag{64.15}$$

This formula is well known in the theory of frequency and phase modulation, and can easily be deduced from the properties of Bessel functions.[2] Thus, we see that the frequency $\omega = \omega_0 - k\omega_1$ (for example), has the mean intensity $\frac{1}{2}J_k^2(pa)$, when averaged over the phase. The amplitude (envelope) a has the Rayleigh distribution

$$p(a) = ae^{-a^2/2} \tag{64.16}$$

Therefore, after averaging over a, the intensity corresponding to the frequency $\omega_0 - k\omega_1$ equals

$$\frac{1}{2}\int_0^\infty ae^{-a^2/2}J_k^2(pa)\,da = \frac{1}{2}\,e^{-p^2}I_k(p^2), \tag{64.17}$$

where the last expression is the same as that given by formula (64.13). The integral in (64.17) is a special case of Weber's second exponential integral.[3]

For pure FM ($n \neq 0$, $m = p = 0$), we have

$$F(\omega) = \frac{1}{4}\int_{-\infty}^{\infty} \exp\{-i(\omega - \omega_0)\tau - \tfrac{1}{2}n^2\omega_0^2 h(\tau)\}\,d\tau, \tag{64.18}$$

and for quasi-sinusoidal modulation, the function $h(\tau)$ is

$$h(\tau) = 2\,\frac{1 - \cos\omega_1\tau}{\omega_1^2}. \tag{64.19}$$

Then, a comparison of formulas (64.10) and (64.18) shows that quasi-sinusoidal FM with modulation index n is completely equivalent to quasi-sinusoidal PM with modulation index

$$p = n\,\frac{\omega_0}{\omega_1}. \tag{64.20}$$

This is a familiar relation in the theory of sinusoidal modulation.

The formulas given above essentially verify the general formulas derived in Sec. 63. In the next two sections, we shall study other applications of these general formulas.

65. Limiting Cases of the Spectral Density

We now consider modulation by a normal process whose spectral density $s(\omega)$ resembles that shown in Fig. 5. We define the correlation time $\delta\tau$ and the bandwidth $\delta\omega$ of the modulating process by using the formulas

$$\delta\tau = \int_0^\infty r(\tau)\,d\tau, \qquad \delta\omega = \frac{\pi}{s(0)}, \tag{65.01}$$

---

[2] G. N. Watson, *op. cit.*, p. 22.

[3] G. N. Watson, *op. cit.*, p. 395.

which are the simplified versions of the corresponding formulas of Sec. 3, obtained for $r(0) = 1$. Then, $\delta\omega$ and $\delta\tau$ are connected by the relation

$$\delta\omega\,\delta\tau = \frac{\pi}{2}. \tag{65.02}$$

In Sec. 63, we reduced the calculation of the spectral density of the modulated sine wave to the evaluation of certain integrals. However, the evaluation of these integrals is in general difficult, since the function $r(\tau)$ and the functions $g(\tau)$ and $h(\tau)$ determined by $r(\tau)$ are usually complicated. On the other hand, for small τ, these functions are approximately equal to

$$r(\tau) = 1, \quad g(\tau) = \tau, \quad h(\tau) = \tau^2 \quad (|\tau| \ll \delta\tau), \tag{65.03}$$

while, for large τ, they are approximately equal to

$$r(\tau) = 0, \quad g(\tau) = \delta\tau, \quad h(\tau) = 2\tau\,\delta\tau \quad (\tau \gg \delta\tau). \tag{65.04}$$

The use of the approximate expressions (65.03) is equivalent to assuming that the spectrum of the modulating process is infinitely narrow, i.e., that

$$s(\omega) = 2\pi\delta(\omega), \qquad r(\tau) = 1. \tag{65.05}$$

Then, formula (63.10) becomes

$$\begin{aligned} F(\omega) &= \frac{1}{4}\int_{-\infty}^{\infty} [(1 - imn\omega_0\tau)^2 + m^2]\exp\{-i(\omega - \omega_0)\tau - \tfrac{1}{2}n^2\omega_0^2\tau^2\}\,d\tau \\ &= \sqrt{\frac{\pi}{2}}\frac{1}{2n\omega_0}\left[1 - \frac{m(\omega - \omega_0)}{n\omega_0}\right]^2 \exp\left\{-\frac{(\omega - \omega_0)^2}{2n^2\omega_0^2}\right\}, \end{aligned} \tag{65.06}$$

while formula (63.12) becomes

$$\begin{aligned} F(\omega) &= \frac{1}{4}\int_{-\infty}^{\infty} \exp\{-i[\omega - \omega_0(1 - 2mn)]\tau - \tfrac{1}{2}n^2\omega_0^2\tau^2 + 2m^2\}\,d\tau \\ &= \sqrt{\frac{\pi}{2}}\frac{1}{2n\omega_0}\exp\left\{2m^2 - \frac{[\omega - \omega_0(1 - 2mn)]^2}{2n^2\omega_0^2}\right\}. \end{aligned} \tag{65.07}$$

Thus, in both cases, it turns out that the presence or absence of PM does not affect the spectral density. This phenomenon is characteristic of the "quasi-static" modulation defined by (65.05), since an "infinitely slow" phase change should not affect the spectral density. Moreover, the spectral bandwidth $n\omega_0$ is determined only by the FM, while the action of the AM is revealed only by the shift of the maximum of the function $F(\omega)$ from the frequency ω_0 to the frequency

$$\omega_0' = \omega_0(1 - 2mn) \tag{65.08}$$

(the AM does not affect the bandwidth). Formula (65.08) is exact for exponential AM, but only approximate for linear AM (valid for $m \ll 1$).

It is not hard to derive formulas (65.06) and (65.07) by an elementary argument. For simplicity, we consider FM without AM ($n \neq 0, m = 0$). Then, to each value of x which changes sufficiently slowly in time, there correspond the frequencies

$$\omega = \pm\omega_0(1 + nx), \tag{65.09}$$

and the intensity of the spectrum associated with each frequency is $\frac{1}{4}$. Therefore, for quasi-static modulation, the spectral density is given by

$$\frac{1}{2\pi} S(\omega)\, d\omega = \frac{1}{4}\,[p(x')\, dx' + p(x'')\, dx''], \tag{65.10}$$

where

$$x' = \frac{\omega - \omega_0}{n\omega_0}, \qquad x'' = -\frac{\omega + \omega_0}{n\omega_0}, \qquad p(x) = \frac{1}{\sqrt{2\pi}}\, e^{-x^2/2}.$$

It follows that

$$S(\omega) = \sqrt{\frac{\pi}{2}}\,\frac{1}{2n\omega_0}\,[e^{-(\omega-\omega_0)^2/2n^2\omega_0^2} + e^{-(\omega+\omega_0)^2/2n^2\omega_0^2}], \tag{65.11}$$

which agrees with the results obtained above, if $m = 0$.

A more exact analysis of (63.10), (63.12) and (63.25) shows that formulas (65.06) and (65.07) are valid under the condition that the parameter

$$q = n\omega_0\,\delta\tau = \frac{\pi}{2}\,\frac{n\omega_0}{\delta\omega} \tag{65.12}$$

is large compared to unity. Then, the spectral bandwidth of the modulated sine wave, given by

$$\Delta\omega \sim n\omega_0 \sim q\,\delta\omega, \tag{65.13}$$

is large compared to $\delta\omega$, the spectral bandwidth of the modulating process.

In the opposite case, when $q \ll 1$, we can substitute the approximate expressions (65.04) into the integrals (63.25). For example, for linear AM, we obtain

$$\begin{aligned} F(\omega) &= \frac{1}{2}\,\mathrm{Re}\left\{[(1 - imn\omega_0\delta\tau)^2 + m^2p^2]e^{-p^2}\int_0^\infty e^{-[i(\omega-\omega_0)+n^2\omega_0^2\delta\tau]\tau}\, d\tau\right\} \\ &= \frac{1}{2}\,e^{-p^2}\,\mathrm{Re}\left\{\frac{(1 - imq)^2 + m^2p^2}{n\omega_0 q + i(\omega - \omega_0)}\right\}. \end{aligned} \tag{65.14}$$

With the extra condition $mq \ll 1$, the function $F(\omega)$ becomes

$$F(\omega) = \frac{(1 + m^2p^2)e^{-p^2}}{2n\omega_0 q}\,\frac{1}{1 + \left(\dfrac{\omega - \omega_0}{n\omega_0 q}\right)^2}, \tag{65.15}$$

from which it follows that in the limiting case $q \ll 1$, AM and PM do not affect the shape of the spectrum. The spectral bandwidth is

$$\Delta\omega \sim n\omega_0 q \sim \frac{2}{\pi} q^2 \,\delta\omega, \tag{65.16}$$

which is small compared to $\delta\omega$.

66. Relation Between the Bandwidths of the Modulating and Modulated Processes

We now calculate the dependence of $\Delta\omega$ on $\delta\omega$ for the case of frequency modulation ($n \neq 0$, $m = p = 0$). We define the (spectral) bandwidth of the *modulating* process by formula (65.01), and the bandwidth of the *modulated* process (i.e., the process obtained as a result of the modulation) by the formula

$$2F(\omega_0)\,\Delta\omega = \int_{-\infty}^{\infty} F(\omega)\,d\omega = \frac{1}{2}\int_{-\infty}^{\infty} S(\omega)\,d\omega = \frac{\pi}{2} \tag{66.01}$$

or

$$\omega = \frac{\pi}{4F(\omega_0)}. \tag{66.02}$$

In fact, for $m = p = 0$, the function

$$F(\omega) = \frac{1}{2}\,\mathrm{Re}\left\{\int_0^{\infty} e^{-i(\omega-\omega_0)\tau - \frac{1}{2}n^2\omega_0^2 h(\tau)}\,d\tau\right\} \tag{66.03}$$

is symmetric with respect to the point $\omega = \omega_0$, where it takes its maximum, and, therefore, the definition (66.02) is analogous to the definition (65.01). (See also the end of Sec. 3.)

It is difficult to calculate the integral (66.03) even for $\omega = \omega_0$, and hence, it is natural to replace the correlation function $r(\tau)$ by the step function

$$\begin{aligned} r(\tau) &= 1 \quad \text{for} \quad |\tau| < \delta\tau, \\ r(\tau) &= 0 \quad \text{for} \quad |\tau| > \delta\tau, \end{aligned} \tag{66.04}$$

so that

$$\begin{aligned} h(\tau) &= \tau^2 \quad \text{for} \quad |\tau| < \delta\tau, \\ h(\tau) &= 2\tau\delta\tau - (\delta\tau)^2 \quad \text{for} \quad |\tau| > \delta\tau. \end{aligned} \tag{66.05}$$

This replacement must be regarded as a *rough approximation* to correlation functions $r(\tau)$ corresponding to spectra of the type shown in Fig. 5. In fact, a correlation function with the exact form (66.04) cannot exist. Making this change, we obtain

$$F(\omega_0) = \frac{1}{2}\left\{\int_0^{\delta\tau} e^{-n^2\omega_0^2\tau^2/2}\,d\tau + e^{n^2\omega_0^2(\delta\tau)^2/2}\int_{\delta\tau}^{\infty} e^{-n^2\omega_0^2\tau\delta\tau}\,d\tau\right\}$$
$$= \sqrt{\frac{\pi}{2}}\frac{1}{n\omega_0}\left[P(q) + \frac{1}{q}P'(q)\right], \tag{66.06}$$

where

$$P(q) = \frac{1}{\sqrt{2\pi}}\int_0^q e^{-t^2/2}\,dt. \tag{66.07}$$

Curve 1 of Fig. 57 shows the dependence of the quantity

$$\frac{\omega}{n\omega_0} = \frac{1}{2}\sqrt{\frac{\pi}{2}}\frac{1}{P(q) + (1/q)P'(q)} \tag{66.08}$$

on the parameter q. In particular, it is clear from Fig. 57 which values of

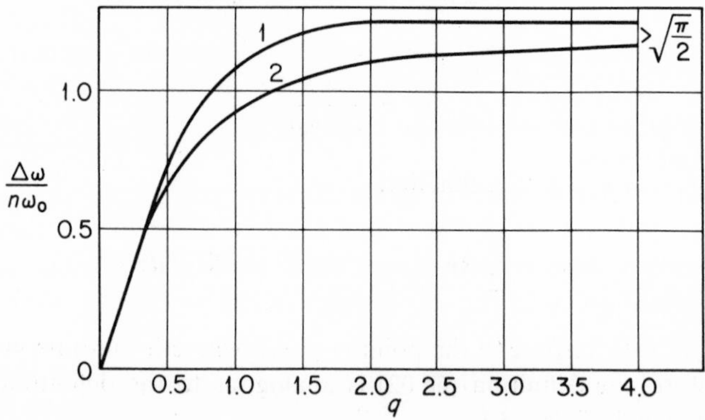

FIG. 57. Spectral bandwidth of the modulated process for random frequency modulation. Curve 1, from formula (66.08); Curve 2, from formula (66.13).

q correspond to the limiting case (65.13) and which correspond to the limiting case (65.16).

Curve 2 of Fig. 57 shows the same curve ($\Delta\omega/n\omega_0$ vs. q) for the case of the correlation function

$$r(\tau) = e^{-|\tau|/\delta\tau}, \tag{66.09}$$

corresponding to the spectral density

$$s(\omega) = \frac{2\delta\tau}{1 + \omega^2(\delta\tau)^2}. \tag{66.10}$$

This is the spectrum obtained when "white noise" is passed through an RC filter with time constant $\delta\tau$. In this case, we have

$$h(\tau) = 2(\delta\tau)^2(\alpha - 1 + e^{-\alpha}), \quad \text{where} \quad \alpha = \frac{\tau}{\delta\tau} > 0 \tag{66.11}$$

and

$$\begin{aligned} F(\omega_0) &= \frac{1}{2}\,\delta\tau e^{q^2} \int_0^\infty e^{-q^2(\alpha+e^{-\alpha})}\,d\alpha \\ &= \frac{1}{2}\,\delta\tau e^{q^2}(q^2)^{-q^2} \int_0^{q^2} t^{q^2-1}e^{-t}\,dt \end{aligned} \tag{66.12}$$

(let $t = q^2e^{-\alpha}$). It follows that

$$\frac{\Delta\omega}{n\omega_0} = \frac{\pi}{2q}\,\frac{e^{-q^2}(q^2)^{q^2}}{(q^2 - 1, q^2)!}, \tag{66.13}$$

where the function

$$(x, y)! = \int_0^y t^x e^{-t}\,dt \tag{66.14}$$

is the "incomplete factorial," originally introduced in tabulating the χ^2 distribution (see, e.g., the formulas of Secs. 38 and 45). To construct curve 2, the graphs of the function $(x, y)!$ given in the book by Jahnke and Emde[4] are adequate.

For small and large values of q, the curves 1 and 2 coincide (as follows from the general considerations of Sec. 65), while for finite q, they vary in the same general way. These curves allow us to estimate the bandwidth of the *modulated* process from a knowledge of the bandwidth of the *modulating* process.

This chapter is based on work done by L. A. Wainstein in 1947, at the suggestion of M. A. Leontovich. Equivalent mathematical results have been obtained independently by many other authors in connection with the most varied problems of engineering and physics. In the next chapter, we shall use the results obtained here to analyze noise due to random reflections (clutter echoes).

---

[4] E. Jahnke and F. Emde, *Tables of Higher Functions*, B. G. Teubner, Leipzig (1952). See p. 23.

11

CLUTTER ECHOES

67. Noise Due to Random Reflections

In radar, we are interested in noise obtained as a result of reflection (or scattering) of electromagnetic waves by raindrops, mist, vegetation and other aggregates of objects irregularly located in space. A statistical treatment of this kind of noise is necessary (and, in fact, possible) because of its "massive" character. For example, a single raindrop gives a scattered field which is small compared to the field produced by the reflection of the useful signal from the radar target, and it is only as a result of the superposition of fields from a large number of scattering objects that one obtains noise which seriously influences the operation of the radar system.

Because of the irregular location and motion of the separate scatterers, the noise caused by "chaotic" reflections from an aggregate of scatterers has to be regarded as a *random process* at the input to the radar receiver. This random process is perforce *normal*, since it is a superposition of a large number of independent (or weakly dependent) terms caused by the fields from the individual scatterers (or groups of scatterers). In our theoretical investigation of clutter, we shall not regard as clutter the noise due to the presence of large objects like buildings, hills, etc., since a statistical treatment of this kind of noise is meaningless; instead we have to talk about the resolution of signals from two or more different objects, about the ways in which the required resolution can be accomplished, etc.

The following difficulty is encountered in theoretical studies of optimum receivers for detecting radar signals in a background of clutter echoes: The random process caused by the chaotic reflections is nonstationary, which makes its correlation properties more complicated, makes it impossible to use a power spectrum point of view, etc. In fact, when a cloud of scatterers is illuminated by a sequence of L pulses [Fig. 58(a)], we receive a random process which comprises only part of the L repetition periods and which is completely absent in the time interval before and after these L periods [Fig. 58(b)]. The nonstationarity of this random process is due to two causes: (1) the finite extent of the region of space occupied by the scatterers, and (2), the finite duration of the transmitted radar signal, or equivalently, its nonstationarity (i.e., inhomogeneity in time).

However, the difficulty just mentioned is easily overcome. In fact, the problem of extracting the useful signal from a background of clutter echoes arises only when the signal itself [indicated by the dashed pulses in Fig. 58(b)] arrives together with the noise. This problem is not changed in any essential way if we imagine that a random process with the same statistical properties is "continued analytically" over the whole repetition period

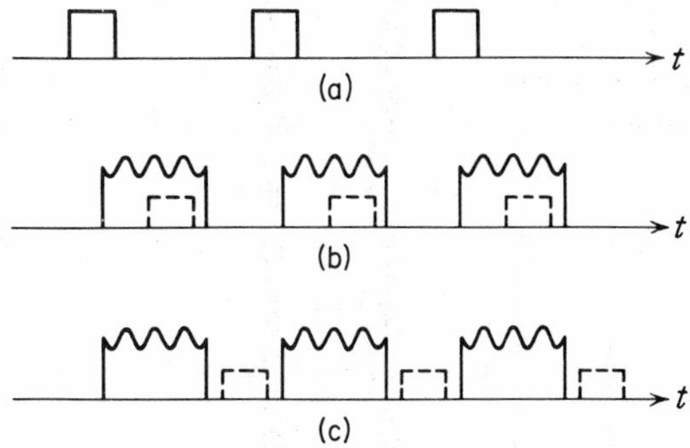

FIG. 58. Radar signals in a background of clutter.

(without any vacant time intervals) or even over the whole infinite time interval $-\infty < t < \infty$. Then, as was done earlier, we assume that the useful signal is present only in the appropriate parts of the original L repetition periods, and we pose the problem of how to extract it from the background of the stationary random process just defined. We note that in analyzing the same problem for pulses which arrive at times when there is no noise [Fig. 58(c)] or when the noise has a different intensity or different correlation properties (scatterers in another part of space), we have to take the noise to be *another* stationary random process.

What is the physical meaning of this "analytic continuation" of the noise, which leads to a stationary random process? The experimentally observed noise [Fig. 58(b)] is caused by a region of space A with finite dimensions; we denote this noise by $n_A(t)$. We now imagine the region A supplemented by another region B, which is also filled with scatterers. Let the region B extend from the minimum to the maximum range within which the radar makes observations, and let it have a particle density (in general, variable) such that when the combined region $A + B$ is illuminated by an infinite periodic sequence of pulses (or other transmitted radar signals), the noise $n_{A+B}(t)$ from the combined region is a stationary random process. Since the original noise is

$$n_A(t) = n_{A+B}(t) - n_B(t), \tag{67.01}$$

where the noise $n_B(t)$ from the "supplementary" region B does not influence radar detection within the region A, we are justified in considering the noise $n_{A+B}(t)$ instead of the noise $n_A(t)$. It is important to note that the process $n_{A+B}(t)$ is obtained as a result of illuminating the region $A + B$ with a signal which repeats itself periodically. This means that in calculating the correlation function and the spectral density of the random process $n_{A+B}(t)$, we have to assume that the region $A + B$ is illuminated during all time and not just during L repetition periods, i.e., we have to "analytically continue" the transmitted wave (but not the received useful signal!) over the whole infinite time interval $-\infty < t < \infty$.

Using physical considerations, we can write the autocorrelation function $R_n(\tau)$ of the stationary random process $n(t)$ in the form

$$R_n(\tau) = R_p(\tau)r(\tau), \tag{67.02}$$

where $R_p(\tau)$ is a periodic function of τ with repetition period T, i.e.,

$$R_p(\tau \pm T) = R_p(\tau), \tag{67.03}$$

while $r(\tau)$ is a slowly varying function satisfying the condition

$$r(0) = 1. \tag{67.04}$$

The meaning of formula (67.02) is very simple. We first assume that the scattering particles do not move. Then, if the transmitted signal is periodic, the process $n(t)$ is also periodic (although it is random within each repetition period T). The autocorrelation function $R_p(\tau)$ of such a process is also a periodic function of τ, as indicated in formula (67.03). In fact, in this case, we can expand the noise $n(t)$ in a Fourier series

$$n(t) = \sum_{k=1}^{\infty} e_k \cos(k\omega_1 t - \vartheta_k), \quad \text{where} \quad \omega_1 = \frac{2\pi}{T}, \tag{67.05}$$

i.e., we can represent $n(t)$ as a superposition of monochromatic processes of the form (6.01), but with random values of e_k and ϑ_k. Regarding a monochromatic process as a limiting case of a quasi-monochromatic process, we obtain an autocorrelation function for (67.05) which is a sum of expressions of the type (6.10). Thus, we arrive at the function

$$R_p(\tau) = \sum_{k=1}^{\infty} P_k \cos k\omega_1\tau, \tag{67.06}$$

where the positive coefficients P_k are equal to

$$P_k = \frac{1}{2}\overline{e_k^2}. \tag{67.07}$$

In general, however, the scattering particles actually move. If we assume that the particles move in a random way ("chaotically") and have no mean velocity, then, after the time interval T, the configuration of the particles (which is randomly changing) will be somewhat different. As a result, the correlation function slowly decreases as $|\tau| \to \infty$, a situation which is taken into account by the factor $r(\tau)$ in formula (67.02).

If the radar signal is a sequence of coherent rectangular pulses of duration $T_0 \ll T$, then the function (67.06) gives a periodic sequence of "triangular r-f correlation pulses," one of which is shown in Fig. 21. The function $r(\tau)$ is usually regarded as constant during time intervals of order T_0, so that $r(\tau)$ is a kind of period-to-period correlation coefficient, characterizing the statistical relation between the values of $n(t)$ at the times t, $t \pm T$, $t \pm 2T$, etc.

Next, we calculate the spectral density of the noise $n(t)$, which has the correlation function (67.02). We have

$$\begin{aligned} S_n(\omega) &= \int_{-\infty}^{\infty} e^{i\omega\tau} R_p(\tau) r(\tau)\, d\tau = \sum_{k=1}^{\infty} P_k \int_{-\infty}^{\infty} e^{i\omega\tau}[\cos k\omega_1\tau] r(\tau)\, d\tau \\ &= \frac{1}{2}\sum_{k=1}^{\infty} P_k \int_{-\infty}^{\infty} [e^{i(\omega-k\omega_1)\tau} + e^{i(\omega+k\omega_1)\tau}] r(\tau)\, d\tau. \end{aligned} \tag{67.08}$$

If we introduce the function

$$s(\omega) = \int_{-\infty}^{\infty} e^{i\omega\tau} r(\tau)\, d\tau, \tag{67.09}$$

then (67.08) can be written in the form

$$S_n(\omega) = \frac{1}{2}\sum_{k=1}^{\infty} P_k[s(\omega - k\omega_1) + s(\omega + k\omega_1)]. \tag{67.10}$$

Thus, because of the random motion of the scatterers, the line spectrum of the periodic signal, originally concentrated at the frequencies $\omega = \pm k\omega_1$, is converted into a continuous spectrum, since each line is "spread out" in a completely definite way, which depends on the form of the function (67.09).

We note that when the cloud of scattering particles is illuminated by a sequence of incoherent pulses (cf. Sec. 21), then the autocorrelation function of the clutter is

$$\begin{aligned} R_n(\tau) &= R_p(\tau) \quad \text{for} \quad -T_0 < \tau < T_0, \\ R_n(\tau) &= 0 \qquad\;\; \text{for} \quad |\tau| > T_0, \end{aligned} \tag{67.11}$$

where T_0 is the pulse duration. In fact, for $|\tau| < T_0$, the autocorrelation function is the same whether the scattering volume is illuminated by coherent or incoherent pulses, since for such values of τ, all that matters is the statistical relation between values of the random process $n(t)$ coming from the same pulses. Therefore, for $|\tau| < T_0$, we can apply formula (67.02), replacing the factor $r(\tau)$ by unity. For larger values of τ (e.g., for $\tau \sim \pm T, \pm 2T$, etc.), we obviously have $R_n(\tau) = 0$, since even when the scatterers do not move, there is no correlation between different reflected pulses (because the phases of the transmitted pulses are random and are not used in detection). Thus, finally, the function $R_n(\tau)$ reduces to a single triangular "correlation pulse" modulating an r-f carrier (see Fig. 21), and the spectral density of the noise is given by formula (21.01).

Below, we shall explain in detail the physical meaning of the formulas given in this section, and in particular, we shall show that the function $s(\omega)$ is simply related to the velocity distribution of the scattering particles. We shall also give a generalization of the formulas derived above, and in particular, we shall take into account the average motion of the scattering particles with respect to the transmitting and receiving antennas, which leads to a frequency shift in the received radiation (the Doppler effect). In this regard, it should be noted that the theory of optimum reception of radar signals in the presence of clutter, as developed in this book, is based entirely on the expression (67.02) for the correlation function of the noise.

A basic difference between noise due to clutter echoes and noise in the receiver itself is the presence of strong correlation usually extending over several repetition periods at least; this correlation is determined by the factor $r(\tau)$ in formula (67.02). If the correlation time $\Delta\tau$ [i.e., the effective width of the function $r(\tau)$] equals

$$\Delta\tau \sim L_0 T, \tag{67.12}$$

then, according to the relation (3.28), the bandwidth of the spectral density $s(\omega)$, i.e., the width of each spectral line in formula (67.10), equals

$$\Delta\omega \sim \frac{\omega_1}{L_0} \tag{67.13}$$

in order of magnitude.

If $L_0 \gg 1$, we have noise which does not change appreciably during the time T; such noise can be compensated effectively by pulse-to-pulse subtraction. In this case, the width of each "line" in the spectrum (67.10) is small compared to the distance between consecutive lines. However, if $L_0 \lesssim 1$, we have "rapidly varying" noise, which changes considerably during the time T. In this case, $\Delta\omega \gtrsim \omega_1$, i.e., the spectral density (67.10) represents a "connected spectrum" in which the spectral lines at $\omega = \pm k\omega_1$ overlap one another.

In the case of incoherent pulses, there is a complete absence of correlation between different repetition periods [see formula (67.11)]. However, in this case, the clutter echoes no longer give a normal random process. In fact, because of the incoherence of the transmitted signals, the phases of the noise in different repetition periods are independent and there is no period-to-period correlation, but there is the same statistical relation between the amplitudes as in the case of coherent signals. This shows an important difference between clutter noise obtained when using incoherent signals and noise which lacks period-to-period correlation because of "natural reasons" (e.g., receiver noise itself or the "rapidly varying" clutter noise considered above).

In Chap. 7, we discussed the case of a radar signal reflected from a scintillating target; such a signal is the result of a superposition of the fields from many "specular points" which simultaneously undergo regular translational motion and random oscillations. The same model is also applicable to describe noise due to clutter echoes, the only difference being that the dimensions of the volume occupied by the scatterers is usually much larger than the dimensions of the radar target. Therefore, the noise is so extended in time that it is convenient to "incorporate" it into a stationary random process in the way described above. However, in studying statistical relations extending from period to period, both the coherent signal train reflected from a scintillating target and the noise due to its random reflection appear in all the theoretical relations in a completely symmetric way (as we saw in Sec. 43 and Secs. 47 to 49).

In the theory of detection of an incoherent train in a background of correlated noise, we restricted ourselves (for simplicity) to the case of normal noise, which is not only uncorrelated from period to period, but also statistically independent from period to period. Thus, the theory of optimum receivers for incoherent signal trains (presented in Chaps. 6 and 7) comprises receiver noise itself and "rapidly varying" clutter noise (resembling signals reflected by a rapidly scintillating target). As far as we know, clutter echoes which have strong period-to-period correlation of amplitude and independent phases have not yet been studied. The theory of detection of incoherent signals in a background of this kind of clutter noise would obviously involve application of the formulas of Sec. 60 to the noise, whereas in Secs. 44 and 45, we only applied these formulas to the useful signals.

68. The Doppler Effect

When electromagnetic radiation is scattered by a moving body, its frequency is changed due to the Doppler effect. In textbooks of physics, the Doppler effect is usually studied for waves radiated (rather than scattered) by a moving body. Therefore, for completeness, we shall now discuss the Doppler effect in the context of radar problems. In doing so, we shall first use the basic concepts of relativity theory, and only afterwards discuss a more elementary derivation.

Thus, suppose that a reflecting object K, moving with constant velocity v, is being observed in the x, y, z coordinate system. Let x', y', z' be a coordinate system attached to the moving body K. Without loss of generality, we can assume that the directions of the x-axis and the x'-axis are parallel to the velocity v, and that the axes y, y' and z, z' are also parallel. Then, the coordinates x, y, z and time t in the fixed system are related to the coordinates x', y', z' and time t' in the system moving with the body K by the Lorentz transformation

$$x' = \frac{x - vt}{\sqrt{1 - \beta^2}}, \quad y' = y, \quad z' = z, \quad t' = \frac{t - (\beta x/c)}{\sqrt{1 - \beta^2}}, \tag{68.01}$$

where

$$\beta = \frac{v}{c}. \tag{68.02}$$

Here, we assume that at the initial instant of time ($t = t' = 0$), the origins of the systems x, y, z and x', y', z' coincide. The inverse Lorentz transformation has the form

$$x = \frac{x' + vt'}{\sqrt{1 - \beta^2}}, \quad y = y', \quad z = z', \quad t = \frac{t' + (\beta x'/c)}{\sqrt{1 - \beta^2}}. \tag{68.03}$$

Now let the transmitting antenna A, which is rigidly attached to the system x, y, z, illuminate the body K with a monochromatic electromagnetic wave. At a sufficiently large distance from the antenna, this wave can be regarded as plane. If the y-axis is chosen so that the direction of propagation of the wave lies in the xy-plane then the phase of the wave equals

$$\Phi = k(x \cos \varphi + y \sin \varphi) - \omega t \qquad \left(k = \frac{\omega}{c}\right) \tag{68.04}$$

(see Fig. 59). This quantity is invariant under the Lorentz transformation, and hence in the system x', y', z', t', we have

$$\Phi = k'(x' \cos \varphi' + y' \sin \varphi') - \omega' t' \quad \left(k' = \frac{\omega'}{c}\right). \tag{68.05}$$

Equating the expressions (68.04) and (68.05), and using the formulas (68.03), we obtain

$$k' \cos \varphi' = k \frac{\cos \varphi - \beta}{\sqrt{1 - \beta^2}}, \qquad k' \sin \varphi' = k \sin \varphi \tag{68.06}$$

and

$$\omega' = \omega \frac{1 - \beta \cos \varphi}{\sqrt{1 - \beta^2}}. \tag{68.07}$$

The last formula gives us the frequency of the wave in the moving coordinate system. Using (68.06) and (68.07), we obtain

$$\cos \varphi' = \frac{\cos \varphi - \beta}{1 - \beta \cos \varphi}, \quad \sin \varphi' = \frac{\sqrt{1 - \beta^2} \sin \varphi}{1 - \beta \cos \varphi}. \tag{68.08}$$

The incident wave with the phase (68.05) is scattered by the body K, which is fixed in the coordinate system x', y', z'. If the scattered wave propagates in the $x'y'$-plane and makes an angle ψ' with the x'-axis, then at a sufficiently large distance from the body K, the scattered radiation is a plane wave with phase

$$\Psi = k'(x' \cos \psi' + y' \sin \psi') - \omega' t' \qquad \left(k' = \frac{\omega'}{c'}\right). \tag{68.09}$$

In the coordinate system x, y, z, this phase can be written in the form

$$\Psi = k_*(x \cos \psi + y \sin \psi) - \omega_* t. \tag{68.10}$$

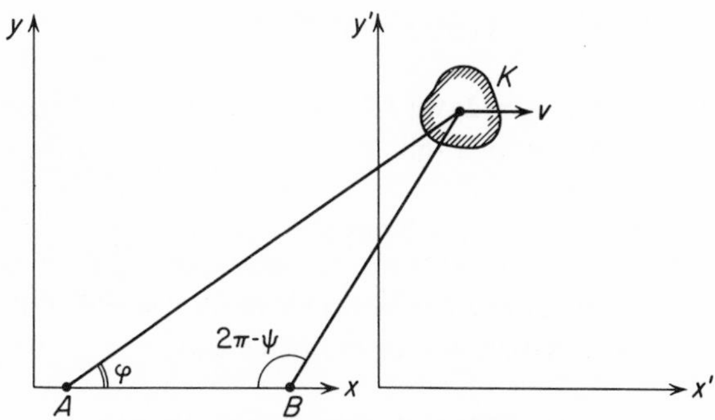

FIG. 59. Illustrating the Doppler effect.

Equating (68.09) and (68.10), and using the Lorentz transformation (68.01), we obtain

$$k_* \cos \psi = k' \frac{\cos \psi' + \beta}{\sqrt{1 - \beta^2}}, \qquad k_* \sin \psi = k' \sin \psi' \tag{68.11}$$

and

$$\omega_* = \omega' \frac{1 + \beta \cos \psi'}{\sqrt{1 - \beta^2}}. \tag{68.12}$$

The relations (68.11) give

$$k_* = \frac{\omega_*}{c}, \quad \cos \psi = \frac{\cos \psi' + \beta}{1 + \beta \cos \psi'}, \quad \sin \psi = \frac{\sqrt{1 - \beta^2} \sin \psi'}{1 + \beta \cos \psi'},$$
$$\cos \psi' = \frac{\cos \psi - \beta}{1 - \beta \cos \psi}, \tag{68.13}$$

and hence formula (68.12) can be written in the form

$$\omega_* = \omega' \frac{\sqrt{1-\beta^2}}{1-\beta\cos\psi}. \tag{68.14}$$

Using formula (68.07), we finally obtain the following expression for the frequency of the wave arriving at the receiving antenna:

$$\omega_* = \omega \frac{1-\beta\cos\varphi}{1-\beta\cos\psi}. \tag{68.15}$$

If the transmitting antenna A and the receiving antenna B coincide, then $\psi = \pi + \varphi$ and

$$\omega_* = \omega \frac{1-\beta\cos\varphi}{1+\beta\cos\varphi}. \tag{68.16}$$

We see that in this case, the frequency change is determined by the radial component of the velocity, since

$$\beta\cos\varphi = \frac{v\cos\varphi}{c} = \frac{v_r}{c} \tag{68.17}$$

(cf. Fig. 59). For $\varphi = \pm\pi/2$, we have $\omega_* = \omega$, i.e., the frequency does not change. For $\beta \ll 1$, formula (68.16) can be rewritten in the simpler form

$$\omega_* \sim \omega(1 - 2\beta\cos\varphi) \sim \frac{\omega}{1+2\beta\cos\varphi}. \tag{68.18}$$

We now give an elementary, but nonrigorous derivation of formula (68.16), for the case $\varphi = 0$. Thus, consider the plane wave

$$E_y^0 = E_0 \cos\omega\left(t - \frac{x}{c}\right), \tag{68.19}$$

which propagates in the direction of the x-axis, and let this wave be reflected from an infinite, perfectly conducting, plane mirror which is perpendicular to the x-axis and moves with velocity v in the direction of the x-axis, so that at time t, the mirror has abscissa

$$x = vt. \tag{68.20}$$

Let the wave reflected by the mirror have the form

$$E_y' = -E_0 \cos\omega_*\left(t + \frac{x}{c}\right). \tag{68.21}$$

Since the boundary condition

$$E_y^0 + E_y' = 0 \quad \text{for} \quad x = vt \tag{68.22}$$

has to be satisfied at the mirror, we arrive at the relation

$$\cos\omega(1-\beta)t = \cos\omega_*(1+\beta)t, \tag{68.23}$$

which is satisfied for all t, provided that the frequency ω_* of the reflected wave equals

$$\omega_* = \omega \frac{1 - \beta}{1 + \beta}, \tag{68.24}$$

a result which agrees with formula (68.16), when $\varphi = 0$. We can also derive (68.16) for $\varphi = \pi$, by making the mirror move along the x-axis in the negative direction; this changes v to $-v$ in formula (68.20) and β to $-\beta$ in formula (68.24). Finally, if the motion of the mirror is perpendicular to the x-axis, it stays in the same position with respect to the x-axis, and hence there can be no frequency change due to the reflection, in complete agreement with formula (68.16).

The Doppler effect for nonmonochromatic waves is considered in Appendix IV.

69. Correlation Function of Noise due to Random Reflections

Let the randomly located particles (scatterers) be illuminated by a wave whose time variation is given by the random function $m(t)$, with spectral density $S_m(\omega)$, and let the αth scatterer produce a reflected signal corresponding to the random process $n_\alpha(t)$, with spectral density $S_{n_\alpha}(\omega)$. Then, the aggregate of all these signals produces clutter noise in the radar receiver. If we denote by η_α the quantity

$$\eta_\alpha = 2\beta_\alpha \cos \varphi_\alpha = \frac{2v_{r\alpha}}{c}, \tag{69.01}$$

where $v_{r\alpha}$ is the radial velocity of the αth scatterer, then the spectral density $S_{n_\alpha}(\omega)$ is

$$S_{n_\alpha}(\omega) = \Gamma_\alpha S_m[\omega(1 + \eta_\alpha)], \tag{69.02}$$

where Γ_α is a constant coefficient which depends on the distance to the particle, its reflecting properties and its orientation, while $S_m(\omega)$ is the spectral density of the transmitted signal.

For a useful signal which occupies a sufficiently narrow frequency band

$$\Delta\omega \ll \omega_0, \tag{69.03}$$

where ω_0 is the carrier frequency, and for values of η_α satisfying the condition

$$|\eta_\alpha| \ll 1, \tag{69.04}$$

we can write formula (69.02) in the form

$$S_{n_\alpha}(\omega) = \Gamma_\alpha S_m(\omega + \zeta_\alpha), \tag{69.05}$$

where $\zeta_\alpha = \omega_0 \eta_\alpha$ and we have neglected the product of the small quantities $\eta_\alpha \Delta\omega$. Formula (69.05) shows that reflection by the αth particle shifts the signal spectrum by the amount ζ_α, due to the Doppler effect, without changing the shape of the spectrum. Under the same conditions, the coefficient Γ_α in formula (69.05) can be regarded as independent of the frequency ω. We note that in practice, the conditions (69.03) and (69.04) can always be considered to be valid.

As a result of the irregular arrangement of the particles in space, the signals reflected by them are added incoherently, so that the total spectral density of the noise equals

$$S_n(\omega) = \int_{-\infty}^{\infty} S_m(\omega + \zeta)W(\zeta)\, d\zeta, \tag{69.06}$$

where $W(\zeta)\, d\zeta$ describes the intensity of the reflections from scatterers producing frequency shifts in the interval $(\zeta, \zeta + d\zeta)$. The function W gives the distribution of radial velocity of the particles, and it can often be taken to be a "bell-shaped" function (like the Maxwell distribution function, which gives the velocity distribution of molecules), whose maximum corresponds to the mean velocity of motion of the particles "as a whole." If the "spread" of the values of ζ about the most probable value $\bar{\zeta}$ is sufficiently small compared to the bandwidth $\Delta\omega$, then in (69.06) we can replace ζ by $\bar{\zeta}$ in the factor $S_m(\omega + \zeta)$ and bring it in front of the integral. This gives the simpler formula

$$S_n(\omega) = S_m(\omega + \bar{\zeta}), \tag{69.07}$$

which for $\bar{\zeta} = 0$ reduces to

$$S_n(\omega) = S_m(\omega). \tag{69.08}$$

For simplicity, here and in what follows, we normalize $S_m(\omega)$ and $W(\zeta)$ in such a way that the relation

$$\int_{-\infty}^{\infty} W(\zeta)\, d\zeta = 1 \tag{69.09}$$

holds.

If for $S_m(\omega)$ we choose the expression (12.14) corresponding to an incoherent sequence of pulses of arbitrary shape, then (69.07) becomes

$$S_n(\omega) = \sigma|M(\omega + \bar{\zeta})|^2, \tag{69.10}$$

and (69.08) gives the expression

$$S_n(\omega) = \sigma|M(\omega)|^2, \tag{69.11}$$

which was used in Sec. 21. Formula (69.11) corresponds to a random configuration of particles at rest, formula (69.07) corresponds to particles moving as a "rigid whole," and formula (69.06) corresponds to particles which move irregularly with respect to each other.

Next, we derive the correlation function corresponding to the spectral density (69.06), for the case where $m(t)$ is a periodic function (which can be regarded as the limiting form of a random process). We first suppose that the function $W(\zeta)$ is even, i.e.,

$$W(-\zeta) = W(\zeta). \tag{69.12}$$

Then we have

$$\begin{aligned} R_n(\tau) &= \frac{1}{2\pi}\int_{-\infty}^{\infty} e^{i\omega\tau} S_n(\omega)\, d\omega \\ &= \frac{1}{2\pi}\int_{-\infty}^{\infty} e^{i\omega\tau} S_m(\omega)\, d\omega \int_{-\infty}^{\infty} e^{-i\zeta\tau} W(\zeta)\, d\zeta. \end{aligned} \tag{69.13}$$

If we define the functions

$$R_m(\tau) = \frac{1}{2\pi}\int_{-\infty}^{\infty} e^{i\omega\tau} S_m(\omega)\, d\omega, \tag{69.14}$$

$$r(\tau) = \int_{-\infty}^{\infty} e^{-i\zeta\tau} W(\zeta)\, d\zeta, \tag{69.15}$$

then we finally obtain

$$R_n(\tau) = R_m(\tau) r(\tau), \tag{69.16}$$

where $R_m(\tau)$ is a periodic function of τ, produced by the reflection of a periodically repeated signal from an aggregate of particles completely at rest, and $r(\tau)$ is the correlation coefficient due to the "chaotic" motion of the particles; here $r(0) = 1$, because of the condition (69.09).

If the condition (69.12) is not satisfied, then the function $r(\tau)$ is not even, and formula (69.16) has to be refined. In this case, we have to take into account the fact that formula (69.05) is valid only for $\omega > 0$, while for $\omega < 0$, the spectral density has to be calculated by using the relation

$$S_n(-\omega) = S_n(\omega). \tag{69.17}$$

Therefore, the autocorrelation function $R_n(\tau)$ equals

$$\begin{aligned} R_n(\tau) &= \frac{1}{2\pi}\int_{-\infty}^{\infty} e^{i\omega\tau} S_n(\omega)\, d\omega = \operatorname{Re}\frac{1}{\pi}\int_{0}^{\infty} e^{i\omega\tau} S_n(\omega)\, d\omega \\ &= \operatorname{Re}\frac{1}{\pi}\int_{-\infty}^{\infty} W(\zeta)\, d\zeta \int_{0}^{\infty} e^{i\omega\tau} S_m(\omega + \zeta)\, d\omega \\ &= \operatorname{Re}\frac{1}{\pi}\int_{-\infty}^{\infty} e^{-i\zeta\tau} W(\zeta)\, d\zeta \int_{\zeta}^{\infty} e^{i\omega\tau} S_m(\omega)\, d\omega. \end{aligned} \tag{69.18}$$

Because of the condition (69.03), we can change the lower limit of the inner integral (69.18) from ζ to 0. Then, instead of the function (69.14), we introduce the new complex function

$$R_m(\tau) = \frac{1}{\pi}\int_{0}^{\infty} e^{i\omega\tau} S_m(\omega)\, d\omega, \tag{69.19}$$

which is no longer a correlation function. Letting $\bar{\zeta}$ denote the frequency shift produced by the mean motion of the particles, i.e.,

$$\bar{\zeta} = \int_{-\infty}^{\infty} \zeta W(\zeta)\, d\zeta, \tag{69.20}$$

we write

$$W(\zeta) = W_0(\zeta - \bar{\zeta}) \tag{69.21}$$

and

$$r(\tau) = \int_{-\infty}^{\infty} e^{-i\zeta\tau} W_0(\zeta)\, d\zeta, \quad \text{where} \quad r(0) = 1. \tag{69.22}$$

Thus, the new complex function $r(\tau)$ is due to the velocity distribution of the particles in a coordinate system moving with the mean velocity of the particles. Bearing in mind that

$$\int_{-\infty}^{\infty} e^{-i\zeta\tau} W(\zeta)\, d\zeta = r(\tau) e^{-i\bar{\zeta}\tau}, \tag{69.23}$$

we can write formula (69.18) in the form

$$R_n(\tau) = \operatorname{Re}\{R_m(\tau) r(\tau) e^{-i\bar{\zeta}\tau}\}. \tag{69.24}$$

If the motion of the particles as a whole can be neglected ($\bar{\zeta} = 0$), and if moreover the function $W_0(\zeta)$ is even, then the function $r(\tau)$ becomes real and even, and we obtain the simple formula

$$R_n(\tau) = R_p(\tau) r(\tau), \tag{69.25}$$

equivalent to (67.02) and (69.16). The first factor

$$R_p(\tau) = \operatorname{Re} R_m(\tau) = \frac{1}{2\pi} \int_{-\infty}^{\infty} e^{i\omega\tau} S_m(\omega)\, d\omega \tag{69.26}$$

is a periodic function of τ, while the second factor gives the additional time decay of the correlation function $R_n(\tau)$ due to the irregular motion of the particles (i.e., the "spread" of their velocities). If $W_0(\zeta)$, the velocity distribution of the particles, is bell-shaped with width $\Delta\zeta$ (cf. the end of Sec. 3), then the factor $r(\tau)$ falls off appreciably for values of τ greater than or equal to the correlation time

$$\Delta\tau \sim \frac{1}{\Delta\zeta}. \tag{69.27}$$

The character of the noise will vary, depending on the relation between $\Delta\tau$ and the repetition period T (cf. the end of Sec. 67).

If we go over to discrete sample values, by sampling H times in each of the L repetition periods, then, according to formula (69.24), the noise correlation function due to random reflections equals

$$\overline{n_{g\varkappa} n_{h\lambda}} = \operatorname{Re}\{R_{gh} r_{\varkappa\lambda} e^{i(\varkappa-\lambda)\Delta\psi}\}, \tag{69.28}$$

where

$$R_{gh} = R_m[(h - g)\,\Delta t] \qquad (g, h = 1, \ldots, H) \tag{69.29}$$

is a complex coefficient describing the correlation within a single period, and

$$r_{\varkappa\lambda} = r[(\lambda - \varkappa)T], \quad r_{\varkappa\varkappa} = 1 \qquad (\varkappa, \lambda = 1, \ldots, L) \tag{69.30}$$

is a complex coefficient describing the period-to-period correlation (which can be regarded as constant during the time of appreciable correlation within a single period). The quantity

$$\Delta\psi = \bar{\zeta}T \tag{69.31}$$

is the phase shift due to the regular motion of the particles as a whole. Since the functions (69.19) and (69.22) satisfy the conditions

$$R_m(-\tau) = R_m^*(\tau), \qquad r(-\tau) = r^*(\tau), \tag{69.32}$$

we have

$$R_{hg} = R_{gh}^*, \qquad r_{\lambda\varkappa} = r_{\varkappa\lambda}^*, \tag{69.33}$$

i.e., the matrices $\|R_{gh}\|$ and $\|r_{\varkappa\lambda}\|$ are Hermitian.

70. Scattering of Radio Waves by Randomly Moving Particles

The scattering of radio waves by randomly moving particles can be studied from a more general point of view. Unfortunately, this more general approach is effective only for monochromatic radiation, so that it has to be used side by side with the formulas of Sec. 69.

Suppose that a monochromatic electromagnetic wave of frequency ω_0 is scattered by randomly moving particles (scatterers). The scattered wave which is incident on the receiving antenna B produces the noise

$$n(t) = \sum_\alpha \gamma_\alpha \cos(\omega_0 t - \Theta_\alpha), \tag{70.01}$$

where the coefficient γ_α gives the amplitude of the wave reradiated in the direction of B by the αth particle, and Θ_α is the phase of this wave, which depends on the distance between the particle and the transmitting antenna A, the distance between the particle and the receiving antenna B, and also on the scattering properties of the particle. The sum is taken over all particles lying within the "scattering volume" V formed by the intersection of the main beams of the antennas A and B (see Fig. 60).

Next, we choose a "center" O in the scattering volume, and we let ϑ denote the angle AOB (so that $\vartheta = 0$ when the transmitting and receiving antennas coincide). Letting P_α denote the center of the αth scatterer, we introduce the angles

$$\chi_\alpha = \angle AOP_\alpha, \qquad \chi'_\alpha = \angle BOP_\alpha. \tag{70.02}$$

If we let ρ_α denote the length of the radius vector joining O to P_α (see Fig. 61), then, if the conditions

$$AO \gg \rho_\alpha, \qquad AO \gg k\rho_\alpha^2, \qquad BO \gg \rho_\alpha, \qquad BO \gg k\rho_\alpha^2 \tag{70.03}$$

are met, we can write the distances from the point P_α to the antennas A and B in the form

$$AP_\alpha = AO - \rho_\alpha \cos \chi_\alpha, \qquad BP_\alpha = BO - \rho_\alpha \cos \chi'_\alpha \tag{70.04}$$

(using the law of cosines), while the phase Θ_α in formula (70.01) equals

$$\Theta_\alpha = k(AO + BO) - k\rho_\alpha(\cos \chi_\alpha + \cos \chi'_\alpha) + \delta_\alpha \qquad \left(k = \frac{\omega_0}{c}\right), \tag{70.05}$$

where the term δ_α is determined by the scatterers themselves and not by their positions.

When the αth scatterer moves, the distance ρ_α and the angles χ_α and χ'_α

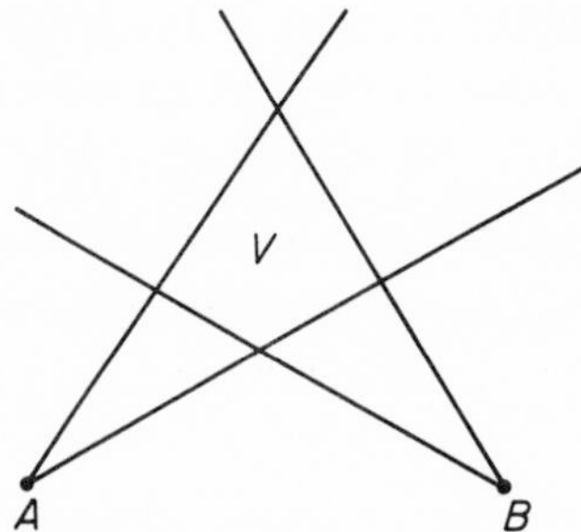

FIG. 60. The scattering volume.

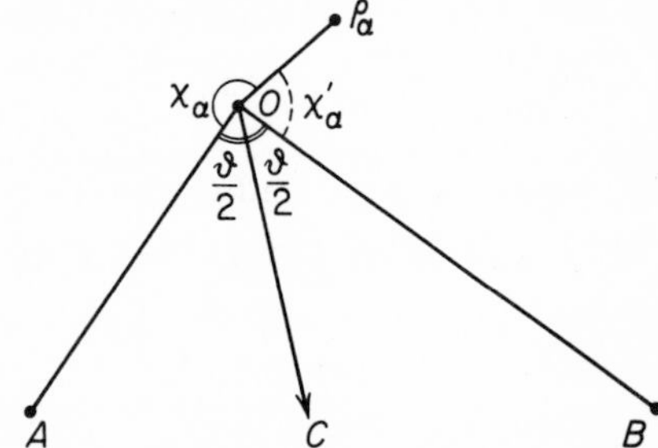

FIG. 61. Illustrating scattering by randomly moving particles.

change, and as a result, the phase Θ_α depends on t. Denoting the constant part of the phase by Θ_α^0 (i.e., the part which is independent of t), we can rewrite (70.05) in the form

$$\Theta_\alpha = \Theta_\alpha^0 - 2k\rho_\alpha \cos \frac{\chi'_\alpha - \chi_\alpha}{2} \cos \frac{\chi'_\alpha + \chi_\alpha}{2}. \tag{70.06}$$

From Fig. 61, we see that

$$\begin{gathered} \chi'_\alpha + \chi_\alpha = 2\pi - \vartheta, \\ \angle COP_\alpha = \frac{\vartheta}{2} + \chi'_\alpha = 2\pi - \frac{\vartheta}{2} - \chi_\alpha = \pi + \frac{\chi'_\alpha - \chi_\alpha}{2}, \end{gathered} \tag{70.07}$$

so that formula (70.06) can be written as

$$\Theta_\alpha = \Theta_\alpha^0 - 2k\xi_\alpha \cos \frac{\vartheta}{2}, \tag{70.08}$$

where

$$\xi_\alpha = -\rho_\alpha \cos\frac{\chi'_\alpha - \chi_\alpha}{2} = \rho_\alpha \cos \angle COP_\alpha \tag{70.09}$$

is the projection of the radius vector joining O to P_α along the line OC, the bisector of the angle AOB.

We now calculate the correlation function of the random process $n(t)$:

$$\begin{aligned}\overline{n(t)n(t-\tau)} &= \sum_{\alpha,\beta} \gamma_\alpha\gamma_\beta \overline{\cos[\omega_0 t - \Theta_\alpha(t)]\cos[\omega_0(t-\tau) - \Theta_\beta(t-\tau)]} \\ &= \frac{1}{2}\sum_{\alpha,\beta}\gamma_\alpha\gamma_\beta \overline{\cos[\omega_0\tau - \Theta_\alpha(t) + \Theta_\beta(t-\tau)]} \\ &= \frac{1}{2}\sum_{\alpha,\beta}\gamma_\alpha\gamma_\beta \overline{\cos[2\omega_0 t - \omega_0\tau - \Theta_\alpha(t) - \Theta_\beta(t-\tau)]}.\end{aligned} \tag{70.10}$$

The necessity of using a statistical approach to the function $n(t)$ is due in the first place, to the irregular configuration of the particles at any instant of time (at the time t, say), and in the second place, to the random motion or "wandering" of the particles in the course of time (during the interval from $t - \tau$ to t, say). According to formula (70.08), we have

$$\begin{aligned}\Theta_\alpha(t) &= \Theta_\alpha(t-\tau) - 2k\cos\frac{\vartheta}{2}[\xi_\alpha(t) - \xi_\alpha(t-\tau)] \\ &= \Theta_\alpha(t-\tau) - 2k\cos\frac{\vartheta}{2}\int_{t-\tau}^{t} v_\alpha(s)\,ds,\end{aligned} \tag{70.11}$$

where v_α is the component of the velocity of the αth scatterer in the direction of the bisector OC. Assuming that the position of the scatterers at time t is "completely random," we have

$$\begin{aligned}&\overline{\cos[\omega_0\tau - \Theta_\alpha(t) + \Theta_\beta(t-\tau)]} = 0 \qquad \text{for } \alpha \neq \beta, \\ &\overline{\cos[2\omega_0 t - \omega_0\tau - \Theta_\alpha(t) - \Theta_\beta(t-\tau)]} = 0 \qquad \text{for any } \alpha \text{ and } \beta.\end{aligned} \tag{70.12}$$

The first of the formulas (70.12) is not valid for $\alpha = \beta$, since then, according to (70.11), the difference

$$\Theta_\alpha(t) - \Theta_\alpha(t-\tau) = -2k\cos\frac{\vartheta}{2}\int_{t-\tau}^{t} v_\alpha(s)\,ds \tag{70.13}$$

appears in the brackets, i.e., when $\alpha = \beta$, the randomness in the phases $\Theta_\alpha(t)$ and $\Theta_\beta(t)$ is cancelled out, and the corresponding statistical average in (70.12) is not zero. Therefore, formula (70.10) becomes

$$\overline{n(t)n(t-\tau)} = \frac{1}{2}\sum_\alpha \gamma_\alpha^2 \overline{\cos\left[\omega_0\tau + 2k\cos\frac{\vartheta}{2}\int_{t-\tau}^{t} v_\alpha(s)\,ds\right]}. \tag{70.14}$$

At this point, we make another simplifying assumption, i.e., we assume that the velocity $v_\alpha(t)$ is a stationary random function of time, whose properties are the same for all the particles in the given scattering volume. Then, in formula (70.14), we can replace

$$\int_{t-\tau}^{t} v_\alpha(s)\,ds \quad \text{by} \quad \int_0^\tau v(t)\,dt, \tag{70.15}$$

and formula (70.14) simplifies to

$$\begin{aligned} R_n(\tau) &= \overline{n(t)n(t-\tau)} \\ &= \frac{1}{2}\sum_\alpha \gamma_\alpha^2 \overline{\cos\left[\omega_0\tau + 2k\cos\frac{\vartheta}{2}\int_0^\tau v(t)\,dt\right]}. \end{aligned} \tag{70.16}$$

Thus, we see that the calculation of the noise correlation function is mathematically equivalent to calculating the correlation function of a source of sinusoidal oscillations which is frequency modulated by a random process. The role of the modulating function is played by the random particle velocity $v(t)$, which can be written in the form

$$v(t) = \bar{v} + \Delta v(t), \tag{70.17}$$

where the velocity $\bar{v}$, which does not depend on t, is the mean velocity of the particles, i.e., their translational velocity as a whole, while $\Delta v(t)$ is the random "fluctuational" velocity of the particles, with mean value equal to zero.

Substituting the expression (70.17) into (70.16), we obtain

$$R_n(\tau) = \frac{1}{2}\sum_\alpha \gamma_\alpha^2 \overline{\cos\left[\omega_*\tau + 2k\cos\frac{\vartheta}{2}\int_0^\tau \Delta v(t)\,dt\right]}, \tag{70.18}$$

where

$$\omega_* = \omega_0 + 2k\bar{v}\cos\frac{\vartheta}{2} = \omega_0\left(1 + 2\frac{\bar{v}}{c}\cos\frac{\vartheta}{2}\right) \tag{70.19}$$

is the frequency of the signal arriving at B, which has been shifted as a result of the Doppler effect. In fact, if we regard the "scattering cloud" as moving like the rigid body K in Fig. 59 (i.e., if we set $\Delta v \equiv 0$), then, using the notation of Fig. 59, we have

$$\psi - \pi = \varphi + \vartheta, \qquad \bar{v} = -v\sin\frac{\varphi + \psi}{2}, \tag{70.20}$$

so that formula (70.19) becomes

$$\omega_* = \omega_0[1 + \beta(\cos\psi - \cos\varphi)], \tag{70.21}$$

which is in complete agreement with formula (68.15) when $\beta \ll 1$.

In the more general case, let

$$\zeta(t) = -2kv(t)\cos\frac{\vartheta}{2} = -2\omega_0\frac{v(t)}{c}\cos\frac{\vartheta}{2}; \tag{70.22}$$

$\zeta(t)$ is the negative of the frequency shift caused by the motion of a particle with velocity $v(t)$ in the direction of the bisector OC (see Fig. 61). Then, we can rewrite formula (70.16) in the form

$$R_n(\tau) = \frac{1}{2}\sum_\alpha \overline{\gamma_a^2\cos\left[\omega_0\tau - \int_0^\tau \zeta(t)\,dt\right]}. \tag{70.23}$$

If the random function $\zeta(t)$ varies sufficiently slowly, then we can use formula (70.23) to derive formula (69.24). In fact, suppose that $\zeta(t)$ changes appreciably only in a time interval of order $\delta\tau$ or larger, where $\delta\tau$ is the correlation time of the velocity of the particles (see Sec. 71 below). Then, if the condition

$$\tau \ll \delta\tau \tag{70.24}$$

is met, we can write

$$\int_0^\tau \zeta(t)\,dt = \zeta\tau, \tag{70.25}$$

where $\zeta = \zeta(0)$ is the initial value of the frequency shift.

Now let $W(\zeta)\,d\zeta$ denote the probability that the frequency shift lies in the interval $(\zeta, \zeta + d\zeta)$; then

$$\overline{\cos(\omega_0 - \zeta)\tau} = \int_{-\infty}^{\infty} W(\zeta)[\cos(\omega_0 - \zeta)\tau]\,d\zeta, \tag{70.26}$$

and the correlation function (70.23) equals

$$R_n(\tau) = R_0\int_{-\infty}^{\infty} W(\zeta)[\cos(\omega_0 - \zeta)\tau]\,d\zeta, \quad \text{where} \quad R_0 = \frac{1}{2}\sum_\alpha \gamma_a^2, \tag{70.27}$$

or

$$R_n(\tau) = \operatorname{Re}\left\{R_0 e^{i\omega_0\tau}\int_{-\infty}^{\infty} e^{-i\zeta\tau}W(\zeta)\,d\zeta\right\}. \tag{70.28}$$

This last formula agrees with (69.24) if the transmitted signal is monochromatic, since then, according to (69.19), we can write

$$R_m(\tau) = R_0 e^{i\omega_0\tau}, \tag{70.29}$$

and moreover

$$r(\tau)e^{-i\bar{\zeta}\tau} = \int_{-\infty}^{\infty} e^{-i\zeta\tau}W(\zeta)\,d\zeta, \tag{70.30}$$

as in formula (69.23).

A comparison of the results of this and the preceding section shows that formula (69.24) cannot be regarded as universally valid, since it implies the expression (70.06) which is valid only if the condition (70.24) is met, i.e., only if the particle velocities vary sufficiently slowly in time. In Sec. 71, we shall derive more general formulas for the correlation function and the spectral density, which are applicable in the case where the condition (70.24) is not met.

Finally, we note that the original formula (70.01) is rigorously valid only for isotropic scatterers, e.g., for scattering by spherical drops of rain or mist. When the scattering particles have other shapes, then, because of their rotation and deformation under actual conditions, the amplitude of the scattered wave depends on time. Therefore, the γ_α in formula (70.01) have to be regarded as functions of time, and we have to write $\overline{\gamma_\alpha(t)\gamma_\beta(t-\tau)}$ instead of $\gamma_\alpha\gamma_\beta$ in (70.10). In this case, formula (70.14) becomes

$$\overline{n(t)n(t-\tau)} = \frac{1}{2}\sum_\alpha \overline{\gamma_\alpha(t)\gamma_\alpha(t-\tau)\cos\left[\omega_0\tau + 2k\cos\frac{\vartheta}{2}\int_{t-\tau}^{t} v_\alpha(s)\,ds\right]}. \tag{70.31}$$

From this it is clear that taking account of the extra effects of rotation and deformation of the scatterers leads to the same expression for the correlation function as when a source of sinusoidal oscillations undergoes simultaneous amplitude and frequency modulation.

In the above analysis, we have not taken into account the fact that some particles leave the scattering volume V (see Fig. 60) and others enter V. This fact can be neglected if the volume V is large enough and the motion of the particles is slow enough.

71. Application of the Theory of Random Modulation to Clutter Echoes

In the preceding section, we obtained the expression (70.23) for the correlation function of the noise due to reflection from randomly moving particles. Regarding $\zeta(t)$ as a stationary random function with mean value $\bar{\zeta}$ and variance

$$(\Delta\zeta)^2 = \overline{(\zeta - \bar{\zeta})^2}, \tag{71.01}$$

we can introduce the new random function

$$x(t) = \frac{\zeta(t) - \bar{\zeta}}{\Delta\zeta}. \tag{71.02}$$

Then we have

$$\zeta(t) = \bar{\zeta} + \Delta\zeta\cdot x(t), \tag{71.03}$$

where $x(t)$ satisfies the relations (62.01), and formula (70.23) becomes

$$R_n(\tau) = \frac{1}{2}\sum_\alpha \gamma_\alpha^2 \overline{\left[\cos\left[\omega_*\tau - \Delta\zeta\int_0^\tau x(t)\,dt\right]\right]}, \tag{71.04}$$

where

$$\omega_* = \omega_0 - \bar{\zeta}.$$

On the other hand, in Chap. 10 we derived formula (63.03), which in the absence of amplitude and phase modulation takes the form

$$R(\tau) = \frac{1}{2}\overline{\cos\left[\omega_0\tau - n\omega_0\int_0^\tau x(t)\,dt\right]}, \tag{71.05}$$

since in taking the average we can replace

$$\Theta_1 - \Theta_2 = n\omega_0\int_{t_2}^{t_1} x(t)\,dt \quad \text{by} \quad n\omega_0\int_0^\tau x(t)\,dt,$$

because of the stationarity of $x(t)$. Then, it is clear that (except for the notation) formula (71.04) differs from (71.05) only by the presence of the factor $\sum_\alpha \gamma_\alpha^2$, which gives the intensity of the noise.

If we assume that the random processes $\zeta(t)$ and $x(t)$ are not only stationary (as assumed previously), but also *normal*, then we can use the first of the formulas (63.09) to transform (71.04) into the form

$$R_n(\tau) = \frac{1}{2}\sum_\alpha \gamma_\alpha^2 e^{-(\Delta\zeta)^2 h(\tau)/2}\cos\omega_*\tau, \tag{71.06}$$

where ω_* is the frequency which takes into account the Doppler effect due to the motion of the particles "as a whole," and the function $h(\tau)$ equals

$$h(\tau) = \int_0^\tau\int_0^\tau r(s_1 - s_2)\,ds_1\,ds_2, \quad \text{where} \quad r(\tau) = \overline{x(t)x(t-\tau)}, \tag{71.07}$$

according to formula (62.18). It should be noted that in this formula, $r(\tau)$ has a different meaning than in all the other formulas of this chapter.

Unlike (70.26), the expression (71.06) is applicable for any relation between τ and $\delta\tau$, where $\delta\tau$ is the correlation time of the random process $x(t)$ [cf. Sec. 70]. However, if the condition (70.24) is met, then, according to formula (65.03), we have

$$R_n(\tau) = \frac{1}{2}\sum_\alpha \gamma_\alpha^2 e^{-(\Delta\zeta)^2\tau^2/2}\cos\omega_*\tau. \tag{71.08}$$

If the opposite condition

$$\tau \gg \delta\tau \tag{71.09}$$

is met, then, according to formula (65.04), we have

$$R_n(\tau) = \frac{1}{2}\sum_\alpha \gamma_\alpha^2 e^{-(\Delta\zeta)^2\tau\delta\tau}\cos\omega_*\tau. \tag{71.10}$$

In other words, the function $r(\tau)$ appearing in formulas (69.24) and (69.28) can fall off in two different ways, i.e.,

$$r(\tau) = e^{-(\Delta\zeta)^2\tau^2/2} \quad \text{for} \quad \tau \ll \delta\tau \tag{71.11}$$

and

$$r(\tau) = e^{-(\Delta\zeta)^2\tau\delta\tau} \quad \text{for} \quad \tau \gg \delta\tau. \tag{71.12}$$

The law (71.11) is easily explained: Since the process $\zeta(t)$ is normal, the instantaneous velocities have a Maxwell distribution, so that

$$W(\zeta) = \frac{1}{\sqrt{2\pi}} \exp\left\{-\frac{(\zeta - \bar{\zeta})^2}{2(\Delta\zeta)^2}\right\}, \tag{71.13}$$

and then formula (70.30) leads to just (71.11). We have essentially discussed both limiting cases, in Sec. 65, except that there we were chiefly concerned with spectral densities and not correlation functions.

In Sec. 48, we showed that the laws (71.11) and (71.12) lead to entirely different schemes for optimum detection of a signal train in a background of clutter echoes. The important thing here is which formula to choose for the function $r(\tau)$ when $\tau = T, 2T$, etc., where T is the repetition period. As we see, on purely theoretical grounds, not only are the limiting laws (71.11) and (71.12) possible, but also the more complicated expression

$$r(\tau) = e^{-(\Delta\zeta)^2 h(\tau)/2}, \tag{71.14}$$

which is valid for $\tau \sim \delta\tau$.

The material in this chapter is largely based on the work of G. S. Gorelik.

Appendix **I**

OPTIMUM RECEIVERS AND STATISTICAL DECISION THEORY

The problem of detecting a signal in a background of random noise is a statistical problem involving the choice of one of two mutually exclusive hypotheses. Suppose that the input function $f(t)$ either consists of the signal $m(t)$ plus the noise $n(t)$, i.e.,

$$f(t) = m(t) + n(t) \tag{I.01}$$

(we denote by $\mathscr{H}_1$ the hypothesis associated with this event), or else reduces to pure noise, i.e.,

$$f(t) = n(t) \tag{I.02}$$

(we denote by $\mathscr{H}_0$ the hypothesis associated with this event). The problem now consists of choosing a decision rule which will allow us to decide in the "best" way which of the two hypotheses $\mathscr{H}_1$ and $\mathscr{H}_0$ is true, from a knowledge of the function $f(t)$. It is obvious that the more we use the properties of the signal and the noise to construct the decision rule, the "better" the decision will be.

Let the random function $f(t)$ be characterized by the probability distribution $P_1(f)$ if the hypothesis $\mathscr{H}_1$ is true and by the distribution $P_0(f)$ if the hypothesis $\mathscr{H}_0$ is true. If instead of the continuous function $f(t)$, we consider H sample values $f_1, \ldots, f_H$, then the functions $P_1(f)$ and $P_0(f)$ are

H-dimensional probability distributions, so that, in more detail, we should write

$$P_1(f) = P_1(f_1, \ldots, f_H), \quad P_0(f) = P_0(f_1, \ldots, f_H), \tag{I.03}$$

where we can go over to the case of a continuous function by letting $\Delta t \to 0$ and $H \to \infty$ (cf. Sec. 26).

For simplicity, we assume that the distributions (I.03) have probability densities $p_1(f)$ and $p_0(f)$, so that

$$\begin{aligned} p_1(f)\,df &= p_1(f_1, \ldots, f_H)\,df_1 \ldots df_H, \\ p_0(f)\,df &= p_0(f_1, \ldots, f_H)\,df_1 \ldots df_H \end{aligned} \tag{I.04}$$

are the probabilities that $f_1, \ldots, f_H$ lie in the appropriate intervals, given that the hypotheses $\mathscr{H}_1$ and $\mathscr{H}_0$, respectively, are true. In these formulas, each input function $f(t)$ is represented by a point with coordinates $f_1, \ldots, f_H$ in an H-dimensional space, and $df_1 \ldots df_H$ is the volume element in this space. We also assume that we know the a priori probabilities of the events corresponding to the hypotheses $\mathscr{H}_1$ and $\mathscr{H}_0$, which we denote by $P(1)$ and $P(0)$ respectively, so that

$$P(1) + P(0) = 1. \tag{I.05}$$

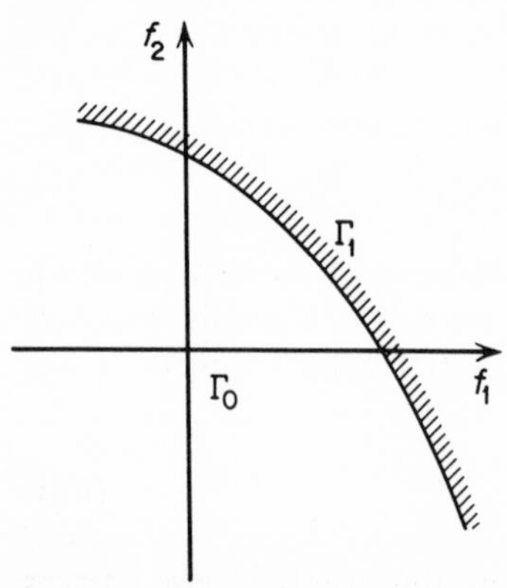

FIG. 62. The regions Γ_1 and Γ_0 corresponding to a decision rule.

The choice of a decision rule consists in decomposing the space of points $(f_1, \ldots, f_H)$ into two regions Γ_1 and Γ_0, such that when the point falls in the region Γ_1, it is decided that the hypothesis $\mathscr{H}_1$ is true, while if the point falls in the region Γ_0, it is decided that the hypothesis $\mathscr{H}_0$ is true. Such a decomposition of the whole space is shown schematically in Fig. 62, for the case $H = 2$. This immediately raises the question of the *optimum* decision rule, i.e., the optimum way of decomposing the space into the regions Γ_1 and Γ_0.

In Chap. 5, we examined optimum receivers for detection, which form the a posteriori probability and compare it with some threshold. There, the quality of the decision was characterized by two probabilities of making *correct* decisions, i.e., the probability of correct detection D (or the probability of choosing the hypothesis $\mathscr{H}_1$ when it is true) and the probability of correct nondetection F_0 (the probability of choosing the hypothesis $\mathscr{H}_0$ when it is true), and two probabilities of making *incorrect* decisions, i.e., the probability of false dismissal D_0 (the probability of choosing the hypothesis $\mathscr{H}_0$ when the hypothesis $\mathscr{H}_1$ is true) and the false alarm probability F (the probability of choosing the hypothesis $\mathscr{H}_1$ when the hypothesis $\mathscr{H}_0$ is true). The following relations

$$D = \int_{\Gamma_1} p_1(f)\, df, \qquad F = \int_{\Gamma_1} p_0(f)\, df,$$
$$D_0 = 1 - D, \qquad F_0 = 1 - F \tag{I.06}$$

are obvious consequences of the definitions.

In the theory of statistical decision functions, the concept of the *costs* of the different types of decisions is introduced. In the simplest detection problem, four costs are introduced, which are denoted by C_D, C_{D_0}, C_F, and C_{F_0}. Here, C_D is the cost of correct detection, C_{D_0} is the cost of false dismissal, C_F is the cost of false alarm, and C_{F_0} is the cost of correct non-detection. We shall assume that the costs satisfy the conditions

$$C_{D_0} > C_D \quad \text{and} \quad C_F > C_{F_0}, \tag{I.07}$$

i.e., the cost of either incorrect decision is greater than the cost of the corresponding correct decision. If the observer bases his decision on any rule and pays the cost corresponding to which of the four possibilities actually occurred, then the *loss function* (also called the *risk function*)

$$R = P(1)DC_D + P(1)D_0C_{D_0} + P(0)FC_F + P(0)F_0C_{F_0} \tag{I.08}$$

obviously gives the average cost of the decision, and the smaller R, the "better" the decision rule. In view of (I.06), we have

$$R = \int_{\Gamma_1} [-P(1)(C_{D_0} - C_D)p_1(f) + P(0)(C_F - C_{F_0})p_0(f)]\, df + P(1)C_{D_0} + P(0)C_{F_0}. \tag{I.09}$$

Following A. Wald, we shall call the decision rule for which the quantity R is a minimum the *optimum decision rule*.

The last two terms of formula (I.09) do not depend on the decision rule (on the regions Γ_1 and Γ_0), and hence the minimum value of R is achieved when the integral in (I.09) is a minimum. Because of the inequalities (I.07), the first term in the integrand in (I.09) is negative or zero, while the second term is positive or zero. Therefore, if we choose the region Γ_1 in such a way that the condition

$$P(1)(C_{D_0} - C_D)p_1(f) \geqslant P(0)(C_F - C_{F_0})p_0(f) \tag{I.10}$$

or

$$\frac{p_1(f)}{p_0(f)} \geqslant \frac{P(0)}{P(1)} \frac{C_F - C_{F_0}}{C_{D_0} - C_D} \tag{I.11}$$

is satisfied, then obviously R will have its minimum value. In fact, if we delete any part of the region Γ_1, in which the condition (I.10) is met, we increase the integral in (I.09), thereby increasing R. Conversely, if we include in the region Γ_1 any volume element in which the inequality opposite to (I.10) holds, then we also increase R. Writing

$$\Lambda = \frac{p_1(f)}{p_0(f)} \tag{I.12}$$

and

$$\Lambda_* = \frac{P(0)}{P(1)} \frac{C_F - C_{F_0}}{C_{D_0} - C_D}, \tag{I.13}$$

we obtain the decision rule

$$\begin{aligned} &\text{If} \quad \Lambda \geqslant \Lambda_*, \quad \text{then the hypothesis } \mathscr{H}_1 \text{ is true;} \\ &\text{If} \quad \Lambda < \Lambda_*, \quad \text{then the hypothesis } \mathscr{H}_0 \text{ is true,} \end{aligned} \tag{I.14}$$

where, to be explicit, we have assigned the case $\Lambda = \Lambda_*$ to the hypothesis $\mathscr{H}_1$. The same kind of decision rule was obtained in Chap. 5 by another argument.

If

$$C_D = C_{F_0} = 0, \qquad C_{D_0} = C_F = 1, \tag{I.15}$$

then the quantity (I.08) equals the total probability of error

$$V = P(1)(1 - D) + P(0)F, \tag{I.16}$$

and the decision rule (I.14) ensures a minimum for the total probability of error, or a maximum for the total probability of making a correct decision

$$W = 1 - V = P(1)D + P(0)(1 - F), \tag{I.17}$$

if the threshold Λ_* is chosen to equal

$$\Lambda_* = \frac{P(0)}{P(1)}. \tag{I.18}$$

We also obtain the threshold (I.18) under the condition

$$C_F - C_{F_0} = C_{D_0} - C_D, \tag{I.19}$$

which is weaker than (I.15).

In the literature, the observer whose decision is based on this rule is customarily called the *ideal observer* (due to Siegert). We see that in constructing the optimum receiver equivalent to this observer, we need to know the a priori probabilities $P(1)$ and $P(0)$, which in many cases involves certain difficulties (cf. Sec. 30). On the other hand, the *Neyman-Pearson observer* does not use the a priori probabilities $P(1)$ and $P(0)$. In fact, according to the Neyman-Pearson criterion, the optimum decision rule should maximize the probability of correct detection for a given false alarm probability. It is not hard to show that the Neyman-Pearson observer bases his decision on the rule (I.14), where, however, the threshold Λ_* is not given by formula (I.13), whose right-hand side contains parameters we do not know, but directly in terms of the false alarm probability, i.e.,

$$\Lambda_* = \Lambda_*(F) \tag{I.20}$$

by using the second of the formulas (I.06).

In statistical decision theory, one also studies the sequential analysis of data as it arrives. Here, the probabilities D_0 and F (or D and F) are specified, but the observation time rather than being fixed, is left as a random variable. Furthermore, the cost of a unit of observation time is also introduced. In this case, Wald has shown that the optimum decision rule minimizing the risk function (which now also depends on the observation time), is the following:

$$\begin{aligned}
&\text{If } \Lambda \geqslant \Lambda^*, && \text{decide that the hypothesis } \mathscr{H}_1 \text{ is true;}\\
&\text{If } \Lambda^* > \Lambda > \Lambda_*, && \text{withhold the decision}\\
& && \qquad\text{(the indeterminate case);}\\
&\text{If } \Lambda \leqslant \Lambda_*, && \text{decide that the hypothesis } \mathscr{H}_0 \text{ is true.}
\end{aligned} \tag{I.21}$$

Here, the thresholds Λ^* and Λ_* are given by the formulas

$$\begin{aligned}
\Lambda^* &= \frac{1-D}{1-F},\\
\Lambda^* &= \frac{D}{F},
\end{aligned} \tag{I.22}$$

and the observation continues until Λ crosses either the threshold Λ^* or the threshold Λ_* for the first time.

Appendix II

THE SIGNAL-TO-NOISE RATIO FOR NONOPTIMUM PROCESSING OF THE INPUT DATA

In situations involving the use of rectangular r-f pulses, the *signal-to-noise ratio* usually means the parameter

$$\rho' = \frac{\text{mean signal power (in a pulse)}}{\text{mean noise power}}. \tag{II.01}$$

If the pulses have constant (nonfluctuating) amplitude and strictly rectangular form, then the "mean signal power" is obtained by averaging over the r-f phase. If the amplitude is a random variable, then extra averaging is carried out over the amplitude.

In Sec. 16, and everywhere else in the book, we defined ρ as the signal-to-noise ratio

$$\rho = \frac{\text{peak signal power}}{\text{mean noise power}} \quad \text{(at the filter output).} \tag{II.02}$$

This parameter was calculated both for optimum linear filters and for nonoptimum linear filters (cf. Chap. 3). If the r-f signal has constant amplitude and if the filtering preserves the rectangular shape of the pulse, then, using the fact that the peak power of a sinusoidal signal is twice as large as its mean power, and comparing formulas (II.01) and (II.02), we obtain

$$\rho' = \frac{1}{2}\rho. \tag{II.03}$$

[For rectangular video pulses (cf. Sec. 18), we obviously have $\rho' = \rho$.] If the amplitude G of the signal is random, and has the Rayleigh distribution

$$p_m(G) = Ge^{-G^2/2}, \tag{II.04}$$

then

$$\overline{G^2} = 2, \tag{II.05}$$

and this formula has to be taken into account in forming the parameter ρ'. As for the parameter ρ, according to Sec. 34, it is given by formula (II.02) with $G = 1$. Hence, for a signal with fluctuating amplitude, we have

$$\rho' = \rho. \tag{II.06}$$

As we saw in Sec. 45, when the filtering is optimum, instead of the parameter ρ, it is sometimes convenient to introduce the parameter ρ' by using formula (II.03) for a constant target and formula (II.06) for a scintillating target, since this makes it easier to compare the detection characteristics of the corresponding receivers.

We have frequently remarked, in various places in the book, that the basic results of the theory of optimum receivers remain valid when the linear filtering (i.e., the processing of the input data within each period) is carried out in a nonoptimum way. This means that the optimum methods for processing the data from period to period, obtained by using the likelihood ratio, are optimum for any *linear* processing of the data within the separate periods, and the calculated receiver operating characteristics (the probabilities F and D) are also applicable; we need only bear in mind that the nonoptimum character of the linear filter decreases the effective signal-to-noise ratio, i.e., the situation is the same as if the noise level were increased somewhat. [As an example of a nonoptimum filter, consider the r-f stage of a receiver which preserves the rectangular shape of the pulses, and use the definition (II.01) for the signal-to-noise ratio of the pulses.]

The statement just made (which is almost obvious from a physical point of view) should really have been proved for each of the most important results of Part II. However, this would have made the exposition too bulky, and hence we have been compelled to confine ourselves to brief remarks. We might hope that a reader who has mastered the basic contents of this book will be able to carry out the necessary proofs by himself, in each special case.

Appendix III

PARADOXES OF DETECTION THEORY

The following mathematical result (which we state in the language of the present book) is proved in a paper by D. Slepian:[1] Consider the detection of a stationary random process $m(t)$, the signal, in a background of another stationary random process $n(t)$, the noise, i.e., consider the problem of deciding whether the input process $f(t)$, which is known in the interval $0 \leqslant t \leqslant T$, contains the signal $m(t)$ [so that $f(t) = m(t) + n(t)$] or does not contain it [so that $f(t) = n(t)$]. Suppose that both processes $m(t)$ and $n(t)$ are normal (Gaussian) with zero means and known spectral densities, and let $m(t) + n(t)$ and $m(t)$ have the spectral densities $S_{m+n}(\omega)$ and $S_n(\omega)$, which are not identically equal. Suppose further that the spectral density $S_{m+n}(\omega)$ is a rational function of ω or vanishes identically outside of some frequency band, and that the same is true of $S_n(\omega)$. Then, if for rational $S_{m+n}(\omega)$ and $S_n(\omega)$, the condition

$$\lim_{\omega \to \pm\infty} \frac{S_{m+n}(\omega)}{S_n(\omega)} \neq 1 \tag{III.01}$$

is met, there exists a decision rule which uses the input function $f(t)$ for $0 \leqslant t \leqslant T$ and guarantees a false alarm probability $F < \varepsilon$ and a detection probability $D > 1 - \varepsilon$, where $\varepsilon > 0$ is any preassigned number. Moreover, this theorem is true for arbitrarily small $T > 0$.

[1] D. Slepian, *Some comments on the detection of Gaussian signals in Gaussian noise*, IRE Trans. on Inform. Theory, **IT-4**, 65 (1958). Many of the results stated in this article (especially, the mathematical ones) can be found in other earlier papers. However, the fundamental importance of these results is explained particularly well in this article.

For the details of the proof and for references to the literature, we refer the reader to Slepian's paper. Here we give only the idea of the proof: If the conditions

$$S_{m+n}(\omega) \equiv 0 \quad \text{and} \quad S_n(\omega) \equiv 0 \quad \text{for} \quad \omega > \omega_0 \quad \text{and} \quad \omega < -\omega_0 \tag{III.02}$$

are satisfied, then the random functions $m(t) + n(t)$ and $n(t)$ are singular (cf. Sec. 13). Then, it can be shown that to determine these functions on the whole infinite interval $-\infty < t < \infty$ and to calculate their correlation functions and spectral densities exactly, it is sufficient to know their behavior in any finite interval $0 \leqslant t \leqslant T$, and, of course, from a knowledge of the spectral densities, we can carry out perfectly reliable detection (with probabilities $F = 0$ and $D = 1$).

If the spectral densities $S_{m+n}(\omega)$ and $S_n(\omega)$ are rational functions of ω, which satisfy the asymptotic relations

$$S_{m+n}(\omega) \sim \frac{a}{\omega^{2l}}, \qquad S_n(\omega) \sim \frac{b}{\omega^{2(l+p)}} \qquad (l = 1, 2, \ldots; p = 0, 1, 2, \ldots), \tag{III.03}$$

as $\omega \rightarrow \pm\infty$, where, according to (III.01), the constants a and b must be different when $p = 0$, then we can carry out detection by using the quantity

$$y_k = \sum_{j=0}^{k-1} \left[z\left(\frac{j+1}{k}T\right) - z\left(\frac{j}{k}T\right)\right]^2, \quad \text{where} \quad z(t) = \frac{d^{l-1}}{dt^{l-1}} f(t). \tag{III.04}$$

In fact, it turns out that for sufficiently large k, the quantity y_k differs by an arbitrarily small amount, with a probability arbitrarily close to unity, from the quantity $(2\pi)^2 aT$, if $f(t) = m(t) + n(t)$, from the quantity $(2\pi)^2 bT$, if $f(t) = n(t)$ with $p = 0$, and from zero, if $f(t) = n(t)$ with $p \geqslant 1$. This proves the theorem when $S_{m+n}(\omega)$ and $S_n(\omega)$ are rational functions. Using the same quantity (III.04), we can also uniquely resolve a random process $m(t) + n(t)$ with a rational spectral density $S_{m+n}(\omega) \sim a/\omega^{2l}$ from a random process $n(t)$ with a spectral density $S_n(\omega)$ which vanishes for $|\omega| > \omega_0$.

The formulation of the theorem just stated can be considerably expanded. In particular, we can take the differences of order l of the function $f(t)$ itself in formula (III.04), instead of first-order differences of the derivatives $(d^{l-1}/dt^{l-1})f(t)$; then, we use only the sample values of the function at the times $t_j = jT/k$, where $j = 0, 1, \ldots, k-1$. Moreover, it can be shown that the theorem is valid for any pair of singular processes $m(t) + n(t)$ and $n(t)$, i.e., instead of the relations (III.02), we need only require that the functions $S_{m+n}(\omega)$ and $S_n(\omega)$ vanish sufficiently rapidly at infinity (see Sec. 13). The assumption that the functions $S_{m+n}(\omega)$ and $S_n(\omega)$ are rational is also unnecessary, and all that is important is that they be bounded for real ω and satisfy the asymptotic relations (III.03) and (III.01). Finally, the random processes under consideration do not have to be normal, at least in the case where they are singular.

Since detection by using the likelihood ratio is optimum (cf. Chap. 5 and Appendix I), then, under the conditions stated above, the decision rule (35.10) must lead to the same values $F < \varepsilon$ and $D > 1 - \varepsilon$, or to even better values. However, direct calculation of the probabilities F and D is difficult.

From the standpoint of physics and engineering, the paradox represented by the given theorem consists in the fact that it enables us to carry out arbitrarily accurate detection of an arbitrarily weak random signal $m(t)$ in a background of arbitrarily strong noise $n(t)$ by using data acquired within an arbitrarily short time interval T. Using this theorem, Slepian arrives at the conclusion that the existing mathematical theory of detection of signals in the presence of noise is not adequate for the detection problems of interest in engineering, and has to be supplemented in at least two ways: (1) The statement that the spectral densities of all the processes involved in the problem are known *exactly* must be abandoned; (2) the statement that the input function $f(t)$ is known *exactly* in the continuous time interval $0 \leqslant t \leqslant T$ (or at discrete instants of time t_j lying arbitrarily close together) must be abandoned. If these additional restrictions were really necessary, then we would first have to renounce the usual statistical theory of detection, presented in this book, and then we would have to start to construct a new theory which would unavoidably be more complex. However, as a matter of fact, the theorem in question does not lead to such radical conclusions, and all the paradoxes which occur can easily be resolved within the context of the existing theory.

In analyzing the given theorem, we shall assume for simplicity that the processes $m(t)$ and $n(t)$ are uncorrelated, so that

$$S_{m+n}(\omega) = S_m(\omega) + S_n(\omega), \tag{III.05}$$

and then the condition (III.01) takes the form

$$\lim_{\omega \to \pm\infty} \frac{S_m(\omega)}{S_n(\omega)} \neq 0. \tag{III.06}$$

Thus, the theorem is valid either when the process $n(t)$ or both processes $m(t)$ and $n(t)$ are singular, or when the bandwidth of the regular process $m(t)$ is not less than that of the noise $n(t)$, i.e., when for sufficiently large frequencies, the spectral density of the useful signal is comparable with or exceeds the spectral density of the noise. However, if we assume that the noise spectrum is wider than the signal spectrum, then the theorem is no longer valid, all the paradoxes vanish, and detection theory leads to conclusions which agree with common sense and engineering practice.

The concept of a stationary random process arose in mathematics as a result of generalizing phenomena like noise in electric circuits and other fluctuation processes, and was then applied to useful signals of a random character (e.g., telegraph signals, telephone conversations, radio transmissions, etc.). However, the mathematical concept of a stationary random process is wider than appears at first glance. For example, in studying the prediction of stationary random processes in Chap. 2, we came across the fact that the theory of prediction leads to results which are sensible from a practical point of view only in the case of regular random processes. Neither random signals nor random noise can serve as the prototype for a singular random process. In fact, a singular random process $n(t)$, for which the "past" uniquely determines the entire "future" conveys no new information and moreover does not impede the detection of an arbitrarily weak signal $m(t)$ of finite duration, since the singular process $n(t)$ can be uniquely extrapolated into the finite time interval in which the signal $m(t)$ appears, and can then be subtracted from the input process $f(t)$, thereby allowing us to ascertain the absence or detect the presence of $m(t)$ with complete reliability. Therefore, that part of the theorem given above which pertains to the detection of a stationary random process $m(t)$ (regular or singular) in the presence of the noise $n(t)$ is completely natural, but, at the same time, cannot lead to any practical results.

However, random processes with rational spectral densities are regular (see Chap. 2), and the part of the theorem pertaining to them needs a more detailed analysis. It is clear from formula (III.04) that in this case, detection is carried out by using the quantity y_k, which contains the differences $z(t_j + 1) - z(t_j)$ for small differences of the argument $t_{j+1} - t_j = T/k$ (since k is assumed to be quite large). As is well known, in forming these differences (and also in calculating the derivative

$$z(t) = \frac{d^{l-1}}{dt^{l-1}} f(t)$$

for $t = t_j$), the significant figures "disappear," i.e., in measuring $f(t)$ with a certain (random) error and carrying out calculations to a finite number of places corresponding to this error, we find y_k with a random error which becomes indefinitely large as $k \to \infty$. This fact prevents us from making practical use of the possibilities inherent in the theorem formulated above, and essentially forces us to introduce into detection theory an additional proposition to the effect that the knowledge of the input process $f(t)$ is *inexact*.

Actually, the nonsystematic errors made in measuring $f(t)$ have the character of extra white noise added to the original process, since they are random and statistically independent. Moreover, the errors committed when $f(t)$ is rounded off to a fixed number of decimal places can also be regarded as white noise. These "measurement" and "mathematical" white noises are normal (Gaussian) and can simply be included in the noise $n(t)$ masking the presence of the useful signal $m(t)$, in just the same way as we incorporate the receiver noise itself [which perturbs the given process $f(t)$ and further distorts it] into the overall noise $n(t)$.

The above considerations show that the noise $n(t)$ always contains an admixture of white noise, which, on the one hand, can be due to physical causes, e.g., thermal noise in resistors, the shot effect, etc.,[2] and on the other hand, allows us to incorporate errors made in reproducing, measuring and processing the input data. The spectral density S_0 of this white noise may be very small over most of the spectrum, but for sufficiently large frequencies it predominates, and

$$\lim_{\omega \to \pm\infty} S_n(\omega) = S_0. \tag{III.07}$$

It follows that the condition (III.06) cannot be satisfied, since the function $S_m(\omega)$ approaches zero as $\omega \to \pm\infty$, inasmuch as the useful signal $m(t)$ has finite average power

$$\overline{m^2} = \frac{1}{2\pi}\int_{-\infty}^{\infty} S_m(\omega)\, d\omega. \tag{III.08}$$

Thus, when we form the quantity y_k, as $k \to \infty$, the main contribution comes from the white noise, which is uncorrelated from sample to sample, while all the other terms in the function $f(t)$, being more slowly varying functions of time, are "subtracted out." Thus, the theorem ceases to be true, and all paradoxes connected with it disappear.

It was pointed out in Sec. 13 that the addition of white noise to a random process leads to a regular process. It follows from what has just been shown that detection theory can also be freed from any paradoxes by taking into account the unavoidable (although possibly very small) admixture of white noise.

Similar paradoxes arise in detecting a signal of known form in the presence of a stationary random process $n(t)$ [the noise]. If, for simplicity, we assume that the input process $f(t)$ is observed during the interval $-\infty < t < \infty$, then the result of optimum linear treatment of the input data can be characterized by the parameter

$$\rho = \frac{1}{2\pi}\int_{-\infty}^{\infty} \frac{|M(\omega)|^2}{S_n(\omega)}\, d\omega, \tag{III.09}$$

the signal-to-noise ratio at the output of the optimum filter [cf. formulas (16.15) and (31.25)]. Here $M(\omega)$ is the amplitude spectrum of the signal $m(t)$, and $S_n(\omega)$ is the power spectrum of the noise. For example, if the signal $m(t)$ is a rectangular pulse, then the function $|M(\omega)|^2$ falls off like

---

[2] See Sec. 61.

ω^{-2} as $\omega \to \pm\infty$ [cf. formulas (20.03) and (20.06)]. For "singular noise" $n(t)$, the function $S_n(\omega)$ falls off much faster as $\omega \to \pm\infty$. Therefore, the integral (III.09) diverges and gives $\rho = \infty$, which corresponds to perfectly reliable detection of an arbitrarily weak signal. Moreover, this detection can be carried out not only by using the optimum filter, but also by extrapolation of the noise (as described above) and by other methods.

The value $\rho = \infty$ can also be obtained when the noise $n(t)$ is a regular random process. For example, if as $\omega \to \pm\infty$, the functions $M(\omega)$ and $S_n(\omega)$ satisfy the asymptotic formulas

$$|M(\omega)|^2 \sim \frac{a}{|\omega|^{2l}}, \quad S_n(\omega) \sim \frac{b}{|\omega|^{2(l+p)}} \qquad (l > \tfrac{1}{2}, p \geqslant -\tfrac{1}{2}), \tag{III.10}$$

which resemble (III.03), then, by using formula (III.09), we again obtain $\rho = \infty$.

Another example of this kind was considered in Sec. 21: If the noise is due to reflections from a large number of objects randomly arranged in space, then, according to formula (21.05), we have

$$S_n(\omega) = \sigma|M(\omega)|^2 \quad \text{and} \quad \rho = \infty, \tag{III.11}$$

so that we can guarantee that $F < \varepsilon$ and $D > 1 - \varepsilon$, even for arbitrarily weak signals, as in the theorem stated above.

The reason why we arrive at these paradoxical results is that we have not taken into account the white noise which to some extent or other is always added to the input process (see above). For example, if S_0 denotes the spectral density of the white noise, formula (III.11) must be replaced by the expression

$$S_n(\omega) = S_0 + \sigma|M(\omega)|^2, \tag{III.12}$$

and then the parameter ρ will be finite (see Sec. 21). In the general case, if we write

$$\lim_{\omega \to \pm\infty} S_n(\omega) = S_0, \tag{III.13}$$

the formula (III.09) leads to a finite value of ρ, if the signal energy

$$E = \int_{-\infty}^{\infty} m^2(t)\,dt = \frac{1}{2\pi}\int_{-\infty}^{\infty} |M(\omega)|^2\,d\omega \tag{III.14}$$

is finite.

In conclusion, we note that instead of letting the white noise have constant spectral density S_0, we can introduce a spectral density $S_0(\omega)$ which is constant in a sufficiently large frequency interval and falls off sufficiently slowly as $\omega \to \pm\infty$. Then, by taking into account the "rapidly fluctuating" normal noise which has the spectral density $S_0(\omega)$, we can reconcile statistical detection theory with reality. In particular, we can free the theory from any paradoxical implications.

Appendix IV

THE DOPPLER EFFECT FOR NONMONOCHROMATIC SIGNALS

In Sec. 68, we considered the frequency change produced in a monochromatic wave when it is reflected from a moving body. According to formula (68.15), the frequency of the reflected wave ω_* is related to the frequency of the incident wave ω by the formula

$$\omega_* = \chi\omega, \tag{IV.01}$$

where the factor

$$\chi = \frac{1 - \beta \cos \varphi}{1 - \beta \cos \psi} \tag{IV.02}$$

depends on the velocity with which the body moves relative to the transmitting and receiving antennas. For a body at rest, we have $\chi = 1$, and for nonrelativistic velocities (i.e., $\beta \ll 1$), the factor χ is near unity; however, even very small frequency changes easily show up experimentally, if the oscillation is observed for a sufficiently long time.

Suppose now that we have a nonmonochromatic wave, which when reflected from a body *at rest* produces the signal

$$m(t) = \frac{1}{2\pi} \int_{-\infty}^{\infty} e^{i\omega t} M(\omega)\, d\omega, \tag{IV.03}$$

at the receiver input, where the Fourier integral allows us to represent $m(t)$ as a superposition of monochromatic waves. If the body *moves*, then due to the Doppler effect, each of these monochromatic waves changes its frequency in accordance with formula (IV.01), and the signal arriving at the receiver is

$$m_*(t) = \frac{1}{2\pi}\int_{-\infty}^{\infty} e^{i\omega_* t} M\left(\frac{\omega_*}{\chi}\right) d\omega_* = \frac{\chi}{2\pi}\int_{-\infty}^{\infty} e^{i\omega\chi t} M(\omega)\, d\omega, \qquad \text{(IV.04)}$$

where $M(\omega)$ is the same function as in formula (IV.03). Thus, an exact treatment shows that the amplitude spectrum $M(\omega)$ is stretched in frequency (if $\chi > 1$). For a sufficiently narrow-band signal, this stretch is equivalent to a shift of the spectrum $M(\omega)$ as a whole by the amount $(\chi - 1)\omega_0$ along the frequency axis (cf. Sec. 36). The signals $m_*(t)$ and $m(t)$ are related by the formula

$$m_*(t) = \chi m(\chi t), \qquad \text{(IV.05)}$$

where the factor χ, which gives the change in amplitude of the signal, is of no practical interest, and moreover is not completely exact (since in our study of the Doppler effect for monochromatic waves, we did not consider the transformation of the amplitude in going over to the moving coordinate system and back). Hence, we shall omit the factor χ.

If the signal $m(t)$ reflected by the fixed body has the form

$$m(t) = e(t) \cos [\omega_0 t - \psi(t) - \theta], \qquad \text{(IV.06)}$$

then the signal $m_*(t)$ reflected by the moving body is

$$m_*(t) = e(\chi t) \cos [\omega_0 \chi t - \psi(\chi t) - \theta]. \qquad \text{(IV.07)}$$

Therefore, in being reflected by the moving body, the carrier frequency ω_0 is replaced by the frequency $\chi\omega_0$, in accordance with formula (IV.01). We took this frequency shift into account in our theory of detection of coherent signal trains. However, besides the shift in carrier frequency, the Doppler effect also produces a change in the form of the signal, or more exactly, in the form of the envelope $e(t)$ and the supplementary phase $\psi(t)$, which are replaced by $e(\chi t)$ and $\psi(\chi t)$, respectively. [In particular, if the radar signal is a rectangular pulse (i.e., a section of a sine wave), then in being reflected by a moving body, the length of the pulse is shortened in the same proportion as the period of the r-f oscillations.] These latter changes in the shape of the signal were not considered anywhere in the book, although in some cases they can be considerable.

Appendix V

SPECULAR POINTS

If electromagnetic radiation is incident on an object of complicated shape, which has "large" dimensions (i.e., dimensions much larger than the wavelength of the radiation), then the chief contribution to the scattered field is due to *specular points* (which, being somewhat "smeared out," are really "patches") occupying a relatively small part of the illuminated surface of the object. The location of these specular points depends strongly on the orientation of the object. To form an intuitive picture of specular points, imagine the sea's surface illuminated by strong sunlight, when the wave motion (which gives the reflecting surface a complicated shape) is not too strong. Then, as a result of the time variation of the form of the sea's surface, the specular points not only move around continuously, but also "jump from wave to wave." Motion of the observer leads to the same kind of motion of the specular points.

The origin of specular points can easily be understood from the point of view of geometrical optics: According to geometrical optics, the wave incident on the object is a bundle of rays (parallel rays, in the case of a plane wave, and divergent rays, in the case of a spherical wave), each of which is reflected from the corresponding surface element of the object, as required by the familiar law of reflection, which determines the direction of the reflected ray. Only some of the reflected rays are incident on the observation point, and a specular point is a point on the surface of the object from which such a ray is reflected. In general, the number of rays incident on the observation point, and hence the number of specular points, increases as the shape of the object becomes more complicated. For example, the sphere, which is the simplest object, has only one specular point.

The notion of specular points is also preserved in the case where geometrical optics has to be replaced or supplemented by diffraction theory. In fact, according to diffraction theory, the scattered wave can be represented as a sum of fields due to various "diffracted rays" coming from the object, each of which begins at some specular point on the surface of the body.

BIBLIOGRAPHY[1]

BOOKS[2]

Arley, N., and K. R. Buch, *Introduction to the Theory of Probability and Statistics*, John Wiley and Sons, Inc., New York (1950).

Baghdady, E. J., editor, *Lectures on Statistical Communication Theory*, McGraw-Hill Book Co., Inc., New York (1961).

Black, H. S., *Modulation Theory*, D. Van Nostrand Co., Inc., Princeton, N.J. (1953).

Blackwell, D., and M. A. Girshick, *Theory of Games and Statistical Decisions*, John Wiley and Sons, Inc., New York (1950).

Cramér, H., *Mathematical Methods of Statistics*, Princeton University Press, Princeton, N.J. (1946).

Cramér, H., *Random Variables and Probability Distributions*, second edition, Cambridge University Press, New York (1961).

Davenport, W. B., Jr., and W. L. Root, *An Introduction to the Theory of Random Signals and Noise*, McGraw-Hill Book Co., Inc., New York (1958).

Fano, R. M., *Transmission of Information*, M.I.T. Technology Press and John Wiley and Sons, Inc., New York (1961).

Feinstein, A., *Foundations of Information Theory*, McGraw-Hill Book Co., Inc., New York (1958).

Helstrom, C. W., *Statistical Theory of Signal Detection*, Pergamon Press, London (1960).

Kerr, D. E., editor, *Propagation of Short Radio Waves*, McGraw-Hill Book Co., Inc., New York (1951).

Laning, J. H., Jr., and R. H. Battin, *Random Processes in Automatic Control*, McGraw-Hill Book Co., Inc., New York (1956).

Lawson, J. L., and G. E. Uhlenbeck, *Threshold Signals*, McGraw-Hill Book Co., Inc., New York (1950).

Lee, Y. W., *Statistical Theory of Communication*, John Wiley and Sons., Inc., New York (1960).

[1] See Translator's Preface.

[2] This list does not contain books specifically cited in the text.

Middleton, D., *An Introduction to Statistical Communication Theory*, McGraw-Hill Book Co., Inc., New York (1960).

Parzen, E., *Modern Probability Theory and Its Applications*, John Wiley and Sons, Inc., New York (1960).

Reza, F. M., *An Introduction to Information Theory*, McGraw-Hill Book Co., Inc., New York (1961).

Schwartz, M., *Information Transmission, Modulation, and Noise*, McGraw-Hill Book Co., Inc., New York (1959).

Solodovnikov, V. V., *Introduction to the Statistical Dynamics of Automatic Control Systems*, translation edited by J. B. Thomas and L. A. Zadeh, Dover Publications, Inc., New York (1960).

Van der Ziel, A., *Noise*, Prentice-Hall, Inc., Englewood Cliffs, N.J. (1954).

Wald, A., *Sequential Analysis*, John Wiley and Sons, Inc., New York (1947).

Wald, A., *Statistical Decision Functions*, John Wiley and Sons, Inc., New York (1950).

Wax, N., editor, *Selected Papers on Noise and Stochastic Processes*, Dover Publications, Inc., New York (1954).

Wiener, N., *Extrapolation, Interpolation, and Smoothing of Stationary Time Series*, M.I.T. Technology Press and John Wiley and Sons, Inc., New York (1950).

PAPERS[3]

Benner, A. H., and R. F. Drenick, *On the problem of optimum detection of pulsed signals in noise*, RCA Rev., **16**, 463 (1955). [Sec. 57]

Bode, H. W., and C. E. Shannon, *A simplified derivation of linear least-square smoothing and prediction theory*, Proc. IRE, **38**, 417 (1950). [Sec. 12]

Davies, I. L., *On determining the presence of signals in noise*, Proc. IEE (London), **99**, 45 (1952). [Chap. 5]

George, S. F., *Effectiveness of crosscorrelation detectors*, Proceedings of the National Electronics Conference, vol. X, p. 109 (1954). [Secs. 18 and 20]

Gorelik, G. S., К теории рассеяния радиоволн на блуждающих неоднородностях (*On the theory of scattering of radio waves by "wandering" inhomogeneities*), Radiotekh. i Elektron., **1**, 695 (1956). [Chap. 11]

Kaplan, E. L., *Signal detection studies with applications*, Bell System Tech. J., **34**, 403 (1955). [Sec. 46]

Middleton, D., *Statistical criteria for the detection of pulsed carriers in noise*, I, II, J. Appl. Phys., **24**, 371, 379 (1953). [Chaps. 5 and 6]

Middleton, D., *Statistical theory of signal detection*, IRE Trans. on Inform. Theory, **IT-3**, 26 (1954). [Chap. 5]

---

[3] The part of the present book to which each paper is relevant is shown in brackets.

Peterson, W. W., T. G. Birdsall, and W. C. Fox, *The theory of signal detectability*, IRE Trans. on Inform. Theory, **IT-4**, 171 (1954). [Chaps. 5 and 6]

Reich, E., and P. Swerling, *Detection of a sine wave in Gaussian noise*, J. Appl. Phys., **24**, 289 (1953). [Sec. 35 and Chap. 6]

Siebert, W. M., *A radar detection philosophy*, IRE Trans. on Inform. Theory, **IT-2**, 204 (1954). [Chap. 5]

Swerling, P., *Maximum angular accuracy of a pulsed search radar*, Proc. IRE, **44**, 1146 (1956). [Chap. 8]

Van Meter, D., and D. Middleton, *Modern statistical approaches to reception in communication theory*, IRE Trans. on Inform. Theory, **IT-4**, 119 (1954). [Chap. 5 and Appendix I]

Wainstein, L. A., Радиолокационное обнаружение "мерцающего объекта" на фоне коррелированных помех, Ч. I, Когерентная пачка сигналов (*Radar detection of a "scintillating object" in a background of correlated noise, Pt. I, A coherent signal train*), Radiotekh. i Elektron., **4**, 735 (1959); Ч. II, Некогерентная пачка сигналов (*Pt. II, An incoherent signal train*), ibid., **4**, 1071 (1959). [Secs. 44 to 49]

Zubakov, V. D., Оптимальное обнаружение при коррелированных помехах (*Optimum detection in correlated noise*), Radiotekh. i Elektron., **3**, 1441 (1958). [Chap. 5]

Zubakov, V. D., Обнаружение сигнала на фоне нормальных шумов и хаотических отражений (*Detection of a signal in a background of normal noise and clutter echoes*), Radiotekh. i Elektron., **4**, 28 (1959). [Chap. 6]

Zubakov, V. D., Обнаружение когерентных сигналов на фоне коррелированных помех (*Detection of coherent signals in a background of correlated noise*), Radiotekh. i Elektron., **4**, 629 (1959). [Chap. 6]

INDEX

I

J

K

L

M

N

S

T

U

V

W

Y

Z